Precalculus: Mathematics for Calculus, Volume 1

includes Enhanced Web Assign access
MATH 161 - Community College of Philadelphia

6th Edition

Stewart | Redlin | Watson

CENGAGE
Learning

Australia • Brazil • Japan • Korea • Mexico • Singapore • Spain • United Kingdom • United States

CENGAGE
Learning™

Precalculus: Mathematics for Calculus, Volume 1: includes Enhanced Web Assign access, MATH 161 - Community College of Philadelphia, 6th Edition

Precalculus: Mathematics for Calculus, 6th Edition
James Stewart | Lothar Redlin | Saleem Watson

Executive Editors:
 Maureen Staudt
 Michael Stranz

Senior Project Development Manager:
 Linda deStefano

Marketing Specialist:
 Courtney Sheldon

Senior Production/Manufacturing Manager:
 Donna M. Brown

PreMedia Manager:
 Joel Brennecke

Sr. Rights Acquisition Account Manager:
 Todd Osborne

Cover Image:
stock.xchng

For product information and technology assistance, contact us at
Cengage Learning Customer & Sales Support, 1-800-354-9706

For permission to use material from this text or product,
submit all requests online at **cengage.com/permissions**
Further permissions questions can be emailed to
permissionrequest@cengage.com

This book contains select works from existing Cengage Learning resources and was produced by Cengage Learning Custom Solutions for collegiate use. As such, those adopting and/or contributing to this work are responsible for editorial content accuracy, continuity and completeness.

Compilation © 2011 Cengage Learning
ISBN-13: 978-1-133-36101-5

ISBN-10: 1-133-36101-3

Cengage Learning
5191 Natorp Boulevard
Mason, Ohio 45040
USA
Cengage Learning is a leading provider of customized learning solutions with office locations around the globe, including Singapore, the United Kingdom, Australia, Mexico, Brazil, and Japan. Locate your local office at:
international.cengage.com/region.

Cengage Learning products are represented in Canada by Nelson Education, Ltd.
For your lifelong learning solutions, visit **www.cengage.com/custom.**
Visit our corporate website at **www.cengage.com.**

Printed in the United States of America

BRIEF CONTENTS

ALSO INCLUDES: STUDENT QUICK START GUIDE FOR EWA CARD

JAMES STEWART received his MS from Stanford University and his PhD from the University of Toronto. He did research at the University of London and was influenced by the famous mathematician George Polya at Stanford University. Stewart is Professor Emeritus at McMaster University and is currently Professor of Mathematics at the University of Toronto. His research field is harmonic analysis and the connections between mathematics and music. James Stewart is the author of a bestselling calculus textbook series published by Brooks/Cole, Cengage Learning, including *Calculus, Calculus: Early Transcendentals*, and *Calculus: Concepts and Contexts*; a series of precalculus texts; and a series of high-school mathematics textbooks.

LOTHAR REDLIN grew up on Vancouver Island, received a Bachelor of Science degree from the University of Victoria, and received a PhD from McMaster University in 1978. He subsequently did research and taught at the University of Washington, the University of Waterloo, and California State University, Long Beach. He is currently Professor of Mathematics at The Pennsylvania State University, Abington Campus. His research field is topology.

SALEEM WATSON received his Bachelor of Science degree from Andrews University in Michigan. He did graduate studies at Dalhousie University and McMaster University, where he received his PhD in 1978. He subsequently did research at the Mathematics Institute of the University of Warsaw in Poland. He also taught at The Pennsylvania State University. He is currently Professor of Mathematics at California State University, Long Beach. His research field is functional analysis.

Stewart, Redlin, and Watson have also published *College Algebra, Trigonometry, Algebra and Trigonometry,* and (with Phyllis Panman) *College Algebra: Concepts and Contexts.*

ABOUT THE COVER

The cover photograph shows the Science Museum in the City of Arts and Sciences in Valencia, Spain, with a planetarium in the distance. Built from 1991 to 1996, it was designed by Santiago Calatrava, a Spanish architect. Calatrava has always been very interested in how mathematics can help him realize the buildings he imagines. As a young student, he taught himself descriptive geometry from books in order to represent three-dimensional objects in two dimensions. Trained as both an engineer and an architect, he wrote a doctoral thesis in 1981 entitled "On the Foldability of Space Frames," which is filled with mathematics, especially geometric transformations. His strength as an engineer enables him to be daring in his architecture.

CONTENTS

PREFACE

What do students really need to know to be prepared for calculus? What tools do instructors really need to assist their students in preparing for calculus? These two questions have motivated the writing of this book.

To be prepared for calculus a student needs not only technical skill but also a clear understanding of concepts. Indeed, *conceptual understanding* and *technical skill* go hand in hand, each reinforcing the other. A student also needs to gain an appreciation for the power and utility of mathematics in *modeling* the real world. Every feature of this textbook is devoted to fostering these goals.

In writing this Sixth Edition our purpose is to further enhance the utility of the book as an instructional tool for teachers and as a learning tool for students. There are several major changes in this edition including a restructuring of each exercise set to better align the exercises with the examples of each section. In this edition each exercise set begins with *Concepts Exercises,* which encourage students to work with basic concepts and to use mathematical vocabulary appropriately. Several chapters have been reorganized and rewritten (as described below) to further focus the exposition on the main concepts; we have added a new chapter on vectors in two and three dimensions. In all these changes and numerous others (small and large) we have retained the main features that have contributed to the success of this book.

New to the Sixth Edition

- **Exercises** More than 20% of the exercises are new. This includes new *Concept* Exercises and new *Cumulative Review* exercises. Key exercises are now linked to examples in the text.

- **Book Companion Website** A new website **www.stewartmath.com** contains *Discovery Projects* for each chapter and *Focus on Problem Solving* sections that highlight different problem-solving principles outlined in the Prologue.

- **CHAPTER 2 Functions** This chapter has been completely rewritten to focus more sharply on the fundamental and crucial concept of *function.* The material on quadratic functions, formerly in this chapter, is now part of the chapter on polynomial functions.

- **CHAPTER 3 Polynomial and Rational Functions** This chapter now begins with a section on quadratic functions, leading to higher degree polynomial functions.

- **CHAPTER 4 Exponential and Logarithmic Functions** The material on the natural exponential function is now in a separate section.

- **CHAPTER 5 Trigonometric Functions: Unit Circle Approach** This chapter includes a new section on inverse trigonometric functions and their graphs. Introducing this topic here reinforces the function concept in the context of trigonometry.

- **CHAPTER 6 Trigonometric Functions: Right Triangle Approach** This chapter includes a new section on inverse trigonometric functions and right triangles (Section 6.4) which is needed in applying the Laws of Sines and Cosines in the following section, as well as for solving trigonometric equations in Chapter 7.

- **CHAPTER 7 Analytic Trigonometry** This chapter has been completely revised. There are two new sections on trigonometric equations (Sections 7.4 and 7.5). The material on this topic (formerly in Section 7.5) has been expanded and revised.

- **CHAPTER 8 Polar Coordinates and Parametric Equations** This chapter is now more sharply focused on the concept of a coordinate system. The section on parametric equations is new to this chapter. The material on vectors is now in its own chapter.

- **CHAPTER 9 Vectors in Two and Three Dimensions** This is a new chapter with a new *Focus on Modeling* section.

- **CHAPTER 10 Systems of Equations and Inequalities** The material on systems of nonlinear equations is now in a separate section.

- **CHAPTER 11 Conic Sections** This chapter is now more closely devoted to the topic of analytic geometry, especially the conic sections; the section on parametric equations has been moved to Chapter 8.

Teaching with the Help of This Book

We are keenly aware that good teaching comes in many forms, and that there are many different approaches to teaching the concepts and skills of precalculus. The organization of the topics in this book is designed to accommodate different teaching styles. For example, the trigonometry chapters have been organized so that either the unit circle approach or the right triangle approach can be taught first. Here are other special features that can be used to complement different teaching styles:

EXERCISE SETS The most important way to foster conceptual understanding and hone technical skill is through the problems that the instructor assigns. To that end we have provided a wide selection of exercises.

- **Concept Exercises** These exercises ask students to use mathematical language to state fundamental facts about the topics of each section.

- **Skills Exercises** Each exercise set is carefully graded, progressing from basic skill-development exercises to more challenging problems requiring synthesis of previously learned material with new concepts.

- **Applications Exercises** We have included substantial applied problems that we believe will capture the interest of students.

- **Discovery, Writing, and Group Learning** Each exercise set ends with a block of exercises labeled *Discovery* ■ *Discussion* ■ *Writing*. These exercises are designed to encourage students to experiment, preferably in groups, with the concepts developed in the section, and then to write about what they have learned, rather than simply look for the answer.

- **Now Try Exercise . . .** At the end of each example in the text the student is directed to a similar exercise in the section that helps reinforce the concepts and skills developed in that example (see, for instance, page 4).

- **Check Your Answer** Students are encouraged to check whether an answer they obtained is reasonable. This is emphasized throughout the text in numerous *Check Your Answer* sidebars that accompany the examples. (See, for instance, page 52).

A COMPLETE REVIEW CHAPTER We have included an extensive review chapter primarily as a handy reference for the basic concepts that are preliminary to this course.

- **Chapter 1** This is the review chapter; it contains the fundamental concepts from algebra and analytic geometry that a student needs in order to begin a precalculus course. As much or as little of this chapter can be covered in class as needed, depending on the background of the students.

- **Chapter 1 Test** The test at the end of Chapter 1 is designed as a diagnostic test for determining what parts of this review chapter need to be taught. It also serves to help students gauge exactly what topics they need to review.

FLEXIBLE APPROACH TO TRIGONOMETRY The trigonometry chapters of this text have been written so that either the right triangle approach or the unit circle approach may be taught first. Putting these two approaches in different chapters, each with its relevant applications, helps to clarify the purpose of each approach. The chapters introducing trigonometry are as follows:

- **Chapter 5 Trigonometric Functions: Unit Circle Approach** This chapter introduces trigonometry through the unit circle approach. This approach emphasizes that the trigonometric functions are functions of real numbers, just like the polynomial and exponential functions with which students are already familiar.
- **Chapter 6 Trigonometric Functions: Right Triangle Approach** This chapter introduces trigonometry through the right triangle approach. This approach builds on the foundation of a conventional high-school course in trigonometry.

Another way to teach trigonometry is to intertwine the two approaches. Some instructors teach this material in the following order: Sections 5.1, 5.2, 6.1, 6.2, 6.3, 5.3, 5.4, 5.5, 5.6, 6.4, 6.5, and 6.6. Our organization makes it easy to do this without obscuring the fact that the two approaches involve distinct representations of the same functions.

GRAPHING CALCULATORS AND COMPUTERS We make use of graphing calculators and computers in examples and exercises throughout the book. Our calculator-oriented examples are always preceded by examples in which students must graph or calculate by hand, so that they can understand precisely what the calculator is doing when they later use it to simplify the routine, mechanical part of their work. The graphing calculator sections, subsections, examples, and exercises, all marked with the special symbol ⬚, are optional and may be omitted without loss of continuity. We use the following capabilities of the calculator.

- **Graphing, Regression, Matrix Algebra** The capabilities of the graphing calculator are used throughout the text to graph and analyze functions, families of functions, and sequences; to calculate and graph regression curves; to perform matrix algebra; to graph linear inequalities; and other powerful uses.
- **Simple Programs** We exploit the programming capabilities of a graphing calculator to simulate real-life situations, to sum series, or to compute the terms of a recursive sequence. (See, for instance, pages 787 and 791.)

FOCUS ON MODELING The "modeling" theme has been used throughout to unify and clarify the many applications of precalculus. We have made a special effort to clarify the essential process of translating problems from English into the language of mathematics (see pages 214 and 636).

- **Constructing Models** There are numerous applied problems throughout the book where students are given a model to analyze (see, for instance, page 228). But the material on modeling, in which students are required to *construct* mathematical models, has been organized into clearly defined sections and subsections (see for example, pages 213, 340, and 427).
- **Focus on Modeling** Each chapter concludes with a *Focus on Modeling* section. The first such section, after Chapter 1, introduces the basic idea of modeling a real-life situation by fitting lines to data (linear regression). Other sections present ways in which polynomial, exponential, logarithmic, and trigonometric functions, and systems of inequalities can all be used to model familiar phenomena from the sciences and from everyday life (see for example pages 296, 357, and 427).

BOOK COMPANION WEBSITE A website that accompanies this book is located at **www. stewartmath.com**. The site includes many useful resources for teaching precalculus, including the following:

- **Discovery Projects** *Discovery Projects* for each chapter are available on the website. Each project provides a challenging but accessible set of activities that enable students (perhaps working in groups) to explore in greater depth an interesting aspect of the topic they have just learned. (See for instance the Discovery Projects *Visualizing a Formula, Relations and Functions, Will the Species Survive?,* and *Computer Graphics I* and *II*.)

- **Focus on Problem Solving** Several *Focus on Problem Solving* sections are available on the website. Each such section highlights one of the problem-solving principles introduced in the Prologue and includes several challenging problems. (See for instance *Recognizing Patterns, Using Analogy, Introducing Something Extra, Taking Cases,* and *Working Backward.*)

MATHEMATICAL VIGNETTES Throughout the book we make use of the margins to provide historical notes, key insights, or applications of mathematics in the modern world. These serve to enliven the material and show that mathematics is an important, vital activity, and that even at this elementary level it is fundamental to everyday life.

- **Mathematical Vignettes** These vignettes include biographies of interesting mathematicians and often include a key insight that the mathematician discovered and which is relevant to precalculus. (See, for instance, the vignettes on Viète, page 49; Salt Lake City, page 84; and radiocarbon dating, page 333).

- **Mathematics in the Modern World** This is a series of vignettes that emphasizes the central role of mathematics in current advances in technology and the sciences (see pages 283, 700, and 759, for example).

REVIEW SECTIONS AND CHAPTER TESTS Each chapter ends with an extensive review section including the following.

- **Concept Check** The *Concept Check* at the end of each chapter is designed to get the students to think about and explain in their own words the ideas presented in the chapter. These can be used as writing exercises, in a classroom discussion setting, or for personal study.

- **Review Exercises** The *Review Exercises* at the end of each chapter recapitulate the basic concepts and skills of the chapter and include exercises that combine the different ideas learned in the chapter.

- **Chapter Test** The review sections conclude with a *Chapter Test* designed to help students gauge their progress.

- **Cumulative Review Tests** The *Cumulative Review Tests* following Chapters 4, 7, 9, 11, and 13 combine skills and concepts from the preceding chapters and are designed to highlight the connections between the topics in these related chapters.

- **Answers** Brief answers to odd-numbered exercises in each section (including the review exercises), and to all questions in the Concepts Exercises and Chapter Tests, are given in the back of the book.

Acknowledgments

We thank the following reviewers for their thoughtful and constructive comments.

REVIEWERS FOR THE FIFTH EDITION Kenneth Berg, University of Maryland; Elizabeth Bowman, University of Alabama at Huntsville; William Cherry, University of North Texas; Barbara Cortzen, DePaul University; Gerry Fitch, Louisiana State University; Lana Grishchenko, Cal Poly State University, San Luis Obispo; Bryce Jenkins, Cal Poly State University, San Luis Obispo; Margaret Mary Jones, Rutgers University; Victoria

Kauffman, University of New Mexico; Sharon Keener, Georgia Perimeter College; YongHee Kim-Park, California State University Long Beach; Mangala Kothari, Rutgers University; Andre Mathurin, Bellarmine College Prep; Donald Robertson, Olympic College; Jude Socrates, Pasadena City College; Enefiok Umana, Georgia Perimeter College; Michele Wallace, Washington State University; and Linda Waymire, Daytona Beach Community College.

REVIEWERS FOR THE SIXTH EDITION Raji Baradwaj, UMBC; Chris Herman, Lorain County Community College; Irina Kloumova, Sacramento City College; Jim McCleery, Skagit Valley College, Whidbey Island Campus; Sally S. Shao, Cleveland State University; David Slutzky, Gainesville State College; Edward Stumpf, Central Carolina Community College; Ricardo Teixeira, University of Texas at Austin; Taixi Xu, Southern Polytechnic State University; and Anna Wlodarczyk, Florida International University.

We are grateful to our colleagues who continually share with us their insights into teaching mathematics. We especially thank Andrew Bulman-Fleming for writing the Study Guide and the Solutions Manual and Doug Shaw at the University of Northern Iowa for writing the Instructor Guide.

We thank Martha Emry, our production service and art editor; her energy, devotion, experience, and intelligence were essential components in the creation of this book. We thank Barbara Willette, our copy editor, for her attention to every detail in the manuscript. We thank Jade Myers and his staff at Matrix Art Services for their attractive and accurate graphs and Precision Graphics for bringing many of our illustrations to life. We thank our designer Lisa Henry for the elegant and appropriate design for the interior of the book.

At Brooks/Cole we especially thank Stacy Green, developmental editor, for guiding and facilitating every aspect of the production of this book. Of the many Brooks/Cole staff involved in this project we particularly thank the following: Jennifer Risden, content project manager, Cynthia Ashton, assistant editor; Lynh Pham, media editor; Vernon Boes, art director; and Myriah Fitzgibbon, marketing manager. They have all done an outstanding job.

Numerous other people were involved in the production of this book—including permissions editors, photo researchers, text designers, typesetters, compositors, proof readers, printers, and many more. We thank them all.

Above all, we thank our editor Gary Whalen. His vast editorial experience, his extensive knowledge of current issues in the teaching of mathematics, and especially his deep interest in mathematics textbooks, have been invaluable resources in the writing of this book.

INSTRUCTOR RESOURCES

Printed

Complete Solution Manual
ISBN-10: 0-8400-6880-8; ISBN-13: 978-0-8400-6880-4
The complete solutions manual provides worked-out solutions to all of the problems in the text.

Instructor's Guide   ISBN-10: 0-8400-6883-2; ISBN-13: 978-0-8400-6883-5
Doug Shaw, author of the Instructor Guides for the widely used Stewart calculus texts, wrote this helpful teaching companion. It contains points to stress, suggested time to allot, text discussion topics, core materials for lectures, workshop/discussion suggestions, group work exercises in a form suitable for handout, solutions to group work exercises, and suggested homework problems.

Media

Enhanced WebAssign   ISBN-10: 0-538-73810-3; ISBN-13: 978-0-538-73810-1
Exclusively from Cengage Learning, Enhanced WebAssign® offers an extensive online program for Precalculus to encourage the practice that's so critical for concept mastery. The meticulously crafted pedagogy and exercises in this text become even more effective in Enhanced WebAssign, supplemented by multimedia tutorial support and immediate feedback as students complete their assignments. Algorithmic problems allow you to assign unique versions to each student. The Practice Another Version feature (activated at your discretion) allows students to attempt the questions with new sets of values until they feel confident enough to work the original problem. Students benefit from a new Premium eBook with highlighting and search features; Personal Study Plans (based on diagnostic quizzing) that identify chapter topics they still need to master; and links to video solutions, interactive tutorials, and even live online help.

ExamView Computerized Testing
ExamView® testing software allows instructors to quickly create, deliver, and customize tests for class in print and online formats, and features automatic grading. Includes a test bank with hundreds of questions customized directly to the text. ExamView is available within the PowerLecture CD-ROM.

Solution Builder   www.cengage.com/solutionbuilder
This online instructor database offers complete worked solutions to all exercises in the text, allowing you to create customized, secure solutions printouts (in PDF format) matched exactly to the problems you assign in class.

PowerLecture with ExamView
ISBN-10: 0-8400-6901-4; ISBN-13: 978-0-8400-6901-6
This CD-ROM provides the instructor with dynamic media tools for teaching. Create, deliver, and customize tests (both print and online) in minutes with ExamView® Computerized Testing Featuring Algorithmic Equations. Easily build solution sets for homework or exams using Solution Builder's online solutions manual. Microsoft® PowerPoint® lecture slides and figures from the book are also included on this CD-ROM.

STUDENT RESOURCES

Printed

Student Solution Manual
ISBN-10: 0-8400-6879-4; ISBN-13: 978-0-8400-6879-8
Contains fully worked-out solutions to all of the odd-numbered exercises in the text, giving students a way to check their answers and ensure that they took the correct steps to arrive at an answer.

Study Guide   ISBN-10: 0-8400-6917-0; ISBN-13: 978-0-8400-6917-7
This carefully crafted learning resource helps students develop their problem-solving skills while reinforcing their understanding with detailed explanations, worked-out examples, and practice problems. Students will also find listings of key ideas to master. Each section of the main text has a corresponding section in the Study Guide.

Media

Enhanced WebAssign   ISBN-10: 0-538-73810-3; ISBN-13: 978-0-538-73810-1
Exclusively from Cengage Learning, Enhanced WebAssign® offers an extensive online program for Precalculus to encourage the practice that's so critical for concept mastery. You'll receive multimedia tutorial support as you complete your assignments. You'll also benefit from a new Premium eBook with highlighting and search features; Personal Study Plans (based on diagnostic quizzing) that identify chapter topics you still need to master; and links to video solutions, interactive tutorials, and even live online help.

Book Companion Website
A new website **www.stewartmath.com** contains *Discovery Projects* for each chapter and *Focus on Problem Solving* sections that highlight different problem-solving principles outlined in the Prologue.

CengageBrain.com
Visit **www.cengagebrain.com** to access additional course materials and companion resources. At the CengageBrain.com home page, search for the ISBN of your title (from the back cover of your book) using the search box at the top of the page. This will take you to the product page where free companion resources can be found.

Text-Specific DVDs   ISBN-10: 0-8400-6882-4; ISBN-13: 978-0-8400-6882-8
The Text-Specific DVDs include new learning objective based lecture videos. These DVDs provide comprehensive coverage of the course—along with additional explanations of concepts, sample problems, and applications—to help students review essential topics.

TO THE STUDENT

This textbook was written for you to use as a guide to mastering precalculus mathematics. Here are some suggestions to help you get the most out of your course.

First of all, you should read the appropriate section of text *before* you attempt your homework problems. Reading a mathematics text is quite different from reading a novel, a newspaper, or even another textbook. You may find that you have to reread a passage several times before you understand it. Pay special attention to the examples, and work them out yourself with pencil and paper as you read. Then do the linked exercises referred to in *"Now Try Exercise . . ."* at the end of each example. With this kind of preparation you will be able to do your homework much more quickly and with more understanding.

Don't make the mistake of trying to memorize every single rule or fact you may come across. Mathematics doesn't consist simply of memorization. Mathematics is a *problem-solving art*, not just a collection of facts. To master the subject you must solve problems— lots of problems. Do as many of the exercises as you can. Be sure to write your solutions in a logical, step-by-step fashion. Don't give up on a problem if you can't solve it right away. Try to understand the problem more clearly—reread it thoughtfully and relate it to what you have learned from your teacher and from the examples in the text. Struggle with it until you solve it. Once you have done this a few times you will begin to understand what mathematics is really all about.

Answers to the odd-numbered exercises, as well as all the answers to each chapter test, appear at the back of the book. If your answer differs from the one given, don't immediately assume that you are wrong. There may be a calculation that connects the two answers and makes both correct. For example, if you get $1/(\sqrt{2} - 1)$ but the answer given is $1 + \sqrt{2}$, your answer *is* correct, because you can multiply both numerator and denominator of your answer by $\sqrt{2} + 1$ to change it to the given answer. In rounding approximate answers, follow the guidelines in the Appendix: *Calculations and Significant Figures*.

The symbol ⊘ is used to warn against committing an error. We have placed this symbol in the margin to point out situations where we have found that many of our students make the same mistake.

cm	centimeter		**mg**	milligram
dB	decibel		**MHz**	megahertz
F	farad		**mi**	mile
ft	foot		**min**	minute
g	gram		**mL**	milliliter
gal	gallon		**mm**	millimeter
h	hour		**N**	Newton
H	henry		**qt**	quart
Hz	Hertz		**oz**	ounce
in.	inch		**s**	second
J	Joule		**Ω**	ohm
kcal	kilocalorie		**V**	volt
kg	kilogram		**W**	watt
km	kilometer		**yd**	yard
kPa	kilopascal		**yr**	year
L	liter		**°C**	degree Celsius
lb	pound		**°F**	degree Fahrenheit
lm	lumen		**K**	Kelvin
M	mole of solute		$\Rightarrow$	implies
	per liter of solution		$\Leftrightarrow$	is equivalent to
m	meter			

MATHEMATICAL VIGNETTES

MATHEMATICS IN THE MODERN WORLD

Chuck Painter /Stanford News Service

GEORGE POLYA (1887–1985) is famous among mathematicians for his ideas on problem solving. His lectures on problem solving at Stanford University attracted overflow crowds whom he held on the edges of their seats, leading them to discover solutions for themselves. He was able to do this because of his deep insight into the psychology of problem solving. His well-known book *How To Solve It* has been translated into 15 languages. He said that Euler (see page 266) was unique among great mathematicians because he explained how he found his results. Polya often said to his students and colleagues, "Yes, I see that your proof is correct, but how did you discover it?" In the preface to *How To Solve It*, Polya writes, "A great discovery solves a great problem but there is a grain of discovery in the solution of any problem. Your problem may be modest; but if it challenges your curiosity and brings into play your inventive faculties, and if you solve it by your own means, you may experience the tension and enjoy the triumph of discovery."

The ability to solve problems is a highly prized skill in many aspects of our lives; it is certainly an important part of any mathematics course. There are no hard and fast rules that will ensure success in solving problems. However, in this Prologue we outline some general steps in the problem-solving process and we give principles that are useful in solving certain problems. These steps and principles are just common sense made explicit. They have been adapted from George Polya's insightful book *How To Solve It*.

1. Understand the Problem

The first step is to read the problem and make sure that you understand it. Ask yourself the following questions:

What is the unknown?
What are the given quantities?
What are the given conditions?

For many problems it is useful to

draw a diagram

and identify the given and required quantities on the diagram. Usually, it is necessary to

introduce suitable notation

In choosing symbols for the unknown quantities, we often use letters such as a, b, c, m, n, x, and y, but in some cases it helps to use initials as suggestive symbols, for instance, V for volume or t for time.

2. Think of a Plan

Find a connection between the given information and the unknown that enables you to calculate the unknown. It often helps to ask yourself explicitly: "How can I relate the given to the unknown?" If you don't see a connection immediately, the following ideas may be helpful in devising a plan.

▶ Try to Recognize Something Familiar

Relate the given situation to previous knowledge. Look at the unknown and try to recall a more familiar problem that has a similar unknown.

▶ **Try to Recognize Patterns**

Certain problems are solved by recognizing that some kind of pattern is occurring. The pattern could be geometric, numerical, or algebraic. If you can see regularity or repetition in a problem, then you might be able to guess what the pattern is and then prove it.

▶ **Use Analogy**

Try to think of an analogous problem, that is, a similar or related problem but one that is easier than the original. If you can solve the similar, simpler problem, then it might give you the clues you need to solve the original, more difficult one. For instance, if a problem involves very large numbers, you could first try a similar problem with smaller numbers. Or if the problem is in three-dimensional geometry, you could look for something similar in two-dimensional geometry. Or if the problem you start with is a general one, you could first try a special case.

▶ **Introduce Something Extra**

You might sometimes need to introduce something new—an auxiliary aid—to make the connection between the given and the unknown. For instance, in a problem for which a diagram is useful, the auxiliary aid could be a new line drawn in the diagram. In a more algebraic problem the aid could be a new unknown that relates to the original unknown.

▶ **Take Cases**

You might sometimes have to split a problem into several cases and give a different argument for each case. For instance, we often have to use this strategy in dealing with absolute value.

▶ **Work Backward**

Sometimes it is useful to imagine that your problem is solved and work backward, step by step, until you arrive at the given data. Then you might be able to reverse your steps and thereby construct a solution to the original problem. This procedure is commonly used in solving equations. For instance, in solving the equation $3x - 5 = 7$, we suppose that x is a number that satisfies $3x - 5 = 7$ and work backward. We add 5 to each side of the equation and then divide each side by 3 to get $x = 4$. Since each of these steps can be reversed, we have solved the problem.

▶ **Establish Subgoals**

In a complex problem it is often useful to set subgoals (in which the desired situation is only partially fulfilled). If you can attain or accomplish these subgoals, then you might be able to build on them to reach your final goal.

▶ **Indirect Reasoning**

Sometimes it is appropriate to attack a problem indirectly. In using **proof by contradiction** to prove that P implies Q, we assume that P is true and Q is false and try to see why this cannot happen. Somehow we have to use this information and arrive at a contradiction to what we absolutely know is true.

▶ **Mathematical Induction**

In proving statements that involve a positive integer n, it is frequently helpful to use the Principle of Mathematical Induction, which is discussed in Section 12.5.

3. Carry Out the Plan

In Step 2, a plan was devised. In carrying out that plan, you must check each stage of the plan and write the details that prove that each stage is correct.

4. Look Back

Having completed your solution, it is wise to look back over it, partly to see whether any errors have been made and partly to see whether you can discover an easier way to solve the problem. Looking back also familiarizes you with the method of solution, which may be useful for solving a future problem. Descartes said, "Every problem that I solved became a rule which served afterwards to solve other problems."

We illustrate some of these principles of problem solving with an example.

PROBLEM | Average Speed

A driver sets out on a journey. For the first half of the distance, she drives at the leisurely pace of 30 mi/h; during the second half she drives 60 mi/h. What is her average speed on this trip?

THINKING ABOUT THE PROBLEM

It is tempting to take the average of the speeds and say that the average speed for the entire trip is

$$\frac{30 + 60}{2} = 45 \text{ mi/h}$$

But is this simple-minded approach really correct?

Try a special case ▶   Let's look at an easily calculated special case. Suppose that the total distance traveled is 120 mi. Since the first 60 mi is traveled at 30 mi/h, it takes 2 h. The second 60 mi is traveled at 60 mi/h, so it takes one hour. Thus, the total time is $2 + 1 = 3$ hours and the average speed is

$$\frac{120}{3} = 40 \text{ mi/h}$$

So our guess of 45 mi/h was wrong.

SOLUTION

Understand the problem ▶   We need to look more carefully at the meaning of average speed. It is defined as

$$\text{average speed} = \frac{\text{distance traveled}}{\text{time elapsed}}$$

Introduce notation ▶   Let d be the distance traveled on each half of the trip. Let t_1 and t_2 be the times taken for the first and second halves of the trip. Now we can write down the information we have

State what is given ▶   been given. For the first half of the trip we have

$$30 = \frac{d}{t_1}$$

and for the second half we have

$$60 = \frac{d}{t_2}$$

Identify the unknown ▶   Now we identify the quantity that we are asked to find:

$$\text{average speed for entire trip} = \frac{\text{total distance}}{\text{total time}} = \frac{2d}{t_1 + t_2}$$

Connect the given
with the unknown ▶   To calculate this quantity, we need to know t_1 and t_2, so we solve the above equations for these times:

$$t_1 = \frac{d}{30} \qquad t_2 = \frac{d}{60}$$

Don't feel bad if you can't solve these problems right away. Problems 1 and 4 were sent to Albert Einstein by his friend Wertheimer. Einstein (and his friend Bucky) enjoyed the problems and wrote back to Wertheimer. Here is part of his reply:

Your letter gave us a lot of amusement. The first intelligence test fooled both of us (Bucky and me). Only on working it out did I notice that no time is available for the downhill run! Mr. Bucky was also taken in by the second example, but I was not. Such drolleries show us how stupid we are!

(See *Mathematical Intelligencer*, Spring 1990, page 41.)

Now we have the ingredients needed to calculate the desired quantity:

$$\text{average speed} = \frac{2d}{t_1 + t_1} = \frac{2d}{\dfrac{d}{30} + \dfrac{d}{60}}$$

$$= \frac{60(2d)}{60\left(\dfrac{d}{30} + \dfrac{d}{60}\right)} \quad \text{Multiply numerator and denominator by 60}$$

$$= \frac{120d}{2d + d} = \frac{120d}{3d} = 40$$

So the average speed for the entire trip is 40 mi/h.

PROBLEMS

1. **Distance, Time, and Speed**   An old car has to travel a 2-mile route, uphill and down. Because it is so old, the car can climb the first mile—the ascent—no faster than an average speed of 15 mi/h. How fast does the car have to travel the second mile—on the descent it can go faster, of course—to achieve an average speed of 30 mi/h for the trip?

2. **Comparing Discounts**   Which price is better for the buyer, a 40% discount or two successive discounts of 20%?

3. **Cutting up a Wire**   A piece of wire is bent as shown in the figure. You can see that one cut through the wire produces four pieces and two parallel cuts produce seven pieces. How many pieces will be produced by 142 parallel cuts? Write a formula for the number of pieces produced by n parallel cuts.

4. **Amoeba Propagation**   An amoeba propagates by simple division; each split takes 3 minutes to complete. When such an amoeba is put into a glass container with a nutrient fluid, the container is full of amoebas in one hour. How long would it take for the container to be filled if we start with not one amoeba, but two?

5. **Batting Averages**   Player A has a higher batting average than player B for the first half of the baseball season. Player A also has a higher batting average than player B for the second half of the season. Is it necessarily true that player A has a higher batting average than player B for the entire season?

6. **Coffee and Cream**   A spoonful of cream is taken from a pitcher of cream and put into a cup of coffee. The coffee is stirred. Then a spoonful of this mixture is put into the pitcher of cream. Is there now more cream in the coffee cup or more coffee in the pitcher of cream?

7. **Wrapping the World**   A ribbon is tied tightly around the earth at the equator. How much more ribbon would you need if you raised the ribbon 1 ft above the equator everywhere? (You don't need to know the radius of the earth to solve this problem.)

8. **Ending Up Where You Started**   A woman starts at a point P on the earth's surface and walks 1 mi south, then 1 mi east, then 1 mi north, and finds herself back at P, the starting point. Describe all points P for which this is possible.   [*Hint:* There are infinitely many such points, all but one of which lie in Antarctica.]

Many more problems and examples that highlight different problem-solving principles are available at the book companion website: **www.stewartmath.com**. You can try them as you progress through the book.

FUNDAMENTALS

In this first chapter we review the real numbers, equations, and the coordinate plane. You are probably already familiar with these concepts, but it is helpful to get a fresh look at how these ideas work together to solve problems and model (or describe) real-world situations.

Let's see how all these ideas are used in a real-life situation: Suppose you get paid $9 an hour at your part-time job. We can *model* your pay y for working x hours by the *equation* $y = 9x$. To find out how many hours you need to work to get paid 200 dollars, we solve the equation $200 = 9x$. Graphing the equation $y = 9x$ in a *coordinate plane* helps us "see" how pay increases with hours worked.

1.1 REAL NUMBERS

Properties of Real Numbers ▶ Addition and Subtraction ▶ Multiplication and Division ▶ The Real Line ▶ Sets and Intervals ▶ Absolute Value and Distance

Let's review the types of numbers that make up the real number system. We start with the **natural numbers**:

$$1, 2, 3, 4, \ldots$$

The **integers** consist of the natural numbers together with their negatives and 0:

$$\ldots, -3, -2, -1, 0, 1, 2, 3, 4, \ldots$$

We construct the **rational numbers** by taking ratios of integers. Thus, any rational number r can be expressed as

$$r = \frac{m}{n}$$

where m and n are integers and $n \neq 0$. Examples are

$$\frac{1}{2} \qquad -\frac{3}{7} \qquad 46 = \frac{46}{1} \qquad 0.17 = \frac{17}{100}$$

(Recall that division by 0 is always ruled out, so expressions like $\frac{3}{0}$ and $\frac{0}{0}$ are undefined.) There are also real numbers, such as $\sqrt{2}$, that cannot be expressed as a ratio of integers and are therefore called **irrational numbers**. It can be shown, with varying degrees of difficulty, that these numbers are also irrational:

$$\sqrt{3} \qquad \sqrt{5} \qquad \sqrt[3]{2} \qquad \pi \qquad \frac{3}{\pi^2}$$

The set of all real numbers is usually denoted by the symbol $\mathbb{R}$. When we use the word *number* without qualification, we will mean "real number." Figure 1 is a diagram of the types of real numbers that we work with in this book.

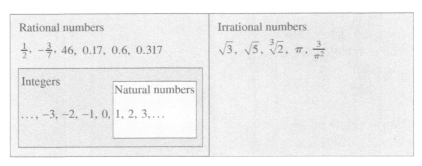

FIGURE 1 The real number system

Every real number has a decimal representation. If the number is rational, then its corresponding decimal is repeating. For example,

$$\frac{1}{2} = 0.5000\ldots = 0.5\overline{0} \qquad\qquad \frac{2}{3} = 0.66666\ldots = 0.\overline{6}$$

$$\frac{157}{495} = 0.3171717\ldots = 0.3\overline{17} \qquad \frac{9}{7} = 1.285714285714\ldots = 1.\overline{285714}$$

(The bar indicates that the sequence of digits repeats forever.) If the number is irrational, the decimal representation is nonrepeating:

$$\sqrt{2} = 1.414213562373095\ldots \qquad \pi = 3.141592653589793\ldots$$

The different types of real numbers were invented to meet specific needs. For example, natural numbers are needed for counting, negative numbers for describing debt or below-zero temperatures, rational numbers for concepts like "half a gallon of milk," and irrational numbers for measuring certain distances, like the diagonal of a square.

A repeating decimal such as

$$x = 3.5474747\ldots$$

is a rational number. To convert it to a ratio of two integers, we write

$$\begin{aligned} 1000x &= 3547.47474747\ldots \\ 10x &= 35.47474747\ldots \\ \hline 990x &= 3512.0 \end{aligned}$$

Thus, $x = \frac{3512}{990}$. (The idea is to multiply x by appropriate powers of 10 and then subtract to eliminate the repeating part.)

If we stop the decimal expansion of any number at a certain place, we get an approximation to the number. For instance, we can write

$$\pi \approx 3.14159265$$

where the symbol $\approx$ is read "is approximately equal to." The more decimal places we retain, the better our approximation.

▼ Properties of Real Numbers

We all know that $2 + 3 = 3 + 2$, and $5 + 7 = 7 + 5$, and $513 + 87 = 87 + 513$, and so on. In algebra, we express all these (infinitely many) facts by writing

$$a + b = b + a$$

where a and b stand for any two numbers. In other words, "$a + b = b + a$" is a concise way of saying that "when we add two numbers, the order of addition doesn't matter." This fact is called the *Commutative Property* for addition. From our experience with numbers we know that the properties in the following box are also valid.

PROPERTIES OF REAL NUMBERS

Property	Example	Description
Commutative Properties		
$a + b = b + a$	$7 + 3 = 3 + 7$	When we add two numbers, order doesn't matter.
$ab = ba$	$3 \cdot 5 = 5 \cdot 3$	When we multiply two numbers, order doesn't matter.
Associative Properties		
$(a + b) + c = a + (b + c)$	$(2 + 4) + 7 = 2 + (4 + 7)$	When we add three numbers, it doesn't matter which two we add first.
$(ab)c = a(bc)$	$(3 \cdot 7) \cdot 5 = 3 \cdot (7 \cdot 5)$	When we multiply three numbers, it doesn't matter which two we multiply first.
Distributive Property		
$a(b + c) = ab + ac$	$2 \cdot (3 + 5) = 2 \cdot 3 + 2 \cdot 5$	When we multiply a number by a sum of two numbers, we get the same result as we would get if we multiply the number by each of the terms and then add the results.
$(b + c)a = ab + ac$	$(3 + 5) \cdot 2 = 2 \cdot 3 + 2 \cdot 5$	

The Distributive Property applies whenever we multiply a number by a sum. Figure 2 explains why this property works for the case in which all the numbers are positive integers, but the property is true for any real numbers a, b, and c.

The Distributive Property is crucial because it describes the way addition and multiplication interact with each other.

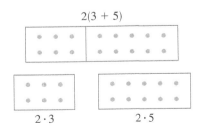

FIGURE 2 The Distributive Property

EXAMPLE 1 | Using the Distributive Property

(a) $2(x + 3) = 2 \cdot x + 2 \cdot 3$ Distributive Property

$= 2x + 6$ Simplify

(b) $(a + b)(x + y) = (a + b)x + (a + b)y$ Distributive Property

$= (ax + bx) + (ay + by)$ Distributive Property

$= ax + bx + ay + by$ Associative Property of Addition

In the last step we removed the parentheses because, according to the Associative Property, the order of addition doesn't matter.

✎ NOW TRY EXERCISE **11**

▼ Addition and Subtraction

🚫 Don't assume that $-a$ is a negative number. Whether $-a$ is negative or positive depends on the value of a. For example, if $a = 5$, then $-a = -5$, a negative number, but if $a = -5$, then $-a = -(-5) = 5$ (Property 2), a positive number.

The number 0 is special for addition; it is called the **additive identity** because $a + 0 = a$ for any real number a. Every real number a has a **negative**, $-a$, that satisfies $a + (-a) = 0$. **Subtraction** is the operation that undoes addition; to subtract a number from another, we simply add the negative of that number. By definition

$$a - b = a + (-b)$$

To combine real numbers involving negatives, we use the following properties.

PROPERTIES OF NEGATIVES	
Property	**Example**
1. $(-1)a = -a$	$(-1)5 = -5$
2. $-(-a) = a$	$-(-5) = 5$
3. $(-a)b = a(-b) = -(ab)$	$(-5)7 = 5(-7) = -(5 \cdot 7)$
4. $(-a)(-b) = ab$	$(-4)(-3) = 4 \cdot 3$
5. $-(a + b) = -a - b$	$-(3 + 5) = -3 - 5$
6. $-(a - b) = b - a$	$-(5 - 8) = 8 - 5$

Property 6 states the intuitive fact that $a - b$ and $b - a$ are negatives of each other. Property 5 is often used with more than two terms:

$$-(a + b + c) = -a - b - c$$

EXAMPLE 2 | Using Properties of Negatives

Let x, y, and z be real numbers.

(a) $-(x + 2) = -x - 2$ Property 5: $-(a + b) = -a - b$

(b) $-(x + y - z) = -x - y - (-z)$ Property 5: $-(a + b) = -a - b$

$= -x - y + z$ Property 2: $-(-a) = a$

✎ NOW TRY EXERCISE **23**

▼ Multiplication and Division

The number 1 is special for multiplication; it is called the **multiplicative identity** because $a \cdot 1 = a$ for any real number a. Every nonzero real number a has an **inverse**, $1/a$, that satisfies $a \cdot (1/a) = 1$. **Division** is the operation that undoes multiplication; to divide by a number, we multiply by the inverse of that number. If $b \neq 0$, then, by definition,

$$a \div b = a \cdot \frac{1}{b}$$

We write $a \cdot (1/b)$ as simply a/b. We refer to a/b as the **quotient** of a and b or as the **fraction** a over b; a is the **numerator** and b is the **denominator** (or **divisor**). To combine real numbers using the operation of division, we use the following properties.

PROPERTIES OF FRACTIONS

Property	Example	Description
1. $\dfrac{a}{b} \cdot \dfrac{c}{d} = \dfrac{ac}{bd}$	$\dfrac{2}{3} \cdot \dfrac{5}{7} = \dfrac{2 \cdot 5}{3 \cdot 7} = \dfrac{10}{21}$	When **multiplying fractions**, multiply numerators and denominators.
2. $\dfrac{a}{b} \div \dfrac{c}{d} = \dfrac{a}{b} \cdot \dfrac{d}{c}$	$\dfrac{2}{3} \div \dfrac{5}{7} = \dfrac{2}{3} \cdot \dfrac{7}{5} = \dfrac{14}{15}$	When **dividing fractions**, invert the divisor and multiply.
3. $\dfrac{a}{c} + \dfrac{b}{c} = \dfrac{a + b}{c}$	$\dfrac{2}{5} + \dfrac{7}{5} = \dfrac{2 + 7}{5} = \dfrac{9}{5}$	When **adding fractions** with the **same denominator**, add the numerators.
4. $\dfrac{a}{b} + \dfrac{c}{d} = \dfrac{ad + bc}{bd}$	$\dfrac{2}{5} + \dfrac{3}{7} = \dfrac{2 \cdot 7 + 3 \cdot 5}{35} = \dfrac{29}{35}$	When **adding fractions** with **different denominators**, find a common denominator. Then add the numerators.
5. $\dfrac{ac}{bc} = \dfrac{a}{b}$	$\dfrac{2 \cdot 5}{3 \cdot 5} = \dfrac{2}{3}$	**Cancel** numbers that are **common factors** in numerator and denominator.
6. If $\dfrac{a}{b} = \dfrac{c}{d}$, then $ad = bc$	$\dfrac{2}{3} = \dfrac{6}{9}$, so $2 \cdot 9 = 3 \cdot 6$	**Cross-multiply.**

When adding fractions with different denominators, we don't usually use Property 4. Instead we rewrite the fractions so that they have the smallest possible common denominator (often smaller than the product of the denominators), and then we use Property 3. This denominator is the **Least Common Denominator (LCD)** described in the next example.

EXAMPLE 3 | Using the LCD to Add Fractions

Evaluate: $\dfrac{5}{36} + \dfrac{7}{120}$

SOLUTION Factoring each denominator into prime factors gives

$$36 = 2^2 \cdot 3^2 \qquad \text{and} \qquad 120 = 2^3 \cdot 3 \cdot 5$$

We find the least common denominator (LCD) by forming the product of all the factors that occur in these factorizations, using the highest power of each factor.

Thus the LCD is $2^3 \cdot 3^2 \cdot 5 = 360$. So

$$\frac{5}{36} + \frac{7}{120} = \frac{5 \cdot 10}{36 \cdot 10} + \frac{7 \cdot 3}{120 \cdot 3} \qquad \text{Use common denominator}$$

$$= \frac{50}{360} + \frac{21}{360} = \frac{71}{360} \qquad \text{Property 3: Adding fractions with the same denominator}$$

✎ NOW TRY EXERCISE **25**

▼ The Real Line

The real numbers can be represented by points on a line, as shown in Figure 3. The positive direction (toward the right) is indicated by an arrow. We choose an arbitrary reference point O, called the **origin**, which corresponds to the real number 0. Given any convenient unit of measurement, each positive number x is represented by the point on the line a distance of x units to the right of the origin, and each negative number $-x$ is represented by the point x units to the left of the origin. The number associated with the point P is called the coordinate of P, and the line is then called a **coordinate line**, or a **real number line**, or simply a **real line**. Often we identify the point with its coordinate and think of a number as being a point on the real line.

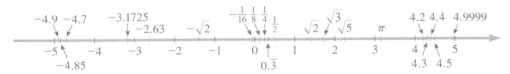

FIGURE 3 The real line

The real numbers are *ordered*. We say that ***a* is less than *b*** and write $a < b$ if $b - a$ is a positive number. Geometrically, this means that a lies to the left of b on the number line. Equivalently, we can say that ***b* is greater than *a*** and write $b > a$. The symbol $a \leq b$ (or $b \geq a$) means that either $a < b$ or $a = b$ and is read "a is less than or equal to b." For instance, the following are true inequalities (see Figure 4):

$$7 < 7.4 < 7.5 \qquad -\pi < -3 \qquad \sqrt{2} < 2 \qquad 2 \leq 2$$

FIGURE 4

▼ Sets and Intervals

A **set** is a collection of objects, and these objects are called the **elements** of the set. If S is a set, the notation $a \in S$ means that a is an element of S, and $b \notin S$ means that b is not an element of S. For example, if Z represents the set of integers, then $-3 \in Z$ but $\pi \notin Z$.

Some sets can be described by listing their elements within braces. For instance, the set A that consists of all positive integers less than 7 can be written as

$$A = \{1, 2, 3, 4, 5, 6\}$$

We could also write A in **set-builder notation** as

$$A = \{x \mid x \text{ is an integer and } 0 < x < 7\}$$

which is read "A is the set of all x such that x is an integer and $0 < x < 7$."

If S and T are sets, then their **union** $S \cup T$ is the set that consists of all elements that are in S *or* T (or in both). The **intersection** of S and T is the set $S \cap T$ consisting of all elements that are in both S *and* T. In other words, $S \cap T$ is the common part of S and T. The **empty set**, denoted by $\varnothing$, is the set that contains no element.

EXAMPLE 4 | Union and Intersection of Sets

If $S = \{1, 2, 3, 4, 5\}$, $T = \{4, 5, 6, 7\}$, and $V = \{6, 7, 8\}$, find the sets $S \cup T$, $S \cap T$, and $S \cap V$.

SOLUTION

$$S \cup T = \{1, 2, 3, 4, 5, 6, 7\} \qquad \text{All elements in } S \text{ or } T$$

$$S \cap T = \{4, 5\} \qquad \text{Elements common to both } S \text{ and } T$$

$$S \cap V = \varnothing \qquad S \text{ and } V \text{ have no element in common}$$

✎ ⌐ NOW TRY EXERCISE **39**

Certain sets of real numbers, called **intervals**, occur frequently in calculus and correspond geometrically to line segments. If $a < b$, then the **open interval** from a to b consists of all numbers between a and b and is denoted (a, b). The **closed interval** from a to b includes the endpoints and is denoted $[a, b]$. Using set-builder notation, we can write

$$(a, b) = \{x \mid a < x < b\} \qquad [a, b] = \{x \mid a \le x \le b\}$$

Note that parentheses ( ) in the interval notation and open circles on the graph in Figure 5 indicate that endpoints are *excluded* from the interval, whereas square brackets [ ] and solid circles in Figure 6 indicate that the endpoints are *included*. Intervals may also include one endpoint but not the other, or they may extend infinitely far in one direction or both. The following table lists the possible types of intervals.

FIGURE 5 The open interval (a, b)

FIGURE 6 The closed interval $[a, b]$

The symbol ∞ ("infinity") does not stand for a number. The notation (a, ∞), for instance, simply indicates that the interval has no endpoint on the right but extends infinitely far in the positive direction.

Notation	Set description	Graph
(a, b)	$\{x \mid a < x < b\}$	
$[a, b]$	$\{x \mid a \le x \le b\}$	
$[a, b)$	$\{x \mid a \le x < b\}$	
$(a, b]$	$\{x \mid a < x \le b\}$	
(a, ∞)	$\{x \mid a < x\}$	
$[a, \infty)$	$\{x \mid a \le x\}$	
$(-\infty, b)$	$\{x \mid x < b\}$	
$(-\infty, b]$	$\{x \mid x \le b\}$	
$(-\infty, \infty)$	$\mathbb{R}$ (set of all real numbers)	

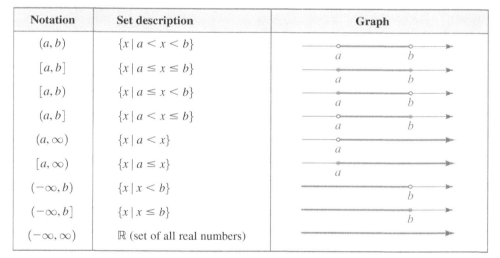

EXAMPLE 5 | Graphing Intervals

Express each interval in terms of inequalities, and then graph the interval.

(a) $[-1, 2) = \{x \mid -1 \le x < 2\}$

(b) $[1.5, 4] = \{x \mid 1.5 \le x \le 4\}$

(c) $(-3, \infty) = \{x \mid -3 < x\}$

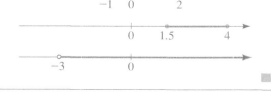

✎ ⌐ NOW TRY EXERCISE **45**

No Smallest or Largest Number in an Open Interval
Any interval contains infinitely many numbers—every point on the graph of an interval corresponds to a real number. In the closed interval $[0, 1]$, the smallest number is 0 and the largest is 1, but the open interval $(0, 1)$ contains no smallest or largest number. To see this, note that 0.01 is close to zero, but 0.001 is closer, 0.0001 is closer yet, and so on. We can always find a number in the interval $(0, 1)$ closer to zero than any given number. Since 0 itself is not in the interval, the interval contains no smallest number. Similarly, 0.99 is close to 1, but 0.999 is closer, 0.9999 closer yet, and so on. Since 1 itself is not in the interval, the interval has no largest number.

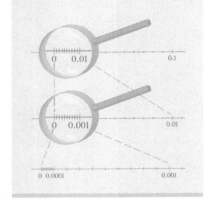

EXAMPLE 6 | Finding Unions and Intersections of Intervals

Graph each set.

(a) $(1, 3) \cap [2, 7]$ **(b)** $(1, 3) \cup [2, 7]$

SOLUTION

(a) The intersection of two intervals consists of the numbers that are in both intervals. Therefore

$$(1, 3) \cap [2, 7] = \{x \mid 1 < x < 3 \text{ and } 2 \le x \le 7\}$$
$$= \{x \mid 2 \le x < 3\} = [2, 3)$$

This set is illustrated in Figure 7.

(b) The union of two intervals consists of the numbers that are in either one interval or the other (or both). Therefore

$$(1, 3) \cup [2, 7] = \{x \mid 1 < x < 3 \text{ or } 2 \le x \le 7\}$$
$$= \{x \mid 1 < x \le 7\} = (1, 7]$$

This set is illustrated in Figure 8.

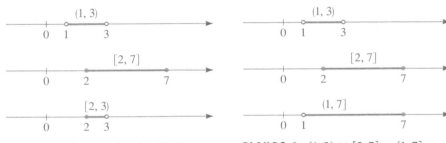

FIGURE 7 $(1, 3) \cap [2, 7] = [2, 3)$ **FIGURE 8** $(1, 3) \cup [2, 7] = (1, 7]$

✎. NOW TRY EXERCISE **59**

▼ Absolute Value and Distance

The **absolute value** of a number a, denoted by $|a|$, is the distance from a to 0 on the real number line (see Figure 9). Distance is always positive or zero, so we have $|a| \ge 0$ for every number a. Remembering that $-a$ is positive when a is negative, we have the following definition.

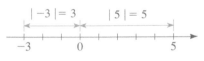

FIGURE 9

DEFINITION OF ABSOLUTE VALUE

If a is a real number, then the **absolute value** of a is

$$|a| = \begin{cases} a & \text{if } a \ge 0 \\ -a & \text{if } a < 0 \end{cases}$$

EXAMPLE 7 | Evaluating Absolute Values of Numbers

(a) $|3| = 3$

(b) $|-3| = -(-3) = 3$

(c) $|0| = 0$

(d) $|3 - \pi| = -(3 - \pi) = \pi - 3$ (since $3 < \pi \Rightarrow 3 - \pi < 0$)

✎. NOW TRY EXERCISE **65**

When working with absolute values, we use the following properties.

PROPERTIES OF ABSOLUTE VALUE

Property	Example	Description
1. $\lvert a \rvert \geq 0$	$\lvert -3 \rvert = 3 \geq 0$	The absolute value of a number is always positive or zero.
2. $\lvert a \rvert = \lvert -a \rvert$	$\lvert 5 \rvert = \lvert -5 \rvert$	A number and its negative have the same absolute value.
3. $\lvert ab \rvert = \lvert a \rvert \lvert b \rvert$	$\lvert -2 \cdot 5 \rvert = \lvert -2 \rvert \lvert 5 \rvert$	The absolute value of a product is the product of the absolute values.
4. $\left\lvert \dfrac{a}{b} \right\rvert = \dfrac{\lvert a \rvert}{\lvert b \rvert}$	$\left\lvert \dfrac{12}{-3} \right\rvert = \dfrac{\lvert 12 \rvert}{\lvert -3 \rvert}$	The absolute value of a quotient is the quotient of the absolute values.

What is the distance on the real line between the numbers -2 and 11? From Figure 10 we see that the distance is 13. We arrive at this by finding either $\lvert 11 - (-2) \rvert = 13$ or $\lvert (-2) - 11 \rvert = 13$. From this observation we make the following definition (see Figure 11).

FIGURE 10

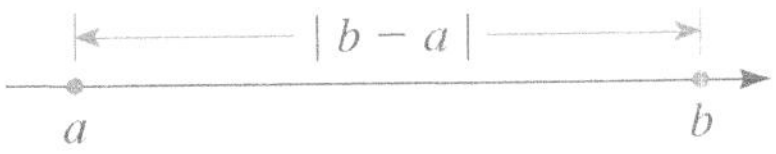

FIGURE 11 Length of a line segment is $\lvert b - a \rvert$

DISTANCE BETWEEN POINTS ON THE REAL LINE

If a and b are real numbers, then the **distance** between the points a and b on the real line is

$$d(a, b) = \lvert b - a \rvert$$

From Property 6 of negatives it follows that

$$\lvert b - a \rvert = \lvert a - b \rvert$$

This confirms that, as we would expect, the distance from a to b is the same as the distance from b to a.

EXAMPLE 8 | Distance Between Points on the Real Line

The distance between the numbers -8 and 2 is

$$d(a, b) = \lvert -8 - 2 \rvert = \lvert -10 \rvert = 10$$

FIGURE 12

We can check this calculation geometrically, as shown in Figure 12.

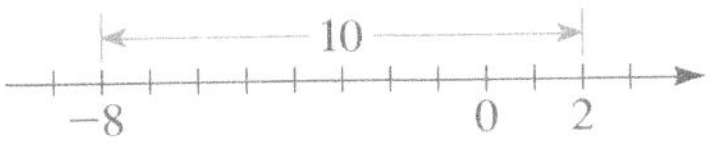

NOW TRY EXERCISE **73**

1.1 EXERCISES

CONCEPTS

1. Give an example of each of the following:
(a) A natural number
(b) An integer that is not a natural number
(c) A rational number that is not an integer
(d) An irrational number

2. Complete each statement and name the property of real numbers you have used.
(a) $ab = $ _____; _____ Property
(b) $a + (b + c) = $ _____; _____ Property
(c) $a(b + c) = $ _____; _____ Property

3. The set of numbers between but not including 2 and 7 can be written as follows:
_____ in set-builder notation and
_____ in interval notation.

4. The symbol $|x|$ stands for the _____ of the number x. If x is not 0, then the sign of $|x|$ is always _____.

SKILLS

5–6 ■ List the elements of the given set that are
(a) natural numbers
(b) integers
(c) rational numbers
(d) irrational numbers

5. $\{0, -10, 50, \frac{22}{7}, 0.538, \sqrt{7}, 1.2\overline{3}, -\frac{1}{3}, \sqrt[3]{2}\}$

6. $\{1.001, 0.333\ldots, -\pi, -11, 11, \frac{13}{15}, \sqrt{16}, 3.14, \frac{15}{3}\}$

7–14 ■ State the property of real numbers being used.

7. $7 + 10 = 10 + 7$

8. $2(3 + 5) = (3 + 5)2$

9. $(x + 2y) + 3z = x + (2y + 3z)$

10. $2(A + B) = 2A + 2B$

11. $(5x + 1)3 = 15x + 3$

12. $(x + a)(x + b) = (x + a)x + (x + a)b$

13. $2x(3 + y) = (3 + y)2x$

14. $7(a + b + c) = 7(a + b) + 7c$

15–18 ■ Rewrite the expression using the given property of real numbers.

15. Commutative Property of addition, $x + 3 = $

16. Associative Property of multiplication, $7(3x) = $

17. Distributive Property, $4(A + B) = $

18. Distributive Property, $5x + 5y = $

19–24 ■ Use properties of real numbers to write the expression without parentheses.

19. $3(x + y)$

20. $(a - b)8$

21. $4(2m)$

22. $\frac{4}{3}(-6y)$

23. $-\frac{5}{2}(2x - 4y)$

24. $(3a)(b + c - 2d)$

25–30 ■ Perform the indicated operations.

25. (a) $\frac{3}{10} + \frac{4}{15}$ (b) $\frac{1}{4} + \frac{1}{5}$

26. (a) $\frac{2}{3} - \frac{3}{5}$ (b) $1 + \frac{5}{8} - \frac{1}{6}$

27. (a) $\frac{2}{3}(6 - \frac{3}{2})$ (b) $0.25(\frac{8}{9} + \frac{1}{2})$

28. (a) $(3 + \frac{1}{4})(1 - \frac{4}{5})$ (b) $(\frac{1}{2} - \frac{1}{3})(\frac{1}{2} + \frac{1}{3})$

29. (a) $\dfrac{\frac{2}{3} - \frac{2}{3}}{2}$ (b) $\dfrac{\frac{1}{12}}{\frac{1}{8} - \frac{1}{9}}$

30. (a) $\dfrac{2 - \frac{3}{4}}{\frac{1}{2} - \frac{1}{3}}$ (b) $\dfrac{\frac{2}{5} + \frac{1}{2}}{\frac{1}{10} + \frac{3}{15}}$

31–32 ■ Place the correct symbol ($<$, $>$, or $=$) in the space.

31. (a) $3 \quad \frac{7}{2}$ (b) $-3 \quad -\frac{7}{2}$ (c) $3.5 \quad \frac{7}{2}$

32. (a) $\frac{2}{3} \quad 0.67$ (b) $\frac{2}{3} \quad -0.67$ (c) $|0.67| \quad |-0.67|$

33–36 ■ State whether each inequality is true or false.

33. (a) $-6 < -10$ (b) $\sqrt{2} > 1.41$

34. (a) $\frac{10}{11} < \frac{12}{13}$ (b) $-\frac{1}{2} < -1$

35. (a) $-\pi > -3$ (b) $8 \le 9$

36. (a) $1.1 > 1.\overline{1}$ (b) $8 \le 8$

37–38 ■ Write each statement in terms of inequalities.

37. (a) x is positive
(b) t is less than 4
(c) a is greater than or equal to π
(d) x is less than $\frac{1}{3}$ and is greater than -5
(e) The distance from p to 3 is at most 5

38. (a) y is negative
(b) z is greater than 1
(c) b is at most 8
(d) w is positive and is less than or equal to 17
(e) y is at least 2 units from π

39–42 ■ Find the indicated set if
$$A = \{1, 2, 3, 4, 5, 6, 7\} \qquad B = \{2, 4, 6, 8\}$$
$$C = \{7, 8, 9, 10\}$$

39. (a) $A \cup B$ (b) $A \cap B$

40. (a) $B \cup C$ (b) $B \cap C$

41. (a) $A \cup C$ (b) $A \cap C$

42. (a) $A \cup B \cup C$ (b) $A \cap B \cap C$

43–44 ■ Find the indicated set if

$$A = \{x \mid x \geq -2\} \qquad B = \{x \mid x < 4\}$$
$$C = \{x \mid -1 < x \leq 5\}$$

43. (a) $B \cup C$ **(b)** $B \cap C$

44. (a) $A \cap C$ **(b)** $A \cap B$

45–50 ■ Express the interval in terms of inequalities, and then graph the interval.

45. $(-3, 0)$ **46.** $(2, 8]$

47. $[2, 8)$ **48.** $[-6, -\frac{1}{2}]$

49. $[2, \infty)$ **50.** $(-\infty, 1)$

51–56 ■ Express the inequality in interval notation, and then graph the corresponding interval.

51. $x \leq 1$ **52.** $1 \leq x \leq 2$

53. $-2 < x \leq 1$ **54.** $x \geq -5$

55. $x > -1$ **56.** $-5 < x < 2$

57–58 ■ Express each set in interval notation.

57. (a)

(b)

58. (a)

(b)

59–64 ■ Graph the set.

59. $(-2, 0) \cup (-1, 1)$ **60.** $(-2, 0) \cap (-1, 1)$

61. $[-4, 6] \cap [0, 8)$ **62.** $[-4, 6) \cup [0, 8)$

63. $(-\infty, -4) \cup (4, \infty)$ **64.** $(-\infty, 6] \cap (2, 10)$

65–70 ■ Evaluate each expression.

65. (a) $|100|$ **(b)** $|-73|$

66. (a) $|\sqrt{5} - 5|$ **(b)** $|10 - \pi|$

67. (a) $||-6| - |-4||$ **(b)** $\dfrac{-1}{|-1|}$

68. (a) $|2 - |-12||$ **(b)** $-1 - |1 - |-1||$

69. (a) $|(-2) \cdot 6|$ **(b)** $|(-\frac{1}{3})(-15)|$

70. (a) $\left|\dfrac{-6}{24}\right|$ **(b)** $\left|\dfrac{7 - 12}{12 - 7}\right|$

71–74 ■ Find the distance between the given numbers.

71.

72.

73. (a) 2 and 17   **(b)** -3 and 21   **(c)** $\frac{11}{8}$ and $-\frac{3}{10}$

74. (a) $\frac{7}{15}$ and $-\frac{1}{21}$ **(b)** -38 and -57 **(c)** -2.6 and -1.8

75–76 ■ Express each repeating decimal as a fraction. (See the margin note on page 2.)

75. (a) $0.\overline{7}$ **(b)** $0.2\overline{8}$ **(c)** $0.\overline{57}$

76. (a) $5.\overline{23}$ **(b)** $1.3\overline{7}$ **(c)** $2.1\overline{35}$

APPLICATIONS

77. Area of a Garden Mary's backyard vegetable garden measures 20 ft by 30 ft, so its area is $20 \times 30 = 600$ ft^2. She decides to make it longer, as shown in the figure, so that the area increases to $A = 20(30 + x)$. Which property of real numbers tells us that the new area can also be written $A = 600 + 20x$?

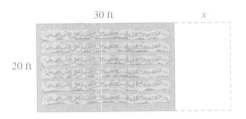

78. Temperature Variation The bar graph shows the daily high temperatures for Omak, Washington, and Geneseo, New York, during a certain week in June. Let T_O represent the temperature in Omak and T_G the temperature in Geneseo. Calculate $T_O - T_G$ and $|T_O - T_G|$ for each day shown. Which of these two values gives more information?

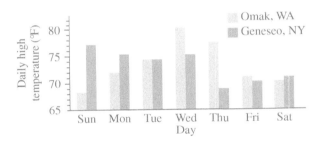

79. Mailing a Package The post office will only accept packages for which the length plus the "girth" (distance around) is no more than 108 inches. Thus, for the package in the figure, we must have

$$L + 2(x + y) \leq 108$$

(a) Will the post office accept a package that is 6 in. wide, 8 in. deep, and 5 ft long? What about a package that measures 2 ft by 2 ft by 4 ft?

(b) What is the greatest acceptable length for a package that has a square base measuring 9 in. by 9 in?

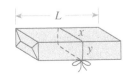
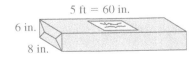

DISCOVERY ▪ DISCUSSION ▪ WRITING

80. Signs of Numbers   Let a, b, and c be real numbers such that $a > 0$, $b < 0$, and $c < 0$. Find the sign of each expression.

(a) $-a$ (b) $-b$ (c) bc

(d) $a - b$ (e) $c - a$ (f) $a + bc$

(g) $ab + ac$ (h) $-abc$ (i) ab^2

81. Sums and Products of Rational and Irrational Numbers   Explain why the sum, the difference, and the product of two rational numbers are rational numbers. Is the product of two irrational numbers necessarily irrational? What about the sum?

82. Combining Rational Numbers with Irrational Numbers   Is $\frac{1}{2} + \sqrt{2}$ rational or irrational? Is $\frac{1}{2} \cdot \sqrt{2}$ rational or irrational? In general, what can you say about the sum of a rational and an irrational number? What about the product?

83. Limiting Behavior of Reciprocals   Complete the tables. What happens to the size of the fraction $1/x$ as x gets large? As x gets small?

x	$1/x$
1	
2	
10	
100	
1000	

x	$1/x$
1.0	
0.5	
0.1	
0.01	
0.001	

84. Irrational Numbers and Geometry   Using the following figure, explain how to locate the point $\sqrt{2}$ on a number line. Can you locate $\sqrt{5}$ by a similar method? What about $\sqrt{6}$? List some other irrational numbers that can be located this way.

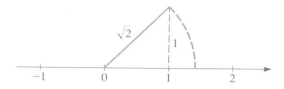

85. Commutative and Noncommutative Operations   We have seen that addition and multiplication are both commutative operations.

(a) Is subtraction commutative?

(b) Is division of nonzero real numbers commutative?

1.2 EXPONENTS AND RADICALS

| Integer Exponents ▶ Rules for Working with Exponents ▶ Scientific Notation ▶ Radicals ▶ Rational Exponents ▶ Rationalizing the Denominator

In this section we give meaning to expressions such as $a^{m/n}$ in which the exponent m/n is a rational number. To do this, we need to recall some facts about integer exponents, radicals, and nth roots.

▼ Integer Exponents

A product of identical numbers is usually written in exponential notation. For example, $5 \cdot 5 \cdot 5$ is written as 5^3. In general, we have the following definition.

EXPONENTIAL NOTATION

If a is any real number and n is a positive integer, then the **nth power** of a is

$$a^n = \underbrace{a \cdot a \cdot \cdots \cdot a}_{n \text{ factors}}$$

The number a is called the **base**, and n is called the **exponent**.

EXAMPLE 1 | Exponential Notation

(a) $\left(\frac{1}{2}\right)^5 = \left(\frac{1}{2}\right)\left(\frac{1}{2}\right)\left(\frac{1}{2}\right)\left(\frac{1}{2}\right)\left(\frac{1}{2}\right) = \frac{1}{32}$

(b) $(-3)^4 = (-3) \cdot (-3) \cdot (-3) \cdot (-3) = 81$

(c) $-3^4 = -(3 \cdot 3 \cdot 3 \cdot 3) = -81$

✎. NOW TRY EXERCISE **15**

Note the distinction between $(-3)^4$ and -3^4. In $(-3)^4$ the exponent applies to -3, but in -3^4 the exponent applies only to 3.

We can state several useful rules for working with exponential notation. To discover the rule for multiplication, we multiply 5^4 by 5^2:

$$5^4 \cdot 5^2 = \underbrace{(5 \cdot 5 \cdot 5 \cdot 5)}_{4 \text{ factors}}\underbrace{(5 \cdot 5)}_{2 \text{ factors}} = \underbrace{5 \cdot 5 \cdot 5 \cdot 5 \cdot 5 \cdot 5}_{6 \text{ factors}} = 5^6 = 5^{4+2}$$

It appears that *to multiply two powers of the same base, we add their exponents*. In general, for any real number a and any positive integers m and n, we have

$$a^m a^n = \underbrace{(a \cdot a \cdots\cdots a)}_{m \text{ factors}}\underbrace{(a \cdot a \cdots\cdots a)}_{n \text{ factors}} = \underbrace{a \cdot a \cdot a \cdots\cdots a}_{m+n \text{ factors}} = a^{m+n}$$

Thus $a^m a^n = a^{m+n}$.

We would like this rule to be true even when m and n are 0 or negative integers. For instance, we must have

$$2^0 \cdot 2^3 = 2^{0+3} = 2^3$$

But this can happen only if $2^0 = 1$. Likewise, we want to have

$$5^4 \cdot 5^{-4} = 5^{4+(-4)} = 5^{4-4} = 5^0 = 1$$

and this will be true if $5^{-4} = 1/5^4$. These observations lead to the following definition.

ZERO AND NEGATIVE EXPONENTS

If $a \neq 0$ is any real number and n is a positive integer, then

$$a^0 = 1 \qquad \text{and} \qquad a^{-n} = \frac{1}{a^n}$$

EXAMPLE 2 | Zero and Negative Exponents

(a) $\left(\frac{4}{7}\right)^0 = 1$

(b) $x^{-1} = \frac{1}{x^1} = \frac{1}{x}$

(c) $(-2)^{-3} = \frac{1}{(-2)^3} = \frac{1}{-8} = -\frac{1}{8}$

✎. NOW TRY EXERCISE **17**

▼ Rules for Working with Exponents

Familiarity with the following rules is essential for our work with exponents and bases. In the table the bases a and b are real numbers, and the exponents m and n are integers.

LAWS OF EXPONENTS

Law	Example	Description
1. $a^m a^n = a^{m+n}$	$3^2 \cdot 3^5 = 3^{2+5} = 3^7$	To multiply two powers of the same number, add the exponents.
2. $\dfrac{a^m}{a^n} = a^{m-n}$	$\dfrac{3^5}{3^2} = 3^{5-2} = 3^3$	To divide two powers of the same number, subtract the exponents.
3. $(a^m)^n = a^{mn}$	$(3^2)^5 = 3^{2\cdot5} = 3^{10}$	To raise a power to a new power, multiply the exponents.
4. $(ab)^n = a^n b^n$	$(3\cdot4)^2 = 3^2 \cdot 4^2$	To raise a product to a power, raise each factor to the power.
5. $\left(\dfrac{a}{b}\right)^n = \dfrac{a^n}{b^n}$	$\left(\dfrac{3}{4}\right)^2 = \dfrac{3^2}{4^2}$	To raise a quotient to a power, raise both numerator and denominator to the power.

PROOF OF LAW 3   If m and n are positive integers, we have

$$(a^m)^n = (\underbrace{a \cdot a \cdots\cdots a}_{m \text{ factors}})^n$$

$$= \underbrace{(\underbrace{a \cdot a \cdots\cdots a}_{m \text{ factors}})(\underbrace{a \cdot a \cdots\cdots a}_{m \text{ factors}}) \cdots (\underbrace{a \cdot a \cdots\cdots a}_{m \text{ factors}})}_{n \text{ groups of factors}}$$

$$= \underbrace{a \cdot a \cdots\cdots a}_{mn \text{ factors}} = a^{mn}$$

The cases for which $m \le 0$ or $n \le 0$ can be proved using the definition of negative exponents. ∎

PROOF OF LAW 4   If n is a positive integer, we have

$$(ab)^n = \underbrace{(ab)(ab) \cdots (ab)}_{n \text{ factors}} = (\underbrace{a \cdot a \cdots\cdots a}_{n \text{ factors}}) \cdot (\underbrace{b \cdot b \cdots\cdots b}_{n \text{ factors}}) = a^n b^n$$

Here we have used the Commutative and Associative Properties repeatedly. If $n \le 0$, Law 4 can be proved by using the definition of negative exponents. ∎

You are asked to prove Laws 2 and 5 in Exercise 94.

EXAMPLE 3 | Using Laws of Exponents

(a) $x^4 x^7 = x^{4+7} = x^{11}$ Law 1: $a^m a^n = a^{m+n}$

(b) $y^4 y^{-7} = y^{4-7} = y^{-3} = \dfrac{1}{y^3}$ Law 1: $a^m a^n = a^{m+n}$

(c) $\dfrac{c^9}{c^5} = c^{9-5} = c^4$ Law 2: $\dfrac{a^m}{a^n} = a^{m-n}$

(d) $(b^4)^5 = b^{4\cdot5} = b^{20}$ Law 3: $(a^m)^n = a^{mn}$

(e) $(3x)^3 = 3^3 x^3 = 27x^3$ Law 4: $(ab)^n = a^n b^n$

(f) $\left(\dfrac{x}{2}\right)^5 = \dfrac{x^5}{2^5} = \dfrac{x^5}{32}$ Law 5: $\left(\dfrac{a}{b}\right)^n = \dfrac{a^n}{b^n}$

✎ NOW TRY EXERCISES **35, 37,** AND **39**

EXAMPLE 4 | Simplifying Expressions with Exponents

Simplify:

(a) $(2a^3b^2)(3ab^4)^3$ **(b)** $\left(\dfrac{x}{y}\right)^3\left(\dfrac{y^2x}{z}\right)^4$

SOLUTION

(a)
$$
\begin{aligned}
(2a^3b^2)(3ab^4)^3 &= (2a^3b^2)[3^3a^3(b^4)^3] && \text{Law 4: } (ab)^n = a^nb^n \\
&= (2a^3b^2)(27a^3b^{12}) && \text{Law 3: } (a^m)^n = a^{mn} \\
&= (2)(27)a^3a^3b^2b^{12} && \text{Group factors with the same base} \\
&= 54a^6b^{14} && \text{Law 1: } a^ma^n = a^{m+n}
\end{aligned}
$$

(b)
$$
\begin{aligned}
\left(\dfrac{x}{y}\right)^3\left(\dfrac{y^2x}{z}\right)^4 &= \dfrac{x^3}{y^3}\dfrac{(y^2)^4x^4}{z^4} && \text{Laws 5 and 4} \\
&= \dfrac{x^3}{y^3}\dfrac{y^8x^4}{z^4} && \text{Law 3} \\
&= (x^3x^4)\left(\dfrac{y^8}{y^3}\right)\dfrac{1}{z^4} && \text{Group factors with the same base} \\
&= \dfrac{x^7y^5}{z^4} && \text{Laws 1 and 2}
\end{aligned}
$$

NOW TRY EXERCISES 43 AND 47

When simplifying an expression, you will find that many different methods will lead to the same result; you should feel free to use any of the rules of exponents to arrive at your own method. We now give two additional laws that are useful in simplifying expressions with negative exponents.

LAWS OF EXPONENTS

Law	Example	Description
6. $\left(\dfrac{a}{b}\right)^{-n} = \left(\dfrac{b}{a}\right)^n$	$\left(\dfrac{3}{4}\right)^{-2} = \left(\dfrac{4}{3}\right)^2$	To raise a fraction to a negative power, invert the fraction and change the sign of the exponent.
7. $\dfrac{a^{-n}}{b^{-m}} = \dfrac{b^m}{a^n}$	$\dfrac{3^{-2}}{4^{-5}} = \dfrac{4^5}{3^2}$	To move a number raised to a power from numerator to denominator or from denominator to numerator, change the sign of the exponent.

PROOF OF LAW 7   Using the definition of negative exponents and then Property 2 of fractions (page 5), we have

$$
\frac{a^{-n}}{b^{-m}} = \frac{1/a^n}{1/b^m} = \frac{1}{a^n}\cdot\frac{b^m}{1} = \frac{b^m}{a^n}
$$

You are asked to prove Law 6 in Exercise 94.

EXAMPLE 5 | Simplifying Expressions with Negative Exponents

Eliminate negative exponents and simplify each expression.

(a) $\dfrac{6st^{-4}}{2s^{-2}t^2}$ **(b)** $\left(\dfrac{y}{3z^3}\right)^{-2}$

SOLUTION

(a) We use Law 7, which allows us to move a number raised to a power from the numerator to the denominator (or vice versa) by changing the sign of the exponent.

t^{-4} moves to denominator and becomes t^4

s^{-2} moves to numerator and becomes s^2

$$\frac{6st^{-4}}{2s^{-2}t^2} = \frac{6ss^2}{2t^2t^4} \qquad \text{Law 7}$$

$$= \frac{3s^3}{t^6} \qquad \text{Law 1}$$

(b) We use Law 6, which allows us to change the sign of the exponent of a fraction by inverting the fraction.

$$\left(\frac{y}{3z^3}\right)^{-2} = \left(\frac{3z^3}{y}\right)^2 \qquad \text{Law 6}$$

$$= \frac{9z^6}{y^2} \qquad \text{Laws 5 and 4}$$

✎ NOW TRY EXERCISE **49**

▼ Scientific Notation

Scientists use exponential notation as a compact way of writing very large numbers and very small numbers. For example, the nearest star beyond the sun, Proxima Centauri, is approximately 40,000,000,000,000 km away. The mass of a hydrogen atom is about 0.00000000000000000000000166 g. Such numbers are difficult to read and to write, so scientists usually express them in *scientific notation.*

SCIENTIFIC NOTATION

A positive number x is said to be written in **scientific notation** if it is expressed as follows:

$$x = a \times 10^n \qquad \text{where } 1 \le a < 10 \text{ and } n \text{ is an integer}$$

For instance, when we state that the distance to the star Proxima Centauri is 4×10^{13} km, the positive exponent 13 indicates that the decimal point should be moved 13 places to the *right*:

$$4 \times 10^{13} = 40,000,000,000,000$$

Move decimal point 13 places to the right

When we state that the mass of a hydrogen atom is 1.66×10^{-24} g, the exponent -24 indicates that the decimal point should be moved 24 places to the *left*:

$$1.66 \times 10^{-24} = 0.00000000000000000000000166$$

Move decimal point 24 places to the left

EXAMPLE 6 | Changing from Decimal to Scientific Notation

Write each number in scientific notation.

(a) 56,920   (b) 0.000093

SOLUTION

(a) $56{,}920 = 5.692 \times 10^4$ (b) $0.000093 = 9.3 \times 10^{-5}$

$\underbrace{\qquad}_{\text{4 places}}$ $\underbrace{\qquad}_{\text{5 places}}$

✎. NOW TRY EXERCISES **77** AND **79**

Scientific notation is often used on a calculator to display a very large or very small number. For instance, if we use a calculator to square the number 1,111,111, the display panel may show (depending on the calculator model) the approximation

$$\boxed{\texttt{1.234568 12}} \quad \text{or} \quad \boxed{\texttt{1.23468 E12}}$$

Here the final digits indicate the power of 10, and we interpret the result as

$$1.234568 \times 10^{12}$$

EXAMPLE 7 | Calculating with Scientific Notation

If $a \approx 0.00046$, $b \approx 1.697 \times 10^{22}$, and $c \approx 2.91 \times 10^{-18}$, use a calculator to approximate the quotient ab/c.

SOLUTION   We could enter the data using scientific notation, or we could use laws of exponents as follows:

$$\frac{ab}{c} \approx \frac{(4.6 \times 10^{-4})(1.697 \times 10^{22})}{2.91 \times 10^{-18}}$$

$$= \frac{(4.6)(1.697)}{2.91} \times 10^{-4+22+18}$$

$$\approx 2.7 \times 10^{36}$$

We state the answer rounded to two significant figures because the least accurate of the given numbers is stated to two significant figures.

✎. NOW TRY EXERCISES **83** AND **85**

▼ Radicals

We know what 2^n means whenever n is an integer. To give meaning to a power, such as $2^{4/5}$, whose exponent is a rational number, we need to discuss radicals.

The symbol $\sqrt{}$ means "the positive square root of." Thus

$$\boxed{\sqrt{a} = b \quad \text{means} \quad b^2 = a \quad \text{and} \quad b \geq 0}$$

Since $a = b^2 \geq 0$, the symbol $\sqrt{a}$ makes sense only when $a \geq 0$. For instance,

$$\sqrt{9} = 3 \quad \text{because} \quad 3^2 = 9 \quad \text{and} \quad 3 \geq 0$$

To use scientific notation on a calculator, press the key labeled $\boxed{\text{E E}}$ or $\boxed{\text{E X P}}$ or $\boxed{\text{E E X}}$ to enter the exponent. For example, to enter the number 3.629×10^{15} on a TI-83 calculator, we enter

$$3.629 \;\boxed{\text{2ND}}\; \boxed{\text{E E}}\; 15$$

and the display reads

$$\texttt{3.629E15}$$

For guidelines on working with significant figures, see the Appendix, *Calculations and Significant Figures.*

It is true that the number 9 has two square roots, 3 and −3, but the notation $\sqrt{9}$ is reserved for the *positive* square root of 9 (sometimes called the *principal square root* of 9). If we want the negative root, we must write $-\sqrt{9}$, which is −3.

Square roots are special cases of *n*th roots. The *n*th root of *x* is the number that, when raised to the *n*th power, gives *x*.

DEFINITION OF *n*th ROOT

If *n* is any positive integer, then the **principal *n*th root** of *a* is defined as follows:

$$\sqrt[n]{a} = b \quad \text{means} \quad b^n = a$$

If *n* is even, we must have $a \geq 0$ and $b \geq 0$.

Thus

$$\sqrt[4]{81} = 3 \quad \text{because} \quad 3^4 = 81 \quad \text{and} \quad 3 \geq 0$$
$$\sqrt[3]{-8} = -2 \quad \text{because} \quad (-2)^3 = -8$$

But $\sqrt{-8}$, $\sqrt[4]{-8}$, and $\sqrt[6]{-8}$ are not defined. (For instance, $\sqrt{-8}$ is not defined because the square of every real number is nonnegative.)

Notice that

$$\sqrt{4^2} = \sqrt{16} = 4 \quad \text{but} \quad \sqrt{(-4)^2} = \sqrt{16} = 4 = |-4|$$

So the equation $\sqrt{a^2} = a$ is not always true; it is true only when $a \geq 0$. However, we can always write $\sqrt{a^2} = |a|$. This last equation is true not only for square roots, but for any even root. This and other rules used in working with *n*th roots are listed in the following box. In each property we assume that all the given roots exist.

PROPERTIES OF *n*th ROOTS

Property	Example
1. $\sqrt[n]{ab} = \sqrt[n]{a}\sqrt[n]{b}$	$\sqrt[3]{-8 \cdot 27} = \sqrt[3]{-8}\sqrt[3]{27} = (-2)(3) = -6$
2. $\sqrt[n]{\dfrac{a}{b}} = \dfrac{\sqrt[n]{a}}{\sqrt[n]{b}}$	$\sqrt[4]{\dfrac{16}{81}} = \dfrac{\sqrt[4]{16}}{\sqrt[4]{81}} = \dfrac{2}{3}$
3. $\sqrt[m]{\sqrt[n]{a}} = \sqrt[mn]{a}$	$\sqrt{\sqrt[3]{729}} = \sqrt[6]{729} = 3$
4. $\sqrt[n]{a^n} = a$ if *n* is odd	$\sqrt[3]{(-5)^3} = -5, \quad \sqrt[5]{2^5} = 2$
5. $\sqrt[n]{a^n} = |a|$ if *n* is even	$\sqrt[4]{(-3)^4} = |-3| = 3$

EXAMPLE 8 | Simplifying Expressions Involving *n*th Roots

(a) $\sqrt[3]{x^4} = \sqrt[3]{x^3 x}$ Factor out the largest cube

$\qquad = \sqrt[3]{x^3}\sqrt[3]{x}$ Property 1: $\sqrt[3]{ab} = \sqrt[3]{a}\sqrt[3]{b}$

$\qquad = x\sqrt[3]{x}$ Property 4: $\sqrt[3]{a^3} = a$

(b) $\sqrt[4]{81x^8 y^4} = \sqrt[4]{81}\sqrt[4]{x^8}\sqrt[4]{y^4}$ Property 1: $\sqrt[4]{abc} = \sqrt[4]{a}\sqrt[4]{b}\sqrt[4]{c}$

$\qquad = 3\sqrt[4]{(x^2)^4}|y|$ Property 5: $\sqrt[4]{a^4} = |a|$

$\qquad = 3x^2|y|$ Property 5: $\sqrt[4]{a^4} = |a|, \ |x^2| = x^2$

✎ NOW TRY EXERCISES **55** AND **57**

It is frequently useful to combine like radicals in an expression such as $2\sqrt{3} + 5\sqrt{3}$. This can be done by using the Distributive Property. Thus

$$2\sqrt{3} + 5\sqrt{3} = (2 + 5)\sqrt{3} = 7\sqrt{3}$$

The next example further illustrates this process.

EXAMPLE 9 | Combining Radicals

Avoid making the following error:

$$\sqrt{a + b} \,\,\cancel{}\,\, \sqrt{a} + \sqrt{b}$$

For instance, if we let $a = 9$ and $b = 16$, then we see the error:

$$\sqrt{9 + 16} \overset{?}{=} \sqrt{9} + \sqrt{16}$$

$$\sqrt{25} \overset{?}{=} 3 + 4$$

$$5 \overset{?}{=} 7 \quad \text{Wrong!}$$

(a) $\sqrt{32} + \sqrt{200} = \sqrt{16 \cdot 2} + \sqrt{100 \cdot 2}$ Factor out the largest squares

$$\qquad\qquad\qquad = \sqrt{16}\sqrt{2} + \sqrt{100}\sqrt{2} \qquad \text{Property 1: } \sqrt{ab} = \sqrt{a}\sqrt{b}$$

$$\qquad\qquad\qquad = 4\sqrt{2} + 10\sqrt{2} = 14\sqrt{2} \qquad \text{Distributive Property}$$

(b) If $b > 0$, then

$$\sqrt{25b} - \sqrt{b^3} = \sqrt{25}\sqrt{b} - \sqrt{b^2}\sqrt{b} \qquad \text{Property 1: } \sqrt{ab} = \sqrt{a}\sqrt{b}$$

$$\qquad\qquad\quad = 5\sqrt{b} - b\sqrt{b} \qquad \text{Property 5, } b > 0$$

$$\qquad\qquad\quad = (5 - b)\sqrt{b} \qquad \text{Distributive Property}$$

✒ **NOW TRY EXERCISES 29 AND 33**

▼ Rational Exponents

To define what is meant by a *rational exponent* or, equivalently, a *fractional exponent* such as $a^{1/3}$, we need to use radicals. To give meaning to the symbol $a^{1/n}$ in a way that is consistent with the Laws of Exponents, we would have to have

$$(a^{1/n})^n = a^{(1/n)n} = a^1 = a$$

So by the definition of nth root,

$$\boxed{a^{1/n} = \sqrt[n]{a}}$$

In general, we define rational exponents as follows.

DEFINITION OF RATIONAL EXPONENTS

For any rational exponent m/n in lowest terms, where m and n are integers and $n > 0$, we define

$$a^{m/n} = (\sqrt[n]{a})^m \qquad \text{or equivalently} \qquad a^{m/n} = \sqrt[n]{a^m}$$

If n is even, then we require that $a \geq 0$.

With this definition it can be proved that *the Laws of Exponents also hold for rational exponents*.

EXAMPLE 10 | Using the Definition of Rational Exponents

(a) $4^{1/2} = \sqrt{4} = 2$

(b) $8^{2/3} = (\sqrt[3]{8})^2 = 2^2 = 4$ Alternative solution: $8^{2/3} = \sqrt[3]{8^2} = \sqrt[3]{64} = 4$

(c) $125^{-1/3} = \dfrac{1}{125^{1/3}} = \dfrac{1}{\sqrt[3]{125}} = \dfrac{1}{5}$ **(d)** $\dfrac{1}{\sqrt[3]{x^4}} = \dfrac{1}{x^{4/3}} = x^{-4/3}$

✒ **NOW TRY EXERCISES 21 AND 23**

EXAMPLE 11 | Using the Laws of Exponents with Rational Exponents

(a) $a^{1/3}a^{7/3} = a^{8/3}$ Law 1: $a^m a^n = a^{m+n}$

(b) $\dfrac{a^{2/5}a^{7/5}}{a^{3/5}} = a^{2/5+7/5-3/5} = a^{6/5}$ Law 1, Law 2: $\dfrac{a^m}{a^n} = a^{m-n}$

(c) $(2a^3b^4)^{3/2} = 2^{3/2}(a^3)^{3/2}(b^4)^{3/2}$ Law 4: $(abc)^n = a^n b^n c^n$

$\qquad\qquad = (\sqrt{2})^3 a^{3(3/2)}b^{4(3/2)}$ Law 3: $(a^m)^n = a^{mn}$

$\qquad\qquad = 2\sqrt{2}a^{9/2}b^6$

(d) $\left(\dfrac{2x^{3/4}}{y^{1/3}}\right)^3 \left(\dfrac{y^4}{x^{-1/2}}\right) = \dfrac{2^3(x^{3/4})^3}{(y^{1/3})^3}\cdot(y^4x^{1/2})$ Laws 5, 4, and 7

$\qquad\qquad = \dfrac{8x^{9/4}}{y}\cdot y^4 x^{1/2}$ Law 3

$\qquad\qquad = 8x^{11/4}y^3$ Laws 1 and 2

✎ NOW TRY EXERCISES **61, 63, 67,** AND **69**

EXAMPLE 12 | Simplifying by Writing Radicals as Rational Exponents

(a) $(2\sqrt{x})(3\sqrt[3]{x}) = (2x^{1/2})(3x^{1/3})$ Definition of rational exponents

$\qquad\qquad = 6x^{1/2+1/3} = 6x^{5/6}$ Law 1

(b) $\sqrt{x\sqrt{x}} = (xx^{1/2})^{1/2}$ Definition of rational exponents

$\qquad\qquad = (x^{3/2})^{1/2}$ Law 1

$\qquad\qquad = x^{3/4}$ Law 3

✎ NOW TRY EXERCISES **71** AND **75**

▼ Rationalizing the Denominator

It is often useful to eliminate the radical in a denominator by multiplying both numerator and denominator by an appropriate expression. This procedure is called **rationalizing the denominator**. If the denominator is of the form $\sqrt{a}$, we multiply numerator and denominator by $\sqrt{a}$. In doing this we multiply the given quantity by 1, so we do not change its value. For instance,

$$\frac{1}{\sqrt{a}} = \frac{1}{\sqrt{a}}\cdot 1 = \frac{1}{\sqrt{a}}\cdot\frac{\sqrt{a}}{\sqrt{a}} = \frac{\sqrt{a}}{a}$$

Note that the denominator in the last fraction contains no radical. In general, if the denominator is of the form $\sqrt[n]{a^m}$ with $m < n$, then multiplying the numerator and denominator by $\sqrt[n]{a^{n-m}}$ will rationalize the denominator, because (for $a > 0$)

$$\sqrt[n]{a^m}\sqrt[n]{a^{n-m}} = \sqrt[n]{a^{m+n-m}} = \sqrt[n]{a^n} = a$$

EXAMPLE 13 | Rationalizing Denominators

This equals 1

(a) $\dfrac{2}{\sqrt{3}} = \dfrac{2}{\sqrt{3}}\cdot\dfrac{\sqrt{3}}{\sqrt{3}} = \dfrac{2\sqrt{3}}{3}$

(b) $\dfrac{1}{\sqrt[3]{x^2}} = \dfrac{1}{\sqrt[3]{x^2}} \dfrac{\sqrt[3]{x}}{\sqrt[3]{x}} = \dfrac{\sqrt[3]{x}}{\sqrt[3]{x^3}} = \dfrac{\sqrt[3]{x}}{x}$

(c) $\sqrt[7]{\dfrac{1}{a^2}} = \dfrac{1}{\sqrt[7]{a^2}} = \dfrac{1}{\sqrt[7]{a^2}} \dfrac{\sqrt[7]{a^5}}{\sqrt[7]{a^5}} = \dfrac{\sqrt[7]{a^5}}{\sqrt[7]{a^7}} = \dfrac{\sqrt[7]{a^5}}{a}$

■ NOW TRY EXERCISES **89** AND **91**

1.2 EXERCISES

CONCEPTS

1. (a) Using exponential notation, we can write the product
$5 \cdot 5 \cdot 5 \cdot 5 \cdot 5 \cdot 5$ as _____.

   (b) In the expression 3^4, the number 3 is called the _____,
   and the number 4 is called the _____.

2. (a) When we multiply two powers with the same base, we
   _____ the exponents. So $3^4 \cdot 3^5 =$ _____.

   (b) When we divide two powers with the same base, we
   _____ the exponents. So $\dfrac{3^5}{3^2} =$ _____.

3. (a) Using exponential notation, we can write $\sqrt[3]{5}$ as _____.

   (b) Using radicals, we can write $5^{1/2}$ as _____.

   (c) Is there a difference between $\sqrt{5^2}$ and $(\sqrt{5})^2$? Explain.

4. Explain what $4^{3/2}$ means, then calculate $4^{3/2}$ in two different ways:
   $(4^{1/2}) =$ _____ or $(4^3) =$ _____

5. Explain how we rationalize a denominator, then complete the
   following steps to rationalize $\dfrac{1}{\sqrt{3}}$:
   $$\dfrac{1}{\sqrt{3}} = \dfrac{1}{\sqrt{3}} \cdot \dfrac{}{} = \dfrac{}{}$$

6. Find the missing power in the following calculation:
   $5^{1/3} \cdot 5^{} = 5$.

SKILLS

7–14 ■ Write each radical expression using exponents, and each
exponential expression using radicals.

	Radical expression	Exponential expression
7.	$\dfrac{1}{\sqrt{5}}$	
8.	$\sqrt[3]{7^2}$	
9.		$4^{2/3}$
10.		$11^{-3/2}$
11.	$\sqrt[5]{5^3}$	
12.		$2^{-1.5}$

	Radical expression	Exponential expression
13.		$a^{2/5}$
14.	$\dfrac{1}{\sqrt{x^5}}$	

15–24 ■ Evaluate each expression.

15. (a) -3^2 **(b)** $(-3)^2$ **(c)** $\left(\tfrac{1}{3}\right)^4 (-3)^2$

16. (a) $5^4 \cdot 5^{-2}$ **(b)** $\dfrac{10^7}{10^4}$ **(c)** $\dfrac{3}{3^{-2}}$

17. (a) $\left(\tfrac{5}{3}\right)^0 2^{-1}$ **(b)** $\dfrac{2^{-3}}{3^0}$ **(c)** $\left(\tfrac{1}{4}\right)^{-2}$

18. (a) $\left(-\tfrac{2}{3}\right)^{-3}$ **(b)** $\left(\tfrac{3}{2}\right)^{-2} \cdot \tfrac{9}{16}$ **(c)** $\left(\tfrac{1}{2}\right)^4 \cdot \left(\tfrac{5}{2}\right)^{-2}$

19. (a) $\sqrt{16}$ **(b)** $\sqrt[4]{16}$ **(c)** $\sqrt[4]{\tfrac{1}{16}}$

20. (a) $\sqrt{64}$ **(b)** $\sqrt[3]{-64}$ **(c)** $\sqrt[5]{-32}$

21. (a) $\sqrt{\tfrac{4}{9}}$ **(b)** $\sqrt[4]{256}$ **(c)** $\sqrt[6]{\tfrac{1}{64}}$

22. (a) $\sqrt{7}\sqrt{28}$ **(b)** $\dfrac{\sqrt{48}}{\sqrt{3}}$ **(c)** $\sqrt[4]{24}\sqrt[4]{54}$

23. (a) $\left(\tfrac{4}{9}\right)^{-1/2}$ **(b)** $(-32)^{2/5}$ **(c)** $-32^{2/5}$

24. (a) $1024^{-0.1}$ **(b)** $\left(-\tfrac{27}{8}\right)^{2/3}$ **(c)** $\left(\tfrac{25}{64}\right)^{-3/2}$

25–28 ■ Evaluate the expression using $x = 3$, $y = 4$, and $z = -1$.

25. $\sqrt{x^2 + y^2}$ **26.** $\sqrt[4]{x^3 + 14y + 2z}$

27. $(9x)^{2/3} + (2y)^{2/3} + z^{2/3}$ **28.** $(xy)^{2z}$

29–34 ■ Simplify the expression.

29. $\sqrt{32} + \sqrt{18}$ **30.** $\sqrt{75} + \sqrt{48}$

31. $\sqrt[5]{96} + \sqrt[5]{3}$ **32.** $\sqrt[4]{48} - \sqrt[4]{3}$

33. $\sqrt{16x} + \sqrt{x^5}$ **34.** $\sqrt[3]{2y^4} - \sqrt[3]{y}$

35–40 ■ Simplify each expression.

35. (a) $x^8 x^2$ **(b)** $(3y^2)(4y^5)$ **(c)** $x^2 x^{-6}$

36. (a) $x^{-5} x^3$ **(b)** $w^{-2} w^{-4} w^6$ **(c)** $z^5 z^{-3} z^{-4}$

37. (a) $\dfrac{y^{10} y^0}{y^7}$ **(b)** $\dfrac{x^6}{x^{10}}$ **(c)** $\dfrac{a^9 a^{-2}}{a}$

38. (a) $\dfrac{z^2 z^4}{z^3 z^{-1}}$ **(b)** $(2y^2)^3$ **(c)** $(8x)^2$

39. (a) $(a^2a^4)^3$ (b) $\left(\dfrac{a^2}{4}\right)^3$ (c) $(3z)^2(6z^2)^{-3}$

40. (a) $(2z^2)^{-5}z^{10}$ (b) $(2a^3a^2)^4$ (c) $\left(\dfrac{3x^4}{4x^2}\right)^2$

41–52 ■ Simplify the expression and eliminate any negative exponents(s).

41. (a) $(4x^2y^4)(2x^5y)$ (b) $(8a^2z)(\tfrac{1}{2}a^3z^4)$

42. (a) $b^4(3ab^3)(2a^2b^{-5})$ (b) $(2s^3t^{-2})(\tfrac{1}{4}s^7t)(16t^4)$

43. (a) $(5x^2y^3)(3x^2y^5)^4$ (b) $(2a^3b^2)^2(5a^2b^5)^3$

44. (a) $(s^{-2}t^2)^2(s^2t)^3$ (b) $(2u^2v^3)^3(3u^{-3}v)^2$

45. (a) $\dfrac{6y^3z}{2yz^2}$ (b) $\dfrac{(xy^2z^3)^4}{(x^2y^2z)^3}$

46. (a) $\dfrac{2x^3y^4}{x^5y^3}$ (b) $\dfrac{(2v^3w)^2}{v^3w^2}$

47. (a) $\left(\dfrac{a^2}{b}\right)^5\left(\dfrac{a^3b^2}{c^3}\right)^3$ (b) $\dfrac{(u^{-1}v^2)^2}{(u^3v^{-2})^3}$

48. (a) $\left(\dfrac{x^4z^2}{4y^5}\right)\left(\dfrac{2x^3y^2}{z^3}\right)^2$ (b) $\dfrac{(rs^2)^3}{(r^{-3}s^2)^2}$

49. (a) $\dfrac{8a^3b^{-4}}{2a^{-5}b^5}$ (b) $\left(\dfrac{y}{5x^{-2}}\right)^{-3}$

50. (a) $\dfrac{5xy^{-2}}{x^{-1}y^{-3}}$ (b) $\left(\dfrac{2a^{-1}b}{a^2b^{-3}}\right)^{-3}$

51. (a) $\left(\dfrac{3a}{b^3}\right)^{-1}$ (b) $\left(\dfrac{q^{-1}r^{-1}s^{-2}}{r^{-5}sq^{-8}}\right)^{-1}$

52. (a) $\left(\dfrac{s^2t^{-4}}{5s^{-1}t}\right)$ (b) $\left(\dfrac{xy^{-2}z^{-3}}{x^2y^3z^{-4}}\right)^{-3}$

53–60 ■ Simplify the expression. Assume that the letters denote any real numbers.

53. $\sqrt[4]{x^4}$ **54.** $\sqrt[5]{x^{10}}$

55. $\sqrt[4]{16x^8}$ **56.** $\sqrt[3]{x^3y^6}$

57. $\sqrt[6]{64a^6b^7}$ **58.** $\sqrt[3]{a^2b}\sqrt[3]{64a^4b}$

59. $\sqrt[3]{\sqrt{64x^6}}$ **60.** $\sqrt[4]{x^4y^2z^2}$

61–70 ■ Simplify the expression and eliminate any negative exponent(s). Assume that all letters denote positive numbers.

61. (a) $x^{3/4}x^{5/4}$ (b) $y^{2/3}y^{4/3}$

62. (a) $(4b)^{1/2}(8b^{1/4})$ (b) $(3a^{3/4})^2(5a^{1/2})$

63. (a) $\dfrac{w^{4/3}w^{2/3}}{w^{1/3}}$ (b) $\dfrac{s^{5/2}(2s^{5/4})^2}{s^{1/2}}$

64. (a) $(8y^3)^{-2/3}$ (b) $(u^4v^6)^{-1/3}$

65. (a) $(8a^6b^{3/2})^{2/3}$ (b) $(4a^6b^8)^{3/2}$

66. (a) $(x^{-5}y^{1/3})^{-3/5}$ (b) $(2x^3y^{-1/4})^2(8y^{-3/2})^{-1/3}$

67. (a) $\dfrac{(8s^3t^3)^{2/3}}{(s^4t^{-8})^{1/4}}$ (b) $\dfrac{(32y^{-5}z^{10})^{1/5}}{(64y^6z^{-12})^{-1/6}}$

68. (a) $\left(\dfrac{x^8y^{-4}}{16y^{4/3}}\right)^{-1/4}$ (b) $\left(\dfrac{-8y^{3/4}}{y^3z^6}\right)^{-1/3}$

69. (a) $\left(\dfrac{x^{-2/3}}{y^{1/2}}\right)\left(\dfrac{x^{-2}}{y^{-3}}\right)^{1/6}$ (b) $\left(\dfrac{4y^3z^{2/3}}{x^{1/2}}\right)^2\left(\dfrac{x^{-3}y^6}{8z^4}\right)^{1/3}$

70. (a) $\left(\dfrac{a^{1/6}b^{-3}}{x^{-1}y}\right)^3\left(\dfrac{x^{-2}b^{-1}}{a^{3/2}y^{1/3}}\right)$ (b) $\dfrac{(9st)^{3/2}}{(27s^3t^{-4})^{2/3}}\left(\dfrac{3s^{-2}}{4t^{1/3}}\right)^{-1}$

71–76 ■ Simplify the expression and eliminate any negative exponents(s). Assume that all letters denote positive numbers.

71. (a) $\sqrt[6]{y^5}\sqrt[3]{y^2}$ (b) $(5\sqrt[3]{x})(2\sqrt[4]{x})$

72. (a) $\sqrt[4]{b^3}\sqrt{b}$ (b) $(2\sqrt{a})(\sqrt[3]{a^2})$

73. (a) $\sqrt{4st^3}\sqrt[6]{s^3t^2}$ (b) $\dfrac{\sqrt[4]{x^7}}{\sqrt[4]{x^3}}$

74. (a) $\sqrt[5]{x^3y^2}\sqrt[10]{x^4y^{16}}$ (b) $\dfrac{\sqrt[3]{8x^2}}{\sqrt{x}}$

75. (a) $\sqrt[3]{y}\sqrt{y}$ (b) $\sqrt{\dfrac{16u^3v}{uv^5}}$

76. (a) $\sqrt{s}\sqrt{s^3}$ (b) $\sqrt[3]{\dfrac{54x^2y^4}{2x^5y}}$

77–78 ■ Write each number in scientific notation.

77. (a) 69,300,000   (b) 7,200,000,000,000
     (c) 0.000028536   (d) 0.0001213

78. (a) 129,540,000   (b) 7,259,000,000
     (c) 0.0000000014   (d) 0.0007029

79–80 ■ Write each number in decimal notation.

79. (a) 3.19×10^5 (b) 2.721×10^8
     (c) 2.670×10^{-8} (d) 9.999×10^{-9}

80. (a) 7.1×10^{14} (b) 6×10^{12}
     (c) 8.55×10^{-3} (d) 6.257×10^{-10}

81–82 ■ Write the number indicated in each statement in scientific notation.

81. (a) A light-year, the distance that light travels in one year, is about 5,900,000,000,000 mi.

    (b) The diameter of an electron is about 0.0000000000004 cm.

    (c) A drop of water contains more than 33 billion billion molecules.

82. (a) The distance from the earth to the sun is about 93 million miles.

    (b) The mass of an oxygen molecule is about 0.0000000000000000000000053 g.

    (c) The mass of the earth is about 5,970,000,000,000,000,000,000,000 kg.

83–88 ■ Use scientific notation, the Laws of Exponents, and a calculator to perform the indicated operations. State your answer rounded to the number of significant digits indicated by the given data.

83. $(7.2 \times 10^{-9})(1.806 \times 10^{-12})$

84. $(1.062 \times 10^{24})(8.61 \times 10^{19})$

85. $\dfrac{1.295643 \times 10^9}{(3.610 \times 10^{-17})(2.511 \times 10^6)}$

86. $\dfrac{(73.1)(1.6341 \times 10^{28})}{0.0000000019}$

87. $\dfrac{(0.0000162)(0.01582)}{(594,621,000)(0.0058)}$

88. $\dfrac{(3.542 \times 10^{-6})^9}{(5.05 \times 10^4)^{12}}$

89–92 ■ Rationalize the denominator.

89. (a) $\dfrac{1}{\sqrt{10}}$ (b) $\sqrt{\dfrac{2}{x}}$ (c) $\sqrt{\dfrac{x}{3}}$

90. (a) $\sqrt{\dfrac{5}{12}}$ (b) $\sqrt{\dfrac{x}{6}}$ (c) $\sqrt{\dfrac{y}{2z}}$

91. (a) $\dfrac{2}{\sqrt[3]{x}}$ (b) $\dfrac{1}{\sqrt[4]{y^3}}$ (c) $\dfrac{x}{y^{2/5}}$

92. (a) $\dfrac{1}{\sqrt[4]{a}}$ (b) $\dfrac{a}{\sqrt[3]{b^2}}$ (c) $\dfrac{1}{c^{3/7}}$

93. Let a, b, and c be real numbers with $a > 0$, $b < 0$, and $c < 0$. Determine the sign of each expression.

(a) b^5 (b) b^{10} (c) ab^2c^3

(d) $(b - a)^3$ (e) $(b - a)^4$ (f) $\dfrac{a^3c^3}{b^6c^6}$

94. Prove the given Laws of Exponents for the case in which m and n are positive integers and $m > n$.

(a) Law 2   (b) Law 5   (c) Law 6

APPLICATIONS

95. Distance to the Nearest Star   Proxima Centauri, the star nearest to our solar system, is 4.3 light-years away. Use the information in Exercise 81(a) to express this distance in miles.

96. Speed of Light   The speed of light is about 186,000 mi/s. Use the information in Exercise 82(a) to find how long it takes for a light ray from the sun to reach the earth.

97. Volume of the Oceans   The average ocean depth is 3.7×10^3 m, and the area of the oceans is 3.6×10^{14} m². What is the total volume of the ocean in liters? (One cubic meter contains 1000 liters.)

98. National Debt   As of July 2010, the population of the United States was 3.070×10^8, and the national debt was 1.320×10^{13} dollars. How much was each person's share of the debt?

99. Number of Molecules   A sealed room in a hospital, measuring 5 m wide, 10 m long, and 3 m high, is filled with pure oxygen. One cubic meter contains 1000 L, and 22.4 L of any gas contains 6.02×10^{23} molecules (Avogadro's number). How many molecules of oxygen are there in the room?

100. How Far Can You See?   Because of the curvature of the earth, the maximum distance D that you can see from the top of a tall building of height h is estimated by the formula

$$D = \sqrt{2rh + h^2}$$

where $r = 3960$ mi is the radius of the earth and D and h are also measured in miles. How far can you see from the observation deck of the Toronto CN Tower, 1135 ft above the ground?

CN Tower

101. Speed of a Skidding Car   Police use the formula $s = \sqrt{30fd}$ to estimate the speed s (in mi/h) at which a car is traveling if it skids d feet after the brakes are applied suddenly. The number f is the coefficient of friction of the road, which is a measure of the "slipperiness" of the road. The table gives some typical estimates for f.

	Tar	Concrete	Gravel
Dry	1.0	0.8	0.2
Wet	0.5	0.4	0.1

(a) If a car skids 65 ft on wet concrete, how fast was it moving when the brakes were applied?

(b) If a car is traveling at 50 mi/h, how far will it skid on wet tar?

102. Distance from the Earth to the Sun It follows from **Kepler's Third Law** of planetary motion that the average distance from a planet to the sun (in meters) is

$$d = \left(\frac{GM}{4\pi^2}\right)^{1/3} T^{2/3}$$

where $M = 1.99 \times 10^{30}$ kg is the mass of the sun, $G = 6.67 \times 10^{-11}$ N $\cdot$ m^2/kg^2 is the gravitational constant, and T is the period of the planet's orbit (in seconds). Use the fact that the period of the earth's orbit is about 365.25 days to find the distance from the earth to the sun.

DISCOVERY ▪ DISCUSSION ▪ WRITING

103. How Big Is a Billion? If you had a million (10^6) dollars in a suitcase, and you spent a thousand (10^3) dollars each day, how many years would it take you to use all the money? Spending at the same rate, how many years would it take you to empty a suitcase filled with a *billion* (10^9) dollars?

104. Easy Powers That Look Hard Calculate these expressions in your head. Use the Laws of Exponents to help you.

(a) $\dfrac{18^5}{9^5}$

(b) $20^6 \cdot (0.5)^6$

105. Limiting Behavior of Powers Complete the following tables. What happens to the nth root of 2 as n gets large? What about the nth root of $\frac{1}{2}$?

n	$2^{1/n}$
1	
2	
5	
10	
100	

n	$\left(\frac{1}{2}\right)^{1/n}$
1	
2	
5	
10	
100	

Construct a similar table for $n^{1/n}$. What happens to the nth root of n as n gets large?

106. Comparing Roots Without using a calculator, determine which number is larger in each pair.

(a) $2^{1/2}$ or $2^{1/3}$

(b) $\left(\frac{1}{2}\right)^{1/2}$ or $\left(\frac{1}{2}\right)^{1/3}$

(c) $7^{1/4}$ or $4^{1/3}$

(d) $\sqrt[3]{5}$ or $\sqrt{3}$

1.3 ALGEBRAIC EXPRESSIONS

Adding and Subtracting Polynomials ▶ Multiplying Algebraic Expressions ▶ Special Product Formulas ▶ Factoring Common Factors ▶ Factoring Trinomials ▶ Special Factoring Formulas ▶ Factoring by Grouping Terms

A **variable** is a letter that can represent any number from a given set of numbers. If we start with variables, such as x, y, and z and some real numbers, and combine them using addition, subtraction, multiplication, division, powers, and roots, we obtain an **algebraic expression**. Here are some examples:

$$2x^2 - 3x + 4 \qquad \sqrt{x} + 10 \qquad \frac{y - 2z}{y^2 + 4}$$

A **monomial** is an expression of the form ax^k, where a is a real number and k is a nonnegative integer. A **binomial** is a sum of two monomials and a **trinomial** is a sum of three monomials. In general, a sum of monomials is called a *polynomial*. For example, the first expression listed above is a polynomial, but the other two are not.

> **POLYNOMIALS**
>
> A **polynomial** in the variable x is an expression of the form
>
> $$a_n x^n + a_{n-1}x^{n-1} + \cdots + a_1 x + a_0$$
>
> where $a_0, a_1, \ldots, a_n$ are real numbers, and n is a nonnegative integer. If $a_n \neq 0$, then the polynomial has **degree n**. The monomials $a_k x^k$ that make up the polynomial are called the **terms** of the polynomial.

Note that the degree of a polynomial is the highest power of the variable that appears in the polynomial.

Polynomial	Type	Terms	Degree
$2x^2 - 3x + 4$	trinomial	$2x^2, -3x, 4$	2
$x^8 + 5x$	binomial	$x^8, 5x$	8
$3 - x + x^2 - \frac{1}{2}x^3$	four terms	$-\frac{1}{2}x^3, x^2, -x, 3$	3
$5x + 1$	binomial	$5x, 1$	1
$9x^5$	monomial	$9x^5$	5
6	monomial	6	0

▼ Adding and Subtracting Polynomials

We **add** and **subtract** polynomials using the properties of real numbers that were discussed in Section 1.1. The idea is to combine **like terms** (that is, terms with the same variables raised to the same powers) using the Distributive Property. For instance,

Distributive Property

$ac + bc = (a + b)c$

$$5x^7 + 3x^7 = (5 + 3)x^7 = 8x^7$$

In subtracting polynomials, we have to remember that if a minus sign precedes an expression in parentheses, then the sign of every term within the parentheses is changed when we remove the parentheses:

$$-(b + c) = -b - c$$

[This is simply a case of the Distributive Property, $a(b + c) = ab + ac$, with $a = -1$.]

EXAMPLE 1 | Adding and Subtracting Polynomials

(a) Find the sum $(x^3 - 6x^2 + 2x + 4) + (x^3 + 5x^2 - 7x)$.

(b) Find the difference $(x^3 - 6x^2 + 2x + 4) - (x^3 + 5x^2 - 7x)$.

SOLUTION

(a) $(x^3 - 6x^2 + 2x + 4) + (x^3 + 5x^2 - 7x)$

$= (x^3 + x^3) + (-6x^2 + 5x^2) + (2x - 7x) + 4$ Group like terms

$= 2x^3 - x^2 - 5x + 4$ Combine like terms

(b) $(x^3 - 6x^2 + 2x + 4) - (x^3 + 5x^2 - 7x)$

$= x^3 - 6x^2 + 2x + 4 - x^3 - 5x^2 + 7x$ Distributive Property

$= (x^3 - x^3) + (-6x^2 - 5x^2) + (2x + 7x) + 4$ Group like terms

$= -11x^2 + 9x + 4$ Combine like terms

✎ . NOW TRY EXERCISES **15** AND **17**

▼ Multiplying Algebraic Expressions

To find the **product** of polynomials or other algebraic expressions, we need to use the Distributive Property repeatedly. In particular, using it three times on the product of two binomials, we get

$$(a + b)(c + d) = a(c + d) + b(c + d) = ac + ad + bc + bd$$

This says that we multiply the two factors by multiplying each term in one factor by each term in the other factor and adding these products. Schematically, we have

The acronym **FOIL** helps us remember that the product of two binomials is the sum of the products of the First terms, the Outer terms, the Inner terms, and the Last terms.

$$(a + b)(c + d) = ac + ad + bc + bd$$

$$\qquad\qquad\qquad \uparrow \quad \uparrow \quad \uparrow \quad \uparrow$$

$$\qquad\qquad\qquad F \quad O \quad I \quad L$$

In general, we can multiply two algebraic expressions by using the Distributive Property and the Laws of Exponents.

EXAMPLE 2 | Multiplying Binomials Using FOIL

$$(2x + 1)(3x - 5) = 6x^2 - 10x + 3x - 5 \qquad \text{Distributive Property}$$
$$\uparrow \qquad \uparrow \qquad \uparrow \qquad \uparrow$$
$$\text{F} \qquad \text{O} \qquad \text{I} \qquad \text{L}$$
$$= 6x^2 - 7x - 5 \qquad \text{Combine like terms}$$

✎ NOW TRY EXERCISE **23**

When we multiply trinomials or other polynomials with more terms, we use the Distributive Property. It is also helpful to arrange our work in table form. The next example illustrates both methods.

EXAMPLE 3 | Multiplying Polynomials

Find the product: $(2x + 3)(x^2 - 5x + 4)$

SOLUTION 1: Using the Distributive Property

$$\begin{aligned}
(2x + 3)(x^2 - 5x + 4) &= 2x(x^2 - 5x + 4) + 3(x^2 - 5x + 4) & \text{Distributive Property} \\
&= (2x \cdot x^2 - 2x \cdot 5x + 2x \cdot 4) + (3 \cdot x^2 - 3 \cdot 5x + 3 \cdot 4) & \text{Distributive Property} \\
&= (2x^3 - 10x^2 + 8x) + (3x^2 - 15x + 12) & \text{Laws of Exponents} \\
&= 2x^3 - 7x^2 - 7x + 12 & \text{Combine like terms}
\end{aligned}$$

SOLUTION 2: Using Table Form

$$
\begin{array}{r}
x^2 - 5x + 4 \\
2x + 3 \\
\hline
3x^2 - 15x + 12 \\
2x^3 - 10x^2 + 8x \\
\hline
2x^3 - 7x^2 - 7x + 12
\end{array}
$$

Multiply $x^2 - 5x + 4$ by 3

Multiply $x^2 - 5x + 4$ by $2x$

Add like terms

✎ NOW TRY EXERCISE **45**

▼ Special Product Formulas

Certain types of products occur so frequently that you should memorize them. You can verify the following formulas by performing the multiplications.

See the *Discovery Project* referenced on page 34 for a geometric interpretation of some of these formulas.

SPECIAL PRODUCT FORMULAS

If A and B are any real numbers or algebraic expressions, then

1. $(A + B)(A - B) = A^2 - B^2$ \qquad Sum and product of same terms

2. $(A + B)^2 = A^2 + 2AB + B^2$ \qquad Square of a sum

3. $(A - B)^2 = A^2 - 2AB + B^2$ \qquad Square of a difference

4. $(A + B)^3 = A^3 + 3A^2B + 3AB^2 + B^3$ \qquad Cube of a sum

5. $(A - B)^3 = A^3 - 3A^2B + 3AB^2 - B^3$ \qquad Cube of a difference

The key idea in using these formulas (or any other formula in algebra) is the **Principle of Substitution**: We may substitute any algebraic expression for any letter in a formula. For example, to find $(x^2 + y^3)^2$ we use Product Formula 2, substituting x^2 for A and y^3 for B, to get

$$(x^2 + y^3)^2 = (x^2)^2 + 2(x^2)(y^3) + (y^3)^2$$

$$(A + B)^2 \;=\; A^2 \;+\; 2AB \;+\; B^2$$

EXAMPLE 4 | Using the Special Product Formulas

Use the Special Product Formulas to find each product.

(a) $(3x + 5)^2$ **(b)** $(x^2 - 2)^3$

SOLUTION

(a) Substituting $A = 3x$ and $B = 5$ in Product Formula 2, we get

$$(3x + 5)^2 = (3x)^2 + 2(3x)(5) + 5^2 = 9x^2 + 30x + 25$$

(b) Substituting $A = x^2$ and $B = 2$ in Product Formula 5, we get

$$(x^2 - 2)^3 = (x^2)^3 - 3(x^2)^2(2) + 3(x^2)(2)^2 - 2^3$$
$$= x^6 - 6x^4 + 12x^2 - 8$$

✎ ⸱ NOW TRY EXERCISES **29** AND **41**

EXAMPLE 5 | Using the Special Product Formulas

Find each product.

(a) $(2x - \sqrt{y})(2x + \sqrt{y})$ **(b)** $(x + y - 1)(x + y + 1)$

SOLUTION

(a) Substituting $A = 2x$ and $B = \sqrt{y}$ in Product Formula 1, we get

$$(2x - \sqrt{y})(2x + \sqrt{y}) = (2x)^2 - (\sqrt{y})^2 = 4x^2 - y$$

(b) If we group $x + y$ together and think of this as one algebraic expression, we can use Product Formula 1 with $A = x + y$ and $B = 1$.

$$(x + y - 1)(x + y + 1) = [(x + y) - 1][(x + y) + 1]$$
$$= (x + y)^2 - 1^2 \qquad \text{Product Formula 1}$$
$$= x^2 + 2xy + y^2 - 1 \qquad \text{Product Formula 2}$$

✎ ⸱ NOW TRY EXERCISES **55** AND **59**

▼ Factoring Common Factors

We use the Distributive Property to expand algebraic expressions. We sometimes need to reverse this process (again using the Distributive Property) by **factoring** an expression as a product of simpler ones. For example, we can write

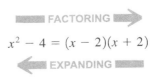

$$x^2 - 4 = (x - 2)(x + 2)$$

We say that $x - 2$ and $x + 2$ are **factors** of $x^2 - 4$.

The easiest type of factoring occurs when the terms have a common factor.

EXAMPLE 6 | Factoring Out Common Factors

Factor each expression.

(a) $3x^2 - 6x$ **(b)** $8x^4y^2 + 6x^3y^3 - 2xy^4$

(c) $(2x + 4)(x - 3) - 5(x - 3)$

SOLUTION

(a) The greatest common factor of the terms $3x^2$ and $-6x$ is $3x$, so we have

$$3x^2 - 6x = 3x(x - 2)$$

(b) We note that

$$8, 6, \text{ and } -2 \text{ have the greatest common factor } 2$$
$$x^4, x^3, \text{ and } x \text{ have the greatest common factor } x$$
$$y^2, y^3, \text{ and } y^4 \text{ have the greatest common factor } y^2$$

So the greatest common factor of the three terms in the polynomial is $2xy^2$, and we have

$$8x^4y^2 + 6x^3y^3 - 2xy^4 = (2xy^2)(4x^3) + (2xy^2)(3x^2y) + (2xy^2)(-y^2)$$
$$= 2xy^2(4x^3 + 3x^2y - y^2)$$

(c) The two terms have the common factor $x - 3$.

$$(2x + 4)(x - 3) - 5(x - 3) = [(2x + 4) - 5](x - 3) \qquad \text{Distributive Property}$$
$$= (2x - 1)(x - 3) \qquad \text{Simplify}$$

✎ **NOW TRY EXERCISES 61, 63, AND 65**

CHECK YOUR ANSWER

Multiplying gives

$$3x(x - 2) = 3x^2 - 6x \quad ✔$$

CHECK YOUR ANSWER

Multiplying gives

$$2xy^2(4x^3 + 3x^2y - y^2)$$
$$= 8x^4y^2 + 6x^3y^3 - 2xy^4 \quad ✔$$

▼ Factoring Trinomials

To factor a trinomial of the form $x^2 + bx + c$, we note that

$$(x + r)(x + s) = x^2 + (r + s)x + rs$$

so we need to choose numbers r and s so that $r + s = b$ and $rs = c$.

EXAMPLE 7 | Factoring $x^2 + bx + c$ by Trial and Error

Factor: $x^2 + 7x + 12$

SOLUTION   We need to find two integers whose product is 12 and whose sum is 7. By trial and error we find that the two integers are 3 and 4. Thus, the factorization is

$$x^2 + 7x + 12 = (x + 3)(x + 4)$$

$$\underset{\text{factors of 12}}{\underline{\qquad\qquad}}$$

CHECK YOUR ANSWER

Multiplying gives

$$(x + 3)(x + 4) = x^2 + 7x + 12 \quad ✔$$

✎ **NOW TRY EXERCISE 67**

To factor a trinomial of the form $ax^2 + bx + c$ with $a \neq 1$, we look for factors of the form $px + r$ and $qx + s$:

$$\overset{\text{factors of } a}{\underset{\text{factors of } c}{ax^2 + bx + c = (px + r)(qx + s)}} = pqx^2 + (ps + qr)x + rs$$

Therefore, we try to find numbers p, q, r, and s such that $pq = a$, $rs = c$, $ps + qr = b$. If these numbers are all integers, then we will have a limited number of possibilities to try for p, q, r, and s.

EXAMPLE 8 | Factoring $ax^2 + bx + c$ by Trial and Error

Factor: $6x^2 + 7x - 5$

SOLUTION   We can factor 6 as $6 \cdot 1$ or $3 \cdot 2$, and -5 as $-5 \cdot 1$ or $5 \cdot (-1)$. By trying these possibilities, we arrive at the factorization

CHECK YOUR ANSWER

Multiplying gives

$(3x + 5)(2x - 1) = 6x^2 + 7x - 5$ ✔

factors of 6

$$6x^2 + 7x - 5 = (3x + 5)(2x - 1)$$

factors of -5

✎. NOW TRY EXERCISE **69**

EXAMPLE 9 | Recognizing the Form of an Expression

Factor each expression.

(a) $x^2 - 2x - 3$ **(b)** $(5a + 1)^2 - 2(5a + 1) - 3$

SOLUTION

(a) $x^2 - 2x - 3 = (x - 3)(x + 1)$ Trial and error

(b) This expression is of the form

$$\square^2 - 2\,\square - 3$$

where $\square$ represents $5a + 1$. This is the same form as the expression in part (a), so it will factor as $(\square - 3)(\square + 1)$.

$$(5a + 1)^2 - 2(5a + 1) - 3 = [(5a + 1) - 3][(5a + 1) + 1]$$
$$= (5a - 2)(5a + 2)$$

✎. NOW TRY EXERCISE **71**

▼ Special Factoring Formulas

Some special algebraic expressions can be factored using the following formulas. The first three are simply Special Product Formulas written backward.

SPECIAL FACTORING FORMULAS	
Formula	**Name**
1. $A^2 - B^2 = (A - B)(A + B)$	Difference of squares
2. $A^2 + 2AB + B^2 = (A + B)^2$	Perfect square
3. $A^2 - 2AB + B^2 = (A - B)^2$	Perfect square
4. $A^3 - B^3 = (A - B)(A^2 + AB + B^2)$	Difference of cubes
5. $A^3 + B^3 = (A + B)(A^2 - AB + B^2)$	Sum of cubes

EXAMPLE 10 | Factoring Differences of Squares

Factor each expression.

(a) $4x^2 - 25$ **(b)** $(x + y)^2 - z^2$

SOLUTION

(a) Using the Difference of Squares Formula with $A = 2x$ and $B = 5$, we have

$$4x^2 - 25 = (2x)^2 - 5^2 = (2x - 5)(2x + 5)$$

$$A^2 \ - \ B^2 \ = \ (A \ - B)(A \ + \ B)$$

(b) We use the Difference of Squares Formula with $A = x + y$ and $B = z$.

$$(x + y)^2 - z^2 = (x + y - z)(x + y + z)$$

✎ NOW TRY EXERCISES **75** AND **109**

EXAMPLE 11 | Factoring Differences and Sums of Cubes

Factor each polynomial.

(a) $27x^3 - 1$ **(b)** $x^6 + 8$

SOLUTION

(a) Using the Difference of Cubes Formula with $A = 3x$ and $B = 1$, we get

$$27x^3 - 1 = (3x)^3 - 1^3 = (3x - 1)[(3x)^2 + (3x)(1) + 1^2]$$
$$= (3x - 1)(9x^2 + 3x + 1)$$

(b) Using the Sum of Cubes Formula with $A = x^2$ and $B = 2$, we have

$$x^6 + 8 = (x^2)^3 + 2^3 = (x^2 + 2)(x^4 - 2x^2 + 4)$$

✎ NOW TRY EXERCISES **77** AND **79**

A trinomial is a perfect square if it is of the form

$$A^2 + 2AB + B^2 \qquad \text{or} \qquad A^2 - 2AB + B^2$$

So we **recognize a perfect square** if the middle term ($2AB$ or $-2AB$) is plus or minus twice the product of the square roots of the outer two terms.

EXAMPLE 12 | Recognizing Perfect Squares

Factor each trinomial.

(a) $x^2 + 6x + 9$ **(b)** $4x^2 - 4xy + y^2$

SOLUTION

(a) Here $A = x$ and $B = 3$, so $2AB = 2 \cdot x \cdot 3 = 6x$. Since the middle term is $6x$, the trinomial is a perfect square. By the Perfect Square Formula we have

$$x^2 + 6x + 9 = (x + 3)^2$$

(b) Here $A = 2x$ and $B = y$, so $2AB = 2 \cdot 2x \cdot y = 4xy$. Since the middle term is $-4xy$, the trinomial is a perfect square. By the Perfect Square Formula we have

$$4x^2 - 4xy + y^2 = (2x - y)^2$$

✎ NOW TRY EXERCISES **105** AND **107**

When we factor an expression, the result can sometimes be factored further. In general, *we first factor out common factors*, then inspect the result to see whether it can be factored by any of the other methods of this section. We repeat this process until we have factored the expression completely.

EXAMPLE 13 | Factoring an Expression Completely

Factor each expression completely.

(a) $2x^4 - 8x^2$ (b) $x^5y^2 - xy^6$

SOLUTION

(a) We first factor out the power of x with the smallest exponent.

$$2x^4 - 8x^2 = 2x^2(x^2 - 4) \qquad \text{Common factor is } 2x^2$$
$$= 2x^2(x - 2)(x + 2) \qquad \text{Factor } x^2 - 4 \text{ as a difference of squares}$$

(b) We first factor out the powers of x and y with the smallest exponents.

$$x^5y^2 - xy^6 = xy^2(x^4 - y^4) \qquad \text{Common factor is } xy^2$$
$$= xy^2(x^2 + y^2)(x^2 - y^2) \qquad \text{Factor } x^4 - y^4 \text{ as a difference of squares}$$
$$= xy^2(x^2 + y^2)(x + y)(x - y) \qquad \text{Factor } x^2 - y^2 \text{ as a difference of squares}$$

✎. NOW TRY EXERCISES **115** AND **117**

In the next example we factor out variables with fractional exponents. This type of factoring occurs in calculus.

EXAMPLE 14 | Factoring Expressions with Fractional Exponents

Factor each expression.

(a) $3x^{3/2} - 9x^{1/2} + 6x^{-1/2}$ (b) $(2 + x)^{-2/3}x + (2 + x)^{1/3}$

SOLUTION

(a) Factor out the power of x with the *smallest exponent*, that is, $x^{-1/2}$.

To factor out $x^{-1/2}$ from $x^{3/2}$, we *subtract* exponents:

$$x^{3/2} = x^{-1/2}(x^{3/2 - (-1/2)})$$
$$= x^{-1/2}(x^{3/2 + 1/2})$$
$$= x^{-1/2}(x^2)$$

$$3x^{3/2} - 9x^{1/2} + 6x^{-1/2} = 3x^{-1/2}(x^2 - 3x + 2) \qquad \text{Factor out } 3x^{-1/2}$$
$$= 3x^{-1/2}(x - 1)(x - 2) \qquad \text{Factor the quadratic } x^2 - 3x + 2$$

(b) Factor out the power of $2 + x$ with the *smallest exponent*, that is, $(2 + x)^{-2/3}$.

$$(2 + x)^{-2/3}x + (2 + x)^{1/3} = (2 + x)^{-2/3}[x + (2 + x)] \qquad \text{Factor out } (2 + x)^{-2/3}$$
$$= (2 + x)^{-2/3}(2 + 2x) \qquad \text{Simplify}$$
$$= 2(2 + x)^{-2/3}(1 + x) \qquad \text{Factor out 2}$$

CHECK YOUR ANSWERS

To see that you have factored correctly, multiply using the Laws of Exponents.

(a) $3x^{-1/2}(x^2 - 3x + 2)$ (b) $(2 + x)^{-2/3}[x + (2 + x)]$
$$= 3x^{3/2} - 9x^{1/2} + 6x^{-1/2} \quad ✔ \qquad\qquad = (2 + x)^{-2/3}x + (2 + x)^{1/3} \quad ✔$$

✎. NOW TRY EXERCISES **91** AND **93**

▼ Factoring by Grouping Terms

Polynomials with at least four terms can sometimes be factored by grouping terms. The following example illustrates the idea.

EXAMPLE 15 | Factoring by Grouping

Factor each polynomial.

(a) $x^3 + x^2 + 4x + 4$ (b) $x^3 - 2x^2 - 3x + 6$

SOLUTION

(a) $x^3 + x^2 + 4x + 4 = (x^3 + x^2) + (4x + 4)$ Group terms

$\quad\quad\quad\quad\quad\quad\quad = x^2(x + 1) + 4(x + 1)$ Factor out common factors

$\quad\quad\quad\quad\quad\quad\quad = (x^2 + 4)(x + 1)$ Factor out $x + 1$ from each term

(b) $x^3 - 2x^2 - 3x + 6 = (x^3 - 2x^2) - (3x - 6)$ Group terms

$\quad\quad\quad\quad\quad\quad\quad = x^2(x - 2) - 3(x - 2)$ Factor out common factors

$\quad\quad\quad\quad\quad\quad\quad = (x^2 - 3)(x - 2)$ Factor out $x - 2$ from each term

✎. NOW TRY EXERCISE **83**

1.3 EXERCISES

CONCEPTS

1. Consider the polynomial $2x^5 + 6x^4 + 4x^3$.

How many terms does this polynomial have? _____

List the terms: _____

What factor is common to each term? _____

Factor the polynomial: $2x^5 + 6x^4 + 4x^3 =$ _____ .

2. To factor the trinomial $x^2 + 7x + 10$, we look for two integers

whose product is _____ and whose sum is _____ .

These integers are _____ and _____ , so the trinomial

factors as _____ .

3. The Special Product Formula for the "square of a sum" is

$(A + B)^2 =$ _____ .

So $(2x + 3)^2 =$ _____ .

4. The Special Product Formula for the "sum and difference

of the same terms" is $(A + B)(A - B) =$ _____ .

So $(5 + x)(5 - x) =$ _____ .

5. The Special Factoring Formula for the "difference of squares"

is $A^2 - B^2 =$ _____ . So $4x^2 - 25$ factors as _____ .

6. The Special Factoring Formula for a "perfect square" is

$A^2 + 2AB + B^2 =$ _____ . So $x^2 + 10x + 25$ factors as

_____ .

SKILLS

7–12 ■ Complete the following table by stating whether the polynomial is a monomial, binomial, or trinomial; then list its terms and state its degree.

Polynomial	Type	Terms	Degree
7. $x^2 - 3x + 7$			
8. $2x^5 + 4x^2$			

Polynomial	Type	Terms	Degree
9. -8			
10. $\frac{1}{2}x^7$			
11. $x - x^2 + x^3 - x^4$			
12. $\sqrt{2}x - \sqrt{3}$			

13–22 ■ Find the sum, difference, or product.

13. $(12x - 7) - (5x - 12)$ **14.** $(5 - 3x) + (2x - 8)$

✎. **15.** $(3x^2 + x + 1) + (2x^2 - 3x - 5)$

16. $(3x^2 + x + 1) - (2x^2 - 3x - 5)$

✎. **17.** $(x^3 + 6x^2 - 4x + 7) - (3x^2 + 2x - 4)$

18. $3(x - 1) + 4(x + 2)$

19. $8(2x + 5) - 7(x - 9)$

20. $4(x^2 - 3x + 5) - 3(x^2 - 2x + 1)$

21. $2(2 - 5t) + t^2(t - 1) - (t^4 - 1)$

22. $5(3t - 4) - (t^2 + 2) - 2t(t - 3)$

23–28 ■ Multiply the algebraic expressions using the FOIL method and simplify.

✎. **23.** $(3t - 2)(7t - 4)$ **24.** $(4s - 1)(2s + 5)$

25. $(3x + 5)(2x - 1)$ **26.** $(7y - 3)(2y - 1)$

27. $(x + 3y)(2x - y)$ **28.** $(4x - 5y)(3x - y)$

29–44 ■ Multiply the algebraic expressions using a Special Product Formula and simplify.

✎. **29.** $(3x + 4)^2$ **30.** $(1 - 2y)^2$

31. $(2u + v)^2$ **32.** $(x - 3y)^2$

33. $(2x + 3y)^2$ **34.** $(r - 2s)^2$

35. $(x + 5)(x - 5)$ **36.** $(y - 3)(y + 3)$

37. $(3x - 4)(3x + 4)$ **38.** $(2y + 5)(2y - 5)$

39. $(\sqrt{x} + 2)(\sqrt{x} - 2)$ **40.** $(\sqrt{y} + \sqrt{2})(\sqrt{y} - \sqrt{2})$

41. $(y + 2)^3$ **42.** $(x - 3)^3$

43. $(1 - 2r)^3$ **44.** $(3 + 2y)^3$

45–60 ■ Perform the indicated operations and simplify.

45. $(x + 2)(x^2 + 2x + 3)$ **46.** $(x + 1)(2x^2 - x + 1)$

47. $(2x - 5)(x^2 - x + 1)$ **48.** $(1 + 2x)(x^2 - 3x + 1)$

49. $\sqrt{x}(x - \sqrt{x})$ **50.** $x^{3/2}(\sqrt{x} - 1/\sqrt{x})$

51. $y^{1/3}(y^{2/3} + y^{5/3})$ **52.** $x^{1/4}(2x^{3/4} - x^{1/4})$

53. $(x^2 - a^2)(x^2 + a^2)$ **54.** $(x^{1/2} + y^{1/2})(x^{1/2} - y^{1/2})$

55. $(\sqrt{a} - b)(\sqrt{a} + b)$

56. $(\sqrt{h^2 + 1} + 1)(\sqrt{h^2 + 1} - 1)$

57. $((x - 1) + x^2)((x - 1) - x^2)$

58. $(x + (2 + x^2))(x - (2 + x^2))$

59. $(2x + y - 3)(2x + y + 3)$ **60.** $(x + y + z)(x - y - z)$

61–66 ■ Factor out the common factor.

61. $-2x^3 + 16x$ **62.** $2x^4 + 4x^3 - 14x^2$

63. $y(y - 6) + 9(y - 6)$ **64.** $(z + 2)^2 - 5(z + 2)$

65. $2x^2y - 6xy^2 + 3xy$ **66.** $-7x^4y^2 + 14xy^3 + 21xy^4$

67–74 ■ Factor the trinomial.

67. $x^2 + 2x - 3$ **68.** $x^2 - 6x + 5$

69. $8x^2 - 14x - 15$ **70.** $6y^2 + 11y - 21$

71. $3x^2 - 16x + 5$ **72.** $5x^2 - 7x - 6$

73. $(3x + 2)^2 + 8(3x + 2) + 12$

74. $2(a + b)^2 + 5(a + b) - 3$

75–82 ■ Use a Special Factoring Formula to factor the expression.

75. $9a^2 - 16$ **76.** $(x + 3)^2 - 4$

77. $27x^3 + y^3$ **78.** $a^3 - b^6$

79. $8s^3 - 125t^3$ **80.** $1 + 1000y^3$

81. $x^2 + 12x + 36$ **82.** $16z^2 - 24z + 9$

83–88 ■ Factor the expression by grouping terms.

83. $x^3 + 4x^2 + x + 4$ **84.** $3x^3 - x^2 + 6x - 2$

85. $2x^3 + x^2 - 6x - 3$ **86.** $-9x^3 - 3x^2 + 3x + 1$

87. $x^3 + x^2 + x + 1$ **88.** $x^5 + x^4 + x + 1$

89–94 ■ Factor the expression completely. Begin by factoring out the lowest power of each common factor.

89. $x^{5/2} - x^{1/2}$ **90.** $3x^{-1/2} + 4x^{1/2} + x^{3/2}$

91. $x^{-3/2} + 2x^{-1/2} + x^{1/2}$ **92.** $(x - 1)^{7/2} - (x - 1)^{3/2}$

93. $(x^2 + 1)^{1/2} + 2(x^2 + 1)^{-1/2}$

94. $x^{-1/2}(x + 1)^{1/2} + x^{1/2}(x + 1)^{-1/2}$

95–124 ■ Factor the expression completely.

95. $12x^3 + 18x$ **96.** $30x^3 + 15x^4$

97. $x^2 - 2x - 8$ **98.** $x^2 - 14x + 48$

99. $2x^2 + 5x + 3$ **100.** $2x^2 + 7x - 4$

101. $9x^2 - 36x - 45$ **102.** $8x^2 + 10x + 3$

103. $49 - 4y^2$ **104.** $4t^2 - 9s^2$

105. $t^2 - 6t + 9$ **106.** $x^2 + 10x + 25$

107. $4x^2 + 4xy + y^2$ **108.** $r^2 - 6rs + 9s^2$

109. $(a + b)^2 - (a - b)^2$ **110.** $\left(1 + \dfrac{1}{x}\right)^2 - \left(1 - \dfrac{1}{x}\right)^2$

111. $x^2(x^2 - 1) - 9(x^2 - 1)$ **112.** $(a^2 - 1)b^2 - 4(a^2 - 1)$

113. $8x^3 - 125$ **114.** $x^6 + 64$

115. $x^3 + 2x^2 + x$ **116.** $3x^3 - 27x$

117. $x^4y^3 - x^2y^5$ **118.** $18y^3x^2 - 2xy^4$

119. $2x^3 + 4x^2 + x + 2$ **120.** $3x^3 + 5x^2 - 6x - 10$

121. $(x - 1)(x + 2)^2 - (x - 1)^2(x + 2)$

122. $y^4(y + 2)^3 + y^5(y + 2)^4$

123. $(a^2 + 1)^2 - 7(a^2 + 1) + 10$

124. $(a^2 + 2a)^2 - 2(a^2 + 2a) - 3$

125–128 ■ Factor the expression completely. (This type of expression arises in calculus when using the "Product Rule.")

125. $5(x^2 + 4)^4(2x)(x - 2)^4 + (x^2 + 4)^5(4)(x - 2)^3$

126. $3(2x - 1)^2(2)(x + 3)^{1/2} + (2x - 1)^3(\frac{1}{2})(x + 3)^{-1/2}$

127. $(x^2 + 3)^{-1/3} - \frac{2}{3}x^2(x^2 + 3)^{-4/3}$

128. $\frac{1}{2}x^{-1/2}(3x + 4)^{1/2} - \frac{3}{2}x^{1/2}(3x + 4)^{-1/2}$

129. **(a)** Show that $ab = \frac{1}{2}[(a + b)^2 - (a^2 + b^2)]$.
  (b) Show that $(a^2 + b^2)^2 - (a^2 - b^2)^2 = 4a^2b^2$.
  (c) Show that
  $$(a^2 + b^2)(c^2 + d^2) = (ac + bd)^2 + (ad - bc)^2$$
  (d) Factor completely: $4a^2c^2 - (a^2 - b^2 + c^2)^2$.

130. Verify Special Factoring Formulas 4 and 5 by expanding their right-hand sides.

APPLICATIONS

131. **Volume of Concrete** A culvert is constructed out of large cylindrical shells cast in concrete, as shown in the figure. Using the formula for the volume of a cylinder given on the inside front cover of this book, explain why the volume of the cylindrical shell is

$$V = \pi R^2 h - \pi r^2 h$$

Factor to show that

$$V = 2\pi \cdot \text{average radius} \cdot \text{height} \cdot \text{thickness}$$

Use the "unrolled" diagram to explain why this makes sense geometrically.

132. Mowing a Field A square field in a certain state park is mowed around the edges every week. The rest of the field is kept unmowed to serve as a habitat for birds and small animals (see the figure). The field measures b feet by b feet, and the mowed strip is x feet wide.

(a) Explain why the area of the mowed portion is $b^2 - (b - 2x)^2$.

(b) Factor the expression in part (a) to show that the area of the mowed portion is also $4x(b - x)$.

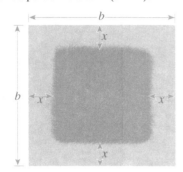

DISCOVERY ▪ DISCUSSION ▪ WRITING

133. Degrees of Sums and Products of Polynomials
Make up several pairs of polynomials, then calculate the sum and product of each pair. On the basis of your experiments and observations, answer the following questions.

(a) How is the degree of the product related to the degrees of the original polynomials?

(b) How is the degree of the sum related to the degrees of the original polynomials?

134. The Power of Algebraic Formulas Use the Difference of Squares Formula to factor $17^2 - 16^2$. Notice that it is easy to calculate the factored form in your head but not so easy to calculate the original form in this way. Evaluate each expression in your head:

(a) $528^2 - 527^2$

(b) $122^2 - 120^2$

(c) $1020^2 - 1010^2$

Now use the Special Product Formula

$$(A + B)(A - B) = A^2 - B^2$$

to evaluate these products in your head:

(d) $79 \cdot 51$

(e) $998 \cdot 1002$

135. Differences of Even Powers

(a) Factor the expressions completely: $A^4 - B^4$ and $A^6 - B^6$.

(b) Verify that $18{,}335 = 12^4 - 7^4$ and that $2{,}868{,}335 = 12^6 - 7^6$.

(c) Use the results of parts (a) and (b) to factor the integers 18,335 and 2,868,335. Then show that in both of these factorizations, all the factors are prime numbers.

136. Factoring $A^n - 1$ Verify these formulas by expanding and simplifying the right-hand side.

$$A^2 - 1 = (A - 1)(A + 1)$$
$$A^3 - 1 = (A - 1)(A^2 + A + 1)$$
$$A^4 - 1 = (A - 1)(A^3 + A^2 + A + 1)$$

On the basis of the pattern displayed in this list, how do you think $A^5 - 1$ would factor? Verify your conjecture. Now generalize the pattern you have observed to obtain a factoring formula for $A^n - 1$, where n is a positive integer.

137. Factoring $x^4 + ax^2 + b$ A trinomial of the form $x^4 + ax^2 + b$ can sometimes be factored easily. For example,

$$x^4 + 3x^2 - 4 = (x^2 + 4)(x^2 - 1)$$

But $x^4 + 3x^2 + 4$ cannot be factored in this way. Instead, we can use the following method.

$$x^4 + 3x^2 + 4 = (x^4 + 4x^2 + 4) - x^2 \qquad \text{Add and subtract } x^2$$

$$= (x^2 + 2)^2 - x^2 \qquad \text{Factor perfect square}$$

$$= [(x^2 + 2) - x][(x^2 + 2) + x] \qquad \text{Difference of squares}$$

$$= (x^2 - x + 2)(x^2 + x + 2)$$

Factor the following, using whichever method is appropriate.

(a) $x^4 + x^2 - 2$

(b) $x^4 + 2x^2 + 9$

(c) $x^4 + 4x^2 + 16$

(d) $x^4 + 2x^2 + 1$

⦿ **DISCOVERY PROJECT** Visualizing a Formula

In this project we discover geometric interpretations of some of the Special Product Formulas. You can find the project at the book companion website: **www.stewartmath.com**

1.4 RATIONAL EXPRESSIONS

| The Domain of an Algebraic Expression ▶ Simplifying Rational Expressions
▶ Multiplying and Dividing Rational Expressions ▶ Adding and Subtracting
Rational Expressions ▶ Compound Fractions ▶ Rationalizing the
Denominator or the Numerator ▶ Avoiding Common Errors

A quotient of two algebraic expressions is called a **fractional expression**. Here are some examples:

$$\frac{2x}{x-1} \qquad \frac{\sqrt{x}+3}{x+1} \qquad \frac{y-2}{y^2+4}$$

A **rational expression** is a fractional expression where both the numerator and denominator are polynomials. For example, the following are rational expressions:

$$\frac{2x}{x-1} \qquad \frac{x}{x^2+1} \qquad \frac{x^3-x}{x^2-5x+6}$$

In this section we learn how to perform algebraic operations on rational expressions.

▼ The Domain of an Algebraic Expression

In general, an algebraic expression may not be defined for all values of the variable. The **domain** of an algebraic expression is the set of real numbers that the variable is permitted to have. The table in the margin gives some basic expressions and their domains.

Expression	Domain
$\dfrac{1}{x}$	$\{x \mid x \neq 0\}$
$\sqrt{x}$	$\{x \mid x \geq 0\}$
$\dfrac{1}{\sqrt{x}}$	$\{x \mid x > 0\}$

EXAMPLE 1 | Finding the Domain of an Expression

Find the domains of the following expressions.

(a) $2x^2 + 3x - 1$ **(b)** $\dfrac{x}{x^2 - 5x + 6}$ **(c)** $\dfrac{\sqrt{x}}{x-5}$

SOLUTION

(a) This polynomial is defined for every x. Thus, the domain is the set $\mathbb{R}$ of real numbers.

(b) We first factor the denominator.

$$\frac{x}{x^2 - 5x + 6} = \frac{x}{(x-2)(x-3)}$$

Denominator would be 0 if
$x = 2$ or $x = 3$

Since the denominator is zero when $x = 2$ or 3, the expression is not defined for these numbers. The domain is $\{x \mid x \neq 2 \text{ and } x \neq 3\}$.

(c) For the numerator to be defined, we must have $x \geq 0$. Also, we cannot divide by zero, so $x \neq 5$.

Must have $x \geq 0$
to take square root $\dfrac{\sqrt{x}}{x-5}$ Denominator would
be 0 if $x = 5$

Thus, the domain is $\{x \mid x \geq 0 \text{ and } x \neq 5\}$.

✎ NOW TRY EXERCISE **11**

▼ Simplifying Rational Expressions

To **simplify rational expressions**, we factor both numerator and denominator and use the following property of fractions:

$$\frac{AC}{BC} = \frac{A}{B}$$

This allows us to **cancel** common factors from the numerator and denominator.

EXAMPLE 2 | Simplifying Rational Expressions by Cancellation

Simplify: $\dfrac{x^2 - 1}{x^2 + x - 2}$

SOLUTION

$$\frac{x^2 - 1}{x^2 + x - 2} = \frac{(x - 1)(x + 1)}{(x - 1)(x + 2)} \quad \text{Factor}$$

$$= \frac{x + 1}{x + 2} \quad \text{Cancel common factors}$$

⊘ We can't cancel the x^2's in $\dfrac{x^2 - 1}{x^2 + x - 2}$ because x^2 is not a factor.

✎ NOW TRY EXERCISE **17**

▼ Multiplying and Dividing Rational Expressions

To **multiply rational expressions**, we use the following property of fractions:

$$\frac{A}{B} \cdot \frac{C}{D} = \frac{AC}{BD}$$

This says that to multiply two fractions we multiply their numerators and multiply their denominators.

EXAMPLE 3 | Multiplying Rational Expressions

Perform the indicated multiplication and simplify: $\dfrac{x^2 + 2x - 3}{x^2 + 8x + 16} \cdot \dfrac{3x + 12}{x - 1}$

SOLUTION We first factor.

$$\frac{x^2 + 2x - 3}{x^2 + 8x + 16} \cdot \frac{3x + 12}{x - 1} = \frac{(x - 1)(x + 3)}{(x + 4)^2} \cdot \frac{3(x + 4)}{x - 1} \quad \text{Factor}$$

$$= \frac{3(x - 1)(x + 3)(x + 4)}{(x - 1)(x + 4)^2} \quad \text{Property of fractions}$$

$$= \frac{3(x + 3)}{x + 4} \quad \text{Cancel common factors}$$

✎ NOW TRY EXERCISE **25**

To **divide rational expressions**, we use the following property of fractions:

$$\frac{A}{B} \div \frac{C}{D} = \frac{A}{B} \cdot \frac{D}{C}$$

This says that to divide a fraction by another fraction, we invert the divisor and multiply.

EXAMPLE 4 | Dividing Rational Expressions

Perform the indicated division and simplify:

$$\frac{x - 4}{x^2 - 4} \div \frac{x^2 - 3x - 4}{x^2 + 5x + 6}$$

SOLUTION

$$\frac{x - 4}{x^2 - 4} \div \frac{x^2 - 3x - 4}{x^2 + 5x + 6} = \frac{x - 4}{x^2 - 4} \cdot \frac{x^2 + 5x + 6}{x^2 - 3x - 4} \qquad \text{Invert and multiply}$$

$$= \frac{(x - 4)(x + 2)(x + 3)}{(x - 2)(x + 2)(x - 4)(x + 1)} \qquad \text{Factor}$$

$$= \frac{x + 3}{(x - 2)(x + 1)} \qquad \text{Cancel common factors}$$

✎ . NOW TRY EXERCISE **31**

▼ Adding and Subtracting Rational Expressions

To **add or subtract rational expressions**, we first find a common denominator and then use the following property of fractions:

Avoid making the following error:

$$\frac{A}{B + C} \quad \text{✗} \quad \frac{A}{B} + \frac{A}{C}$$

For instance, if we let $A = 2$, $B = 1$, and $C = 1$, then we see the error:

$$\frac{2}{1 + 1} \stackrel{?}{=} \frac{2}{1} + \frac{2}{1}$$

$$\frac{2}{2} \stackrel{?}{=} 2 + 2$$

$$1 \stackrel{?}{=} 4 \quad \text{Wrong!}$$

$$\boxed{\frac{A}{C} + \frac{B}{C} = \frac{A + B}{C}}$$

Although any common denominator will work, it is best to use the **least common denominator** (LCD) as explained in Section 1.1. The LCD is found by factoring each denominator and taking the product of the distinct factors, using the highest power that appears in any of the factors.

EXAMPLE 5 | Adding and Subtracting Rational Expressions

Perform the indicated operations and simplify:

(a) $\dfrac{3}{x - 1} + \dfrac{x}{x + 2}$ **(b)** $\dfrac{1}{x^2 - 1} - \dfrac{2}{(x + 1)^2}$

SOLUTION

(a) Here the LCD is simply the product $(x - 1)(x + 2)$.

$$\frac{3}{x - 1} + \frac{x}{x + 2} = \frac{3(x + 2)}{(x - 1)(x + 2)} + \frac{x(x - 1)}{(x - 1)(x + 2)} \qquad \text{Write fractions using LCD}$$

$$= \frac{3x + 6 + x^2 - x}{(x - 1)(x + 2)} \qquad \text{Add fractions}$$

$$= \frac{x^2 + 2x + 6}{(x - 1)(x + 2)} \qquad \text{Combine terms in numerator}$$

(b) The LCD of $x^2 - 1 = (x - 1)(x + 1)$ and $(x + 1)^2$ is $(x - 1)(x + 1)^2$.

$$\frac{1}{x^2 - 1} - \frac{2}{(x + 1)^2} = \frac{1}{(x - 1)(x + 1)} - \frac{2}{(x + 1)^2} \qquad \text{Factor}$$

$$= \frac{(x + 1) - 2(x - 1)}{(x - 1)(x + 1)^2} \qquad \begin{array}{l}\text{Combine fractions}\\\text{using LCD}\end{array}$$

$$= \frac{x + 1 - 2x + 2}{(x - 1)(x + 1)^2} \qquad \text{Distributive Property}$$

$$= \frac{3 - x}{(x - 1)(x + 1)^2} \qquad \begin{array}{l}\text{Combine terms in}\\\text{numerator}\end{array}$$

NOW TRY EXERCISES **43** AND **45**

▼ Compound Fractions

A **compound fraction** is a fraction in which the numerator, the denominator, or both, are themselves fractional expressions.

EXAMPLE 6 | Simplifying a Compound Fraction

Simplify: $\dfrac{\dfrac{x}{y} + 1}{1 - \dfrac{y}{x}}$

SOLUTION 1 We combine the terms in the numerator into a single fraction. We do the same in the denominator. Then we invert and multiply.

$$\frac{\dfrac{x}{y} + 1}{1 - \dfrac{y}{x}} = \frac{\dfrac{x + y}{y}}{\dfrac{x - y}{x}} = \frac{x + y}{y} \cdot \frac{x}{x - y}$$

$$= \frac{x(x + y)}{y(x - y)}$$

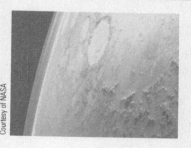

Courtesy of NASA

Error-Correcting Codes

The pictures sent back by the *Pathfinder* spacecraft from the surface of Mars on July 4, 1997, were astoundingly clear. But few viewing these pictures were aware of the complex mathematics used to accomplish that feat. The distance to Mars is enormous, and the background noise (or static) is many times stronger than the original signal emitted by the spacecraft. So, when scientists receive the signal, it is full of errors. To get a clear picture, the errors must be found and corrected. This same problem of errors is routinely encountered in transmitting bank records when you use an ATM machine or voice when you are talking on the telephone.

To understand how errors are found and corrected, we must first understand that to transmit pictures, sound, or text we transform them into bits (the digits 0 or 1; see page 30). To help the receiver recognize errors, the message is "coded" by inserting additional bits. For example, suppose you want to transmit the message "10100." A very simple-minded code is as follows: Send each digit a million times. The person receiving the message reads it in blocks of a million digits. If the first block is mostly 1's, he concludes that you are probably trying to transmit a 1, and so on. To say that this code is not efficient is a bit of an understatement; it requires sending a million times more data than the original message. Another method inserts "check digits." For example, for each block of eight digits insert a ninth digit; the inserted digit is 0 if there is an even number of 1's in the block and 1 if there is an odd number. So, if a single digit is wrong (a 0 changed to a 1, or vice versa), the check digits allow us to recognize that an error has occurred. This method does not tell us where the error is, so we can't correct it. Modern error-correcting codes use interesting mathematical algorithms that require inserting relatively few digits but that allow the receiver to not only recognize, but also correct, errors. The first error-correcting code was developed in the 1940s by Richard Hamming at MIT. It is interesting to note that the English language has a built-in error correcting mechanism; to test it, try reading this error-laden sentence: Gve mo libty ox giv ne deth.

SOLUTION 2 We find the LCD of all the fractions in the expression, then multiply numerator and denominator by it. In this example the LCD of all the fractions is xy. Thus

$$\frac{\dfrac{x}{y} + 1}{1 - \dfrac{y}{x}} = \frac{\dfrac{x}{y} + 1}{1 - \dfrac{y}{x}} \cdot \frac{xy}{xy} \qquad \text{Multiply numerator and denominator by } xy$$

$$= \frac{x^2 + xy}{xy - y^2} \qquad \text{Simplify}$$

$$= \frac{x(x + y)}{y(x - y)} \qquad \text{Factor}$$

✎. NOW TRY EXERCISES **59** AND **61**

The next two examples show situations in calculus that require the ability to work with fractional expressions.

EXAMPLE 7 | Simplifying a Compound Fraction

Simplify: $\dfrac{\dfrac{1}{a + h} - \dfrac{1}{a}}{h}$

SOLUTION We begin by combining the fractions in the numerator using a common denominator.

$$\frac{\dfrac{1}{a + h} - \dfrac{1}{a}}{h} = \frac{\dfrac{a - (a + h)}{a(a + h)}}{h} \qquad \begin{array}{l}\text{Combine fractions in the}\\\text{numerator}\end{array}$$

$$= \frac{a - (a + h)}{a(a + h)} \cdot \frac{1}{h} \qquad \begin{array}{l}\text{Property 2 of fractions (invert}\\\text{divisor and multiply)}\end{array}$$

$$= \frac{a - a - h}{a(a + h)} \cdot \frac{1}{h} \qquad \text{Distributive Property}$$

$$= \frac{-h}{a(a + h)} \cdot \frac{1}{h} \qquad \text{Simplify}$$

$$= \frac{-1}{a(a + h)} \qquad \begin{array}{l}\text{Property 5 of fractions}\\\text{(cancel common factors)}\end{array}$$

✎. NOW TRY EXERCISE **69**

EXAMPLE 8 | Simplifying a Compound Fraction

Simplify: $\dfrac{(1 + x^2)^{1/2} - x^2(1 + x^2)^{-1/2}}{1 + x^2}$

SOLUTION 1 Factor $(1 + x^2)^{-1/2}$ from the numerator.

Factor out the power of $1 + x^2$ with the *smallest* exponent, in this case $(1 + x^2)^{-1/2}$.

$$\frac{(1 + x^2)^{1/2} - x^2(1 + x^2)^{-1/2}}{1 + x^2} = \frac{(1 + x^2)^{-1/2}[(1 + x^2) - x^2]}{1 + x^2}$$

$$= \frac{(1 + x^2)^{-1/2}}{1 + x^2} = \frac{1}{(1 + x^2)^{3/2}}$$

SOLUTION 2 Since $(1 + x^2)^{-1/2} = 1/(1 + x^2)^{1/2}$ is a fraction, we can clear all fractions by multiplying numerator and denominator by $(1 + x^2)^{1/2}$.

$$\frac{(1 + x^2)^{1/2} - x^2(1 + x^2)^{-1/2}}{1 + x^2} = \frac{(1 + x^2)^{1/2} - x^2(1 + x^2)^{-1/2}}{1 + x^2} \cdot \frac{(1 + x^2)^{1/2}}{(1 + x^2)^{1/2}}$$

$$= \frac{(1 + x^2) - x^2}{(1 + x^2)^{3/2}} = \frac{1}{(1 + x^2)^{3/2}}$$

✎. NOW TRY EXERCISE **77**

▼ Rationalizing the Denominator or the Numerator

If a fraction has a denominator of the form $A + B\sqrt{C}$, we may rationalize the denominator by multiplying numerator and denominator by the **conjugate radical** $A - B\sqrt{C}$. This works because, by Special Product Formula 1 in Section 1.3, the product of the denominator and its conjugate radical does not contain a radical:

$$(A + B\sqrt{C})(A - B\sqrt{C}) = A^2 - B^2C$$

EXAMPLE 9 | Rationalizing the Denominator

Rationalize the denominator: $\dfrac{1}{1 + \sqrt{2}}$

SOLUTION We multiply both the numerator and the denominator by the conjugate radical of $1 + \sqrt{2}$, which is $1 - \sqrt{2}$.

Special Product Formula 1
$(A + B)(A - B) = A^2 - B^2$

$$\frac{1}{1 + \sqrt{2}} = \frac{1}{1 + \sqrt{2}} \cdot \frac{1 - \sqrt{2}}{1 - \sqrt{2}} \qquad \text{Multiply numerator and denominator by the conjugate radical}$$

$$= \frac{1 - \sqrt{2}}{1^2 - (\sqrt{2})^2} \qquad \text{Special Product Formula 1}$$

$$= \frac{1 - \sqrt{2}}{1 - 2} = \frac{1 - \sqrt{2}}{-1} = \sqrt{2} - 1$$

✎. NOW TRY EXERCISE **81**

EXAMPLE 10 | Rationalizing the Numerator

Rationalize the numerator: $\dfrac{\sqrt{4 + h} - 2}{h}$

SOLUTION We multiply numerator and denominator by the conjugate radical $\sqrt{4 + h} + 2$.

Special Product Formula 1
$(A + B)(A - B) = A^2 - B^2$

$$\frac{\sqrt{4 + h} - 2}{h} = \frac{\sqrt{4 + h} - 2}{h} \cdot \frac{\sqrt{4 + h} + 2}{\sqrt{4 + h} + 2} \qquad \text{Multiply numerator and denominator by the conjugate radical}$$

$$= \frac{(\sqrt{4 + h})^2 - 2^2}{h(\sqrt{4 + h} + 2)} \qquad \text{Special Product Formula 1}$$

$$= \frac{4 + h - 4}{h(\sqrt{4 + h} + 2)}$$

$$= \frac{h}{h(\sqrt{4 + h} + 2)} = \frac{1}{\sqrt{4 + h} + 2} \qquad \text{Property 5 of fractions (cancel common factors)}$$

✎. NOW TRY EXERCISE **87**

▼ Avoiding Common Errors

 Don't make the mistake of applying properties of multiplication to the operation of addition. Many of the common errors in algebra involve doing just that. **The following table states several properties of multiplication and illustrates the error in applying them to addition.**

Correct multiplication property	Common error with addition
$(a \cdot b)^2 = a^2 \cdot b^2$	$(a + b)^2 \neq a^2 + b^2$
$\sqrt{a \cdot b} = \sqrt{a}\,\sqrt{b} \quad (a, b \geq 0)$	$\sqrt{a + b} \neq \sqrt{a} + \sqrt{b}$
$\sqrt{a^2 \cdot b^2} = a \cdot b \quad (a, b \geq 0)$	$\sqrt{a^2 + b^2} \neq a + b$
$\dfrac{1}{a} \cdot \dfrac{1}{b} = \dfrac{1}{a \cdot b}$	$\dfrac{1}{a} + \dfrac{1}{b} \neq \dfrac{1}{a + b}$
$\dfrac{ab}{a} = b$	$\dfrac{a + b}{a} \neq b$
$a^{-1} \cdot b^{-1} = (a \cdot b)^{-1}$	$a^{-1} + b^{-1} \neq (a + b)^{-1}$

To verify that the equations in the right-hand column are wrong, simply substitute numbers for a and b and calculate each side. For example, if we take $a = 2$ and $b = 2$ in the fourth error, we find that the left-hand side is

$$\frac{1}{a} + \frac{1}{b} = \frac{1}{2} + \frac{1}{2} = 1$$

whereas the right-hand side is

$$\frac{1}{a + b} = \frac{1}{2 + 2} = \frac{1}{4}$$

Since $1 \neq \frac{1}{4}$, the stated equation is wrong. You should similarly convince yourself of the error in each of the other equations. (See Exercise 105.)

1.4 EXERCISES

CONCEPTS

1. Which of the following are rational expressions?

(a) $\dfrac{3x}{x^2 - 1}$ **(b)** $\dfrac{\sqrt{x + 1}}{2x + 3}$ **(c)** $\dfrac{x(x^2 - 1)}{x + 3}$

2. To simplify a rational expression, we cancel *factors* that are common to the _____ and _____. So the expression

$$\frac{(x + 1)(x + 2)}{(x + 3)(x + 2)}$$

simplifies to _____.

3. To multiply two rational expressions, we multiply their _____ together and multiply their _____ together.

So $\dfrac{2}{x + 1} \cdot \dfrac{x}{x + 3}$ is the same as _____.

4. Consider the expression $\dfrac{1}{x} - \dfrac{2}{x + 1} - \dfrac{x}{(x + 1)^2}$.

(a) How many terms does this expression have?

(b) Find the least common denominator of all the terms.

(c) Perform the addition and simplify.

SKILLS

5–12 ■ Find the domain of the expression.

5. $4x^2 - 10x + 3$

6. $-x^4 + x^3 + 9x$

7. $\dfrac{2x + 1}{x - 4}$

8. $\dfrac{2t^2 - 5}{3t + 6}$

9. $\sqrt{x + 3}$

10. $\dfrac{1}{\sqrt{x - 1}}$

11. $\dfrac{x^2 + 1}{x^2 - x - 2}$

12. $\dfrac{\sqrt{2x}}{x + 1}$

13–22 ■ Simplify the rational expression.

13. $\dfrac{3(x + 2)(x - 1)}{6(x - 1)^2}$

14. $\dfrac{4(x^2 - 1)}{12(x + 2)(x - 1)}$

15. $\dfrac{x - 2}{x^2 - 4}$

16. $\dfrac{x^2 - x - 2}{x^2 - 1}$

17. $\dfrac{x^2 + 6x + 8}{x^2 + 5x + 4}$

18. $\dfrac{x^2 - x - 12}{x^2 + 5x + 6}$

19. $\dfrac{y^2 + y}{y^2 - 1}$

20. $\dfrac{y^2 - 3y - 18}{2y^2 + 5y + 3}$

21. $\dfrac{2x^3 - x^2 - 6x}{2x^2 - 7x + 6}$

22. $\dfrac{1 - x^2}{x^3 - 1}$

23–38 ■ Perform the multiplication or division and simplify.

23. $\dfrac{4x}{x^2 - 4} \cdot \dfrac{x + 2}{16x}$

24. $\dfrac{x^2 - 25}{x^2 - 16} \cdot \dfrac{x + 4}{x + 5}$

25. $\dfrac{x^2 - 2x - 15}{x^2 - 9} \cdot \dfrac{x + 3}{x - 5}$

26. $\dfrac{x^2 + 2x - 3}{x^2 - 2x - 3} \cdot \dfrac{3 - x}{3 + x}$

27. $\dfrac{t - 3}{t^2 + 9} \cdot \dfrac{t + 3}{t^2 - 9}$

28. $\dfrac{x^2 - x - 6}{x^2 + 2x} \cdot \dfrac{x^3 + x^2}{x^2 - 2x - 3}$

29. $\dfrac{x^2 + 7x + 12}{x^2 + 3x + 2} \cdot \dfrac{x^2 + 5x + 6}{x^2 + 6x + 9}$

30. $\dfrac{x^2 + 2xy + y^2}{x^2 - y^2} \cdot \dfrac{2x^2 - xy - y^2}{x^2 - xy - 2y^2}$

31. $\dfrac{x + 3}{4x^2 - 9} \div \dfrac{x^2 + 7x + 12}{2x^2 + 7x - 15}$

32. $\dfrac{2x + 1}{2x^2 + x - 15} \div \dfrac{6x^2 - x - 2}{x + 3}$

33. $\dfrac{2x^2 + 3x + 1}{x^2 + 2x - 15} \div \dfrac{x^2 + 6x + 5}{2x^2 - 7x + 3}$

34. $\dfrac{4y^2 - 9}{2y^2 + 9y - 18} \div \dfrac{2y^2 + y - 3}{y^2 + 5y - 6}$

35. $\dfrac{\dfrac{x^3}{x + 1}}{\dfrac{x}{x^2 + 2x + 1}}$

36. $\dfrac{\dfrac{2x^2 - 3x - 2}{x^2 - 1}}{\dfrac{2x^2 + 5x + 2}{x^2 + x - 2}}$

37. $\dfrac{x/y}{z}$

38. $\dfrac{x}{y/z}$

39–58 ■ Perform the addition or subtraction and simplify.

39. $2 + \dfrac{x}{x + 3}$

40. $\dfrac{2x - 1}{x + 4} - 1$

41. $\dfrac{1}{x + 5} + \dfrac{2}{x - 3}$

42. $\dfrac{1}{x + 1} + \dfrac{1}{x - 1}$

43. $\dfrac{1}{x + 1} - \dfrac{1}{x + 2}$

44. $\dfrac{x}{x - 4} - \dfrac{3}{x + 6}$

45. $\dfrac{x}{(x + 1)^2} + \dfrac{2}{x + 1}$

46. $\dfrac{5}{2x - 3} - \dfrac{3}{(2x - 3)^2}$

47. $u + 1 + \dfrac{u}{u + 1}$

48. $\dfrac{2}{a^2} - \dfrac{3}{ab} + \dfrac{4}{b^2}$

49. $\dfrac{1}{x^2} + \dfrac{1}{x^2 + x}$

50. $\dfrac{1}{x} + \dfrac{1}{x^2} + \dfrac{1}{x^3}$

51. $\dfrac{2}{x + 3} - \dfrac{1}{x^2 + 7x + 12}$

52. $\dfrac{x}{x^2 - 4} + \dfrac{1}{x - 2}$

53. $\dfrac{1}{x + 3} + \dfrac{1}{x^2 - 9}$

54. $\dfrac{x}{x^2 + x - 2} - \dfrac{2}{x^2 - 5x + 4}$

55. $\dfrac{2}{x} + \dfrac{3}{x - 1} - \dfrac{4}{x^2 - x}$

56. $\dfrac{x}{x^2 - x - 6} - \dfrac{1}{x + 2} - \dfrac{2}{x - 3}$

57. $\dfrac{1}{x^2 + 3x + 2} - \dfrac{1}{x^2 - 2x - 3}$

58. $\dfrac{1}{x + 1} - \dfrac{2}{(x + 1)^2} + \dfrac{3}{x^2 - 1}$

59–68 ■ Simplify the compound fractional expression.

59. $\dfrac{x + \dfrac{1}{x + 2}}{x - \dfrac{1}{x + 2}}$

60. $\dfrac{1 + \dfrac{1}{c - 1}}{1 - \dfrac{1}{c - 1}}$

61. $\dfrac{\dfrac{x + 2}{x - 1} - \dfrac{x - 3}{x - 2}}{x + 2}$

62. $\dfrac{\dfrac{x - 3}{x - 4} - \dfrac{x + 2}{x + 1}}{x + 3}$

63. $\dfrac{\dfrac{x}{y} - \dfrac{y}{x}}{\dfrac{1}{x^2} - \dfrac{1}{y^2}}$

64. $x - \dfrac{y}{\dfrac{x}{y} + \dfrac{y}{x}}$

65. $\dfrac{x^{-2} - y^{-2}}{x^{-1} + y^{-1}}$

66. $\dfrac{x^{-1} + y^{-1}}{(x + y)^{-1}}$

67. $1 - \dfrac{1}{1 - \dfrac{1}{x}}$

68. $1 + \dfrac{1}{1 + \dfrac{1}{1 + x}}$

69–74 ■ Simplify the fractional expression. (Expressions like these arise in calculus.)

69. $\dfrac{\dfrac{1}{1 + x + h} - \dfrac{1}{1 + x}}{h}$

70. $\dfrac{\dfrac{1}{\sqrt{x + h}} - \dfrac{1}{\sqrt{x}}}{h}$

71. $\dfrac{\dfrac{1}{(x + h)^2} - \dfrac{1}{x^2}}{h}$

72. $\dfrac{(x + h)^3 - 7(x + h) - (x^3 - 7x)}{h}$

73. $\sqrt{1 + \left(\dfrac{x}{\sqrt{1 - x^2}}\right)^2}$

74. $\sqrt{1 + \left(x^3 - \dfrac{1}{4x^3}\right)^2}$

75–80 ■ Simplify the expression. (This type of expression arises in calculus when using the "quotient rule.")

75. $\dfrac{3(x + 2)^2(x - 3)^2 - (x + 2)^3(2)(x - 3)}{(x - 3)^4}$

76. $\dfrac{2x(x + 6)^4 - x^2(4)(x + 6)^3}{(x + 6)^8}$

77. $\dfrac{2(1 + x)^{1/2} - x(1 + x)^{-1/2}}{x + 1}$

78. $\dfrac{(1 - x^2)^{1/2} + x^2(1 - x^2)^{-1/2}}{1 - x^2}$

79. $\dfrac{3(1 + x)^{1/3} - x(1 + x)^{-2/3}}{(1 + x)^{2/3}}$

80. $\dfrac{(7 - 3x)^{1/2} + \frac{3}{2}x(7 - 3x)^{-1/2}}{7 - 3x}$

81–86 ■ Rationalize the denominator.

81. $\dfrac{1}{2 - \sqrt{3}}$

82. $\dfrac{2}{3 - \sqrt{5}}$

83. $\dfrac{2}{\sqrt{2} + \sqrt{7}}$

84. $\dfrac{1}{\sqrt{x} + 1}$

85. $\dfrac{y}{\sqrt{3} + \sqrt{y}}$

86. $\dfrac{2(x - y)}{\sqrt{x} - \sqrt{y}}$

87–92 ■ Rationalize the numerator.

87. $\dfrac{1 - \sqrt{5}}{3}$

88. $\dfrac{\sqrt{3} + \sqrt{5}}{2}$

89. $\dfrac{\sqrt{r} + \sqrt{2}}{5}$

90. $\dfrac{\sqrt{x} - \sqrt{x + h}}{h\sqrt{x}\sqrt{x + h}}$

91. $\sqrt{x^2 + 1} - x$

92. $\sqrt{x + 1} - \sqrt{x}$

93–100 ■ State whether the given equation is true for all values of the variables. (Disregard any value that makes a denominator zero.)

93. $\dfrac{16 + a}{16} = 1 + \dfrac{a}{16}$

94. $\dfrac{b}{b - c} = 1 - \dfrac{b}{c}$

95. $\dfrac{2}{4 + x} = \dfrac{1}{2} + \dfrac{2}{x}$

96. $\dfrac{x + 1}{y + 1} = \dfrac{x}{y}$

97. $\dfrac{x}{x + y} = \dfrac{1}{1 + y}$

98. $2\left(\dfrac{a}{b}\right) = \dfrac{2a}{2b}$

99. $\dfrac{-a}{b} = -\dfrac{a}{b}$

100. $\dfrac{1 + x + x^2}{x} = \dfrac{1}{x} + 1 + x$

APPLICATIONS

101. **Electrical Resistance** If two electrical resistors with resistances R_1 and R_2 are connected in parallel (see the figure), then the total resistance R is given by

$$R = \dfrac{1}{\dfrac{1}{R_1} + \dfrac{1}{R_2}}$$

(a) Simplify the expression for R.

(b) If $R_1 = 10$ ohms and $R_2 = 20$ ohms, what is the total resistance R?

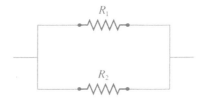

102. **Average Cost** A clothing manufacturer finds that the cost of producing x shirts is $500 + 6x + 0.01x^2$ dollars.

(a) Explain why the average cost per shirt is given by the rational expression

$$A = \dfrac{500 + 6x + 0.01x^2}{x}$$

(b) Complete the table by calculating the average cost per shirt for the given values of x.

x	Average cost
10	
20	
50	
100	
200	
500	
1000	

DISCOVERY ■ DISCUSSION ■ WRITING

103. **Limiting Behavior of a Rational Expression** The rational expression

$$\dfrac{x^2 - 9}{x - 3}$$

is not defined for $x = 3$. Complete the tables and determine what value the expression approaches as x gets closer and closer to 3. Why is this reasonable? Factor the numerator of the expression and simplify to see why.

x	$\dfrac{x^2 - 9}{x - 3}$
2.80	
2.90	
2.95	
2.99	
2.999	

x	$\dfrac{x^2 - 9}{x - 3}$
3.20	
3.10	
3.05	
3.01	
3.001	

104. **Is This Rationalization?** In the expression $2/\sqrt{x}$ we would eliminate the radical if we were to square both numerator and denominator. Is this the same thing as rationalizing the denominator?

105. **Algebraic Errors** The left-hand column in the table on the following page lists some common algebraic errors. In each case, give an example using numbers that show that the formula is not valid. An example of this type, which shows that a statement is false, is called a *counterexample*.

Algebraic error	Counterexample
$\dfrac{1}{a} + \dfrac{1}{b} \overset{\times}{=} \dfrac{1}{a+b}$	$\dfrac{1}{2} + \dfrac{1}{2} \neq \dfrac{1}{2+2}$
$(a+b)^2 \overset{\times}{=} a^2 + b^2$	
$\sqrt{a^2 + b^2} \overset{\times}{=} a + b$	
$\dfrac{a+b}{a} \overset{\times}{=} b$	
$(a^3 + b^3)^{1/3} \overset{\times}{=} a + b$	
$a^m / a^n \overset{\times}{=} a^{m/n}$	
$a^{-1/n} \overset{\times}{=} \dfrac{1}{a^n}$	

106. The Form of an Algebraic Expression An algebraic expression may look complicated, but its "form" is always simple; it must be a sum, a product, a quotient, or a power. For example, consider the following expressions:

$$(1+x^2)^2 + \left(\frac{x+2}{x+1}\right)^3 \qquad (1+x)\left(1 + \frac{x+5}{1+x^4}\right)$$

$$\frac{5-x^3}{1+\sqrt{1+x^2}} \qquad \sqrt{\frac{1+x}{1-x}}$$

With appropriate choices for A and B, the first has the form $A + B$, the second AB, the third A/B, and the fourth $A^{1/2}$. Recognizing the form of an expression helps us expand, simplify, or factor it correctly. Find the form of the following algebraic expressions.

(a) $x + \sqrt{1 + \dfrac{1}{x}}$ 　　　**(b)** $(1+x^2)(1+x)^3$

(c) $\sqrt[3]{x^4(4x^2+1)}$ 　　　**(d)** $\dfrac{1 - 2\sqrt{1+x}}{1 + \sqrt{1+x^2}}$

1.5 EQUATIONS

Solving Linear Equations ▶ Solving Quadratic Equations ▶ Other Types of Equations

An equation is a statement that two mathematical expressions are equal. For example,

$$3 + 5 = 8$$

is an equation. Most equations that we study in algebra contain variables, which are symbols (usually letters) that stand for numbers. In the equation

$$4x + 7 = 19$$

the letter x is the variable. We think of x as the "unknown" in the equation, and our goal is to find the value of x that makes the equation true. The values of the unknown that make the equation true are called the **solutions** or **roots** of the equation, and the process of finding the solutions is called **solving the equation**.

Two equations with exactly the same solutions are called **equivalent equations**. To solve an equation, we try to find a simpler, equivalent equation in which the variable stands alone on one side of the "equal" sign. Here are the properties that we use to solve an equation. (In these properties, A, B, and C stand for any algebraic expressions, and the symbol $\Leftrightarrow$ means "is equivalent to.")

$x = 3$ is a solution of the equation $4x + 7 = 19$, because substituting $x = 3$ makes the equation true:

$$x = 3$$

$$4(3) + 7 \overset{?}{=} 19 \quad ✔$$

PROPERTIES OF EQUALITY

Property	Description
1. $A = B \iff A + C = B + C$	Adding the same quantity to both sides of an equation gives an equivalent equation.
2. $A = B \iff CA = CB \quad (C \neq 0)$	Multiplying both sides of an equation by the same nonzero quantity gives an equivalent equation.

These properties require that you *perform the same operation on both sides of an equation* when solving it. Thus, if we say "*add* -7" when solving an equation, that is just a short way of saying "*add* -7 to each side of the equation."

▼ Solving Linear Equations

The simplest type of equation is a *linear equation*, or first-degree equation, which is an equation in which each term is either a constant or a nonzero multiple of the variable.

LINEAR EQUATIONS

A **linear equation** in one variable is an equation equivalent to one of the form

$$ax + b = 0$$

where a and b are real numbers and x is the variable.

Here are some examples that illustrate the difference between linear and nonlinear equations.

Linear equations	Nonlinear equations	
$4x - 5 = 3$	$x^2 + 2x = 8$	Not linear; contains the square of the variable
$2x = \frac{1}{2}x - 7$	$\sqrt{x} - 6x = 0$	Not linear; contains the square root of the variable
$x - 6 = \dfrac{x}{3}$	$\dfrac{3}{x} - 2x = 1$	Not linear; contains the reciprocal of the variable

EXAMPLE 1 | Solving a Linear Equation

Solve the equation $7x - 4 = 3x + 8$.

SOLUTION   We solve this by changing it to an equivalent equation with all terms that have the variable x on one side and all constant terms on the other.

$$7x - 4 = 3x + 8 \qquad \text{Given equation}$$
$$(7x - 4) + 4 = (3x + 8) + 4 \qquad \text{Add 4}$$
$$7x = 3x + 12 \qquad \text{Simplify}$$
$$7x - 3x = (3x + 12) - 3x \qquad \text{Subtract } 3x$$
$$4x = 12 \qquad \text{Simplify}$$
$$\tfrac{1}{4} \cdot 4x = \tfrac{1}{4} \cdot 12 \qquad \text{Multiply by } \tfrac{1}{4}$$
$$x = 3 \qquad \text{Simplify}$$

Because it is important to CHECK YOUR ANSWER, we do this in many of our examples. In these checks, LHS stands for "left-hand side" and RHS stands for "right-hand side" of the original equation.

CHECK YOUR ANSWER

$x = 3$:

	$x = 3$	$x = 3$
	LHS $= 7(3) - 4$	RHS $= 3(3) + 8$
	$= 17$	$= 17$

LHS $=$ RHS   ✔

✎. NOW TRY EXERCISE 15

Many formulas in the sciences involve several variables, and it is often necessary to express one of the variables in terms of the others. In the next example we solve for a variable in Newton's Law of Gravity.

This is Newton's Law of Gravity. It gives the gravitational force F between two masses m and M that are a distance r apart. The constant G is the universal gravitational constant.

EXAMPLE 2 | Solving for One Variable in Terms of Others

Solve for the variable M in the equation

$$F = G\frac{mM}{r^2}$$

SOLUTION Although this equation involves more than one variable, we solve it as usual by isolating M on one side and treating the other variables as we would numbers.

$$F = \left(\frac{Gm}{r^2}\right)M \qquad \text{Factor } M \text{ from RHS}$$

$$\left(\frac{r^2}{Gm}\right)F = \left(\frac{r^2}{Gm}\right)\left(\frac{Gm}{r^2}\right)M \qquad \text{Multiply by reciprocal of } \frac{Gm}{r^2}$$

$$\frac{r^2F}{Gm} = M \qquad \text{Simplify}$$

The solution is $M = \dfrac{r^2F}{Gm}$.

✎. NOW TRY EXERCISE **29**

EXAMPLE 3 | Solving for One Variable in Terms of Others

The surface area A of the closed rectangular box shown in Figure 1 can be calculated from the length l, the width w, and the height h according to the formula

$$A = 2lw + 2wh + 2lh$$

Solve for w in terms of the other variables in this equation.

SOLUTION Although this equation involves more than one variable, we solve it as usual by isolating w on one side, treating the other variables as we would numbers.

$$A = (2lw + 2wh) + 2lh \qquad \text{Collect terms involving } w$$

$$A - 2lh = 2lw + 2wh \qquad \text{Subtract } 2lh$$

$$A - 2lh = (2l + 2h)w \qquad \text{Factor } w \text{ from RHS}$$

$$\frac{A - 2lh}{2l + 2h} = w \qquad \text{Divide by } 2l + 2h$$

The solution is $w = \dfrac{A - 2lh}{2l + 2h}$.

✎. NOW TRY EXERCISE **31**

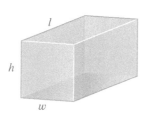

FIGURE 1 A closed rectangular box

▼ Solving Quadratic Equations

Linear equations are first-degree equations like $2x + 1 = 5$ or $4 - 3x = 2$. Quadratic equations are second-degree equations like $x^2 + 2x - 3 = 0$ or $2x^2 + 3 = 5x$.

Quadratic Equations

$$x^2 - 2x - 8 = 0$$

$$3x + 10 = 4x^2$$

$$\tfrac{1}{2}x^2 + \tfrac{1}{3}x - \tfrac{1}{6} = 0$$

> ### QUADRATIC EQUATIONS
>
> A **quadratic equation** is an equation of the form
>
> $$ax^2 + bx + c = 0$$
>
> where a, b, and c are real numbers with $a \neq 0$.

Some quadratic equations can be solved by factoring and using the following basic property of real numbers.

> **ZERO-PRODUCT PROPERTY**
>
> $$AB = 0 \quad \text{if and only if} \quad A = 0 \quad \text{or} \quad B = 0$$

 This means that if we can factor the left-hand side of a quadratic (or other) equation, then we can solve it by setting each factor equal to 0 in turn. This method works only when the right-hand side of the equation is 0.

EXAMPLE 4 | Solving a Quadratic Equation by Factoring

Solve the equation $x^2 + 5x = 24$.

SOLUTION   We must first rewrite the equation so that the right-hand side is 0.

$$x^2 + 5x = 24$$
$$x^2 + 5x - 24 = 0 \qquad \text{Subtract 24}$$
$$(x - 3)(x + 8) = 0 \qquad \text{Factor}$$
$$x - 3 = 0 \quad \text{or} \quad x + 8 = 0 \qquad \text{Zero-Product Property}$$
$$x = 3 \qquad\qquad x = -8 \qquad \text{Solve}$$

The solutions are $x = 3$ and $x = -8$.

↝ . NOW TRY EXERCISE **43**

CHECK YOUR ANSWERS

$x = 3$:

$(3)^2 + 5(3) = 9 + 15 = 24$ ✔

$x = -8$:

$(-8)^2 + 5(-8) = 64 - 40 = 24$ ✔

Do you see why one side of the equation must be 0 in Example 4? Factoring the equation as $x(x + 5) = 24$ does not help us find the solutions, since 24 can be factored in infinitely many ways, such as $6 \cdot 4$, $\frac{1}{2} \cdot 48$, $\left(-\frac{2}{5}\right) \cdot (-60)$, and so on.

A quadratic equation of the form $x^2 - c = 0$, where c is a positive constant, factors as $(x - \sqrt{c})(x + \sqrt{c}) = 0$, so the solutions are $x = \sqrt{c}$ and $x = -\sqrt{c}$. We often abbreviate this as $x = \pm\sqrt{c}$.

> **SOLVING A SIMPLE QUADRATIC EQUATION**
>
> The solutions of the equation $x^2 = c$ are $x = \sqrt{c}$ and $x = -\sqrt{c}$.

EXAMPLE 5 | Solving Simple Quadratics

Solve each equation.

(a) $x^2 = 5$ **(b)** $(x - 4)^2 = 5$

SOLUTION

(a) From the principle in the preceding box, we get $x = \pm\sqrt{5}$.

(b) We can take the square root of each side of this equation as well.

$$(x - 4)^2 = 5$$
$$x - 4 = \pm\sqrt{5} \qquad \text{Take the square root}$$
$$x = 4 \pm \sqrt{5} \qquad \text{Add 4}$$

The solutions are $x = 4 + \sqrt{5}$ and $x = 4 - \sqrt{5}$.

↝ . NOW TRY EXERCISES **51** AND **53**

See page 30 for how to recognize when a quadratic expression is a perfect square.

Completing the Square

The area of the blue region is

$$x^2 + 2\left(\frac{b}{2}\right)x = x^2 + bx$$

Add a small square of area $(b/2)^2$ to "complete" the square.

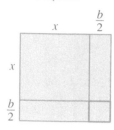

As we saw in Example 5, if a quadratic equation is of the form $(x \pm a)^2 = c$, then we can solve it by taking the square root of each side. In an equation of this form the left-hand side is a *perfect square*: the square of a linear expression in x. So if a quadratic equation does not factor readily, then we can solve it using the technique of **completing the square**. This means that we add a constant to an expression to make it a perfect square. For example, to make $x^2 - 6x$ a perfect square, we must add 9, since $x^2 - 6x + 9 = (x - 3)^2$.

COMPLETING THE SQUARE

To make $x^2 + bx$ a perfect square, add $\left(\dfrac{b}{2}\right)^2$, the square of half the coefficient of x. This gives the perfect square

$$x^2 + bx + \left(\frac{b}{2}\right)^2 = \left(x + \frac{b}{2}\right)^2$$

EXAMPLE 6 | Solving Quadratic Equations by Completing the Square

Solve each equation.

(a) $x^2 - 8x + 13 = 0$　　　**(b)** $3x^2 - 12x + 6 = 0$

SOLUTION

⊘ When completing the square, make sure the coefficient of x^2 is 1. If it isn't, you must factor this coefficient from both terms that contain x:

$$ax^2 + bx = a\left(x^2 + \frac{b}{a}x\right)$$

Then complete the square inside the parentheses. Remember that the term added inside the parentheses is multiplied by a.

(a)

$x^2 - 8x + 13 = 0$	Given equation
$x^2 - 8x = -13$	Subtract 13
$x^2 - 8x + 16 = -13 + 16$	Complete the square: add $\left(\dfrac{-8}{2}\right)^2 = 16$
$(x - 4)^2 = 3$	Perfect square
$x - 4 = \pm\sqrt{3}$	Take square root
$x = 4 \pm \sqrt{3}$	Add 4

(b) After subtracting 6 from each side of the equation, we must factor the coefficient of x^2 (the 3) from the left side to put the equation in the correct form for completing the square.

$3x^2 - 12x + 6 = 0$	Given equation
$3x^2 - 12x = -6$	Subtract 6
$3(x^2 - 4x) = -6$	Factor 3 from LHS

Now we complete the square by adding $(-2)^2 = 4$ *inside* the parentheses. Since everything inside the parentheses is multiplied by 3, this means that we are actually adding $3 \cdot 4 = 12$ to the left side of the equation. Thus, we must add 12 to the right side as well.

$3(x^2 - 4x + 4) = -6 + 3 \cdot 4$	Complete the square: add 4
$3(x - 2)^2 = 6$	Perfect square
$(x - 2)^2 = 2$	Divide by 3
$x - 2 = \pm\sqrt{2}$	Take square root
$x = 2 \pm \sqrt{2}$	Add 2

NOW TRY EXERCISES **55** AND **59**

We can use the technique of completing the square to derive a formula for the roots of the general quadratic equation $ax^2 + bx + c = 0$.

THE QUADRATIC FORMULA

The roots of the quadratic equation $ax^2 + bx + c = 0$, where $a \neq 0$, are

$$x = \frac{-b \pm \sqrt{b^2 - 4ac}}{2a}$$

PROOF First, we divide each side of the equation by a and move the constant to the right side, giving

$$x^2 + \frac{b}{a}x = -\frac{c}{a} \qquad \text{Divide by } a$$

We now complete the square by adding $(b/2a)^2$ to each side of the equation:

$$x^2 + \frac{b}{a}x + \left(\frac{b}{2a}\right)^2 = -\frac{c}{a} + \left(\frac{b}{2a}\right)^2 \qquad \text{Complete the square: Add } \left(\frac{b}{2a}\right)^2$$

$$\left(x + \frac{b}{2a}\right)^2 = \frac{-4ac + b^2}{4a^2} \qquad \text{Perfect square}$$

$$x + \frac{b}{2a} = \pm\frac{\sqrt{b^2 - 4ac}}{2a} \qquad \text{Take square root}$$

$$x = \frac{-b \pm \sqrt{b^2 - 4ac}}{2a} \qquad \text{Subtract } \frac{b}{2a}$$

The Quadratic Formula could be used to solve the equations in Examples 4 and 6. You should carry out the details of these calculations.

EXAMPLE 7 | Using the Quadratic Formula

Find all solutions of each equation.

(a) $3x^2 - 5x - 1 = 0$ **(b)** $4x^2 + 12x + 9 = 0$ **(c)** $x^2 + 2x + 2 = 0$

SOLUTION

(a) In this quadratic equation $a = 3$, $b = -5$, and $c = -1$.

$$b = -5$$
$$3x^2 - 5x - 1 = 0$$
$$a = 3 \qquad c = -1$$

By the Quadratic Formula,

$$x = \frac{-(-5) \pm \sqrt{(-5)^2 - 4(3)(-1)}}{2(3)} = \frac{5 \pm \sqrt{37}}{6}$$

If approximations are desired, we can use a calculator to obtain

$$x = \frac{5 + \sqrt{37}}{6} \approx 1.8471 \qquad \text{and} \qquad x = \frac{5 - \sqrt{37}}{6} \approx -0.1805$$

(b) Using the Quadratic Formula with $a = 4$, $b = 12$, and $c = 9$ gives

$$x = \frac{-12 \pm \sqrt{(12)^2 - 4 \cdot 4 \cdot 9}}{2 \cdot 4} = \frac{-12 \pm 0}{8} = -\frac{3}{2}$$

This equation has only one solution, $x = -\frac{3}{2}$.

Another Method
$$4x^2 + 12x + 9 = 0$$
$$(2x + 3)^2 = 0$$
$$2x + 3 = 0$$
$$x = -\frac{3}{2}$$

FRANÇOIS VIÈTE (1540–1603) had a successful political career before taking up mathematics late in life. He became one of the most famous French mathematicians of the 16th century. Viète introduced a new level of abstraction in algebra by using letters to stand for *known* quantities in an equation. Before Viète's time, each equation had to be solved on its own. For instance, the quadratic equations

$$3x^2 + 2x + 8 = 0$$
$$5x^2 - 6x + 4 = 0$$

had to be solved separately by completing the square. Viète's idea was to consider all quadratic equations at once by writing

$$ax^2 + bx + c = 0$$

where a, b, and c are known quantities. Thus, he made it possible to write a *formula* (in this case, the quadratic formula) involving a, b, and c that can be used to solve all such equations in one fell swoop.

Viète's mathematical genius proved quite valuable during a war between France and Spain. To communicate with their troops, the Spaniards used a complicated code that Viète managed to decipher. Unaware of Viète's accomplishment, the Spanish king, Philip II, protested to the Pope, claiming that the French were using witchcraft to read his messages.

(c) Using the Quadratic Formula with $a = 1$, $b = 2$, and $c = 2$ gives

$$x = \frac{-2 \pm \sqrt{2^2 - 4 \cdot 2}}{2} = \frac{-2 \pm \sqrt{-4}}{2} = \frac{-2 \pm 2\sqrt{-1}}{2} = -1 \pm \sqrt{-1}$$

Since the square of any real number is nonnegative, $\sqrt{-1}$ is undefined in the real number system. The equation has no real solution.

✎. NOW TRY EXERCISES **65, 69**, AND **75**

In Section 3.5 we study the complex number system, in which the square roots of negative numbers do exist. The equation in Example 7(c) does have solutions in the complex number system.

The quantity $b^2 - 4ac$ that appears under the square root sign in the quadratic formula is called the *discriminant* of the equation $ax^2 + bx + c = 0$ and is given the symbol D. If $D < 0$, then $\sqrt{b^2 - 4ac}$ is undefined, and the quadratic equation has no real solution, as in Example 7(c). If $D = 0$, then the equation has only one real solution, as in Example 7(b). Finally, if $D > 0$, then the equation has two distinct real solutions, as in Example 7(a). The following box summarizes these observations.

THE DISCRIMINANT

The **discriminant** of the general quadratic $ax^2 + bx + c = 0$ $(a \neq 0)$ is $D = b^2 - 4ac$.

1. If $D > 0$, then the equation has two distinct real solutions.

2. If $D = 0$, then the equation has exactly one real solution.

3. If $D < 0$, then the equation has no real solution.

EXAMPLE 8 | Using the Discriminant

Use the discriminant to determine how many real solutions each equation has.

(a) $x^2 + 4x - 1 = 0$ **(b)** $4x^2 - 12x + 9 = 0$ **(c)** $\frac{1}{3}x^2 - 2x + 4 = 0$

SOLUTION

(a) The discriminant is $D = 4^2 - 4(1)(-1) = 20 > 0$, so the equation has two distinct real solutions.

(b) The discriminant is $D = (-12)^2 - 4 \cdot 4 \cdot 9 = 0$, so the equation has exactly one real solution.

(c) The discriminant is $D = (-2)^2 - 4(\frac{1}{3})4 = -\frac{4}{3} < 0$, so the equation has no real solution.

✎. NOW TRY EXERCISES **79, 81**, AND **83**

Now let's consider a real-life situation that can be modeled by a quadratic equation.

EXAMPLE 9 | The Path of a Projectile

An object thrown or fired straight upward at an initial speed of v_0 ft/s will reach a height of h feet after t seconds, where h and t are related by the formula

This formula depends on the fact that acceleration due to gravity is constant near the earth's surface. Here we neglect the effect of air resistance.

$$h = -16t^2 + v_0 t$$

Suppose that a bullet is shot straight upward with an initial speed of 800 ft/s. Its path is shown in Figure 2.

(a) When does the bullet fall back to ground level?

(b) When does it reach a height of 6400 ft?

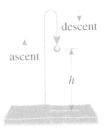

FIGURE 2

6400 ft

2 mi

10,000 ft

(c) When does it reach a height of 2 mi?

(d) How high is the highest point the bullet reaches?

SOLUTION Since the initial speed in this case is $v_0 = 800$ ft/s, the formula is

$$h = -16t^2 + 800t$$

(a) Ground level corresponds to $h = 0$, so we must solve the equation

$$0 = -16t^2 + 800t \qquad \text{Set } h = 0$$

$$0 = -16t(t - 50) \qquad \text{Factor}$$

Thus, $t = 0$ or $t = 50$. This means the bullet starts ($t = 0$) at ground level and returns to ground level after 50 s.

(b) Setting $h = 6400$ gives the equation

$$6400 = -16t^2 + 800t \qquad \text{Set } h = 6400$$

$$16t^2 - 800t + 6400 = 0 \qquad \text{All terms to LHS}$$

$$t^2 - 50t + 400 = 0 \qquad \text{Divide by 16}$$

$$(t - 10)(t - 40) = 0 \qquad \text{Factor}$$

$$t = 10 \quad \text{or} \quad t = 40 \qquad \text{Solve}$$

The bullet reaches 6400 ft after 10 s (on its ascent) and again after 40 s (on its descent to earth).

(c) Two miles is $2 \times 5280 = 10{,}560$ ft.

$$10{,}560 = -16t^2 + 800t \qquad \text{Set } h = 10{,}560$$

$$16t^2 - 800t + 10{,}560 = 0 \qquad \text{All terms to LHS}$$

$$t^2 - 50t + 660 = 0 \qquad \text{Divide by 16}$$

The discriminant of this equation is $D = (-50)^2 - 4(660) = -140$, which is negative. Thus, the equation has no real solution. The bullet never reaches a height of 2 mi.

(d) Each height the bullet reaches is attained twice, once on its ascent and once on its descent. The only exception is the highest point of its path, which is reached only once. This means that for the highest value of h, the following equation has only one solution for t:

$$h = -16t^2 + 800t$$

$$16t^2 - 800t + h = 0 \qquad \text{All terms to LHS}$$

This in turn means that the discriminant D of the equation is 0, so

$$D = (-800)^2 - 4(16)h = 0$$

$$640{,}000 - 64h = 0$$

$$h = 10{,}000$$

The maximum height reached is 10,000 ft.

✎ . NOW TRY EXERCISE **111**

▼ Other Types of Equations

So far we have learned how to solve linear and quadratic equations. Now we study other types of equations, including those that involve higher powers, fractional expressions, and radicals.

EXAMPLE 10 | An Equation Involving Fractional Expressions

Solve the equation $\dfrac{3}{x} + \dfrac{5}{x+2} = 2$.

SOLUTION   We eliminate the denominators by multiplying each side by the lowest common denominator.

$$\left(\frac{3}{x} + \frac{5}{x+2}\right)x(x+2) = 2x(x+2) \qquad \text{Multiply by LCD } x(x+2)$$

$$3(x+2) + 5x = 2x^2 + 4x \qquad \text{Expand}$$

$$8x + 6 = 2x^2 + 4x \qquad \text{Expand LHS}$$

$$0 = 2x^2 - 4x - 6 \qquad \text{Subtract } 8x + 6$$

$$0 = x^2 - 2x - 3 \qquad \text{Divide both sides by 2}$$

$$0 = (x-3)(x+1) \qquad \text{Factor}$$

$$x - 3 = 0 \quad \text{or} \quad x + 1 = 0 \qquad \text{Zero-Product Property}$$

$$x = 3 \qquad\qquad x = -1 \qquad \text{Solve}$$

We must check our answers because multiplying by an expression that contains the variable can introduce extraneous solutions. From *Check Your Answers* we see that the solutions are $x = 3$ and -1.

✎. NOW TRY EXERCISE **85**

When you solve an equation that involves radicals, you must be especially careful to check your final answers. The next example demonstrates why.

EXAMPLE 11 | An Equation Involving a Radical

Solve the equation $2x = 1 - \sqrt{2-x}$.

SOLUTION   To eliminate the square root, we first isolate it on one side of the equal sign, then square:

$$2x - 1 = -\sqrt{2-x} \qquad \text{Subtract 1}$$

$$(2x-1)^2 = 2 - x \qquad \text{Square each side}$$

$$4x^2 - 4x + 1 = 2 - x \qquad \text{Expand LHS}$$

$$4x^2 - 3x - 1 = 0 \qquad \text{Add } -2 + x$$

$$(4x+1)(x-1) = 0 \qquad \text{Factor}$$

$$4x + 1 = 0 \quad \text{or} \quad x - 1 = 0 \qquad \text{Zero-Product Property}$$

$$x = -\tfrac{1}{4} \qquad\qquad x = 1 \qquad \text{Solve}$$

The values $x = -\frac{1}{4}$ and $x = 1$ are only potential solutions. We must check them to see if they satisfy the original equation. From *Check Your Answers* we see that $x = -\frac{1}{4}$ is a solution but $x = 1$ is not. The only solution is $x = -\frac{1}{4}$.

✎. NOW TRY EXERCISE **91**

When we solve an equation, we may end up with one or more **extraneous solutions**, that is, potential solutions that do not satisfy the original equation. In Example 11 the value $x = 1$ is an extraneous solution. Extraneous solutions may be introduced when we square each side of an equation because the operation of squaring can turn a false equation into a true one. For example, $-1 \neq 1$, but $(-1)^2 = 1^2$. Thus, the squared equation

---

CHECK YOUR ANSWERS

$x = 3$:

$$\text{LHS} = \frac{3}{3} + \frac{5}{3+2}$$

$$= 1 + 1 = 2$$

$$\text{RHS} = 2$$

$$\text{LHS} = \text{RHS} \quad ✔$$

$x = -1$:

$$\text{LHS} = \frac{3}{-1} + \frac{5}{-1+2}$$

$$= -3 + 5 = 2$$

$$\text{RHS} = 2$$

$$\text{LHS} = \text{RHS} \quad ✔$$

CHECK YOUR ANSWERS

$x = -\frac{1}{4}$:

$$\text{LHS} = 2\left(-\tfrac{1}{4}\right) = -\tfrac{1}{2}$$

$$\text{RHS} = 1 - \sqrt{2 - \left(-\tfrac{1}{4}\right)}$$

$$= 1 - \sqrt{\tfrac{9}{4}}$$

$$= 1 - \tfrac{3}{2} = -\tfrac{1}{2}$$

$$\text{LHS} = \text{RHS} \quad ✔$$

$x = 1$:

$$\text{LHS} = 2(1) = 2$$

$$\text{RHS} = 1 - \sqrt{2 - 1}$$

$$= 1 - 1 = 0$$

$$\text{LHS} \neq \text{RHS} \quad ✗$$

may be true for more values of the variable than the original equation. That is why you must always check your answers to make sure that each satisfies the original equation.

An equation of the form $aW^2 + bW + c = 0$, where W is an algebraic expression, is an equation of **quadratic type**. We solve equations of quadratic type by substituting for the algebraic expression, as we see in the next two examples.

EXAMPLE 12 | A Fourth-Degree Equation of Quadratic Type

Find all solutions of the equation $x^4 - 8x^2 + 8 = 0$.

SOLUTION If we set $W = x^2$, then we get a quadratic equation in the new variable W:

$$(x^2)^2 - 8x^2 + 8 = 0 \qquad \text{Write } x^4 \text{ as } (x^2)^2$$

$$W^2 - 8W + 8 = 0 \qquad \text{Let } W = x^2$$

$$W = \frac{-(-8) \pm \sqrt{(-8)^2 - 4 \cdot 8}}{2} = 4 \pm 2\sqrt{2} \qquad \text{Quadratic Formula}$$

$$x^2 = 4 \pm 2\sqrt{2} \qquad W = x^2$$

$$x = \pm\sqrt{4 \pm 2\sqrt{2}} \qquad \text{Take square roots}$$

So, there are four solutions:

$$\sqrt{4 + 2\sqrt{2}}, \qquad \sqrt{4 - 2\sqrt{2}}, \qquad -\sqrt{4 + 2\sqrt{2}}, \qquad -\sqrt{4 - 2\sqrt{2}}$$

Using a calculator, we obtain the approximations $x \approx 2.61, 1.08, -2.61, -1.08$.

✎. NOW TRY EXERCISE **95**

EXAMPLE 13 | An Equation Involving Fractional Powers

Find all solutions of the equation $x^{1/3} + x^{1/6} - 2 = 0$.

SOLUTION This equation is of quadratic type because if we let $W = x^{1/6}$, then $W^2 = (x^{1/6})^2 = x^{1/3}$.

$$x^{1/3} + x^{1/6} - 2 = 0$$

$$W^2 + W - 2 = 0 \qquad \text{Let } W = x^{1/6}$$

$$(W - 1)(W + 2) = 0 \qquad \text{Factor}$$

$$W - 1 = 0 \quad \text{or} \quad W + 2 = 0 \qquad \text{Zero-Product Property}$$

$$W = 1 \qquad\qquad W = -2 \qquad \text{Solve}$$

$$x^{1/6} = 1 \qquad\qquad x^{1/6} = -2 \qquad W = x^{1/6}$$

$$x = 1^6 = 1 \qquad\qquad x = (-2)^6 = 64 \qquad \text{Take the 6th power}$$

From *Check Your Answers* we see that $x = 1$ is a solution but $x = 64$ is not. The only solution is $x = 1$.

CHECK YOUR ANSWERS

$x = 1$:

$\quad$ LHS $= 1^{1/3} + 1^{1/6} - 2 = 0$

$\quad$ RHS $= 0$

$\quad$ LHS $=$ RHS $\quad$ ✔

$x = 64$:

$\quad$ LHS $= 64^{1/3} + 64^{1/6} - 2$

$\qquad\quad = 4 + 2 - 2 = 4$

$\quad$ RHS $= 0$

$\quad$ LHS $\neq$ RHS $\quad$ ✗

✎. NOW TRY EXERCISE **99**

When solving equations that involve absolute values, we usually take cases.

EXAMPLE 14 | An Absolute Value Equation

Solve the equation $|2x - 5| = 3$.

SOLUTION By the definition of absolute value, $|2x - 5| = 3$ is equivalent to

$$
\begin{array}{lll}
2x - 5 = 3 & \text{or} & 2x - 5 = -3 \\
2x = 8 & & 2x = 2 \\
x = 4 & & x = 1
\end{array}
$$

The solutions are $x = 1$, $x = 4$.

✎. NOW TRY EXERCISE **105**

1.5 EXERCISES

CONCEPTS

1. *True or false?*
   (a) Adding the same number to each side of an equation always gives an equivalent equation.
   (b) Multiplying each side of an equation by the same number always gives an equivalent equation.
   (c) Squaring each side of an equation always gives an equivalent equation.

2. Explain how you would use each method to solve the equation $x^2 - 4x - 5 = 0$.
   (a) By factoring: _____
   (b) By completing the square: _____
   (c) By using the Quadratic Formula: _____

3. (a) The solutions of the equation $x^2(x - 4) = 0$ are _____.
   (b) To solve the equation $x^3 - 4x^2 = 0$, we _____ the left-hand side.

4. Solve the equation $\sqrt{2x} + x = 0$ by doing the following steps.
   (a) Isolate the radical: _____.
   (b) Square both sides: _____.
   (c) The solutions of the resulting quadratic equation are _____.
   (d) The solution(s) that satisfy the original equation are _____.

5. The equation $(x + 1)^2 - 5(x + 1) + 6 = 0$ is of _____ type. To solve the equation, we set $W =$ _____. The resulting quadratic equation is _____.

6. The equation $x^6 + 7x^3 - 8 = 0$ is of _____ type. To solve the equation, we set $W =$ _____. The resulting quadratic equation is _____.

SKILLS

7–10 ■ Determine whether the given value is a solution of the equation.

7. $4x + 7 = 9x - 3$
   (a) $x = -2$ (b) $x = 2$

8. $1 - [2 - (3 - x)] = 4x - (6 + x)$
   (a) $x = 2$ (b) $x = 4$

9. $\dfrac{1}{x} - \dfrac{1}{x - 4} = 1$
   (a) $x = 2$ (b) $x = 4$

10. $\dfrac{x^{3/2}}{x - 6} = x - 8$
    (a) $x = 4$ (b) $x = 8$

11–28 ■ The given equation is either linear or equivalent to a linear equation. Solve the equation.

11. $2x + 7 = 31$

12. $5x - 3 = 4$

13. $\frac{1}{2}x - 8 = 1$

14. $3 + \frac{1}{3}x = 5$

15. $-7w = 15 - 2w$

16. $5t - 13 = 12 - 5t$

17. $\frac{1}{2}y - 2 = \frac{1}{3}y$

18. $\dfrac{z}{5} = \dfrac{3}{10}z + 7$

19. $2(1 - x) = 3(1 + 2x) + 5$

20. $\dfrac{2}{3}y + \dfrac{1}{2}(y - 3) = \dfrac{y + 1}{4}$

21. $x - \frac{1}{3}x - \frac{1}{2}x - 5 = 0$

22. $2x - \dfrac{x}{2} + \dfrac{x + 1}{4} = 6x$

23. $\dfrac{1}{x} = \dfrac{4}{3x} + 1$

24. $\dfrac{2x - 1}{x + 2} = \dfrac{4}{5}$

25. $\dfrac{3}{x + 1} - \dfrac{1}{2} = \dfrac{1}{3x + 3}$

26. $\dfrac{4}{x - 1} + \dfrac{2}{x + 1} = \dfrac{35}{x^2 - 1}$

27. $(t - 4)^2 = (t + 4)^2 + 32$

28. $\sqrt{3}x + \sqrt{12} = \dfrac{x + 5}{\sqrt{3}}$

29–42 ■ Solve the equation for the indicated variable.

29. $PV = nRT$;   for R

30. $F = G\dfrac{mM}{r^2}$;   for m

31. $P = 2l + 2w$; for w

32. $\dfrac{1}{R} = \dfrac{1}{R_1} + \dfrac{1}{R_2}$; for R_1

33. $\dfrac{ax + b}{cx + d} = 2$; for x

34. $a - 2[b - 3(c - x)] = 6$; for x

35. $a^2 x + (a - 1) = (a + 1)x$; for x

36. $\dfrac{a + 1}{b} = \dfrac{a - 1}{b} + \dfrac{b + 1}{a}$; for a

37. $V = \frac{1}{3}\pi r^2 h$; for r

38. $F = G\dfrac{mM}{r^2}$; for r

39. $a^2 + b^2 = c^2$; for b

40. $A = P\left(1 + \dfrac{i}{100}\right)^2$; for i

41. $h = \frac{1}{2}gt^2 + v_0 t$; for t

42. $S = \dfrac{n(n + 1)}{2}$; for n

43–54 ■ Solve the equation by factoring.

43. $x^2 + x - 12 = 0$

44. $x^2 + 3x - 4 = 0$

45. $x^2 - 7x + 12 = 0$

46. $x^2 + 8x + 12 = 0$

47. $4x^2 - 4x - 15 = 0$

48. $2y^2 + 7y + 3 = 0$

49. $3x^2 + 5x = 2$

50. $6x(x - 1) = 21 - x$

51. $2x^2 = 8$

52. $3x^2 - 27 = 0$

53. $(3x + 2)^2 = 10$

54. $(2x - 1)^2 = 8$

55–62 ■ Solve the equation by completing the square.

55. $x^2 + 2x - 5 = 0$

56. $x^2 - 4x + 2 = 0$

57. $x^2 - 6x - 11 = 0$

58. $x^2 + 3x - \frac{7}{4} = 0$

59. $2x^2 + 8x + 1 = 0$

60. $3x^2 - 6x - 1 = 0$

61. $4x^2 - x = 0$

62. $x^2 = \frac{3}{4}x - \frac{1}{8}$

63–78 ■ Find all real solutions of the quadratic equation.

63. $x^2 - 2x - 15 = 0$

64. $x^2 + 5x - 6 = 0$

65. $x^2 - 7x + 10 = 0$

66. $x^2 + 30x + 200 = 0$

67. $2x^2 + x - 3 = 0$

68. $3x^2 + 7x + 4 = 0$

69. $3x^2 + 6x - 5 = 0$

70. $x^2 - 6x + 1 = 0$

71. $z^2 - \frac{3}{2}z + \frac{9}{16} = 0$

72. $2y^2 - y - \frac{1}{2} = 0$

73. $4x^2 + 16x - 9 = 0$

74. $0 = x^2 - 4x + 1$

75. $w^2 = 3(w - 1)$

76. $3 + 5z + z^2 = 0$

77. $10y^2 - 16y + 5 = 0$

78. $25x^2 + 70x + 49 = 0$

79–84 ■ Use the discriminant to determine the number of real solutions of the equation. Do not solve the equation.

79. $x^2 - 6x + 1 = 0$

80. $3x^2 = 6x - 9$

81. $x^2 + 2.20x + 1.21 = 0$

82. $x^2 + 2.21x + 1.21 = 0$

83. $4x^2 + 5x + \frac{13}{8} = 0$

84. $x^2 + rx - s = 0$ $(s > 0)$

85–108 ■ Find all real solutions of the equation.

85. $\dfrac{1}{x - 1} + \dfrac{1}{x + 2} = \dfrac{5}{4}$

86. $\dfrac{10}{x} - \dfrac{12}{x - 3} + 4 = 0$

87. $\dfrac{x^2}{x + 100} = 50$

88. $\dfrac{1}{x - 1} - \dfrac{2}{x^2} = 0$

89. $\dfrac{x + 5}{x - 2} = \dfrac{5}{x + 2} + \dfrac{28}{x^2 - 4}$

90. $\dfrac{x}{2x + 7} - \dfrac{x + 1}{x + 3} = 1$

91. $\sqrt{2x + 1} + 1 = x$

92. $\sqrt{5 - x} + 1 = x - 2$

93. $2x + \sqrt{x + 1} = 8$

94. $\sqrt{\sqrt{x - 5} + x} = 5$

95. $x^4 - 13x^2 + 40 = 0$

96. $x^4 - 5x^2 + 4 = 0$

97. $2x^4 + 4x^2 + 1 = 0$

98. $x^6 - 2x^3 - 3 = 0$

99. $x^{4/3} - 5x^{2/3} + 6 = 0$

100. $\sqrt{x} - 3\sqrt[4]{x} - 4 = 0$

101. $4(x + 1)^{1/2} - 5(x + 1)^{3/2} + (x + 1)^{5/2} = 0$

102. $x^{1/2} + 3x^{-1/2} = 10x^{-3/2}$

103. $x^{1/2} - 3x^{1/3} = 3x^{1/6} - 9$ **104.** $x - 5\sqrt{x} + 6 = 0$

105. $|3x + 5| = 1$

106. $|2x| = 3$

107. $|x - 4| = 0.01$

108. $|x - 6| = -1$

APPLICATIONS

109–110 ■ **Falling-Body Problems** Suppose an object is dropped from a height h_0 above the ground. Then its height after t seconds is given by $h = -16t^2 + h_0$, where h is measured in feet. Use this information to solve the problem.

109. If a ball is dropped from 288 ft above the ground, how long does it take to reach ground level?

110. A ball is dropped from the top of a building 96 ft tall.
  (a) How long will it take to fall half the distance to ground level?
  (b) How long will it take to fall to ground level?

111–112 ■ **Falling-Body Problems** Use the formula $h = -16t^2 + v_0 t$ discussed in Example 9.

111. A ball is thrown straight upward at an initial speed of $v_0 = 40$ ft/s.
  (a) When does the ball reach a height of 24 ft?
  (b) When does it reach a height of 48 ft?
  (c) What is the greatest height reached by the ball?
  (d) When does the ball reach the highest point of its path?
  (e) When does the ball hit the ground?

112. How fast would a ball have to be thrown upward to reach a maximum height of 100 ft?   [*Hint:* Use the discriminant of the equation $16t^2 - v_0 t + h = 0$.]

113. **Shrinkage in Concrete Beams** As concrete dries, it shrinks—the higher the water content, the greater the shrinkage. If a concrete beam has a water content of w kg/m³, then it will shrink by a factor

$$S = \dfrac{0.032w - 2.5}{10{,}000}$$

where S is the fraction of the original beam length that disappears due to shrinkage.

  (a) A beam 12.025 m long is cast in concrete that contains 250 kg/m³ water. What is the shrinkage factor S? How long will the beam be when it has dried?

(b) A beam is 10.014 m long when wet. We want it to shrink to 10.009 m, so the shrinkage factor should be $S = 0.00050$. What water content will provide this amount of shrinkage?

114. The Lens Equation If F is the focal length of a convex lens and an object is placed at a distance x from the lens, then its image will be at a distance y from the lens, where F, x, and y are related by the *lens equation*

$$\frac{1}{F} = \frac{1}{x} + \frac{1}{y}$$

Suppose that a lens has a focal length of 4.8 cm and that the image of an object is 4 cm closer to the lens than the object itself. How far from the lens is the object?

115. Fish Population The fish population in a certain lake rises and falls according to the formula

$$F = 1000(30 + 17t - t^2)$$

Here F is the number of fish at time t, where t is measured in years since January 1, 2002, when the fish population was first estimated.

(a) On what date will the fish population again be the same as it was on January 1, 2002?

(b) By what date will all the fish in the lake have died?

116. Fish Population A large pond is stocked with fish. The fish population P is modeled by the formula $P = 3t + 10\sqrt{t} + 140$, where t is the number of days since the fish were first introduced into the pond. How many days will it take for the fish population to reach 500?

117. Profit A small-appliance manufacturer finds that the profit P (in dollars) generated by producing x microwave ovens per week is given by the formula $P = \frac{1}{10}x(300 - x)$ provided that $0 \le x \le 200$. How many ovens must be manufactured in a given week to generate a profit of $1250?

118. Gravity If an imaginary line segment is drawn between the centers of the earth and the moon, then the net gravitational force F acting on an object situated on this line segment is

$$F = \frac{-K}{x^2} + \frac{0.012K}{(239 - x)^2}$$

where $K > 0$ is a constant and x is the distance of the object from the center of the earth, measured in thousands of miles. How far from the center of the earth is the "dead spot" where no net gravitational force acts upon the object? (Express your answer to the nearest thousand miles.)

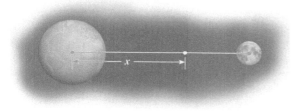

119. Depth of a Well One method for determining the depth of a well is to drop a stone into it and then measure the time it takes until the splash is heard. If d is the depth of the well (in feet) and t_1 the time (in seconds) it takes for the stone to fall, then $d = 16t_1^2$, so $t_1 = \sqrt{d}/4$. Now if t_2 is the time it takes for the sound to travel back up, then $d = 1090t_2$ because the speed of sound is 1090 ft/s. So $t_2 = d/1090$. Thus, the total time elapsed between dropping the stone and hearing the splash is

$$t_1 + t_2 = \frac{\sqrt{d}}{4} + \frac{d}{1090}$$

How deep is the well if this total time is 3 s?

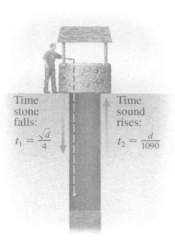

DISCOVERY ▪ DISCUSSION ▪ WRITING

120. A Family of Equations The equation

$$3x + k - 5 = kx - k + 1$$

is really a **family of equations**, because for each value of k, we get a different equation with the unknown x. The letter k is called a **parameter** for this family. What value should we pick for k to make the given value of x a solution of the resulting equation?

(a) $x = 0$ **(b)** $x = 1$ **(c)** $x = 2$

121. Proof That 0 = 1? The following steps appear to give equivalent equations, which seem to prove that $1 = 0$. Find the error.

$x = 1$	Given
$x^2 = x$	Multiply by x
$x^2 - x = 0$	Subtract x
$x(x - 1) = 0$	Factor
$\dfrac{x(x - 1)}{x - 1} = \dfrac{0}{x - 1}$	Divide by $x - 1$
$x = 0$	Simplify
$1 = 0$	Given $x = 1$

122. Volumes of Solids The sphere, cylinder, and cone shown here all have the same radius r and the same volume V.

(a) Use the volume formulas given on the inside front cover of this book, to show that

$$\tfrac{4}{3}\pi r^3 = \pi r^2 h_1 \qquad \text{and} \qquad \tfrac{4}{3}\pi r^3 = \tfrac{1}{3}\pi r^2 h_2$$

(b) Solve these equations for h_1 and h_2.

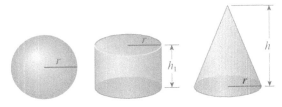

123. Relationship Between Roots and Coefficients
The Quadratic Formula gives us the roots of a quadratic equation from its coefficients. We can also obtain the coefficients from the roots. For example, find the roots of the equation $x^2 - 9x + 20 = 0$ and show that the product of the roots is the constant term 20 and the sum of the roots is 9, the negative of the coefficient of x. Show that the same relationship between roots and coefficients holds for the following equations:

$$x^2 - 2x - 8 = 0$$

$$x^2 + 4x + 2 = 0$$

Use the Quadratic Formula to prove that in general, if the equation $x^2 + bx + c = 0$ has roots r_1 and r_2, then $c = r_1 r_2$ and $b = -(r_1 + r_2)$.

124. Solving an Equation in Different Ways We have learned several different ways to solve an equation in this section. Some equations can be tackled by more than one method. For example, the equation $x - \sqrt{x} - 2 = 0$ is of quadratic type. We can solve it by letting $\sqrt{x} = u$ and $x = u^2$, and factoring. Or we could solve for $\sqrt{x}$, square each side, and then solve the resulting quadratic equation. Solve the following equations using both methods indicated, and show that you get the same final answers.

(a) $x - \sqrt{x} - 2 = 0$ quadratic type; solve for the radical, and square

(b) $\dfrac{12}{(x-3)^2} + \dfrac{10}{x-3} + 1 = 0$ quadratic type; multiply by LCD

1.6 MODELING WITH EQUATIONS

Making and Using Models ▶ Problems About Interest ▶ Problems About Area or Length ▶ Problems About Mixtures ▶ Problems About the Time Needed to Do a Job ▶ Problems About Distance, Rate, and Time

Many problems in the sciences, economics, finance, medicine, and numerous other fields can be translated into algebra problems; this is one reason that algebra is so useful. In this section we use equations as mathematical models to solve real-life problems.

▼ Making and Using Models

We will use the following guidelines to help us set up equations that model situations described in words. To show how the guidelines can help you to set up equations, we note them as we work each example in this section.

GUIDELINES FOR MODELING WITH EQUATIONS

1. **Identify the Variable.** Identify the quantity that the problem asks you to find. This quantity can usually be determined by a careful reading of the question that is posed at the end of the problem. Then **introduce notation** for the variable (call it x or some other letter).

2. **Translate from Words to Algebra.** Read each sentence in the problem again, and express all the quantities mentioned in the problem in terms of the variable you defined in Step 1. To organize this information, it is sometimes helpful to **draw a diagram** or **make a table**.

3. **Set Up the Model.** Find the crucial fact in the problem that gives a relationship between the expressions you listed in Step 2. **Set up an equation** (or **model**) that expresses this relationship.

4. **Solve the Equation and Check Your Answer.** Solve the equation, check your answer, and express it as a sentence that answers the question posed in the problem.

The following example illustrates how these guidelines are used to translate a "word problem" into the language of algebra.

EXAMPLE 1 | Renting a Car

A car rental company charges $30 a day and 15¢ a mile for renting a car. Helen rents a car for two days, and her bill comes to $108. How many miles did she drive?

SOLUTION

Identify the variable.   We are asked to find the number of miles Helen has driven. So we let

$$x = \text{number of miles driven}$$

Translate from words to algebra.   Now we translate all the information given in the problem into the language of algebra.

In Words	In Algebra
Number of miles driven	x
Mileage cost (at $0.15 per mile)	$0.15x$
Daily cost (at $30 per day)	$2(30)$

Set up the model.   Now we set up the model.

mileage cost	+	daily cost	=	total cost

$$0.15x + 2(30) = 108$$

Solve.   Now we solve for x.

$$0.15x = 48 \qquad \text{Subtract 60}$$

$$x = \frac{48}{0.15} \qquad \text{Divide by 0.15}$$

$$x = 320 \qquad \text{Calculator}$$

CHECK YOUR ANSWER

total cost = mileage cost + daily cost

$= 0.15(320) + 2(30)$

$= 108$ ✔

Helen drove her rental car 320 miles.

✎. NOW TRY EXERCISE **19**

In the examples and exercises that follow, we construct equations that model problems in many different real-life situations.

▼ Problems About Interest

When you borrow money from a bank or when a bank "borrows" your money by keeping it for you in a savings account, the borrower in each case must pay for the privilege of using the money. The fee that is paid is called **interest**. The most basic type of interest is **simple interest**, which is just an annual percentage of the total amount borrowed or deposited. The amount of a loan or deposit is called the **principal** P. The annual percentage paid for the use of this money is the **interest rate** r. We will use the variable t to stand for the number of years that the money is on deposit and the variable I to stand for the total interest earned. The following **simple interest formula** gives the amount of interest I earned when a principal P is deposited for t years at an interest rate r.

$$I = Prt$$

When using this formula, remember to convert r from a percentage to a decimal. For example, in decimal form, 5% is 0.05. So at an interest rate of 5%, the interest paid on a $1000 deposit over a 3-year period is $I = Prt = 1000(0.05)(3) = \$150$.

EXAMPLE 2 | Interest on an Investment

Mary inherits $100,000 and invests it in two certificates of deposit. One certificate pays 6% and the other pays $4\frac{1}{2}$% simple interest annually. If Mary's total interest is $5025 per year, how much money is invested at each rate?

SOLUTION

Identify the variable. The problem asks for the amount she has invested at each rate. So we let

$$x = \text{the amount invested at 6\%}$$

Translate from words to algebra. Since Mary's total inheritance is $100,000, it follows that she invested $100,000 - x$ at $4\frac{1}{2}$%. We translate all the information given into the language of algebra.

In Words	In Algebra
Amount invested at 6%	x
Amount invested at $4\frac{1}{2}$%	$100{,}000 - x$
Interest earned at 6%	$0.06x$
Interest earned at $4\frac{1}{2}$%	$0.045(100{,}000 - x)$

Set up the model. We use the fact that Mary's total interest is $5025 to set up the model.

$$\underset{\text{interest at 6\%}}{\underbrace{}} + \underset{\text{interest at } 4\frac{1}{2}\%}{\underbrace{}} = \underset{\text{total interest}}{\underbrace{}}$$

$$0.06x + 0.045(100{,}000 - x) = 5025$$

Solve. Now we solve for x.

$$0.06x + 4500 - 0.045x = 5025 \qquad \text{Distributive Property}$$

$$0.015x + 4500 = 5025 \qquad \text{Combine the } x\text{-terms}$$

$$0.015x = 525 \qquad \text{Subtract 4500}$$

$$x = \frac{525}{0.015} = 35{,}000 \qquad \text{Divide by 0.015}$$

So Mary has invested $35,000 at 6% and the remaining $65,000 at $4\frac{1}{2}$%.

CHECK YOUR ANSWER

$$\text{total interest} = 6\% \text{ of } \$35{,}000 + 4\tfrac{1}{2}\% \text{ of } \$65{,}000$$

$$= \$2100 + \$2925 = \$5025 \qquad ✔$$

NOW TRY EXERCISE **21**

▼ Problems About Area or Length

When we use algebra to model a physical situation, we must sometimes use basic formulas from geometry. For example, we may need a formula for an area or a perimeter, or the formula that relates the sides of similar triangles, or the Pythagorean Theorem. Most of these formulas are listed in the front endpapers of this book. The next two examples use these geometric formulas to solve some real-world problems.

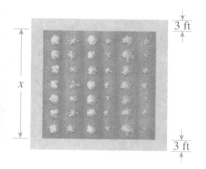

3 ft

x

3 ft

FIGURE 1

EXAMPLE 3 | Dimensions of a Garden

A square garden has a walkway 3 ft wide around its outer edge, as shown in Figure 1. If the area of the entire garden, including the walkway, is 18,000 ft², what are the dimensions of the planted area?

SOLUTION

Identify the variable. We are asked to find the length and width of the planted area. So we let

$$x = \text{the length of the planted area}$$

Translate from words to algebra. Next, translate the information from Figure 1 into the language of algebra.

In Words	In Algebra
Length of planted area	x
Length of entire garden	$x + 6$
Area of entire garden	$(x + 6)^2$

Set up the model. We now set up the model.

$$\text{area of entire garden} = 18,000 \text{ ft}^2$$

$$(x + 6)^2 = 18,000$$

Solve. Now we solve for x.

$$x + 6 = \sqrt{18,000} \qquad \text{Take square roots}$$
$$x = \sqrt{18,000} - 6 \qquad \text{Subtract 6}$$
$$x \approx 128$$

The planted area of the garden is about 128 ft by 128 ft.

✎. NOW TRY EXERCISE **47**

EXAMPLE 4 | Dimensions of a Building Lot

A rectangular building lot is 8 ft longer than it is wide and has an area of 2900 ft². Find the dimensions of the lot.

SOLUTION

Identify the variable. We are asked to find the width and length of the lot. So let

$$w = \text{width of lot}$$

Translate from words to algebra. Then we translate the information given in the problem into the language of algebra (see Figure 2).

In Words	In Algebra
Width of lot	w
Length of Lot	$w + 8$

Set up the model. Now we set up the model.

$$\begin{array}{ccc} \text{width} & \text{length} & \text{area} \\ \text{of lot} & \cdot \quad \text{of lot} & = \quad \text{of lot} \end{array}$$

$$w(w + 8) = 2900$$

Solve.   Now we solve for w.

$$w^2 + 8w = 2900 \qquad \text{Expand}$$

$$w^2 + 8w - 2900 = 0 \qquad \text{Subtract 2900}$$

$$(w - 50)(w + 58) = 0 \qquad \text{Factor}$$

$$w = 50 \quad \text{or} \quad w = -58 \qquad \text{Zero-Product Property}$$

Since the width of the lot must be a positive number, we conclude that $w = 50$ ft. The length of the lot is $w + 8 = 50 + 8 = 58$ ft.

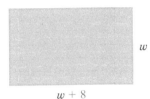

FIGURE 2

$w + 8$

✎ NOW TRY EXERCISE **39**

EXAMPLE 5 | Determining the Height of a Building Using Similar Triangles

A man who is 6 ft tall wishes to find the height of a certain four-story building. He measures its shadow and finds it to be 28 ft long, while his own shadow is $3\frac{1}{2}$ ft long. How tall is the building?

SOLUTION

Identify the variable.   The problem asks for the height of the building. So let

$$h = \text{the height of the building}$$

Translate from words to algebra.   We use the fact that the triangles in Figure 3 are similar. Recall that for any pair of similar triangles the ratios of corresponding sides are equal. Now we translate these observations into the language of algebra.

In Words	In Algebra
Height of building	h
Ratio of height to base in large triangle	$\frac{h}{28}$
Ratio of height to base in small triangle	$\frac{6}{3.5}$

FIGURE 3

Set up the model. Since the large and small triangles are similar, we get the equation

$$\boxed{\begin{array}{c}\text{ratio of height to}\\ \text{base in large triangle}\end{array}} = \boxed{\begin{array}{c}\text{ratio of height to}\\ \text{base in small triangle}\end{array}}$$

$$\frac{h}{28} = \frac{6}{3.5}$$

Solve. Now we solve for h.

$$h = \frac{6 \cdot 28}{3.5} = 48 \qquad \text{Multiply by 28}$$

So the building is 48 ft tall.

NOW TRY EXERCISE **51**

▼ Problems About Mixtures

Many real-world problems involve mixing different types of substances. For example, construction workers may mix cement, gravel, and sand; fruit juice from concentrate may involve mixing different types of juices. Problems involving mixtures and concentrations make use of the fact that if an amount x of a substance is dissolved in a solution with volume V, then the concentration C of the substance is given by

$$C = \frac{x}{V}$$

So if 10 g of sugar is dissolved in 5 L of water, then the sugar concentration is $C = 10/5 = 2$ g/L. Solving a mixture problem usually requires us to analyze the amount x of the substance that is in the solution. When we solve for x in this equation, we see that $x = CV$. Note that in many mixture problems the concentration C is expressed as a percentage, as in the next example.

EXAMPLE 6 | Mixtures and Concentration

A manufacturer of soft drinks advertises their orange soda as "naturally flavored," although it contains only 5% orange juice. A new federal regulation stipulates that to be called "natural," a drink must contain at least 10% fruit juice. How much pure orange juice must this manufacturer add to 900 gal of orange soda to conform to the new regulation?

SOLUTION

Identify the variable. The problem asks for the amount of pure orange juice to be added. So let

$$x = \text{the amount (in gallons) of pure orange juice to be added}$$

Translate from words to algebra. In any problem of this type—in which two different substances are to be mixed—drawing a diagram helps us to organize the given information (see Figure 4).

The information in the figure can be translated into the language of algebra, as follows:

In Words	In Algebra
Amount of orange juice to be added	x
Amount of the mixture	$900 + x$
Amount of orange juice in the first vat	$0.05(900) = 45$
Amount of orange juice in the second vat	$1 \cdot x = x$
Amount of orange juice in the mixture	$0.10(900 + x)$

	5% juice	100% juice	10% juice
Volume	900 gallons	x gallons	$900 + x$ gallons
Amount of orange juice	5% of 900 gallons = 45 gallons	100% of x gallons = x gallons	10% of $900 + x$ gallons = $0.1(900 + x)$ gallons

FIGURE 4

Set up the model.   To set up the model, we use the fact that the total amount of orange juice in the mixture is equal to the orange juice in the first two vats.

$$\begin{pmatrix} \text{amount of} \\ \text{orange juice} \\ \text{in first vat} \end{pmatrix} + \begin{pmatrix} \text{amount of} \\ \text{orange juice} \\ \text{in second vat} \end{pmatrix} = \begin{pmatrix} \text{amount of} \\ \text{orange juice} \\ \text{in mixture} \end{pmatrix}$$

$$45 + x = 0.1(900 + x) \qquad \text{From Figure 4}$$

Solve.   Now we solve for x.

$$45 + x = 90 + 0.1x \qquad \text{Distributive Property}$$

$$0.9x = 45 \qquad \text{Subtract } 0.1x \text{ and } 45$$

$$x = \frac{45}{0.9} = 50 \qquad \text{Divide by } 0.9$$

The manufacturer should add 50 gal of pure orange juice to the soda.

CHECK YOUR ANSWER

amount of juice before mixing = 5% of 900 gal + 50 gal pure juice

= 45 gal + 50 gal = 95 gal

amount of juice after mixing = 10% of 950 gal = 95 gal

Amounts are equal.   ✔

✎ NOW TRY EXERCISE **53**

▼ Problems About the Time Needed to Do a Job

When solving a problem that involves determining how long it takes several workers to complete a job, we use the fact that if a person or machine takes H time units to complete the task, then in one time unit the fraction of the task that has been completed is $1/H$. For example, if a worker takes 5 hours to mow a lawn, then in 1 hour the worker will mow 1/5 of the lawn.

EXAMPLE 7 | Time Needed to Do a Job

Because of an anticipated heavy rainstorm, the water level in a reservoir must be lowered by 1 ft. Opening spillway A lowers the level by this amount in 4 hours, whereas opening the smaller spillway B does the job in 6 hours. How long will it take to lower the water level by 1 ft if both spillways are opened?

SOLUTION Identify the variable.   We are asked to find the time needed to lower the level by 1 ft if both spillways are open. So let

$$x = \text{the time (in hours) it takes to lower the water level}$$
$$\text{by 1 ft if both spillways are open}$$

Translate from words to algebra.   Finding an equation relating x to the other quantities in this problem is not easy. Certainly x is not simply $4 + 6$, because that would mean that together the two spillways require longer to lower the water level than either spillway alone. Instead, *we look at the fraction of the job that can be done in 1 hour by each spillway.*

In Words	In Algebra
Time it takes to lower level 1 ft with A and B together	x h
Distance A lowers level in 1 h	$\frac{1}{4}$ ft
Distance B lowers level in 1 h	$\frac{1}{6}$ ft
Distance A and B together lower levels in 1 h	$\frac{1}{x}$ ft

Set up the model.   Now we set up the model.

$$\boxed{\text{fraction done by A}} + \boxed{\text{fraction done by B}} = \boxed{\text{fraction done by both}}$$

$$\frac{1}{4} + \frac{1}{6} = \frac{1}{x}$$

Solve.   Now we solve for x.

$$3x + 2x = 12 \qquad \text{Multiply by the LCD, } 12x$$
$$5x = 12 \qquad \text{Add}$$
$$x = \frac{12}{5} \qquad \text{Divide by 5}$$

It will take $2\frac{2}{5}$ hours, or 2 h 24 min, to lower the water level by 1 ft if both spillways are open.

✎. NOW TRY EXERCISE **61**

▼ Problems About Distance, Rate, and Time

The next example deals with distance, rate (speed), and time. The formula to keep in mind here is

$$\boxed{\text{distance} = \text{rate} \times \text{time}}$$

where the rate is either the constant speed or average speed of a moving object. For example, driving at 60 mi/h for 4 hours takes you a distance of $60 \cdot 4 = 240$ mi.

EXAMPLE 8 | A Distance-Speed-Time Problem

A jet flew from New York to Los Angeles, a distance of 4200 km. The speed for the return trip was 100 km/h faster than the outbound speed. If the total trip took 13 hours, what was the jet's speed from New York to Los Angeles?

SOLUTION Identify the variable.   We are asked for the speed of the jet from New York to Los Angeles. So let

$$s = \text{speed from New York to Los Angeles}$$

Then $\qquad\qquad s + 100 = \text{speed from Los Angeles to New York}$

Translate from words to algebra.   Now we organize the information in a table. We fill in the "Distance" column first, since we know that the cities are 4200 km apart. Then we fill in the "Speed" column, since we have expressed both speeds (rates) in terms of the variable s. Finally, we calculate the entries for the "Time" column, using

$$\text{time} = \frac{\text{distance}}{\text{rate}}$$

	Distance (km)	Speed (km/h)	Time (h)
N.Y. to L.A.	4200	s	$\dfrac{4200}{s}$
L.A. to N.Y.	4200	$s + 100$	$\dfrac{4200}{s + 100}$

Set up the model.   The total trip took 13 hours, so we have the model

$$\begin{array}{ccc} \text{time from} \\ \text{N.Y. to L.A.} \end{array} + \begin{array}{ccc} \text{time from} \\ \text{L.A. to N.Y.} \end{array} = \begin{array}{ccc} \text{total} \\ \text{time} \end{array}$$

$$\frac{4200}{s} + \frac{4200}{s + 100} = 13$$

Solve.   Multiplying by the common denominator, $s(s + 100)$, we get

$$4200(s + 100) + 4200s = 13s(s + 100)$$

$$8400s + 420{,}000 = 13s^2 + 1300s$$

$$0 = 13s^2 - 7100s - 420{,}000$$

Although this equation does factor, with numbers this large it is probably quicker to use the Quadratic Formula and a calculator.

$$s = \frac{7100 \pm \sqrt{(-7100)^2 - 4(13)(-420{,}000)}}{2(13)}$$

$$= \frac{7100 \pm 8500}{26}$$

$$s = 600 \qquad \text{or} \qquad s = \frac{-1400}{26} \approx -53.8$$

Since s represents speed, we reject the negative answer and conclude that the jet's speed from New York to Los Angeles was 600 km/h.

✎. NOW TRY EXERCISE **67**

EXAMPLE 9 | Energy Expended in Bird Flight

Ornithologists have determined that some species of birds tend to avoid flights over large bodies of water during daylight hours, because air generally rises over land and falls over water in the daytime, so flying over water requires more energy. A bird is released from point A on an island, 5 mi from B, the nearest point on a straight shoreline. The bird flies to a point C on the shoreline and then flies along the shoreline to its nesting area D, as shown in Figure 5. Suppose the bird has 170 kcal of energy reserves. It uses 10 kcal/mi flying over land and 14 kcal/mi flying over water.

(a) Where should the point C be located so that the bird uses exactly 170 kcal of energy during its flight?

(b) Does the bird have enough energy reserves to fly directly from A to D?

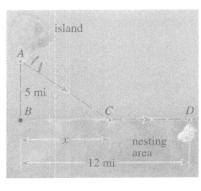

FIGURE 5

SOLUTION

(a) Identify the variable. We are asked to find the location of C. So let

$$x = \text{distance from } B \text{ to } C$$

Translate from words to algebra. From the figure, and from the fact that

$$\text{energy used} = \text{energy per mile} \times \text{miles flown}$$

we determine the following:

In Words	In Algebra	
Distance from B to C	x	
Distance flown over water (from A to C)	$\sqrt{x^2 + 25}$	Pythagorean Theorem
Distance flown over land (from C to D)	$12 - x$	
Energy used over water	$14\sqrt{x^2 + 25}$	
Energy used over land	$10(12 - x)$	

Set up the model. Now we set up the model.

$$\begin{array}{ccc} \text{total energy} \\ \text{used} \end{array} = \begin{array}{c} \text{energy used} \\ \text{over water} \end{array} + \begin{array}{c} \text{energy used} \\ \text{over land} \end{array}$$

$$170 = 14\sqrt{x^2 + 25} + 10(12 - x)$$

Solve. To solve this equation, we eliminate the square root by first bringing all other terms to the left of the equal sign and then squaring each side.

$$170 - 10(12 - x) = 14\sqrt{x^2 + 25} \qquad \text{Isolate square-root term on RHS}$$

$$50 + 10x = 14\sqrt{x^2 + 25} \qquad \text{Simplify LHS}$$

$$(50 + 10x)^2 = (14)^2(x^2 + 25) \qquad \text{Square each side}$$

$$2500 + 1000x + 100x^2 = 196x^2 + 4900 \qquad \text{Expand}$$

$$0 = 96x^2 - 1000x + 2400 \qquad \text{All terms to RHS}$$

This equation could be factored, but because the numbers are so large it is easier to use the Quadratic Formula and a calculator:

$$x = \frac{1000 \pm \sqrt{(-1000)^2 - 4(96)(2400)}}{2(96)}$$

$$= \frac{1000 \pm 280}{192} = 6\frac{2}{3} \quad \text{or} \quad 3\frac{3}{4}$$

Point C should be either $6\frac{2}{3}$ mi or $3\frac{3}{4}$ mi from B so that the bird uses exactly 170 kcal of energy during its flight.

(b) By the Pythagorean Theorem (see page 219), the length of the route directly from A to D is $\sqrt{5^2 + 12^2} = 13$ mi, so the energy the bird requires for that route is $14 \times 13 = 182$ kcal. This is more energy than the bird has available, so it can't use this route.

NOW TRY EXERCISE 83

1.6 EXERCISES

CONCEPTS

1. Explain in your own words what it means for an equation to model a real-world situation, and give an example.

2. In the formula $I = Prt$ for simple interest, P stands for

_____, r for _____, and t for _____.

3. Give a formula for the area of the geometric figure.

(a) A square of side x: $A =$ _____.

(b) A rectangle of length l and width w: $A =$ _____.

(c) A circle of radius r: $A =$ _____.

4. Balsamic vinegar contains 5% acetic acid, so a 32-oz bottle of balsamic vinegar contains _____ ounces of acetic acid.

5. A painter paints a wall in x hours, so the fraction of the wall that she paints in 1 hour is _____.

6. The formula $d = rt$ models the distance d traveled by an object moving at the constant rate r in time t. Find formulas for the following quantities.

$$r = \text{_____} \qquad t = \text{_____} .$$

SKILLS

7–18 ■ Express the given quantity in terms of the indicated variable.

7. The sum of three consecutive integers; $n =$ first integer of the three

8. The sum of three consecutive integers; $n =$ middle integer of the three

9. The average of three test scores if the first two scores are 78 and 82; $s =$ third test score

10. The average of four quiz scores if each of the first three scores is 8; $q =$ fourth quiz score

11. The interest obtained after one year on an investment at $2\frac{1}{2}\%$ simple interest per year; $x =$ number of dollars invested

12. The total rent paid for an apartment if the rent is $795 a month; $n =$ number of months

13. The area (in ft^2) of a rectangle that is three times as long as it is wide; $w =$ width of the rectangle (in ft)

14. The perimeter (in cm) of a rectangle that is 5 cm longer than it is wide; $w =$ width of the rectangle (in cm)

15. The distance (in mi) that a car travels in 45 min; $s =$ speed of the car (in mi/h)

16. The time (in hours) it takes to travel a given distance at 55 mi/h; $d =$ given distance (in mi)

17. The concentration (in oz/gal) of salt in a mixture of 3 gal of brine containing 25 oz of salt to which some pure water has been added; $x =$ volume of pure water added (in gal)

18. The value (in cents) of the change in a purse that contains twice as many nickels as pennies, four more dimes than nickels, and as many quarters as dimes and nickels combined; $p =$ number of pennies

APPLICATIONS

19. Renting a Truck   A rental company charges $65 a day and 20 cents a mile for renting a truck. Michael rented a truck for 3 days, and his bill came to $275. How many miles did he drive?

20. Cell Phone Costs   A cell phone company charges a monthly fee of $10 for the first 1000 text messages and 10 cents for each additional text message. Miriam's bill for text messages for the month of June is $38.50. How many text messages did she send that month?

21. Investments   Phyllis invested $12,000, a portion earning a simple interest rate of $4\frac{1}{2}\%$ per year and the rest earning a rate of 4% per year. After 1 year the total interest earned on these investments was $525. How much money did she invest at each rate?

22. Investments   If Ben invests $4000 at 4% interest per year, how much additional money must he invest at $5\frac{1}{2}\%$ annual interest to ensure that the interest he receives each year is $4\frac{1}{2}\%$ of the total amount invested?

23. Investments   What annual rate of interest would you have to earn on an investment of $3500 to ensure receiving $262.50 interest after 1 year?

24. Investments   Jack invests $1000 at a certain annual interest rate, and he invests another $2000 at an annual rate that is one-half percent higher. If he receives a total of $190 interest in 1 year, at what rate is the $1000 invested?

25. Salaries   An executive in an engineering firm earns a monthly salary plus a Christmas bonus of $8500. If she earns a total of $97,300 per year, what is her monthly salary?

26. Salaries   A woman earns 15% more than her husband. Together they make $69,875 per year. What is the husband's annual salary?

27. Inheritance   Craig is saving to buy a vacation home. He inherits some money from a wealthy uncle, then combines this with the $22,000 he has already saved and doubles the total in a lucky investment. He ends up with $134,000—just enough to buy a cabin on the lake. How much did he inherit?

28. Overtime Pay   Helen earns $7.50 an hour at her job, but if she works more than 35 hours in a week, she is paid $1\frac{1}{2}$ times her regular salary for the overtime hours worked. One week her gross pay was $352.50. How many overtime hours did she work that week?

29. Labor Costs   A plumber and his assistant work together to replace the pipes in an old house. The plumber charges $45 an hour for his own labor and $25 an hour for his assistant's labor. The plumber works twice as long as his assistant on this job, and the labor charge on the final bill is $4025. How long did the plumber and his assistant work on this job?

30. A Riddle A father is four times as old as his daughter. In 6 years, he will be three times as old as she is. How old is the daughter now?

31. A Riddle A movie star, unwilling to give his age, posed the following riddle to a gossip columnist: "Seven years ago, I was eleven times as old as my daughter. Now I am four times as old as she is." How old is the movie star?

32. Career Home Runs During his major league career, Hank Aaron hit 41 more home runs than Babe Ruth hit during his career. Together they hit 1469 home runs. How many home runs did Babe Ruth hit?

33. Value of Coins A change purse contains an equal number of pennies, nickels, and dimes. The total value of the coins is $1.44. How many coins of each type does the purse contain?

34. Value of Coins Mary has $3.00 in nickels, dimes, and quarters. If she has twice as many dimes as quarters and five more nickels than dimes, how many coins of each type does she have?

35. Length of a Garden A rectangular garden is 25 ft wide. If its area is 1125 ft^2, what is the length of the garden?

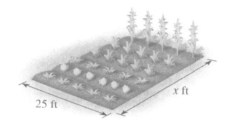

25 ft

x ft

36. Width of a Pasture A pasture is twice as long as it is wide. Its area is 115,200 ft^2. How wide is the pasture?

37. Dimensions of a Lot A square plot of land has a building 60 ft long and 40 ft wide at one corner. The rest of the land outside the building forms a parking lot. If the parking lot has area 12,000 ft^2, what are the dimensions of the entire plot of land?

38. Dimensions of a Lot A half-acre building lot is five times as long as it is wide. What are its dimensions? [*Note:* 1 acre = 43,560 ft^2.]

39. Dimensions of a Garden A rectangular garden is 10 ft longer than it is wide. Its area is 875 ft^2. What are its dimensions?

40. Dimensions of a Room A rectangular bedroom is 7 ft longer than it is wide. Its area is 228 ft^2. What is the width of the room?

41. Dimensions of a Garden A farmer has a rectangular garden plot surrounded by 200 ft of fence. Find the length and width of the garden if its area is 2400 ft^2.

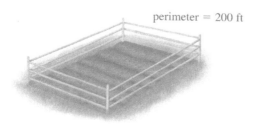

perimeter = 200 ft

42. Dimensions of a Lot A parcel of land is 6 ft longer than it is wide. Each diagonal from one corner to the opposite corner is 174 ft long. What are the dimensions of the parcel?

43. Dimensions of a Lot A rectangular parcel of land is 50 ft wide. The length of a diagonal between opposite corners is 10 ft more than the length of the parcel. What is the length of the parcel?

44. Dimensions of a Track A running track has the shape shown in the figure, with straight sides and semicircular ends. If the length of the track is 440 yd and the two straight parts are each 110 yd long, what is the radius of the semicircular parts (to the nearest yard)?

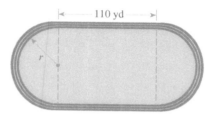

110 yd

r

45. Length and Area Find the length x in the figure. The area of the shaded region is given.

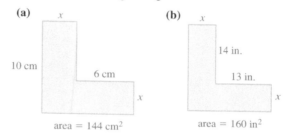

(a)

x

10 cm

6 cm

x

area = 144 cm^2

(b)

x

14 in.

13 in.

x

area = 160 in^2

46. Length and Area Find the length y in the figure. The area of the shaded region is given.

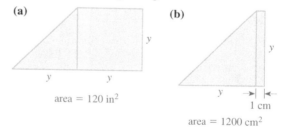

(a)

y

y y

area = 120 in^2

(b)

y

y 1 cm

area = 1200 cm^2

47. Framing a Painting Ali paints with watercolors on a sheet of paper 20 in. wide by 15 in. high. He then places this sheet on a mat so that a uniformly wide strip of the mat shows all around the picture. The perimeter of the mat is 102 in. How wide is the strip of the mat showing around the picture?

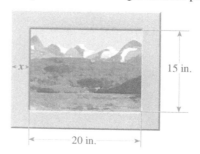

x

15 in.

20 in.

48. Dimensions of a Poster A poster has a rectangular printed area 100 cm by 140 cm and a blank strip of uniform width around the edges. The perimeter of the poster is $1\frac{1}{2}$ times the perimeter of the printed area. What is the width of the blank strip?

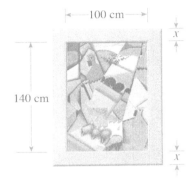

49. Reach of a Ladder A $19\frac{1}{2}$-foot ladder leans against a building. The base of the ladder is $7\frac{1}{2}$ ft from the building. How high up the building does the ladder reach?

50. Height of a Flagpole A flagpole is secured on opposite sides by two guy wires, each of which is 5 ft longer than the pole. The distance between the points where the wires are fixed to the ground is equal to the length of one guy wire. How tall is the flagpole (to the nearest inch)?

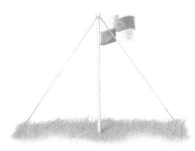

51. Length of a Shadow A man is walking away from a lamppost with a light source 6 m above the ground. The man is 2 m tall. How long is the man's shadow when he is 10 m from the lamppost? [*Hint:* Use similar triangles.]

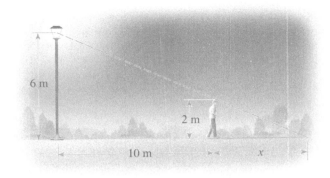

52. Height of a Tree A woodcutter determines the height of a tall tree by first measuring a smaller one 125 ft away, then moving so that his eyes are in the line of sight along the tops of the trees and measuring how far he is standing from the small tree (see the figure). Suppose the small tree is 20 ft tall, the man is 25 ft from the small tree, and his eye level is 5 ft above the ground. How tall is the taller tree?

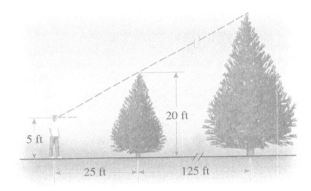

53. Mixture Problem What quantity of a 60% acid solution must be mixed with a 30% solution to produce 300 mL of a 50% solution?

54. Mixture Problem What quantity of pure acid must be added to 300 mL of a 50% acid solution to produce a 60% acid solution?

55. Mixture Problem A jeweler has five rings, each weighing 18 g, made of an alloy of 10% silver and 90% gold. She decides to melt down the rings and add enough silver to reduce the gold content to 75%. How much silver should she add?

56. Mixture Problem A pot contains 6 L of brine at a concentration of 120 g/L. How much of the water should be boiled off to increase the concentration to 200 g/L?

57. Mixture Problem The radiator in a car is filled with a solution of 60% antifreeze and 40% water. The manufacturer of the antifreeze suggests that for summer driving, optimal cooling of the engine is obtained with only 50% antifreeze. If the capacity of the radiator is 3.6 L, how much coolant should be drained and replaced with water to reduce the antifreeze concentration to the recommended level?

58. Mixture Problem A health clinic uses a solution of bleach to sterilize petri dishes in which cultures are grown. The sterilization tank contains 100 gal of a solution of 2% ordinary household bleach mixed with pure distilled water. New research indicates that the concentration of bleach should be 5% for complete sterilization. How much of the solution should be drained and replaced with bleach to increase the bleach content to the recommended level?

59. Mixture Problem A bottle contains 750 mL of fruit punch with a concentration of 50% pure fruit juice. Jill drinks 100 mL of the punch and then refills the bottle with an equal amount of a cheaper brand of punch. If the concentration of juice in the bottle is now reduced to 48%, what was the concentration in the punch that Jill added?

60. Mixture Problem A merchant blends tea that sells for $3.00 a pound with tea that sells for $2.75 a pound to produce 80 lb of a mixture that sells for $2.90 a pound. How many pounds of each type of tea does the merchant use in the blend?

61. Sharing a Job Candy and Tim share a paper route. It takes Candy 70 min to deliver all the papers, and it takes Tim 80 min. How long does it take the two when they work together?

62. Sharing a Job Stan and Hilda can mow the lawn in 40 min if they work together. If Hilda works twice as fast as Stan, how long does it take Stan to mow the lawn alone?

63. Sharing a Job Betty and Karen have been hired to paint the houses in a new development. Working together, the women can paint a house in two-thirds the time that it takes Karen working alone. Betty takes 6 h to paint a house alone. How long does it take Karen to paint a house working alone?

64. Sharing a Job Next-door neighbors Bob and Jim use hoses from both houses to fill Bob's swimming pool. They know that it takes 18 h using both hoses. They also know that Bob's hose, used alone, takes 20% less time than Jim's hose alone. How much time is required to fill the pool by each hose alone?

65. Sharing a Job Henry and Irene working together can wash all the windows of their house in 1 h 48 min. Working alone, it takes Henry $1\frac{1}{2}$ h more than Irene to do the job. How long does it take each person working alone to wash all the windows?

66. Sharing a Job Jack, Kay, and Lynn deliver advertising flyers in a small town. If each person works alone, it takes Jack 4 h to deliver all the flyers, and it takes Lynn 1 h longer than it takes Kay. Working together, they can deliver all the flyers in 40% of the time it takes Kay working alone. How long does it take Kay to deliver all the flyers alone?

67. Distance, Speed, and Time Wendy took a trip from Davenport to Omaha, a distance of 300 mi. She traveled part of the way by bus, which arrived at the train station just in time for Wendy to complete her journey by train. The bus averaged 40 mi/h, and the train averaged 60 mi/h. The entire trip took $5\frac{1}{2}$ h. How long did Wendy spend on the train?

68. Distance, Speed, and Time Two cyclists, 90 mi apart, start riding toward each other at the same time. One cycles twice as fast as the other. If they meet 2 h later, at what average speed is each cyclist traveling?

69. Distance, Speed, and Time A pilot flew a jet from Montreal to Los Angeles, a distance of 2500 mi. On the return trip, the average speed was 20% faster than the outbound speed. The round-trip took 9 h 10 min. What was the speed from Montreal to Los Angeles?

70. Distance, Speed, and Time A woman driving a car 14 ft long is passing a truck 30 ft long. The truck is traveling at 50 mi/h. How fast must the woman drive her car so that she can pass the truck completely in 6 s, from the position shown in figure (a) to the position shown in figure (b)? [*Hint:* Use feet and seconds instead of miles and hours.]

(a)

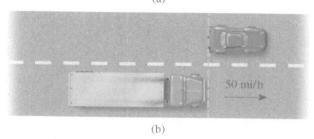

(b)

71. Distance, Speed, and Time A salesman drives from Ajax to Barrington, a distance of 120 mi, at a steady speed. He then increases his speed by 10 mi/h to drive the 150 mi from Barrington to Collins. If the second leg of his trip took 6 min more time than the first leg, how fast was he driving between Ajax and Barrington?

72. Distance, Speed, and Time Kiran drove from Tortula to Cactus, a distance of 250 mi. She increased her speed by 10 mi/h for the 360-mi trip from Cactus to Dry Junction. If the total trip took 11 h, what was her speed from Tortula to Cactus?

73. Distance, Speed, and Time It took a crew 2 h 40 min to row 6 km upstream and back again. If the rate of flow of the stream was 3 km/h, what was the rowing speed of the crew in still water?

74. Speed of a Boat Two fishing boats depart a harbor at the same time, one traveling east, the other south. The eastbound boat travels at a speed 3 mi/h faster than the southbound boat. After two hours the boats are 30 mi apart. Find the speed of the southbound boat.

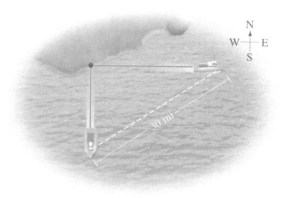

75. Law of the Lever The figure shows a lever system, similar to a seesaw that you might find in a children's playground. For the system to balance, the product of the weight and its distance from the fulcrum must be the same on each side; that is,

$$w_1x_1 = w_2x_2$$

This equation is called the **law of the lever** and was first discovered by Archimedes (see page 729).

A woman and her son are playing on a seesaw. The boy is at one end, 8 ft from the fulcrum. If the son weighs 100 lb and the mother weighs 125 lb, where should the woman sit so that the seesaw is balanced?

76. Law of the Lever A plank 30 ft long rests on top of a flat-roofed building, with 5 ft of the plank projecting over the edge, as shown in the figure. A worker weighing 240 lb sits on one end of the plank. What is the largest weight that can be hung on the projecting end of the plank if it is to remain in balance? (Use the law of the lever stated in Exercise 75.)

77. Dimensions of a Box A large plywood box has a volume of 180 ft³. Its length is 9 ft greater than its height, and its width is 4 ft less than its height. What are the dimensions of the box?

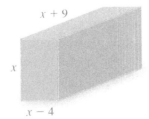

78. Radius of a Sphere A jeweler has three small solid spheres made of gold, of radius 2 mm, 3 mm, and 4 mm. He decides to melt these down and make just one sphere out of them. What will the radius of this larger sphere be?

79. Dimensions of a Box A box with a square base and no top is to be made from a square piece of cardboard by cutting 4-in. squares from each corner and folding up the sides, as shown in the figure. The box is to hold 100 in³. How big a piece of cardboard is needed?

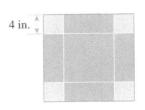
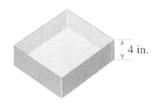

80. Dimensions of a Can A cylindrical can has a volume of 40π cm³ and is 10 cm tall. What is its diameter? [*Hint:* Use the volume formula listed on the inside front cover of this book.]

81. Radius of a Tank A spherical tank has a capacity of 750 gallons. Using the fact that one gallon is about 0.1337 ft³, find the radius of the tank (to the nearest hundredth of a foot).

82. Dimensions of a Lot A city lot has the shape of a right triangle whose hypotenuse is 7 ft longer than one of the other sides. The perimeter of the lot is 392 ft. How long is each side of the lot?

83. Construction Costs The town of Foxton lies 10 mi north of an abandoned east-west road that runs through Grimley, as shown in the figure. The point on the abandoned road closest to Foxton is 40 mi from Grimley. County officials are about to build a new road connecting the two towns. They have determined that restoring the old road would cost $100,000 per mile, whereas building a new road would cost $200,000 per mile. How much of the abandoned road should be used (as indicated in the figure) if the officials intend to spend exactly $6.8 million? Would it cost less than this amount to build a new road connecting the towns directly?

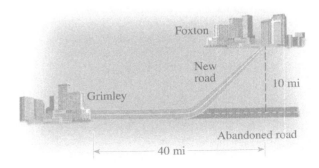

84. Distance, Speed, and Time A boardwalk is parallel to and 210 ft inland from a straight shoreline. A sandy beach lies between the boardwalk and the shoreline. A man is standing on the boardwalk, exactly 750 ft across the sand from his beach umbrella, which is right at the shoreline. The man walks 4 ft/s on the boardwalk and 2 ft/s on the sand. How far should he walk on the boardwalk before veering off onto the sand if he wishes to reach his umbrella in exactly 4 min 45 s?

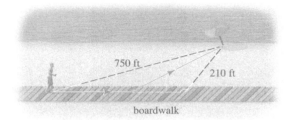

750 ft

210 ft

boardwalk

85. Volume of Grain Grain is falling from a chute onto the ground, forming a conical pile whose diameter is always three times its height. How high is the pile (to the nearest hundredth of a foot) when it contains 1000 ft³ of grain?

86. TV Monitors Two television monitors sitting side by side on a shelf in an appliance store have the same screen height. One has a conventional screen, which is 5 in. wider than it is high. The other has a wider, high-definition screen, which is 1.8 times as wide as it is high. The diagonal measure of the wider screen is 14 in. more than the diagonal measure of the smaller screen. What is the height of the screens, correct to the nearest 0.1 in.?

87. Dimensions of a Structure A storage bin for corn consists of a cylindrical section made of wire mesh, surmounted by a conical tin roof, as shown in the figure. The height of the roof is one-third the height of the entire structure. If the total volume of the structure is 1400π ft³ and its radius is 10 ft, what is its height? [*Hint:* Use the volume formulas listed on the inside front cover of this book.]

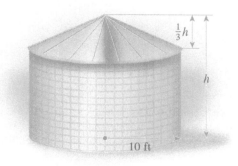

$\frac{1}{3}h$

h

10 ft

88. Comparing Areas A wire 360 in. long is cut into two pieces. One piece is formed into a square, and the other is formed into a circle. If the two figures have the same area, what are the lengths of the two pieces of wire (to the nearest tenth of an inch)?

89. An Ancient Chinese Problem This problem is taken from a Chinese mathematics textbook called *Chui-chang suan-shu*, or *Nine Chapters on the Mathematical Art*, which was written about 250 B.C.

A 10-ft-long stem of bamboo is broken in such a way that its tip touches the ground 3 ft from the base of the stem, as shown in the figure. What is the height of the break?

[*Hint:* Use the Pythagorean Theorem.]

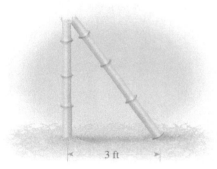

3 ft

DISCOVERY ■ DISCUSSION ■ WRITING

90. Historical Research Read the biographical notes on Pythagoras (page 219), Euclid (page 497), and Archimedes (page 729). Choose one of these mathematicians and find out more about him from the library or on the Internet. Write a short essay on your findings. Include both biographical information and a description of the mathematics for which he is famous.

91. A Babylonian Quadratic Equation The ancient Babylonians knew how to solve quadratic equations. Here is a problem from a cuneiform tablet found in a Babylonian school dating back to about 2000 B.C.

I have a reed, I know not its length. I broke from it one cubit, and it fit 60 times along the length of my field. I restored to the reed what I had broken off, and it fit 30 times along the width of my field. The area of my field is 375 square nindas. What was the original length of the reed?

Solve this problem. Use the fact that 1 ninda = 12 cubits.

⦵ **DISCOVERY PROJECT** **Equations Through the Ages**

In this project we study equations that were created and solved by the ancient peoples of Egypt, Babylon, India, and China. You can find the project at the book companion website: **www.stewartmath.com**

1.7 INEQUALITIES

Solving Linear Inequalities ▶ Solving Nonlinear Inequalities ▶ Absolute Value Inequalities ▶ Modeling with Inequalities

Some problems in algebra lead to **inequalities** instead of equations. An inequality looks just like an equation, except that in the place of the equal sign is one of the symbols, $<$, $>$, $\leq$, or $\geq$. Here is an example of an inequality:

$$4x + 7 \leq 19$$

x	$4x + 7 \leq 19$	
1	$11 \leq 19$	✔
2	$15 \leq 19$	✔
3	$19 \leq 19$	✔
4	$23 \leq 19$	✗
5	$27 \leq 19$	✗

The table in the margin shows that some numbers satisfy the inequality and some numbers don't.

To **solve** an inequality that contains a variable means to find all values of the variable that make the inequality true. Unlike an equation, an inequality generally has infinitely many solutions, which form an interval or a union of intervals on the real line. The following illustration shows how an inequality differs from its corresponding equation:

		Solution	Graph
Equation:	$4x + 7 = 19$	$x = 3$	
Inequality:	$4x + 7 \leq 19$	$x \leq 3$	

To solve inequalities, we use the following rules to isolate the variable on one side of the inequality sign. These rules tell us when two inequalities are *equivalent* (the symbol $\Leftrightarrow$ means "is equivalent to"). In these rules the symbols A, B, and C stand for real numbers or algebraic expressions. Here we state the rules for inequalities involving the symbol $\leq$, but they apply to all four inequality symbols.

RULES FOR INEQUALITIES

Rule   **Description**

1. $A \leq B \quad \Leftrightarrow \quad A + C \leq B + C$

    Adding the same quantity to each side of an inequality gives an equivalent inequality.

2. $A \leq B \quad \Leftrightarrow \quad A - C \leq B - C$

    Subtracting the same quantity from each side of an inequality gives an equivalent inequality.

3. If $C > 0$, then $A \leq B \quad \Leftrightarrow \quad CA \leq CB$

    Multiplying each side of an inequality by the same *positive* quantity gives an equivalent inequality.

4. If $C < 0$, then $A \leq B \quad \Leftrightarrow \quad CA \geq CB$

    Multiplying each side of an inequality by the same *negative* quantity *reverses the direction* of the inequality.

5. If $A > 0$ and $B > 0$,

    then $A \leq B \quad \Leftrightarrow \quad \dfrac{1}{A} \geq \dfrac{1}{B}$

    Taking reciprocals of each side of an inequality involving *positive* quantities *reverses the direction* of the inequality.

6. If $A \leq B$ and $C \leq D$,

    then $A + C \leq B + D$

    Inequalities can be added.

 Pay special attention to Rules 3 and 4. Rule 3 says that we can multiply (or divide) each side of an inequality by a *positive* number, but Rule 4 says that if we multiply each side of an inequality by a *negative* number, then we reverse the direction of the inequality. For example, if we start with the inequality

$$3 < 5$$

and multiply by 2, we get

$$6 < 10$$

but if we multiply by -2, we get

$$-6 > -10$$

▼ Solving Linear Inequalities

An inequality is **linear** if each term is constant or a multiple of the variable. To solve a linear inequality, we isolate the variable on one side of the inequality sign.

EXAMPLE 1 | Solving a Linear Inequality

Solve the inequality $3x < 9x + 4$ and sketch the solution set.

SOLUTION

$3x < 9x + 4$	Given inequality
$3x - 9x < 9x + 4 - 9x$	Subtract $9x$
$-6x < 4$	Simplify
$\left(-\frac{1}{6}\right)(-6x) > \left(-\frac{1}{6}\right)(4)$	Multiply by $-\frac{1}{6}$ and reverse inequality
$x > -\frac{2}{3}$	Simplify

The solution set consists of all numbers greater than $-\frac{2}{3}$. In other words the solution of the inequality is the interval $\left(-\frac{2}{3}, \infty\right)$. It is graphed in Figure 1.

✎. NOW TRY EXERCISE **21**　　　　　　▩

Multiplying by the negative number $-\frac{1}{6}$ reverses the direction of the inequality.

FIGURE 1

EXAMPLE 2 | Solving a Pair of Simultaneous Inequalities

Solve the inequalities $4 \le 3x - 2 < 13$.

SOLUTION　The solution set consists of all values of x that satisfy both of the inequalities $4 \le 3x - 2$ and $3x - 2 < 13$. Using Rules 1 and 3, we see that the following inequalities are equivalent:

$4 \le 3x - 2 < 13$	Given inequality
$6 \le 3x < 15$	Add 2
$2 \le x < 5$	Divide by 3

FIGURE 2

Therefore, the solution set is $[2, 5)$, as shown in Figure 2.

✎. NOW TRY EXERCISE **31**　　　　　　▩

▼ Solving Nonlinear Inequalities

To solve inequalities involving squares and other powers of the variable, we use factoring, together with the following principle.

THE SIGN OF A PRODUCT OR QUOTIENT

If a product or a quotient has an *even* number of *negative* factors, then its value is *positive*.

If a product or a quotient has an *odd* number of *negative* factors, then its value is *negative*.

For example, to solve the inequality $x^2 - 5x \leq -6$, we first move all terms to the left-hand side and factor to get

$$(x - 2)(x - 3) \leq 0$$

This form of the inequality says that the product $(x - 2)(x - 3)$ must be negative or zero, so to solve the inequality, we must determine where each factor is negative or positive (because the sign of a product depends on the sign of the factors). The details are explained in Example 3, in which we use the following guidelines.

GUIDELINES FOR SOLVING NONLINEAR INEQUALITIES

1. **Move All Terms to One Side.** If necessary, rewrite the inequality so that all nonzero terms appear on one side of the inequality sign. If the nonzero side of the inequality involves quotients, bring them to a common denominator.

2. **Factor.** Factor the nonzero side of the inequality.

3. **Find the Intervals.** Determine the values for which each factor is zero. These numbers will divide the real line into intervals. List the intervals that are determined by these numbers.

4. **Make a Table or Diagram.** Use test values to make a table or diagram of the signs of each factor on each interval. In the last row of the table determine the sign of the product (or quotient) of these factors.

5. **Solve.** Determine the solution of the inequality from the last row of the sign table. Be sure to check whether the inequality is satisfied by some or all of the endpoints of the intervals. (This may happen if the inequality involves $\leq$ or $\geq$.)

 The factoring technique that is described in these guidelines works only if all nonzero terms appear on one side of the inequality symbol. If the inequality is not written in this form, first rewrite it, as indicated in Step 1.

EXAMPLE 3 | Solving a Quadratic Inequality

Solve the inequality $x^2 \leq 5x - 6$.

SOLUTION We will follow the guidelines given above.

Move all terms to one side. We move all the terms to the left-hand side.

$$x^2 \leq 5x - 6 \qquad \text{Given inequality}$$
$$x^2 - 5x + 6 \leq 0 \qquad \text{Subtract } 5x, \text{ add } 6$$

Factor. Factoring the left-hand side of the inequality, we get

$$(x - 2)(x - 3) \leq 0 \qquad \text{Factor}$$

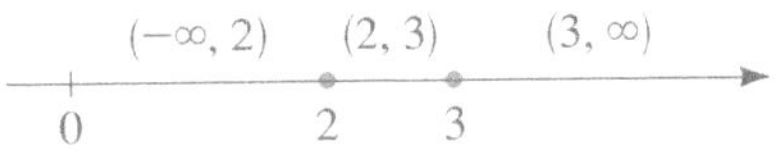

Find the intervals. The factors of the left-hand side are $x - 2$ and $x - 3$. These factors are zero when x is 2 and 3, respectively. As shown in Figure 3, the numbers 2 and 3 divide the real line into the three intervals

$$(-\infty, 2), (2, 3), (3, \infty)$$

The factors $x - 2$ and $x - 3$ change sign only at 2 and 3, respectively. So these factors maintain their sign on each of these three intervals.

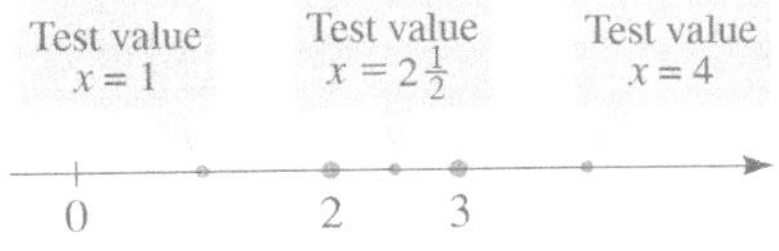

Make a table or diagram. To determine the sign of each factor on each of the intervals that we found, we use **test values**. We choose a number inside each interval and check the sign of the factors $x - 2$ and $x - 3$ at the number we chose. For the interval $(-\infty, 2)$, let's choose the test value 1 (see Figure 4). Substituting 1 for x in the factors $x - 2$ and $x - 3$, we get

$$x - 2 = 1 - 2 = -1 < 0$$
$$x - 3 = 1 - 3 = -2 < 0$$

FIGURE 3

$(-\infty, 2) \quad (2, 3) \quad (3, \infty)$

$0 \qquad 2 \qquad 3$

FIGURE 4

Test value $x = 1$ Test value $x = 2\frac{1}{2}$ Test value $x = 4$

$0 \qquad 2 \qquad 3$

So both factors are negative on this interval. Notice that we need to check only one test value for each interval because the factors $x - 2$ and $x - 3$ do not change sign on any of the three intervals we found.

Using the test values $x = 2\frac{1}{2}$ and $x = 4$ for the intervals $(2, 3)$ and $(3, \infty)$ (see Figure 4), respectively, we construct the following sign table. The final row of the table is obtained from the fact that the expression in the last row is the product of the two factors.

Interval	$(-\infty, 2)$	$(2, 3)$	$(3, \infty)$
Sign of $x - 2$ Sign of $x - 3$	– –	+ –	+ +
Sign of $(x - 2)(x - 3)$	+	–	+

If you prefer, you can represent this information on a real line, as in the following sign diagram. The vertical lines indicate the points at which the real line is divided into intervals:

	2		3	
Sign of $x - 2$	–		+		+
Sign of $x - 3$	–		–		+
Sign of $(x - 2)(x - 3)$	+		–		+

Solve. We read from the table or the diagram that $(x - 2)(x - 3)$ is negative on the interval $(2, 3)$. Thus, the solution of the inequality $(x - 2)(x - 3) \leq 0$ is

$$\{x \mid 2 \leq x \leq 3\} = [2, 3]$$

We have included the endpoints 2 and 3 because we seek values of x such that the product is either less than *or equal to* zero. The solution is illustrated in Figure 5.

FIGURE 5

✎. NOW TRY EXERCISE **41**

EXAMPLE 4 | Solving an Inequality with Repeated Factors

Solve the inequality $x(x - 1)^2(x - 3) < 0$.

SOLUTION All nonzero terms are already on one side of the inequality, and the nonzero side of the inequality is already factored. So we begin by finding the intervals for this inequality.

Find the intervals. The factors of the left-hand side are x, $(x - 1)^2$, and $x - 3$. These are zero when $x = 0, 1, 3$. These numbers divide the real line into the intervals

$$(-\infty, 0), (0, 1), (1, 3), (3, \infty)$$

Make a diagram. We make the following diagram, using test points to determine the sign of each factor in each interval.

	0		1		3	
Sign of x	–		+		+		+
Sign of $(x - 1)^2$	+		+		+		+
Sign of $(x - 3)$	–		–		–		+
Sign of $x(x - 1)^2(x - 3)$	+		–		–		+

Solve. From the diagram we see that $x(x-1)^2(x-3) < 0$ for x in the interval $(0, 1)$ or for x in $(1, 3)$. So the solution set is the union of these two intervals:

$$(0, 1) \cup (1, 3)$$

The solution set is graphed in Figure 6.

FIGURE 6

NOW TRY EXERCISE **53**

EXAMPLE 5 | Solving an Inequality Involving a Quotient

Solve the inequality $\dfrac{1+x}{1-x} \geq 1$.

SOLUTION

Move all terms to one side. We move the terms to the left-hand side and simplify using a common denominator.

$$\frac{1+x}{1-x} \geq 1 \qquad \text{Given inequality}$$

$$\frac{1+x}{1-x} - 1 \geq 0 \qquad \text{Subtract 1}$$

$$\frac{1+x}{1-x} - \frac{1-x}{1-x} \geq 0 \qquad \text{Common denominator } 1 - x$$

$$\frac{1+x-1+x}{1-x} \geq 0 \qquad \text{Combine the fractions}$$

$$\frac{2x}{1-x} \geq 0 \qquad \text{Simplify}$$

Find the intervals. The factors of the left-hand side are $2x$ and $1 - x$. These are zero when x is 0 and 1. These numbers divide the real line into the intervals

$$(-\infty, 0), (0, 1), (1, \infty)$$

Make a diagram. We make the following diagram using test points to determine the sign of each factor in each interval.

	0		1	
Sign of $2x$	$-$		$+$	$+$
Sign of $1 - x$	$+$		$+$	$-$
Sign of $\dfrac{2x}{1-x}$	$-$		$+$	$-$

Solve. From the diagram we see that $\dfrac{2x}{1-x} \geq 0$ for x in the interval $[0, 1)$. We include the endpoint 0 because the original inequality requires that the quotient be greater than *or equal to* 1. However, we do not include the other endpoint 1 because the quotient in the inequality is not defined at 1. So the solution set is the interval

$$[0, 1)$$

The solution set is graphed in Figure 7.

NOW TRY EXERCISE **59**

FIGURE 7

It is tempting to simply multiply both sides of the inequality by $1 - x$ (as you would if this were an *equation*). But this doesn't work because we don't know whether $1 - x$ is positive or negative, so we can't tell whether the inequality needs to be reversed. (See Exercise 123.)

Example 5 shows that we should always check the endpoints of the solution set to see whether they satisfy the original inequality.

▼ Absolute Value Inequalities

We use the following properties to solve inequalities that involve absolute value.

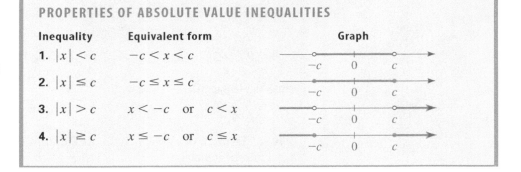

These properties hold when x is replaced by any algebraic expression. (In the figures we assume that $c > 0$.)

PROPERTIES OF ABSOLUTE VALUE INEQUALITIES

Inequality	Equivalent form	Graph
1. $\lvert x \rvert < c$	$-c < x < c$	
2. $\lvert x \rvert \le c$	$-c \le x \le c$	
3. $\lvert x \rvert > c$	$x < -c \quad$ or $\quad c < x$	
4. $\lvert x \rvert \ge c$	$x \le -c \quad$ or $\quad c \le x$	

FIGURE 8

These properties can be proved using the definition of absolute value. To prove Property 1, for example, note that the inequality $\lvert x \rvert < c$ says that the distance from x to 0 is less than c, and from Figure 8 you can see that this is true if and only if x is between $-c$ and c.

EXAMPLE 6 | Solving an Absolute Value Inequality

Solve the inequality $\lvert x - 5 \rvert < 2$.

SOLUTION 1 The inequality $\lvert x - 5 \rvert < 2$ is equivalent to

$$-2 < x - 5 < 2 \qquad \text{Property 1}$$
$$3 < x < 7 \qquad \text{Add 5}$$

The solution set is the open interval $(3, 7)$.

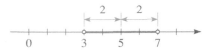

FIGURE 9

SOLUTION 2 Geometrically, the solution set consists of all numbers x whose distance from 5 is less than 2. From Figure 9 we see that this is the interval $(3, 7)$.

✐ NOW TRY EXERCISE **79**

EXAMPLE 7 | Solving an Absolute Value Inequality

Solve the inequality $\lvert 3x + 2 \rvert \ge 4$.

SOLUTION By Property 4 the inequality $\lvert 3x + 2 \rvert \ge 4$ is equivalent to

$$
\begin{array}{lll}
3x + 2 \ge 4 & \text{or} & 3x + 2 \le -4 \\
3x \ge 2 & & 3x \le -6 \qquad \text{Subtract 2} \\
x \ge \tfrac{2}{3} & & x \le -2 \qquad \text{Divide by 3}
\end{array}
$$

So the solution set is

$$\left\{ x \mid x \le -2 \quad \text{or} \quad x \ge \tfrac{2}{3} \right\} = (-\infty, -2] \cup \left[\tfrac{2}{3}, \infty \right)$$

The set is graphed in Figure 10.

FIGURE 10

✐ NOW TRY EXERCISE **83**

▼ Modeling with Inequalities

Modeling real-life problems frequently leads to inequalities because we are often interested in determining when one quantity is more (or less) than another.

EXAMPLE 8 | Carnival Tickets

A carnival has two plans for tickets.

> Plan A: $5 entrance fee and 25¢ each ride
>
> Plan B: $2 entrance fee and 50¢ each ride

How many rides would you have to take for Plan A to be less expensive than Plan B?

SOLUTION Identify the variable. We are asked for the number of rides for which Plan A is less expensive than Plan B. So let

$$x = \text{number of rides}$$

Translate from words to algebra. The information in the problem may be organized as follows.

In Words	In Algebra
Number of rides	x
Cost with Plan A	$5 + 0.25x$
Cost with Plan B	$2 + 0.50x$

Set up the model. Now we set up the model.

$$\begin{pmatrix} \text{cost with} \\ \text{Plan A} \end{pmatrix} < \begin{pmatrix} \text{cost with} \\ \text{Plan B} \end{pmatrix}$$

$$5 + 0.25x < 2 + 0.50x$$

Solve. Now we solve for x.

$$3 + 0.25x < 0.50x \qquad \text{Subtract 2}$$
$$3 < 0.25x \qquad \text{Subtract } 0.25x$$
$$12 < x \qquad \text{Divide by 0.25}$$

So if you plan to take *more than* 12 rides, Plan A is less expensive.

✎. NOW TRY EXERCISE **107**

EXAMPLE 9 | Relationship Between Fahrenheit and Celsius Scales

The instructions on a bottle of medicine indicate that the bottle should be stored at a temperature between 5°C and 30°C. What range of temperatures does this correspond to on the Fahrenheit scale?

SOLUTION The relationship between degrees Celsius (C) and degrees Fahrenheit (F) is given by the equation $C = \frac{5}{9}(F - 32)$. Expressing the statement on the bottle in terms of inequalities, we have

$$5 < C < 30$$

So the corresponding Fahrenheit temperatures satisfy the inequalities

$$5 < \tfrac{5}{9}(F - 32) < 30 \qquad \text{Substitute } C = \tfrac{5}{9}(F - 32)$$
$$\tfrac{9}{5} \cdot 5 < F - 32 < \tfrac{9}{5} \cdot 30 \qquad \text{Multiply by } \tfrac{9}{5}$$
$$9 < F - 32 < 54 \qquad \text{Simplify}$$
$$9 + 32 < F < 54 + 32 \qquad \text{Add 32}$$
$$41 < F < 86 \qquad \text{Simplify}$$

The medicine should be stored at a temperature between 41°F and 86°F.

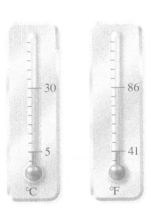

✎. NOW TRY EXERCISE **105**

1.7 EXERCISES

CONCEPTS

1. Fill in the blank with an appropriate inequality sign.

   (a) If $x < 5$, then $x - 3$ _____ 2.

   (b) If $x \le 5$, then $3x$ _____ 15.

   (c) If $x \ge 2$, then $-3x$ _____ -6.

   (d) If $x < -2$, then $-x$ _____ 2.

2. *True or false?*
   (a) If $x(x + 1) > 0$, then x and $x + 1$ are either both positive or both negative.
   (b) If $x(x + 1) > 5$, then x and $x + 1$ are each greater than 5.

3. (a) The solution of the inequality $|x| \le 3$ is the interval

   _____ .

   (b) The solution of the inequality $|x| \ge 3$ is a union of two intervals _____ $\cup$ _____ .

4. (a) The set of all points on the real line whose distance from zero is less than 3 can be described by the absolute value inequality $|x|$ _____ .

   (b) The set of all points on the real line whose distance from zero is greater than 3 can be described by the absolute value inequality $|x|$ _____ .

SKILLS

5–10 ■ Let $S = \{-2, -1, 0, \frac{1}{2}, 1, \sqrt{2}, 2, 4\}$. Determine which elements of S satisfy the inequality.

5. $3 - 2x \le \frac{1}{2}$

6. $2x - 1 \ge x$

7. $1 < 2x - 4 \le 7$

8. $-2 \le 3 - x < 2$

9. $\dfrac{1}{x} \le \dfrac{1}{2}$

10. $x^2 + 2 < 4$

11–34 ■ Solve the linear inequality. Express the solution using interval notation and graph the solution set.

11. $2x \le 7$

12. $-4x \ge 10$

13. $2x - 5 > 3$

14. $3x + 11 < 5$

15. $7 - x \ge 5$

16. $5 - 3x \le -16$

17. $2x + 1 < 0$

18. $0 < 5 - 2x$

19. $3x + 11 \le 6x + 8$

20. $6 - x \ge 2x + 9$

21. $\frac{1}{2}x - \frac{2}{3} > 2$

22. $\frac{2}{5}x + 1 < \frac{1}{5} - 2x$

23. $\frac{1}{3}x + 2 < \frac{1}{6}x - 1$

24. $\frac{2}{3} - \frac{1}{2}x \ge \frac{1}{6} + x$

25. $4 - 3x \le -(1 + 8x)$

26. $2(7x - 3) \le 12x + 16$

27. $2 \le x + 5 < 4$

28. $5 \le 3x - 4 \le 14$

29. $-1 < 2x - 5 < 7$

30. $1 < 3x + 4 \le 16$

31. $-2 < 8 - 2x \le -1$

32. $-3 \le 3x + 7 \le \frac{1}{2}$

33. $\dfrac{1}{6} < \dfrac{2x - 13}{12} \le \dfrac{2}{3}$

34. $-\dfrac{1}{2} \le \dfrac{4 - 3x}{5} \le \dfrac{1}{4}$

35–72 ■ Solve the nonlinear inequality. Express the solution using interval notation and graph the solution set.

35. $(x + 2)(x - 3) < 0$

36. $(x - 5)(x + 4) \ge 0$

37. $x(2x + 7) \ge 0$

38. $x(2 - 3x) \le 0$

39. $x^2 - 3x - 18 \le 0$

40. $x^2 + 5x + 6 > 0$

41. $2x^2 + x \ge 1$

42. $x^2 < x + 2$

43. $3x^2 - 3x < 2x^2 + 4$

44. $5x^2 + 3x \ge 3x^2 + 2$

45. $x^2 > 3(x + 6)$

46. $x^2 + 2x > 3$

47. $x^2 < 4$

48. $x^2 \ge 9$

49. $(x + 2)(x - 1)(x - 3) \le 0$

50. $(x - 5)(x - 2)(x + 1) > 0$

51. $(x - 4)(x + 2)^2 < 0$

52. $(x + 3)^2(x + 1) > 0$

53. $(x - 2)^2(x - 3)(x + 1) \le 0$

54. $x^2(x^2 - 1) \ge 0$

55. $x^3 - 4x > 0$

56. $16x \le x^3$

57. $\dfrac{x - 3}{x + 1} \ge 0$

58. $\dfrac{2x + 6}{x - 2} < 0$

59. $\dfrac{4x}{2x + 3} > 2$

60. $-2 < \dfrac{x + 1}{x - 3}$

61. $\dfrac{2x + 1}{x - 5} \le 3$

62. $\dfrac{3 + x}{3 - x} \ge 1$

63. $\dfrac{4}{x} < x$

64. $\dfrac{x}{x + 1} > 3x$

65. $1 + \dfrac{2}{x + 1} \le \dfrac{2}{x}$

66. $\dfrac{3}{x - 1} - \dfrac{4}{x} \ge 1$

67. $\dfrac{6}{x - 1} - \dfrac{6}{x} \ge 1$

68. $\dfrac{x}{2} \ge \dfrac{5}{x + 1} + 4$

69. $\dfrac{x + 2}{x + 3} < \dfrac{x - 1}{x - 2}$

70. $\dfrac{1}{x + 1} + \dfrac{1}{x + 2} \le 0$

71. $x^4 > x^2$

72. $x^5 > x^2$

73–88 ■ Solve the absolute value inequality. Express the answer using interval notation and graph the solution set.

73. $|x| \le 4$

74. $|3x| < 15$

75. $|2x| > 7$

76. $\frac{1}{2}|x| \ge 1$

77. $|x - 5| \le 3$

78. $|x + 1| \ge 1$

79. $|2x - 3| \le 0.4$

80. $|5x - 2| < 6$

81. $|3x - 2| \ge 5$

82. $|8x + 3| > 12$

83. $\left|\dfrac{x - 2}{3}\right| < 2$

84. $\left|\dfrac{x + 1}{2}\right| \ge 4$

85. $|x + 6| < 0.001$

86. $3 - |2x + 4| \le 1$

87. $8 - |2x - 1| \ge 6$

88. $7|x + 2| + 5 > 4$

89–92 ■ A phrase describing a set of real numbers is given. Express the phrase as an inequality involving an absolute value.

89. All real numbers x less than 3 units from 0

90. All real numbers x more than 2 units from 0

91. All real numbers x at least 5 units from 7

92. All real numbers x at most 4 units from 2

93–98 ■ A set of real numbers is graphed. Find an inequality involving an absolute value that describes the set.

93.
$$-5 \; -4 \; -3 \; -2 \; -1 \;\; 0 \;\; 1 \;\; 2 \;\; 3 \;\; 4 \;\; 5$$

94.
$$-5 \; -4 \; -3 \; -2 \; -1 \;\; 0 \;\; 1 \;\; 2 \;\; 3 \;\; 4 \;\; 5$$

95.
$$-5 \; -4 \; -3 \; -2 \; -1 \;\; 0 \;\; 1 \;\; 2 \;\; 3 \;\; 4 \;\; 5$$

96.
$$-5 \; -4 \; -3 \; -2 \; -1 \;\; 0 \;\; 1 \;\; 2 \;\; 3 \;\; 4 \;\; 5$$

97.
$$-5 \; -4 \; -3 \; -2 \; -1 \;\; 0 \;\; 1 \;\; 2 \;\; 3 \;\; 4 \;\; 5$$

98.
$$-5 \; -4 \; -3 \; -2 \; -1 \;\; 0 \;\; 1 \;\; 2 \;\; 3 \;\; 4 \;\; 5$$

99–102 ■ Determine the values of the variable for which the expression is defined as a real number.

99. $\sqrt{16 - 9x^2}$

100. $\sqrt{3x^2 - 5x + 2}$

101. $\left(\dfrac{1}{x^2 - 5x - 14}\right)^{1/2}$

102. $\sqrt[4]{\dfrac{1 - x}{2 + x}}$

103. Solve the inequality for x, assuming that a, b, and c are positive constants.

    (a) $a(bx - c) \geq bc$ **(b)** $a \leq bx + c < 2a$

104. Suppose that a, b, c, and d are positive numbers such that

$$\frac{a}{b} < \frac{c}{d}$$

Show that $\dfrac{a}{b} < \dfrac{a + c}{b + d} < \dfrac{c}{d}$.

APPLICATIONS

105. Temperature Scales Use the relationship between C and F given in Example 9 to find the interval on the Fahrenheit scale corresponding to the temperature range $20 \leq C \leq 30$.

106. Temperature Scales What interval on the Celsius scale corresponds to the temperature range $50 \leq F \leq 95$?

107. Car Rental Cost A car rental company offers two plans for renting a car.

    Plan A: $30 per day and 10¢ per mile

    Plan B: $50 per day with free unlimited mileage

    For what range of miles will Plan B save you money?

108. Long-Distance Cost A telephone company offers two long-distance plans.

    Plan A: $25 per month and 5¢ per minute

    Plan B: $5 per month and 12¢ per minute

    For how many minutes of long-distance calls would Plan B be financially advantageous?

109. Driving Cost It is estimated that the annual cost of driving a certain new car is given by the formula

$$C = 0.35m + 2200$$

where m represents the number of miles driven per year and C is the cost in dollars. Jane has purchased such a car and decides to budget between $6400 and $7100 for next year's driving costs. What is the corresponding range of miles that she can drive her new car?

110. Air Temperature As dry air moves upward, it expands and, in so doing, cools at a rate of about 1°C for each 100-meter rise, up to about 12 km.
    (a) If the ground temperature is 20°C, write a formula for the temperature at height h.
    (b) What range of temperatures can be expected if a plane takes off and reaches a maximum height of 5 km?

111. Airline Ticket Price A charter airline finds that on its Saturday flights from Philadelphia to London all 120 seats will be sold if the ticket price is $200. However, for each $3 increase in ticket price, the number of seats sold decreases by one.
    (a) Find a formula for the number of seats sold if the ticket price is P dollars.
    (b) Over a certain period the number of seats sold for this flight ranged between 90 and 115. What was the corresponding range of ticket prices?

112. Accuracy of a Scale A coffee merchant sells a customer 3 lb of Hawaiian Kona at $6.50 per pound. The merchant's scale is accurate to within ± 0.03 lb. By how much could the customer have been overcharged or undercharged because of possible inaccuracy in the scale?

113. Gravity The gravitational force F exerted by the earth on an object having a mass of 100 kg is given by the equation

$$F = \frac{4{,}000{,}000}{d^2}$$

where d is the distance (in km) of the object from the center of the earth, and the force F is measured in newtons (N). For what distances will the gravitational force exerted by the earth on this object be between 0.0004 N and 0.01 N?

114. Bonfire Temperature In the vicinity of a bonfire the temperature T in °C at a distance of x meters from the center of the fire was given by

$$T = \frac{600{,}000}{x^2 + 300}$$

At what range of distances from the fire's center was the temperature less than 500°C?

115. Falling Ball   Using calculus, it can be shown that if a ball is thrown upward with an initial velocity of 16 ft/s from the top of a building 128 ft high, then its height h above the ground t seconds later will be

$$h = 128 + 16t - 16t^2$$

During what time interval will the ball be at least 32 ft above the ground?

116. Gas Mileage   The gas mileage g (measured in mi/gal) for a particular vehicle, driven at v mi/h, is given by the formula $g = 10 + 0.9v - 0.01v^2$, as long as v is between 10 mi/h and 75 mi/h. For what range of speeds is the vehicle's mileage 30 mi/gal or better?

117. Stopping Distance   For a certain model of car the distance d required to stop the vehicle if it is traveling at v mi/h is given by the formula

$$d = v + \frac{v^2}{20}$$

where d is measured in feet. Kerry wants her stopping distance not to exceed 240 ft. At what range of speeds can she travel?

118. Manufacturer's Profit   If a manufacturer sells x units of a certain product, revenue R and cost C (in dollars) are given by

$$R = 20x$$

$$C = 2000 + 8x + 0.0025x^2$$

Use the fact that

$$\text{profit} = \text{revenue} - \text{cost}$$

to determine how many units the manufacturer should sell to enjoy a profit of at least $2400.

119. Fencing a Garden   A determined gardener has 120 ft of deer-resistant fence. She wants to enclose a rectangular vegetable garden in her backyard, and she wants the area that is enclosed to be at least 800 ft². What range of values is possible for the length of her garden?

120. Thickness of a Laminate   A company manufactures industrial laminates (thin nylon-based sheets) of thickness 0.020 in, with a tolerance of 0.003 in.

(a) Find an inequality involving absolute values that describes the range of possible thickness for the laminate.

(b) Solve the inequality you found in part (a).

121. Range of Height   The average height of adult males is 68.2 in, and 95% of adult males have height h that satisfies the inequality

$$\left| \frac{h - 68.2}{2.9} \right| \le 2$$

Solve the inequality to find the range of heights.

DISCOVERY ▪ DISCUSSION ▪ WRITING

122. Do Powers Preserve Order?   If $a < b$, is $a^2 < b^2$? (Check both positive and negative values for a and b.) If $a < b$, is $a^3 < b^3$? On the basis of your observations, state a general rule about the relationship between a^n and b^n when $a < b$ and n is a positive integer.

123. What's Wrong Here?   It is tempting to try to solve an inequality like an equation. For instance, we might try to solve $1 < 3/x$ by multiplying both sides by x, to get $x < 3$, so the solution would be $(-\infty, 3)$. But that's wrong; for example, $x = -1$ lies in this interval but does not satisfy the original inequality. Explain why this method doesn't work (think about the *sign* of x). Then solve the inequality correctly.

124. Using Distances to Solve Absolute Value Inequalities   Recall that $|a - b|$ is the distance between a and b on the number line. For any number x, what do $|x - 1|$ and $|x - 3|$ represent? Use this interpretation to solve the inequality $|x - 1| < |x - 3|$ geometrically. In general, if $a < b$, what is the solution of the inequality $|x - a| < |x - b|$?

1.8 COORDINATE GEOMETRY

The Coordinate Plane ▶ The Distance and Midpoint Formulas ▶ Graphs of Equations in Two Variables ▶ Intercepts ▶ Circles ▶ Symmetry

The *coordinate plane* is the link between algebra and geometry. In the coordinate plane we can draw graphs of algebraic equations. The graphs, in turn, allow us to "see" the relationship between the variables in the equation. In this section we study the coordinate plane.

▼ The Coordinate Plane

The Cartesian plane is named in honor of the French mathematician René Descartes (1596–1650), although another Frenchman, Pierre Fermat (1601–1665), also invented the principles of coordinate geometry at the same time. (See their biographies on pages 181 and 99.)

Just as points on a line can be identified with real numbers to form the coordinate line, points in a plane can be identified with ordered pairs of numbers to form the **coordinate plane** or **Cartesian plane**. To do this, we draw two perpendicular real lines that intersect at 0 on each line. Usually, one line is horizontal with positive direction to the right and is called the ***x*-axis**; the other line is vertical with positive direction upward and is called the ***y*-axis**. The point of intersection of the *x*-axis and the *y*-axis is the **origin *O***, and the two axes divide the plane into four **quadrants**, labeled I, II, III, and IV in Figure 1. (The points *on* the coordinate axes are not assigned to any quadrant.)

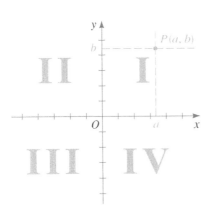

FIGURE 1

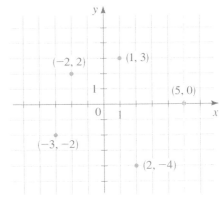

FIGURE 2

Although the notation for a point (a, b) is the same as the notation for an open interval (a, b), the context should make clear which meaning is intended.

Any point *P* in the coordinate plane can be located by a unique **ordered pair** of numbers (a, b), as shown in Figure 1. The first number *a* is called the ***x*-coordinate** of *P*; the second number *b* is called the ***y*-coordinate** of *P*. We can think of the coordinates of *P* as its "address," because they specify its location in the plane. Several points are labeled with their coordinates in Figure 2.

EXAMPLE 1 | Graphing Regions in the Coordinate Plane

Describe and sketch the regions given by each set.

(a) $\{(x, y) \mid x \geq 0\}$ **(b)** $\{(x, y) \mid y = 1\}$ **(c)** $\{(x, y) \mid |y| < 1\}$

SOLUTION

(a) The points whose *x*-coordinates are 0 or positive lie on the *y*-axis or to the right of it, as shown in Figure 3(a).

(b) The set of all points with *y*-coordinate 1 is a horizontal line one unit above the *x*-axis, as in Figure 3(b).

(c) Recall from Section 1.7 that

$$|y| < 1 \qquad \text{if and only if} \qquad -1 < y < 1$$

So the given region consists of those points in the plane whose *y*-coordinates lie between -1 and 1. Thus, the region consists of all points that lie between (but not on) the horizontal lines $y = 1$ and $y = -1$. These lines are shown as broken lines in Figure 3(c) to indicate that the points on these lines do not lie in the set.

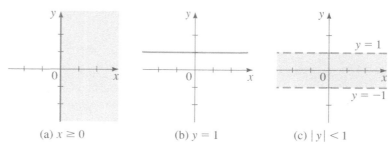

(a) $x \geq 0$ (b) $y = 1$ (c) $|y| < 1$

FIGURE 3

NOW TRY EXERCISES **23**, **25**, AND **29**

▼ The Distance and Midpoint Formulas

We now find a formula for the distance $d(A, B)$ between two points $A(x_1, y_1)$ and $B(x_2, y_2)$ in the plane. Recall from Section 1.1 that the distance between points a and b on a number line is $d(a, b) = |b - a|$. So from Figure 4 we see that the distance between the points $A(x_1, y_1)$ and $C(x_2, y_1)$ on a horizontal line must be $|x_2 - x_1|$, and the distance between $B(x_2, y_2)$ and $C(x_2, y_1)$ on a vertical line must be $|y_2 - y_1|$.

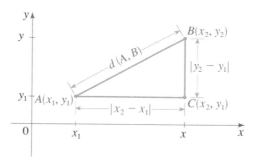

FIGURE 4

Since triangle *ABC* is a right triangle, the Pythagorean Theorem gives

$$d(A, B) = \sqrt{|x_2 - x_1|^2 + |y_2 - y_1|^2} = \sqrt{(x_2 - x_1)^2 + (y_2 - y_1)^2}$$

DISTANCE FORMULA

The distance between the points $A(x_1, y_1)$ and $B(x_2, y_2)$ in the plane is

$$d(A, B) = \sqrt{(x_2 - x_1)^2 + (y_2 - y_1)^2}$$

EXAMPLE 2 | Applying the Distance Formula

Which of the points $P(1, -2)$ or $Q(8, 9)$ is closer to the point $A(5, 3)$?

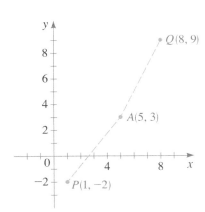

FIGURE 5

SOLUTION By the Distance Formula we have

$$d(P, A) = \sqrt{(5 - 1)^2 + [3 - (-2)]^2} = \sqrt{4^2 + 5^2} = \sqrt{41}$$

$$d(Q, A) = \sqrt{(5 - 8)^2 + (3 - 9)^2} = \sqrt{(-3)^2 + (-6)^2} = \sqrt{45}$$

This shows that $d(P, A) < d(Q, A)$, so P is closer to A (see Figure 5).

NOW TRY EXERCISE **33**

Now let's find the coordinates (x, y) of the midpoint M of the line segment that joins the point $A(x_1, y_1)$ to the point $B(x_2, y_2)$. In Figure 6 notice that triangles APM and MQB are congruent because $d(A, M) = d(M, B)$ and the corresponding angles are equal.

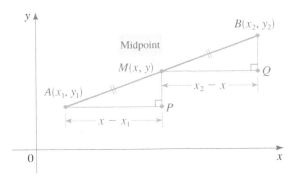

FIGURE 6

It follows that $d(A, P) = d(M, Q)$, so

$$x - x_1 = x_2 - x$$

Solving this equation for x, we get $2x = x_1 + x_2$, so $x = \dfrac{x_1 + x_2}{2}$. Similarly, $y = \dfrac{y_1 + y_2}{2}$.

MIDPOINT FORMULA

The midpoint of the line segment from $A(x_1, y_1)$ to $B(x_2, y_2)$ is

$$\left(\frac{x_1 + x_2}{2}, \frac{y_1 + y_2}{2} \right)$$

EXAMPLE 3 | Applying the Midpoint Formula

Show that the quadrilateral with vertices $P(1, 2)$, $Q(4, 4)$, $R(5, 9)$, and $S(2, 7)$ is a parallelogram by proving that its two diagonals bisect each other.

SOLUTION If the two diagonals have the same midpoint, then they must bisect each other. The midpoint of the diagonal PR is

$$\left(\frac{1 + 5}{2}, \frac{2 + 9}{2} \right) = \left(3, \frac{11}{2} \right)$$

and the midpoint of the diagonal QS is

$$\left(\frac{4 + 2}{2}, \frac{4 + 7}{2} \right) = \left(3, \frac{11}{2} \right)$$

so each diagonal bisects the other, as shown in Figure 7. (A theorem from elementary geometry states that the quadrilateral is therefore a parallelogram.)

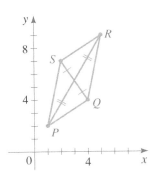

FIGURE 7

NOW TRY EXERCISE **37**

▼ Graphs of Equations in Two Variables

Fundamental Principle of Analytic Geometry

A point (x, y) lies on the graph of an equation if and only if its coordinates satisfy the equation.

An **equation in two variables**, such as $y = x^2 + 1$, expresses a relationship between two quantities. A point (x, y) **satisfies** the equation if it makes the equation true when the values for x and y are substituted into the equation. For example, the point $(3, 10)$ satisfies the equation $y = x^2 + 1$ because $10 = 3^2 + 1$, but the point $(1, 3)$ does not, because $3 \neq 1^2 + 1$.

> **THE GRAPH OF AN EQUATION**
>
> The **graph** of an equation in x and y is the set of all points (x, y) in the coordinate plane that satisfy the equation.

The graph of an equation is a curve, so to graph an equation, we plot as many points as we can, then connect them by a smooth curve.

EXAMPLE 4 | Sketching a Graph by Plotting Points

Sketch the graph of the equation $2x - y = 3$.

SOLUTION We first solve the given equation for y to get

$$y = 2x - 3$$

This helps us calculate the y-coordinates in the following table.

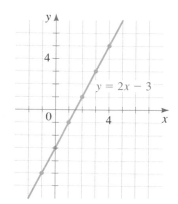

FIGURE 8

x	$y = 2x - 3$	(x, y)
-1	-5	$(-1, -5)$
0	-3	$(0, -3)$
1	-1	$(1, -1)$
2	1	$(2, 1)$
3	3	$(3, 3)$
4	5	$(4, 5)$

Of course, there are infinitely many points on the graph, and it is impossible to plot all of them. But the more points we plot, the better we can imagine what the graph represented by the equation looks like. We plot the points we found in Figure 8; they appear to lie on a line. So we complete the graph by joining the points by a line. (In Section 1.10 we verify that the graph of this equation is indeed a line.)

✎. NOW TRY EXERCISE **59**

A detailed discussion of parabolas and their geometric properties is presented in Chapter 10.

EXAMPLE 5 | Sketching a Graph by Plotting Points

Sketch the graph of the equation $y = x^2 - 2$.

SOLUTION We find some of the points that satisfy the equation in the following table. In Figure 9 we plot these points and then connect them by a smooth curve. A curve with this shape is called a *parabola*.

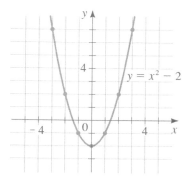

FIGURE 9

x	$y = x^2 - 2$	(x, y)
-3	7	$(-3, 7)$
-2	2	$(-2, 2)$
-1	-1	$(-1, -1)$
0	-2	$(0, -2)$
1	-1	$(1, -1)$
2	2	$(2, 2)$
3	7	$(3, 7)$

✎. NOW TRY EXERCISE **63**

EXAMPLE 6 | Graphing an Absolute Value Equation

Sketch the graph of the equation $y = |x|$.

SOLUTION   We make a table of values:

x	$y = |x|$	(x, y)
-3	3	$(-3, 3)$
-2	2	$(-2, 2)$
-1	1	$(-1, 1)$
0	0	$(0, 0)$
1	1	$(1, 1)$
2	2	$(2, 2)$
3	3	$(3, 3)$

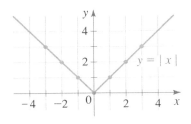

FIGURE 10

In Figure 10 we plot these points and use them to sketch the graph of the equation.

◆ NOW TRY EXERCISE 75

▼ Intercepts

The x-coordinates of the points where a graph intersects the x-axis are called the **x-intercepts** of the graph and are obtained by setting $y = 0$ in the equation of the graph. The y-coordinates of the points where a graph intersects the y-axis are called the **y-intercepts** of the graph and are obtained by setting $x = 0$ in the equation of the graph.

DEFINITION OF INTERCEPTS

Intercepts	How to find them	Where they are on the graph
x-intercepts: The x-coordinates of points where the graph of an equation intersects the x-axis	Set $y = 0$ and solve for x	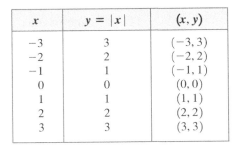
y-intercepts: The y-coordinates of points where the graph of an equation intersects the y-axis	Set $x = 0$ and solve for y	

EXAMPLE 7 | Finding Intercepts

Find the x- and y-intercepts of the graph of the equation $y = x^2 - 2$.

SOLUTION   To find the x-intercepts, we set $y = 0$ and solve for x. Thus

$$0 = x^2 - 2 \qquad \text{Set } y = 0$$
$$x^2 = 2 \qquad \text{Add 2 to each side}$$
$$x = \pm\sqrt{2} \qquad \text{Take the square root}$$

The x-intercepts are $\sqrt{2}$ and $-\sqrt{2}$.

To find the y-intercepts, we set $x = 0$ and solve for y. Thus

$$y = 0^2 - 2 \qquad \text{Set } x = 0$$

$$y = -2$$

The y-intercept is -2.

The graph of this equation was sketched in Example 5. It is repeated in Figure 11 with the x- and y-intercepts labeled.

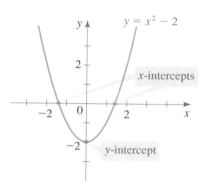

FIGURE 11

⬥ NOW TRY EXERCISE **65**

▼ Circles

So far, we have discussed how to find the graph of an equation in x and y. The converse problem is to find an equation of a graph, that is, an equation that represents a given curve in the xy-plane. Such an equation is satisfied by the coordinates of the points on the curve and by no other point. This is the other half of the fundamental principle of analytic geometry as formulated by Descartes and Fermat. The idea is that if a geometric curve can be represented by an algebraic equation, then the rules of algebra can be used to analyze the curve.

As an example of this type of problem, let's find the equation of a circle with radius r and center (h, k). By definition the circle is the set of all points $P(x, y)$ whose distance from the center $C(h, k)$ is r (see Figure 12). Thus P is on the circle if and only if $d(P, C) = r$. From the distance formula we have

$$\sqrt{(x - h)^2 + (y - k)^2} = r$$

$$(x - h)^2 + (y - k)^2 = r^2 \qquad \text{Square each side}$$

This is the desired equation.

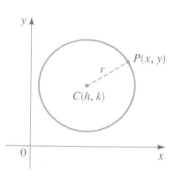

FIGURE 12

EQUATION OF A CIRCLE

An equation of the circle with center (h, k) and radius r is

$$(x - h)^2 + (y - k)^2 = r^2$$

This is called the **standard form** for the equation of the circle. If the center of the circle is the origin $(0, 0)$, then the equation is

$$x^2 + y^2 = r^2$$

EXAMPLE 8 | Graphing a Circle

Graph each equation.

(a) $x^2 + y^2 = 25$ **(b)** $(x - 2)^2 + (y + 1)^2 = 25$

SOLUTION

(a) Rewriting the equation as $x^2 + y^2 = 5^2$, we see that this is an equation of the circle of radius 5 centered at the origin. Its graph is shown in Figure 13.

(b) Rewriting the equation as $(x - 2)^2 + (y + 1)^2 = 5^2$, we see that this is an equation of the circle of radius 5 centered at $(2, -1)$. Its graph is shown in Figure 14.

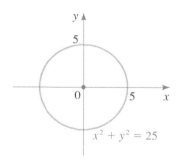

$x^2 + y^2 = 25$

FIGURE 13

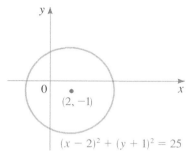

$(x - 2)^2 + (y + 1)^2 = 25$

FIGURE 14

✎. NOW TRY EXERCISES **87** AND **89**

EXAMPLE 9 | Finding an Equation of a Circle

(a) Find an equation of the circle with radius 3 and center $(2, -5)$.

(b) Find an equation of the circle that has the points $P(1, 8)$ and $Q(5, -6)$ as the endpoints of a diameter.

SOLUTION

(a) Using the equation of a circle with $r = 3$, $h = 2$, and $k = -5$, we obtain

$$(x - 2)^2 + (y + 5)^2 = 9$$

The graph is shown in Figure 15.

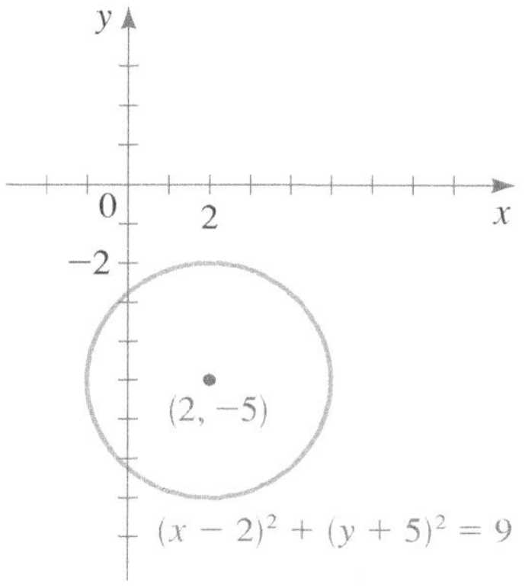

(b) We first observe that the center is the midpoint of the diameter PQ, so by the Midpoint Formula the center is

$$\left(\frac{1 + 5}{2}, \frac{8 - 6}{2}\right) = (3, 1)$$

The radius r is the distance from P to the center, so by the Distance Formula

$$r^2 = (3 - 1)^2 + (1 - 8)^2 = 2^2 + (-7)^2 = 53$$

Therefore, the equation of the circle is

$$(x - 3)^2 + (y - 1)^2 = 53$$

The graph is shown in Figure 16.

✎. NOW TRY EXERCISES **93** AND **97**

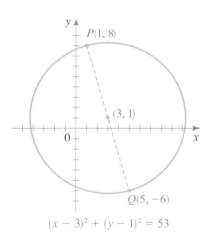

$(x - 2)^2 + (y + 5)^2 = 9$

FIGURE 15

$P(1, 8)$

$(3, 1)$

$Q(5, -6)$

$(x - 3)^2 + (y - 1)^2 = 53$

FIGURE 16

Let's expand the equation of the circle in the preceding example.

$$(x - 3)^2 + (y - 1)^2 = 53 \quad \text{Standard form}$$
$$x^2 - 6x + 9 + y^2 - 2y + 1 = 53 \quad \text{Expand the squares}$$
$$x^2 - 6x + y^2 - 2y = 43 \quad \text{Subtract 10 to get expanded form}$$

Completing the square is used in many contexts in algebra. In Section 1.5 we used completing the square to solve quadratic equations.

Suppose we are given the equation of a circle in expanded form. Then to find its center and radius, we must put the equation back in standard form. That means that we must reverse the steps in the preceding calculation, and to do that we need to know what to add to an expression like $x^2 - 6x$ to make it a perfect square—that is, we need to complete the square, as in the next example.

EXAMPLE 10 | Identifying an Equation of a Circle

Show that the equation $x^2 + y^2 + 2x - 6y + 7 = 0$ represents a circle, and find the center and radius of the circle.

SOLUTION   We first group the x-terms and y-terms. Then we complete the square within each grouping. That is, we complete the square for $x^2 + 2x$ by adding $\left(\frac{1}{2} \cdot 2\right)^2 = 1$, and we complete the square for $y^2 - 6y$ by adding $\left[\frac{1}{2} \cdot (-6)\right]^2 = 9$.

$$(x^2 + 2x \quad) + (y^2 - 6y \quad) = -7 \qquad \text{Group terms}$$

$$(x^2 + 2x + 1) + (y^2 - 6y + 9) = -7 + 1 + 9 \qquad \begin{array}{l}\text{Complete the square by} \\ \text{adding 1 and 9 to each side}\end{array}$$

$$(x + 1)^2 + (y - 3)^2 = 3 \qquad \text{Factor and simplify}$$

We must add the same numbers to *each side* to maintain equality.

Comparing this equation with the standard equation of a circle, we see that $h = -1$, $k = 3$, and $r = \sqrt{3}$, so the given equation represents a circle with center $(-1, 3)$ and radius $\sqrt{3}$.

✎ NOW TRY EXERCISE **103**

▼ Symmetry

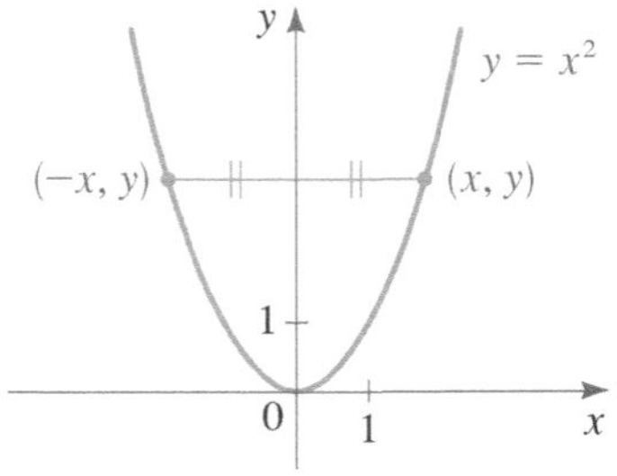

Figure 17 shows the graph of $y = x^2$. Notice that the part of the graph to the left of the y-axis is the mirror image of the part to the right of the y-axis. The reason is that if the point (x, y) is on the graph, then so is $(-x, y)$, and these points are reflections of each other about the y-axis. In this situation we say that the graph is **symmetric with respect to the y-axis**. Similarly, we say that a graph is **symmetric with respect to the x-axis** if whenever the point (x, y) is on the graph, then so is $(x, -y)$. A graph is **symmetric with respect to the origin** if whenever (x, y) is on the graph, so is $(-x, -y)$.

FIGURE 17

DEFINITION OF SYMMETRY

Type of symmetry	How to test for symmetry	What the graph looks like (figures in this section)	Geometric meaning
Symmetry with respect to the x-axis	The equation is unchanged when y is replaced by $-y$	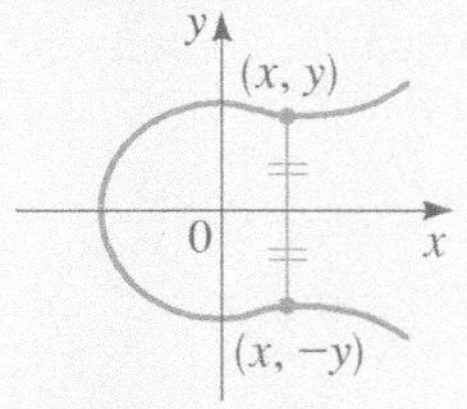 (Figures 13, 18)	Graph is unchanged when reflected in the x-axis
Symmetry with respect to the y-axis	The equation is unchanged when x is replaced by $-x$	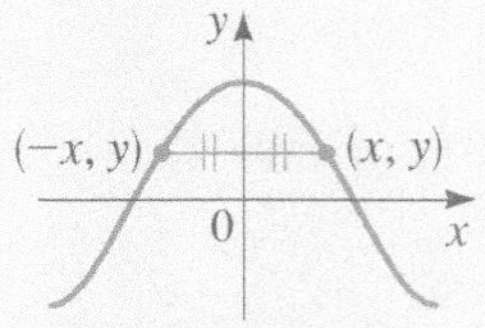 (Figures 9, 10, 11, 13, 17)	Graph is unchanged when reflected in the y-axis
Symmetry with respect to the origin	The equation is unchanged when x is replaced by $-x$ and y by $-y$	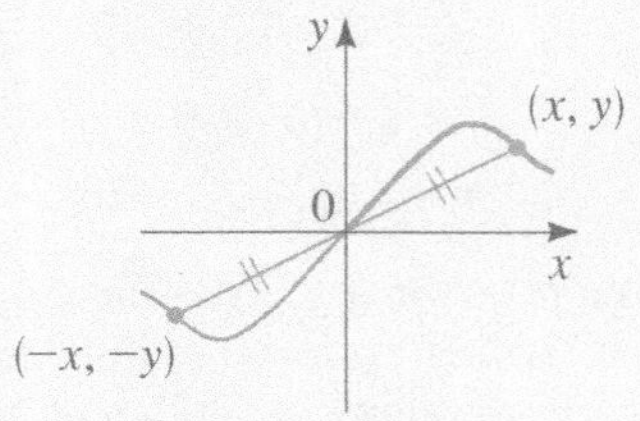 (Figures 13, 19)	Graph is unchanged when rotated 180° about the origin

The remaining examples in this section show how symmetry helps us sketch the graphs of equations.

EXAMPLE 11 | Using Symmetry to Sketch a Graph

Test the equation $x = y^2$ for symmetry and sketch the graph.

SOLUTION   If y is replaced by $-y$ in the equation $x = y^2$, we get

$$x = (-y)^2 \qquad \text{Replace } y \text{ by } -y$$

$$x = y^2 \qquad \text{Simplify}$$

and so the equation is unchanged. Therefore, the graph is symmetric about the x-axis. But changing x to $-x$ gives the equation $-x = y^2$, which is not the same as the original equation, so the graph is not symmetric about the y-axis.

We use the symmetry about the x-axis to sketch the graph by first plotting points just for $y > 0$ and then reflecting the graph in the x-axis, as shown in Figure 18.

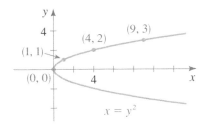

FIGURE 18

y	$x = y^2$	(x, y)
0	0	$(0, 0)$
1	1	$(1, 1)$
2	4	$(4, 2)$
3	9	$(9, 3)$

✎ NOW TRY EXERCISE **77**

EXAMPLE 12 | Using Symmetry to Sketch a Graph

Test the equation $y = x^3 - 9x$ for symmetry and sketch its graph.

SOLUTION   If we replace x by $-x$ and y by $-y$ in the equation, we get

$$-y = (-x)^3 - 9(-x) \qquad \text{Replace } x \text{ by } -x \text{ and } y \text{ by } -y$$

$$-y = -x^3 + 9x \qquad \text{Simplify}$$

$$y = x^3 - 9x \qquad \text{Multiply by } -1$$

and so the equation is unchanged. This means that the graph is symmetric with respect to the origin. We sketch it by first plotting points for $x > 0$ and then using symmetry about the origin (see Figure 19).

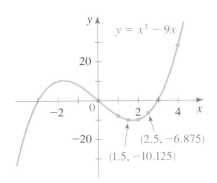

FIGURE 19

x	$y = x^3 - 9x$	(x, y)
0	0	$(0, 0)$
1	-8	$(1, -8)$
1.5	-10.125	$(1.5, -10.125)$
2	-10	$(2, -10)$
2.5	-6.875	$(2.5, -6.875)$
3	0	$(3, 0)$
4	28	$(4, 28)$

✎ NOW TRY EXERCISE **79**

1.8 EXERCISES

CONCEPTS

1. The point that is 3 units to the right of the y-axis and 5 units below the x-axis has coordinates (____ , ____).

2. The distance between the points (a, b) and (c, d) is _____. So the distance between $(1, 2)$ and $(7, 10)$ is _____ .

3. The point midway between (a, b) and (c, d) is _____ . So the point midway between $(1, 2)$ and $(7, 10)$ is _____ .

4. If the point $(2, 3)$ is on the graph of an equation in x and y, then the equation is satisfied when we replace x by _____ and y by _____ . Is the point $(2, 3)$ on the graph of the equation $2y = x + 1$?

5. (a) To find the x-intercept(s) of the graph of an equation, we set _____ equal to 0 and solve for _____ . So the x-intercept of $2y = x + 1$ is _____ .

   (b) To find the y-intercept(s) of the graph of an equation, we set _____ equal to 0 and solve for _____ . So the y-intercept of $2y = x + 1$ is _____ .

6. The graph of the equation $(x - 1)^2 + (y - 2)^2 = 9$ is a circle with center (____ , ____) and radius _____ .

SKILLS

7. Plot the given points in a coordinate plane.

   $(2, 3), (-2, 3), (4, 5), (4, -5), (-4, 5), (-4, -5)$

8. Find the coordinates of the points shown in the figure.

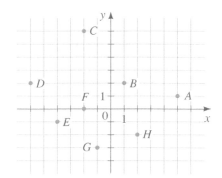

9–12 ■ A pair of points is graphed.

   (a) Find the distance between them.

   (b) Find the midpoint of the segment that joins them.

9. 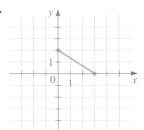   **10.**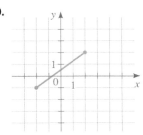

11. 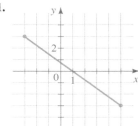   **12.**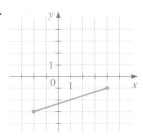

13–18 ■ A pair of points is graphed.

   (a) Plot the points in a coordinate plane.

   (b) Find the distance between them.

   (c) Find the midpoint of the segment that joins them.

13. $(0, 8), (6, 16)$ 14. $(-2, 5), (10, 0)$

15. $(-3, -6), (4, 18)$ 16. $(-1, -1), (9, 9)$

17. $(6, -2), (-6, 2)$ 18. $(0, -6), (5, 0)$

19. Draw the rectangle with vertices $A(1, 3), B(5, 3), C(1, -3)$, and $D(5, -3)$ on a coordinate plane. Find the area of the rectangle.

20. Draw the parallelogram with vertices $A(1, 2), B(5, 2), C(3, 6)$, and $D(7, 6)$ on a coordinate plane. Find the area of the parallelogram.

21. Plot the points $A(1, 0), B(5, 0), C(4, 3)$, and $D(2, 3)$ on a coordinate plane. Draw the segments AB, BC, CD, and DA. What kind of quadrilateral is $ABCD$, and what is its area?

22. Plot the points $P(5, 1), Q(0, 6)$, and $R(-5, 1)$ on a coordinate plane. Where must the point S be located so that the quadrilateral $PQRS$ is a square? Find the area of this square.

23–32 ■ Sketch the region given by the set.

23. $\{(x, y) \mid x \geq 3\}$ 24. $\{(x, y) \mid y < 3\}$

25. $\{(x, y) \mid y = 2\}$ 26. $\{(x, y) \mid x = -1\}$

27. $\{(x, y) \mid 1 < x < 2\}$ 28. $\{(x, y) \mid 0 \leq y \leq 4\}$

29. $\{(x, y) \mid |x| > 4\}$ 30. $\{(x, y) \mid |y| \leq 2\}$

31. $\{(x, y) \mid x \geq 1 \text{ and } y < 3\}$

32. $\{(x, y) \mid |x| \leq 2 \text{ and } |y| \leq 3\}$

33. Which of the points $A(6, 7)$ or $B(-5, 8)$ is closer to the origin?

34. Which of the points $C(-6, 3)$ or $D(3, 0)$ is closer to the point $E(-2, 1)$?

35. Which of the points $P(3, 1)$ or $Q(-1, 3)$ is closer to the point $R(-1, -1)$?

36. (a) Show that the points $(7, 3)$ and $(3, 7)$ are the same distance from the origin.

    (b) Show that the points (a, b) and (b, a) are the same distance from the origin.

37. Show that the triangle with vertices $A(0, 2)$, $B(-3, -1)$, and $C(-4, 3)$ is isosceles.

38. Find the area of the triangle shown in the figure.

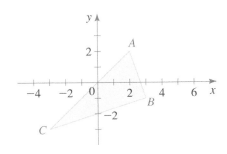

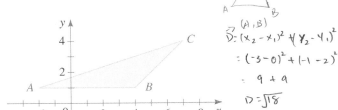

39. Refer to triangle ABC in the figure below.

    (a) Show that triangle ABC is a right triangle by using the converse of the Pythagorean Theorem (see page 219).

    (b) Find the area of triangle ABC.

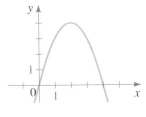

40. Show that the triangle with vertices $A(6, -7)$, $B(11, -3)$, and $C(2, -2)$ is a right triangle by using the converse of the Pythagorean Theorem. Find the area of the triangle.

41. Show that the points $A(-2, 9)$, $B(4, 6)$, $C(1, 0)$, and $D(-5, 3)$ are the vertices of a square.

42. Show that the points $A(-1, 3)$, $B(3, 11)$, and $C(5, 15)$ are collinear by showing that $d(A, B) + d(B, C) = d(A, C)$.

43. Find a point on the y-axis that is equidistant from the points $(5, -5)$ and $(1, 1)$.

44. Find the lengths of the medians of the triangle with vertices $A(1, 0)$, $B(3, 6)$, and $C(8, 2)$. (A *median* is a line segment from a vertex to the midpoint of the opposite side.)

45. Plot the points $P(-1, -4)$, $Q(1, 1)$, and $R(4, 2)$ on a coordinate plane. Where should the point S be located so that the figure $PQRS$ is a parallelogram?

46. If $M(6, 8)$ is the midpoint of the line segment AB and if A has coordinates $(2, 3)$, find the coordinates of B.

47. (a) Sketch the parallelogram with vertices $A(-2, -1)$, $B(4, 2)$, $C(7, 7)$, and $D(1, 4)$.

    (b) Find the midpoints of the diagonals of this parallelogram.

    (c) From part (b) show that the diagonals bisect each other.

48. The point M in the figure is the midpoint of the line segment AB. Show that M is equidistant from the vertices of triangle ABC.

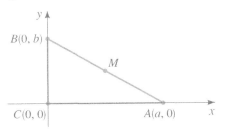

49–52 ■ Determine whether the given points are on the graph of the equation.

49. $x - 2y - 1 = 0$; $(0, 0), (1, 0), (-1, -1)$

50. $y(x^2 + 1) = 1$; $(1, 1), \left(1, \frac{1}{2}\right), \left(-1, \frac{1}{2}\right)$

51. $x^2 + xy + y^2 = 4$; $(0, -2), (1, -2), (2, -2)$

52. $x^2 + y^2 = 1$; $(0, 1), \left(\frac{1}{\sqrt{2}}, \frac{1}{\sqrt{2}}\right), \left(\frac{\sqrt{3}}{2}, \frac{1}{2}\right)$

53–56 ■ An equation and its graph are given. Find the x- and y-intercepts.

53. $y = 4x - x^2$

54. $\dfrac{x^2}{9} + \dfrac{y^2}{4} = 1$

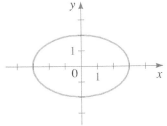

55. $x^4 + y^2 - xy = 16$

56. $x^2 + y^3 - x^2y^2 = 64$

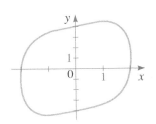

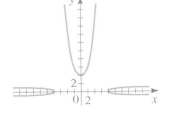

57–76 ■ Make a table of values and sketch the graph of the equation. Find the x- and y-intercepts and test for symmetry.

57. $y = -x + 4$

58. $y = 3x + 3$

59. $2x - y = 6$

60. $x + y = 3$

61. $y = 1 - x^2$

62. $y = x^2 + 2$

63. $4y = x^2$

64. $8y = x^3$

65. $y = x^2 - 9$

66. $y = 9 - x^2$

67. $xy = 2$

68. $y = \sqrt{x + 4}$

69. $y = \sqrt{4 - x^2}$

70. $y = -\sqrt{4 - x^2}$

71. $x + y^2 = 4$

72. $x = y^3$

73. $y = 16 - x^4$

74. $x = |y|$

75. $y = 4 - |x|$

76. $y = |4 - x|$

77–82 ■ Test the equation for symmetry.

77. $y = x^4 + x^2$

78. $x = y^4 - y^2$

79. $x^2y^2 + xy = 1$

80. $x^4y^4 + x^2y^2 = 1$

81. $y = x^3 + 10x$

82. $y = x^2 + |x|$

83–86 ■ Complete the graph using the given symmetry property.

83. Symmetric with respect to the y-axis

84. Symmetric with respect to the x-axis

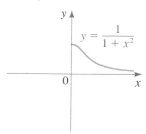

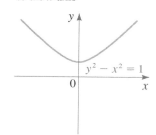

85. Symmetric with respect to the origin

86. Symmetric with respect to the origin

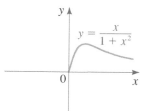

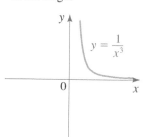

87–92 ■ Find the center and radius of the circle and sketch its graph

87. $x^2 + y^2 = 9$

88. $x^2 + y^2 = 5$

89. $(x - 3)^2 + y^2 = 16$

90. $x^2 + (y - 2)^2 = 4$

91. $(x + 3)^2 + (y - 4)^2 = 25$

92. $(x + 1)^2 + (y + 2)^2 = 36$

93–100 ■ Find an equation of the circle that satisfies the given conditions.

93. Center $(2, -1)$; radius 3

94. Center $(-1, -4)$; radius 8

95. Center at the origin; passes through $(4, 7)$

96. Center $(-1, 5)$; passes through $(-4, -6)$

97. Endpoints of a diameter are $P(-1, 1)$ and $Q(5, 9)$

98. Endpoints of a diameter are $P(-1, 3)$ and $Q(7, -5)$

99. Center $(7, -3)$; tangent to the x-axis

100. Circle lies in the first quadrant, tangent to both x-and y-axes; radius 5

101–102 ■ Find the equation of the circle shown in the figure.

101. **102.**

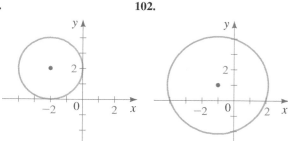

103–108 ■ Show that the equation represents a circle, and find the center and radius of the circle.

103. $x^2 + y^2 - 4x + 10y + 13 = 0$

104. $x^2 + y^2 + 6y + 2 = 0$

105. $x^2 + y^2 - \frac{1}{2}x + \frac{1}{2}y = \frac{1}{8}$

106. $x^2 + y^2 + \frac{1}{2}x + 2y + \frac{1}{16} = 0$

107. $2x^2 + 2y^2 - 3x = 0$

108. $3x^2 + 3y^2 + 6x - y = 0$

109–110 ■ Sketch the region given by the set.

109. $\{(x, y) \mid x^2 + y^2 \le 1\}$

110. $\{(x, y) \mid x^2 + y^2 > 4\}$

111. Find the area of the region that lies outside the circle $x^2 + y^2 = 4$ but inside the circle

$$x^2 + y^2 - 4y - 12 = 0$$

112. Sketch the region in the coordinate plane that satisfies both the inequalities $x^2 + y^2 \le 9$ and $y \ge |x|$. What is the area of this region?

APPLICATIONS

113. Distances in a City A city has streets that run north and south and avenues that run east and west, all equally spaced. Streets and avenues are numbered sequentially, as shown in the figure. The *walking* distance between points A and B is 7 blocks—that is, 3 blocks east and 4 blocks north. To find the *straight-line* distance d, we must use the Distance Formula.

(a) Find the straight-line distance (in blocks) between A and B.

(b) Find the walking distance and the straight-line distance between the corner of 4th St. and 2nd Ave. and the corner of 11th St. and 26th Ave.

(c) What must be true about the points P and Q if the walking distance between P and Q equals the straight-line distance between P and Q?

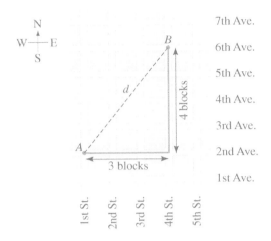

114. Halfway Point Two friends live in the city described in Exercise 113, one at the corner of 3rd St. and 7th Ave., the other at the corner of 27th St. and 17th Ave. They frequently meet at a coffee shop halfway between their homes.

(a) At what intersection is the coffee shop located?

(b) How far must each of them walk to get to the coffee shop?

115. Orbit of a Satellite A satellite is in orbit around the moon. A coordinate plane containing the orbit is set up with the center of the moon at the origin, as shown in the graph, with distances measured in megameters (Mm). The equation of the satellite's orbit is

$$\frac{(x-3)^2}{25} + \frac{y^2}{16} = 1$$

(a) From the graph, determine the closest and the farthest that the satellite gets to the center of the moon.

(b) There are two points in the orbit with y-coordinates 2. Find the x-coordinates of these points, and determine their distances to the center of the moon.

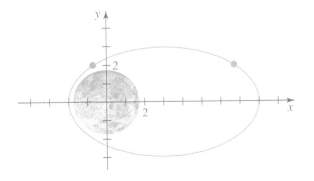

DISCOVERY ■ DISCUSSION ■ WRITING

116. Shifting the Coordinate Plane Suppose that each point in the coordinate plane is shifted 3 units to the right and 2 units upward.

(a) The point $(5, 3)$ is shifted to what new point?

(b) The point (a, b) is shifted to what new point?

(c) What point is shifted to $(3, 4)$?

(d) Triangle ABC in the figure has been shifted to triangle $A'B'C'$. Find the coordinates of the points A', B', and C'.

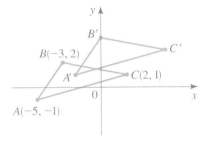

117. Reflecting in the Coordinate Plane Suppose that the y-axis acts as a mirror that reflects each point to the right of it into a point to the left of it.

(a) The point $(3, 7)$ is reflected to what point?

(b) The point (a, b) is reflected to what point?

(c) What point is reflected to $(-4, -1)$?

(d) Triangle ABC in the figure is reflected to triangle $A'B'C'$. Find the coordinates of the points A', B', and C'.

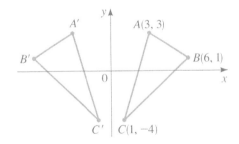

118. Completing a Line Segment Plot the points $M(6, 8)$ and $A(2, 3)$ on a coordinate plane. If M is the midpoint of the line segment AB, find the coordinates of B. Write a brief description of the steps you took to find B, and your reasons for taking them.

119. Completing a Parallelogram Plot the points $P(0, 3)$, $Q(2, 2)$, and $R(5, 3)$ on a coordinate plane. Where should the point S be located so that the figure $PQRS$ is a parallelogram? Write a brief description of the steps you took and your reasons for taking them.

120. Circle, Point, or Empty Set? Complete the squares in the general equation $x^2 + ax + y^2 + by + c = 0$ and simplify the result as much as possible. Under what conditions on the coefficients a, b, and c does this equation represent a circle? A single point? The empty set? In the case that the equation does represent a circle, find its center and radius.

121. Do the Circles Intersect?

(a) Find the radius of each circle in the pair and the distance between their centers; then use this information to determine whether the circles intersect.

(i) $(x - 2)^2 + (y - 1)^2 = 9$;
$(x - 6)^2 + (y - 4)^2 = 16$

(ii) $x^2 + (y - 2)^2 = 4$;
$(x - 5)^2 + (y - 14)^2 = 9$

(iii) $(x - 3)^2 + (y + 1)^2 = 1$;
$(x - 2)^2 + (y - 2)^2 = 25$

(b) How can you tell, just by knowing the radii of two circles and the distance between their centers, whether the circles intersect? Write a short paragraph describing how you would decide this and draw graphs to illustrate your answer.

122. Making a Graph Symmetric The graph shown in the figure is not symmetric about the *x*-axis, the *y*-axis, or the origin. Add more line segments to the graph so that it exhibits the indicated symmetry. In each case, add as little as possible.

(a) Symmetry about the *x*-axis

(b) Symmetry about the *y*-axis

(c) Symmetry about the origin

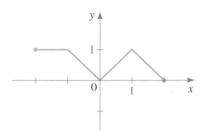

1.9 GRAPHING CALCULATORS; SOLVING EQUATIONS AND INEQUALITIES GRAPHICALLY

| Using a Graphing Calculator ▶ Solving Equations Graphically ▶ Solving Inequalities Graphically

In Sections 1.5 and 1.7 we solved equations and inequalities algebraically. In Section 1.8 we learned how to sketch the graph of an equation in a coordinate plane. In this section we use graphs to solve equations and inequalities. To do this, we must first draw a graph using a graphing device. So we begin by giving a few guidelines to help us use graphing devices effectively.

▼ Using a Graphing Calculator

A graphing calculator or computer displays a rectangular portion of the graph of an equation in a display window or viewing screen, which we call a **viewing rectangle**. The default screen often gives an incomplete or misleading picture, so it is important to choose the viewing rectangle with care. If we choose the *x*-values to range from a minimum value of Xmin = *a* to a maximum value of Xmax = *b* and the *y*-values to range from a minimum value of Ymin = *c* to a maximum value of Ymax = *d*, then the displayed portion of the graph lies in the rectangle

$$[a, b] \times [c, d] = \{(x, y) \mid a \le x \le b, c \le y \le d\}$$

as shown in Figure 1. We refer to this as the $[a, b]$ by $[c, d]$ viewing rectangle.

The graphing device draws the graph of an equation much as you would. It plots points of the form (x, y) for a certain number of values of *x*, equally spaced between *a* and *b*. If the equation is not defined for an *x*-value or if the corresponding *y*-value lies outside the viewing rectangle, the device ignores this value and moves on to the next *x*-value. The machine connects each point to the preceding plotted point to form a representation of the graph of the equation.

FIGURE 1 The viewing rectangle $[a, b]$ by $[c, d]$

EXAMPLE 1 | Choosing an Appropriate Viewing Rectangle

Graph the equation $y = x^2 + 3$ in an appropriate viewing rectangle.

SOLUTION Let's experiment with different viewing rectangles. We start with the viewing rectangle $[-2, 2]$ by $[-2, 2]$, so we set

$$\text{Xmin} = -2 \qquad \text{Ymin} = -2$$

$$\text{Xmax} = 2 \qquad \text{Ymax} = 2$$

The resulting graph in Figure 2(a) is blank! This is because $x^2 \geq 0$, so $x^2 + 3 \geq 3$ for all x. Thus, the graph lies entirely above the viewing rectangle, so this viewing rectangle is not appropriate. If we enlarge the viewing rectangle to $[-4, 4]$ by $[-4, 4]$, as in Figure 2(b), we begin to see a portion of the graph.

Now let's try the viewing rectangle $[-10, 10]$ by $[-5, 30]$. The graph in Figure 2(c) seems to give a more complete view of the graph. If we enlarge the viewing rectangle even further, as in Figure 2(d), the graph doesn't show clearly that the y-intercept is 3.

So the viewing rectangle $[-10, 10]$ by $[-5, 30]$ gives an appropriate representation of the graph.

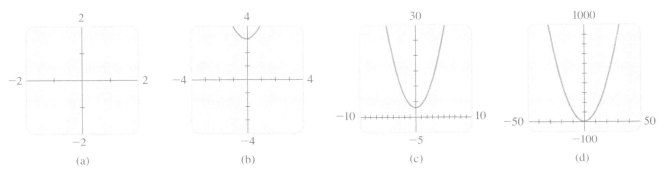

FIGURE 2 Graphs of $y = x^2 + 3$

NOW TRY EXERCISE **5**

EXAMPLE 2 | Two Graphs on the Same Screen

Graph the equations $y = 3x^2 - 6x + 1$ and $y = 0.23x - 2.25$ together in the viewing rectangle $[-1, 3]$ by $[-2.5, 1.5]$. Do the graphs intersect in this viewing rectangle?

SOLUTION Figure 3(a) shows the essential features of both graphs. One is a parabola, and the other is a line. It looks as if the graphs intersect near the point $(1, -2)$. However, if we zoom in on the area around this point as shown in Figure 3(b), we see that although the graphs almost touch, they do not actually intersect.

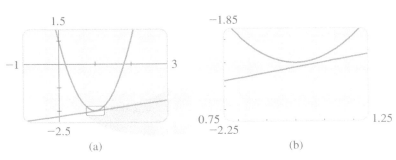

FIGURE 3

NOW TRY EXERCISE **23**

You can see from Examples 1 and 2 that the choice of a viewing rectangle makes a big difference in the appearance of a graph. If you want an overview of the essential features of a graph, you must choose a relatively large viewing rectangle to obtain a global view of the graph. If you want to investigate the details of a graph, you must zoom in to a small viewing rectangle that shows just the feature of interest.

Most graphing calculators can only graph equations in which y is isolated on one side of the equal sign. The next example shows how to graph equations that don't have this property.

EXAMPLE 3 | Graphing a Circle

Graph the circle $x^2 + y^2 = 1$.

SOLUTION We first solve for y, to isolate it on one side of the equal sign.

$$y^2 = 1 - x^2 \qquad \text{Subtract } x^2$$

$$y = \pm\sqrt{1 - x^2} \qquad \text{Take square roots}$$

Therefore, the circle is described by the graphs of *two* equations:

$$y = \sqrt{1 - x^2} \qquad \text{and} \qquad y = -\sqrt{1 - x^2}$$

The graph in Figure 4(c) looks somewhat flattened. Most graphing calculators allow you to set the scales on the axes so that circles really look like circles. On the TI-82 and TI-83, from the ZOOM menu, choose ZSquare to set the scales appropriately. (On the TI-86 the command is Zsq.)

The first equation represents the top half of the circle (because $y \geq 0$), and the second represents the bottom half of the circle (because $y \leq 0$). If we graph the first equation in the viewing rectangle $[-2, 2]$ by $[-2, 2]$, we get the semicircle shown in Figure 4(a). The graph of the second equation is the semicircle in Figure 4(b). Graphing these semicircles together on the same viewing screen, we get the full circle in Figure 4(c).

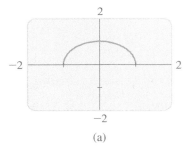
(a)

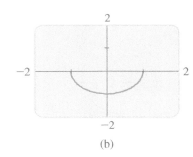
(b)

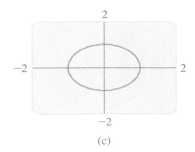
(c)

FIGURE 4 Graphing the equation $x^2 + y^2 = 1$

✎ NOW TRY EXERCISE **27**

▼ Solving Equations Graphically

In Section 1.5 we learned how to solve equations. To solve an equation such as

$$3x - 5 = 0$$

we used the **algebraic method**. This means that we used the rules of algebra to isolate x on one side of the equation. We view x as an *unknown,* and we use the rules of algebra to hunt it down. Here are the steps in the solution:

$$3x - 5 = 0$$

$$3x = 5 \qquad \text{Add 5}$$

$$x = \tfrac{5}{3} \qquad \text{Divide by 3}$$

So the solution is $x = \tfrac{5}{3}$.

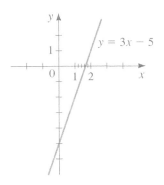

$y = 3x - 5$

FIGURE 5

We can also solve this equation by the **graphical method**. In this method we view x as a *variable* and sketch the graph of the equation

$$y = 3x - 5$$

Different values for x give different values for y. Our goal is to find the value of x for which $y = 0$. From the graph in Figure 5 we see that $y = 0$ when $x \approx 1.7$. Thus, the solution is $x \approx 1.7$. Note that from the graph we obtain an approximate solution. We summarize these methods in the box below.

SOLVING AN EQUATION

Algebraic Method

Use the rules of algebra to isolate the unknown x on one side of the equation.

Example: $2x = 6 - x$

$$3x = 6 \qquad \text{Add } x$$
$$x = 2 \qquad \text{Divide by 3}$$

The solution is $x = 2$.

Graphical Method

Move all terms to one side and set equal to y. Sketch the graph to find the value of x where $y = 0$.

Example: $2x = 6 - x$

$$0 = 6 - 3x$$

Set $y = 6 - 3x$ and graph.

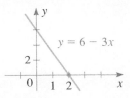

$y = 6 - 3x$

From the graph, the solution is $x \approx 2$.

The advantage of the algebraic method is that it gives exact answers. Also, the process of unraveling the equation to arrive at the answer helps us to understand the algebraic structure of the equation. On the other hand, for many equations it is difficult or impossible to isolate x.

The graphical method gives a numerical approximation to the answer. This is an advantage when a numerical answer is desired. (For example, an engineer might find an answer expressed as $x \approx 2.6$ more immediately useful than $x = \sqrt{7}$.) Also, graphing an equation helps us to visualize how the solution is related to other values of the variable.

The *Discovery Project* referenced on page 263 describes a numerical method for solving equations.

PIERRE DE FERMAT (1601–1665) was a French lawyer who became interested in mathematics at the age of 30. Because of his job as a magistrate, Fermat had little time to write complete proofs of his discoveries and often wrote them in the margin of whatever book he was reading at the time. After his death, his copy of Diophantus' *Arithmetica* (see page 20) was found to contain a particularly tantalizing comment. Where Diophantus discusses the solutions of $x^2 + y^2 = z^2$ (for example, $x = 3$, $y = 4$, and $z = 5$), Fermat states in the margin that for $n \geq 3$ there are no natural number solutions to the equation $x^n + y^n = z^n$. In other words, it's impossible for a cube to equal the sum of two cubes, a fourth power to equal the sum of two fourth powers, and so on. Fermat writes, "I have discovered a truly wonderful proof for this but the margin is too small to contain it." All the other margin comments in Fermat's copy of *Arithmetica* have been proved. This one, however, remained unproved, and it came to be known as "Fermat's Last Theorem."

In 1994, Andrew Wiles of Princeton University announced a proof of Fermat's Last Theorem, an astounding 350 years after it was conjectured. His proof is one of the most widely reported mathematical results in the popular press.

EXAMPLE 4 | Solving a Quadratic Equation Algebraically and Graphically

Solve the quadratic equations algebraically and graphically.

(a) $x^2 - 4x + 2 = 0$ **(b)** $x^2 - 4x + 4 = 0$ **(c)** $x^2 - 4x + 6 = 0$

SOLUTION 1: Algebraic

We use the Quadratic Formula to solve each equation.

The Quadratic Formula is discussed on page 49.

(a) $x = \dfrac{-(-4) \pm \sqrt{(-4)^2 - 4 \cdot 1 \cdot 2}}{2} = \dfrac{4 \pm \sqrt{8}}{2} = 2 \pm \sqrt{2}$

There are two solutions, $x = 2 + \sqrt{2}$ and $x = 2 - \sqrt{2}$.

(b) $x = \dfrac{-(-4) \pm \sqrt{(-4)^2 - 4 \cdot 1 \cdot 4}}{2} = \dfrac{4 \pm \sqrt{0}}{2} = 2$

There is just one solution, $x = 2$.

(c) $x = \dfrac{-(-4) \pm \sqrt{(-4)^2 - 4 \cdot 1 \cdot 6}}{2} = \dfrac{4 \pm \sqrt{-8}}{2}$

There is no real solution.

SOLUTION 2: Graphical

We graph the equations $y = x^2 - 4x + 2$, $y = x^2 - 4x + 4$, and $y = x^2 - 4x + 6$ in Figure 6. By determining the x-intercepts of the graphs, we find the following solutions.

(a) $x \approx 0.6$ and $x \approx 3.4$

(b) $x = 2$

(c) There is no x-intercept, so the equation has no solution.

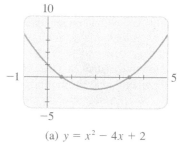

(a) $y = x^2 - 4x + 2$

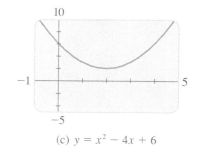

(b) $y = x^2 - 4x + 4$

(c) $y = x^2 - 4x + 6$

FIGURE 6

✎ NOW TRY EXERCISE **35**

© National Portrait Gallery

ALAN TURING (1912–1954) was at the center of two pivotal events of the 20th century: World War II and the invention of computers. At the age of 23 Turing made his mark on mathematics by solving an important problem in the foundations of mathematics that had been posed by David Hilbert at the 1928 International Congress of Mathematicians (see page 683). In this research he invented a theoretical machine, now called a Turing machine, which was the in- spiration for modern digital computers. During World War II Turing was in charge of the British effort to decipher secret German codes. His complete success in this endeavor played a decisive role in the Allies' victory. To carry out the numerous logical steps that are required to break a coded message, Turing developed decision procedures similar to modern computer programs. After the war he helped to develop the first electronic computers in Britain. He also did pioneering work on artificial intelligence and computer models of biological processes. At the age of 42 Turing died of poisoning after eating an apple that had mysteriously been laced with cyanide.

The graphs in Figure 6 show visually why a quadratic equation may have two solutions, one solution, or no real solution. We proved this fact algebraically in Section 1.5 when we studied the discriminant.

EXAMPLE 5 | Another Graphical Method

Solve the equation algebraically and graphically: $5 - 3x = 8x - 20$

SOLUTION 1: Algebraic

$$5 - 3x = 8x - 20$$
$$-3x = 8x - 25 \qquad \text{Subtract 5}$$
$$-11x = -25 \qquad \text{Subtract } 8x$$
$$x = \frac{-25}{-11} = 2\tfrac{3}{11} \qquad \text{Divide by } -11 \text{ and simplify}$$

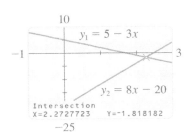

FIGURE 7

SOLUTION 2: Graphical

We could move all terms to one side of the equal sign, set the result equal to y, and graph the resulting equation. But to avoid all this algebra, we graph two equations instead:

$$y_1 = 5 - 3x \qquad \text{and} \qquad y_2 = 8x - 20$$

The solution of the original equation will be the value of x that makes y_1 equal to y_2; that is, the solution is the x-coordinate of the intersection point of the two graphs. Using the $\boxed{\text{TRACE}}$ feature or the `intersect` command on a graphing calculator, we see from Figure 7 that the solution is $x \approx 2.27$.

✎. NOW TRY EXERCISE **31**

In the next example we use the graphical method to solve an equation that is extremely difficult to solve algebraically.

EXAMPLE 6 | Solving an Equation in an Interval

Solve the equation

$$x^3 - 6x^2 + 9x = \sqrt{x}$$

in the interval $[1, 6]$.

SOLUTION We are asked to find all solutions x that satisfy $1 \le x \le 6$, so we will graph the equation in a viewing rectangle for which the x-values are restricted to this interval.

$$x^3 - 6x^2 + 9x = \sqrt{x}$$
$$x^3 - 6x^2 + 9x - \sqrt{x} = 0 \qquad \text{Subtract } \sqrt{x}$$

We can also use the `zero` command to find the solutions, as shown in Figures 8(a) and 8(b).

Figure 8 shows the graph of the equation $y = x^3 - 6x^2 + 9x - \sqrt{x}$ in the viewing rectangle $[1, 6]$ by $[-5, 5]$. There are two x-intercepts in this viewing rectangle; zooming in, we see that the solutions are $x \approx 2.18$ and $x \approx 3.72$.

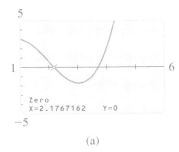
(a)

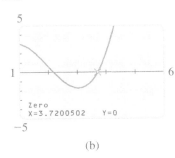
(b)

FIGURE 8

✎. NOW TRY EXERCISE **43**

The equation in Example 6 actually has four solutions. You are asked to find the other two in Exercise 71.

EXAMPLE 7 | Intensity of Light

Two light sources are 10 m apart. One is three times as intense as the other. The light intensity L (in lux) at a point x meters from the weaker source is given by

$$L = \frac{10}{x^2} + \frac{30}{(10 - x)^2}$$

(See Figure 9.) Find the points at which the light intensity is 4 lux.

FIGURE 9

SOLUTION We need to solve the equation

$$4 = \frac{10}{x^2} + \frac{30}{(10 - x)^2}$$

The graphs of

$$y_1 = 4 \qquad \text{and} \qquad y_2 = \frac{10}{x^2} + \frac{30}{(10 - x)^2}$$

are shown in Figure 10. Zooming in (or using the `intersect` command), we find two solutions, $x \approx 1.67431$ and $x \approx 7.1927193$. So the light intensity is 4 lux at the points that are 1.67 m and 7.19 m from the weaker source.

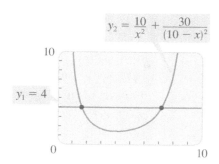

FIGURE 10

✎. NOW TRY EXERCISE **73**

▼ Solving Inequalities Graphically

Inequalities can be solved graphically. To describe the method, we solve

$$x^2 - 5x + 6 \leq 0$$

This inequality was solved algebraically in Example 3 of Section 1.7. To solve the inequality graphically, we draw the graph of

$$y = x^2 - 5x + 6$$

Our goal is to find those values of x for which $y \leq 0$. These are simply the x-values for which the graph lies below the x-axis. From Figure 11 we see that the solution of the inequality is the interval $[2, 3]$.

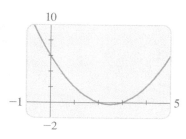

FIGURE 11 $x^2 - 5x + 6 \leq 0$

EXAMPLE 8 | Solving an Inequality Graphically

Solve the inequality $3.7x^2 + 1.3x - 1.9 \le 2.0 - 1.4x$.

SOLUTION   We graph the equations

$$y_1 = 3.7x^2 + 1.3x - 1.9 \qquad \text{and} \qquad y_2 = 2.0 - 1.4x$$

in the same viewing rectangle in Figure 12. We are interested in those values of x for which $y_1 \le y_2$; these are points for which the graph of y_2 lies on or above the graph of y_1. To determine the appropriate interval, we look for the x-coordinates of points where the graphs intersect. We conclude that the solution is (approximately) the interval $[-1.45, 0.72]$.

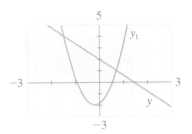

FIGURE 12
$y_1 = 3.7x^2 + 1.3x - 1.9$
$y_2 = 2.0 - 1.4x$

✎ . NOW TRY EXERCISE **59**

EXAMPLE 9 | Solving an Inequality Graphically

Solve the inequality $x^3 - 5x^2 \ge -8$.

SOLUTION   We write the inequality as

$$x^3 - 5x^2 + 8 \ge 0$$

and then graph the equation

$$y = x^3 - 5x^2 + 8$$

in the viewing rectangle $[-6, 6]$ by $[-15, 15]$, as shown in Figure 13. The solution of the inequality consists of those intervals on which the graph lies on or above the x-axis. By moving the cursor to the x-intercepts, we find that, rounded to one decimal place, the solution is $[-1.1, 1.5] \cup [4.6, \infty)$.

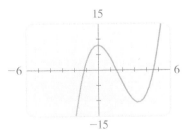

FIGURE 13 $x^3 - 5x^2 + 8 \ge 0$

✎ . NOW TRY EXERCISE **61**

1.9 EXERCISES

CONCEPTS

1. The solutions of the equation $x^2 - 2x - 3 = 0$ are the
   _____-intercepts of the graph of $y = x^2 - 2x - 3$.

2. The solutions of the inequality $x^2 - 2x - 3 > 0$ are the
   x-coordinates of the points on the graph of $y = x^2 - 2x - 3$
   that lie _____ the x-axis.

3. The figure shows a graph of $y = x^4 - 3x^3 - x^2 + 3x$.
   Use the graph to do the following.
   (a) Find the solutions of the equation $x^4 - 3x^3 - x^2 + 3x = 0$.
   (b) Find the solutions of the inequality $x^4 - 3x^3 - x^2 + 3x \le 0$.

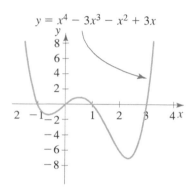

4. The figure shows the graphs of $y = 5x - x^2$ and $y = 4$. Use
   the graphs to do the following.
   (a) Find the solutions of the equation $5x - x^2 = 4$.
   (b) Find the solutions of the inequality $5x - x^2 > 4$.

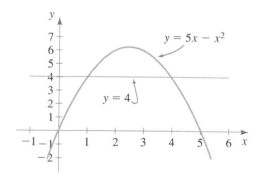

SKILLS

5–10 ■ Use a graphing calculator or computer to decide which
viewing rectangle (a)–(d) produces the most appropriate graph
of the equation.

5. $y = x^4 + 2$
   (a) $[-2, 2]$ by $[-2, 2]$
   (b) $[0, 4]$ by $[0, 4]$
   (c) $[-8, 8]$ by $[-4, 40]$
   (d) $[-40, 40]$ by $[-80, 800]$

6. $y = x^2 + 7x + 6$
   (a) $[-5, 5]$ by $[-5, 5]$
   (b) $[0, 10]$ by $[-20, 100]$
   (c) $[-15, 8]$ by $[-20, 100]$
   (d) $[-10, 3]$ by $[-100, 20]$

7. $y = 100 - x^2$
   (a) $[-4, 4]$ by $[-4, 4]$
   (b) $[-10, 10]$ by $[-10, 10]$
   (c) $[-15, 15]$ by $[-30, 110]$
   (d) $[-4, 4]$ by $[-30, 110]$

8. $y = 2x^2 - 1000$
   (a) $[-10, 10]$ by $[-10, 10]$
   (b) $[-10, 10]$ by $[-100, 100]$
   (c) $[-10, 10]$ by $[-1000, 1000]$
   (d) $[-25, 25]$ by $[-1200, 200]$

9. $y = 10 + 25x - x^3$
   (a) $[-4, 4]$ by $[-4, 4]$
   (b) $[-10, 10]$ by $[-10, 10]$
   (c) $[-20, 20]$ by $[-100, 100]$
   (d) $[-100, 100]$ by $[-200, 200]$

10. $y = \sqrt{8x - x^2}$
    (a) $[-4, 4]$ by $[-4, 4]$
    (b) $[-5, 5]$ by $[0, 100]$
    (c) $[-10, 10]$ by $[-10, 40]$
    (d) $[-2, 10]$ by $[-2, 6]$

11–22 ■ Determine an appropriate viewing rectangle for the equation, and use it to draw the graph.

11. $y = 100x^2$
12. $y = -100x^2$
13. $y = 4 + 6x - x^2$
14. $y = 0.3x^2 + 1.7x - 3$
15. $y = \sqrt[4]{256 - x^2}$
16. $y = \sqrt{12x - 17}$
17. $y = 0.01x^3 - x^2 + 5$
18. $y = x(x + 6)(x - 9)$
19. $y = x^4 - 4x^3$
20. $y = \dfrac{x}{x^2 + 25}$
21. $y = 1 + |x - 1|$
22. $y = 2x - |x^2 - 5|$

23–26 ■ Do the graphs intersect in the given viewing rectangle? If
they do, how many points of intersection are there?

23. $y = -3x^2 + 6x - \frac{1}{2}$, $y = \sqrt{7 - \frac{7}{12}x^2}$; $[-4, 4]$ by $[-1, 3]$
24. $y = \sqrt{49 - x^2}$, $y = \frac{1}{5}(41 - 3x)$; $[-8, 8]$ by $[-1, 8]$
25. $y = 6 - 4x - x^2$, $y = 3x + 18$; $[-6, 2]$ by $[-5, 20]$
26. $y = x^3 - 4x$, $y = x + 5$; $[-4, 4]$ by $[-15, 15]$

27. Graph the circle $x^2 + y^2 = 9$ by solving for y and graphing
    two equations as in Example 3.

28. Graph the circle $(y - 1)^2 + x^2 = 1$ by solving for y and
    graphing two equations as in Example 3.

29. Graph the equation $4x^2 + 2y^2 = 1$ by solving for y and
    graphing two equations corresponding to the negative and
    positive square roots. (This graph is called an *ellipse*.)

30. Graph the equation $y^2 - 9x^2 = 1$ by solving for y and graphing the two equations corresponding to the positive and negative square roots. (This graph is called a *hyperbola*.)

31–42 ■ Solve the equation both algebraically and graphically.

31. $x - 4 = 5x + 12$

32. $\frac{1}{2}x - 3 = 6 + 2x$

33. $\frac{2}{x} + \frac{1}{2x} = 7$

34. $\frac{4}{x+2} - \frac{6}{2x} = \frac{5}{2x+4}$

35. $x^2 - 32 = 0$

36. $x^3 + 16 = 0$

37. $x^2 + 9 = 0$

38. $x^2 + 3 = 2x$

39. $16x^4 = 625$

40. $2x^5 - 243 = 0$

41. $(x - 5)^4 - 80 = 0$

42. $6(x + 2)^5 = 64$

43–50 ■ Solve the equation graphically in the given interval. State each answer rounded to two decimals.

43. $x^2 - 7x + 12 = 0$; $[0, 6]$

44. $x^2 - 0.75x + 0.125 = 0$; $[-2, 2]$

45. $x^3 - 6x^2 + 11x - 6 = 0$; $[-1, 4]$

46. $16x^3 + 16x^2 = x + 1$; $[-2, 2]$

47. $x - \sqrt{x + 1} = 0$; $[-1, 5]$

48. $1 + \sqrt{x} = \sqrt{1 + x^2}$; $[-1, 5]$

49. $x^{1/3} - x = 0$; $[-3, 3]$

50. $x^{1/2} + x^{1/3} - x = 0$; $[-1, 5]$

51–54 ■ Use the graphical method to solve the equation in the indicated exercise from Section 1.5.

51. Exercise 91

52. Exercise 92

53. Exercise 97

54. Exercise 98

55–58 ■ Find all real solutions of the equation, rounded to two decimals.

55. $x^3 - 2x^2 - x - 1 = 0$

56. $x^4 - 8x^2 + 2 = 0$

57. $x(x - 1)(x + 2) = \frac{1}{6}x$

58. $x^4 = 16 - x^3$

59–66 ■ Find the solutions of the inequality by drawing appropriate graphs. State each answer rounded to two decimals.

59. $x^2 \le 3x + 10$

60. $0.5x^2 + 0.875x \le 0.25$

61. $x^3 + 11x \le 6x^2 + 6$

62. $16x^3 + 24x^2 > -9x - 1$

63. $x^{1/3} < x$

64. $\sqrt{0.5x^2 + 1} \le 2|x|$

65. $(x + 1)^2 < (x - 1)^2$

66. $(x + 1)^2 \le x^3$

67–70 ■ Use the graphical method to solve the inequality in the indicated exercise from Section 1.7.

67. Exercise 43

68. Exercise 44

69. Exercise 53

70. Exercise 54

71. In Example 6 we found two solutions of the equation $x^3 - 6x^2 + 9x = \sqrt{x}$, the solutions that lie between 1 and 6. Find two more solutions, correct to two decimals.

APPLICATIONS

72. Estimating Profit   An appliance manufacturer estimates that the profit y (in dollars) generated by producing x cooktops per month is given by the equation

$$y = 10x + 0.5x^2 - 0.001x^3 - 5000$$

where $0 \le x \le 450$.
   (a) Graph the equation.
   (b) How many cooktops must be produced to begin generating a profit?
   (c) For what range of values of x is the company's profit greater than \$15,000?

73. How Far Can You See?   If you stand on a ship in a calm sea, then your height x (in ft) above sea level is related to the farthest distance y (in mi) that you can see by the equation

$$y = \sqrt{1.5x + \left(\frac{x}{5280}\right)^2}$$

   (a) Graph the equation for $0 \le x \le 100$.
   (b) How high up do you have to be to be able to see 10 mi?

DISCOVERY ▪ DISCUSSION ▪ WRITING

74. Misleading Graphs   Write a short essay describing different ways in which a graphing calculator might give a misleading graph of an equation.

75. Algebraic and Graphical Solution Methods   Write a short essay comparing the algebraic and graphical methods for solving equations. Make up your own examples to illustrate the advantages and disadvantages of each method.

76. Equation Notation on Graphing Calculators   When you enter the following equations into your calculator, how does what you see on the screen differ from the usual way of writing the equations? (Check your user's manual if you're not sure.)
   (a) $y = |x|$
   (b) $y = \sqrt[5]{x}$
   (c) $y = \dfrac{x}{x - 1}$
   (d) $y = x^3 + \sqrt[3]{x + 2}$

77. Enter Equations Carefully   A student wishes to graph the equations

$$y = x^{1/3} \quad \text{and} \quad y = \frac{x}{x + 4}$$

on the same screen, so he enters the following information into his calculator:

$$Y_1 = X \wedge 1/3 \qquad Y_2 = X/X + 4$$

The calculator graphs two lines instead of the equations he wanted. What went wrong?

1.10 LINES

The Slope of a Line ▶ Point-Slope Form of the Equation of a Line ▶ Slope-Intercept Form of the Equation of a Line ▶ Vertical and Horizontal Lines ▶ General Equation of a Line ▶ Parallel and Perpendicular Lines ▶ Modeling with Linear Equations: Slope as Rate of Change

In this section we find equations for straight lines lying in a coordinate plane. The equations will depend on how the line is inclined, so we begin by discussing the concept of slope.

▼ The Slope of a Line

We first need a way to measure the "steepness" of a line, or how quickly it rises (or falls) as we move from left to right. We define *run* to be the distance we move to the right and *rise* to be the corresponding distance that the line rises (or falls). The *slope* of a line is the ratio of rise to run:

$$\text{slope} = \frac{\text{rise}}{\text{run}}$$

Figure 1 shows situations in which slope is important. Carpenters use the term *pitch* for the slope of a roof or a staircase; the term *grade* is used for the slope of a road.

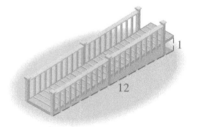

Slope of a ramp
Slope $= \frac{1}{12}$

Pitch of a roof
Slope $= \frac{1}{3}$

Grade of a road
Slope $= \frac{8}{100}$

FIGURE 1

If a line lies in a coordinate plane, then the **run** is the change in the *x*-coordinate and the **rise** is the corresponding change in the *y*-coordinate between any two points on the line (see Figure 2). This gives us the following definition of slope.

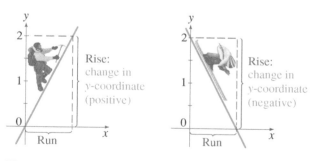

FIGURE 2

SLOPE OF A LINE

The **slope** m of a nonvertical line that passes through the points $A(x_1, y_1)$ and $B(x_2, y_2)$ is

$$m = \frac{\text{rise}}{\text{run}} = \frac{y_2 - y_1}{x_2 - x_1}$$

The slope of a vertical line is not defined.

The slope is independent of which two points are chosen on the line. We can see that this is true from the similar triangles in Figure 3:

$$\frac{y_2 - y_1}{x_2 - x_1} = \frac{y_2' - y_1'}{x_2' - x_1'}$$

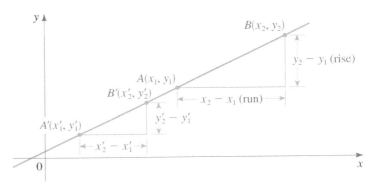

FIGURE 3

Figure 4 shows several lines labeled with their slopes. Notice that lines with positive slope slant upward to the right, whereas lines with negative slope slant downward to the right. The steepest lines are those for which the absolute value of the slope is the largest; a horizontal line has slope zero.

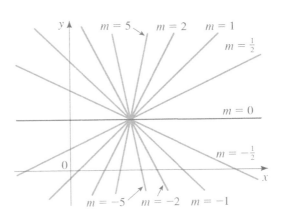

FIGURE 4 Lines with various slopes

EXAMPLE 1 | Finding the Slope of a Line Through Two Points

Find the slope of the line that passes through the points $P(2, 1)$ and $Q(8, 5)$.

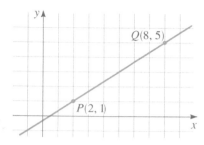

FIGURE 5

SOLUTION Since any two different points determine a line, only one line passes through these two points. From the definition the slope is

$$m = \frac{y_2 - y_1}{x_2 - x_1} = \frac{5 - 1}{8 - 2} = \frac{4}{6} = \frac{2}{3}$$

This says that for every 3 units we move to the right, the line rises 2 units. The line is drawn in Figure 5.

◆ NOW TRY EXERCISE 5

▼ Point-Slope Form of the Equation of a Line

Now let's find the equation of the line that passes through a given point $P(x_1, y_1)$ and has slope m. A point $P(x, y)$ with $x \neq x_1$ lies on this line if and only if the slope of the line through P_1 and P is equal to m (see Figure 6), that is,

$$\frac{y - y_1}{x - x_1} = m$$

This equation can be rewritten in the form $y - y_1 = m(x - x_1)$; note that the equation is also satisfied when $x = x_1$ and $y = y_1$. Therefore, it is an equation of the given line.

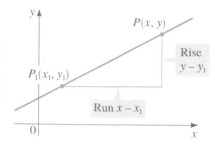

FIGURE 6

POINT-SLOPE FORM OF THE EQUATION OF A LINE

An equation of the line that passes through the point (x_1, y_1) and has slope m is

$$y - y_1 = m(x - x_1)$$

EXAMPLE 2 | Finding the Equation of a Line with Given Point and Slope

(a) Find an equation of the line through $(1, -3)$ with slope $-\frac{1}{2}$.

(b) Sketch the line.

SOLUTION

(a) Using the point-slope form with $m = -\frac{1}{2}$, $x_1 = 1$, and $y_1 = -3$, we obtain an equation of the line as

$$y + 3 = -\tfrac{1}{2}(x - 1) \qquad \text{Slope } m = -\tfrac{1}{2}, \text{ point } (1, -3)$$
$$2y + 6 = -x + 1 \qquad \text{Multiply by 2}$$
$$x + 2y + 5 = 0 \qquad \text{Rearrange}$$

(b) The fact that the slope is $-\frac{1}{2}$ tells us that when we move to the right 2 units, the line drops 1 unit. This enables us to sketch the line in Figure 7.

◆ NOW TRY EXERCISE 19

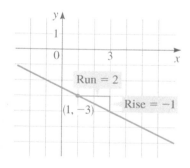

FIGURE 7

EXAMPLE 3 | Finding the Equation of a Line Through Two Given Points

Find an equation of the line through the points $(-1, 2)$ and $(3, -4)$.

SOLUTION The slope of the line is

$$m = \frac{-4 - 2}{3 - (-1)} = -\frac{6}{4} = -\frac{3}{2}$$

We can use *either* point, $(-1, 2)$ *or* $(3, -4)$, in the point-slope equation. We will end up with the same final answer.

Using the point-slope form with $x_1 = -1$ and $y_1 = 2$, we obtain

$$y - 2 = -\tfrac{3}{2}(x + 1) \qquad \text{Slope } m = -\tfrac{3}{2}, \text{ point } (-1, 2)$$

$$2y - 4 = -3x - 3 \qquad \text{Multiply by 2}$$

$$3x + 2y - 1 = 0 \qquad \text{Rearrange}$$

◆ NOW TRY EXERCISE **23**

▼ Slope-Intercept Form of the Equation of a Line

Suppose a nonvertical line has slope m and y-intercept b (see Figure 8). This means that the line intersects the y-axis at the point $(0, b)$, so the point-slope form of the equation of the line, with $x = 0$ and $y = b$, becomes

$$y - b = m(x - 0)$$

This simplifies to $y = mx + b$, which is called the **slope-intercept form** of the equation of a line.

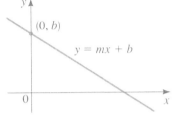

FIGURE 8

SLOPE-INTERCEPT FORM OF THE EQUATION OF A LINE

An equation of the line that has slope m and y-intercept b is

$$y = mx + b$$

EXAMPLE 4 | Lines in Slope-Intercept Form

(a) Find the equation of the line with slope 3 and y-intercept -2.

(b) Find the slope and y-intercept of the line $3y - 2x = 1$.

SOLUTION

(a) Since $m = 3$ and $b = -2$, from the slope-intercept form of the equation of a line we get

$$y = 3x - 2$$

(b) We first write the equation in the form $y = mx + b$:

$$3y - 2x = 1$$

$$3y = 2x + 1 \qquad \text{Add } 2x$$

$$y = \tfrac{2}{3}x + \tfrac{1}{3} \qquad \text{Divide by 3}$$

From the slope-intercept form of the equation of a line, we see that the slope is $m = \tfrac{2}{3}$ and the y-intercept is $b = \tfrac{1}{3}$.

◆ NOW TRY EXERCISES **25** AND **47**

Slope y-intercept

$y = \tfrac{2}{3}x + \tfrac{1}{3}$

▼ Vertical and Horizontal Lines

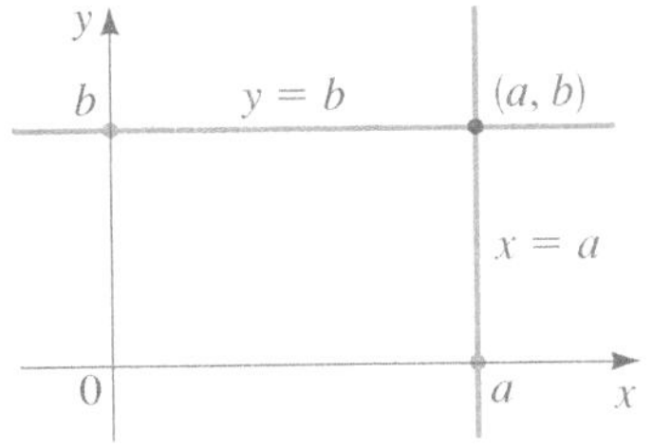

If a line is horizontal, its slope is $m = 0$, so its equation is $y = b$, where b is the y-intercept (see Figure 9). A vertical line does not have a slope, but we can write its equation as $x = a$, where a is the x-intercept, because the x-coordinate of every point on the line is a.

FIGURE 9

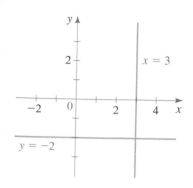

FIGURE 10

EXAMPLE 5 | Vertical and Horizontal Lines

(a) An equation for the vertical line through $(3, 5)$ is $x = 3$.

(b) The graph of the equation $x = 3$ is a vertical line with x-intercept 3.

(c) An equation for the horizontal line through $(8, -2)$ is $y = -2$.

(d) The graph of the equation $y = -2$ is a horizontal line with y-intercept -2.

The lines are graphed in Figure 10.

✎. NOW TRY EXERCISES **29** AND **33**

▼ General Equation of a Line

A **linear equation** is an equation of the form

$$Ax + By + C = 0$$

where A, B, and C are constants and A and B are not both 0. The equation of a line is a linear equation:

- A nonvertical line has the equation $y = mx + b$ or $-mx + y - b = 0$, which is a linear equation with $A = -m$, $B = 1$, and $C = -b$.
- A vertical line has the equation $x = a$ or $x - a = 0$, which is a linear equation with $A = 1$, $B = 0$, and $C = -a$.

Conversely, the graph of a linear equation is a line.

- If $B \neq 0$, the equation becomes

$$y = -\frac{A}{B}x - \frac{C}{B} \qquad \text{Divide by } B$$

and this is the slope-intercept form of the equation of a line (with $m = -A/B$ and $b = -C/B$).

- If $B = 0$, the equation becomes

$$Ax + C = 0 \qquad \text{Set } B = 0$$

or $x = -C/A$, which represents a vertical line.

We have proved the following.

EXAMPLE 6 | Graphing a Linear Equation

Sketch the graph of the equation $2x - 3y - 12 = 0$.

SOLUTION 1 Since the equation is linear, its graph is a line. To draw the graph, it is enough to find any two points on the line. The intercepts are the easiest points to find.

x-intercept: Substitute $y = 0$, to get $2x - 12 = 0$, so $x = 6$

y-intercept: Substitute $x = 0$, to get $-3y - 12 = 0$, so $y = -4$

With these points we can sketch the graph in Figure 11.

SOLUTION 2 We write the equation in slope-intercept form:

$$2x - 3y - 12 = 0$$
$$2x - 3y = 12 \qquad \text{Add 12}$$
$$-3y = -2x + 12 \qquad \text{Subtract } 2x$$
$$y = \tfrac{2}{3}x - 4 \qquad \text{Divide by } -3$$

This equation is in the form $y = mx + b$, so the slope is $m = \frac{2}{3}$ and the y-intercept is $b = -4$. To sketch the graph, we plot the y-intercept and then move 3 units to the right and 2 units up as shown in Figure 12.

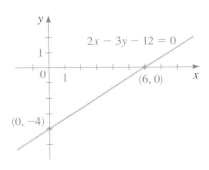

FIGURE 11   **FIGURE 12**

◆ . NOW TRY EXERCISE **53**

▼ Parallel and Perpendicular Lines

Since slope measures the steepness of a line, it seems reasonable that parallel lines should have the same slope. In fact, we can prove this.

> **PARALLEL LINES**
>
> Two nonvertical lines are parallel if and only if they have the same slope.

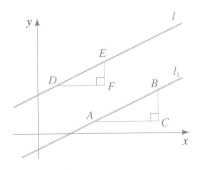

FIGURE 13

PROOF Let the lines l_1 and l_2 in Figure 13 have slopes m_1 and m_2. If the lines are parallel, then the right triangles ABC and DEF are similar, so

$$m_1 = \frac{d(B, C)}{d(A, C)} = \frac{d(E, F)}{d(D, F)} = m_2$$

Conversely, if the slopes are equal, then the triangles will be similar, so $\angle BAC = \angle EDF$ and the lines are parallel.

EXAMPLE 7 | Finding the Equation of a Line Parallel to a Given Line

Find an equation of the line through the point $(5, 2)$ that is parallel to the line $4x + 6y + 5 = 0$.

SOLUTION   First we write the equation of the given line in slope-intercept form.

$$4x + 6y + 5 = 0$$

$$6y = -4x - 5 \qquad \text{Subtract } 4x + 5$$

$$y = -\tfrac{2}{3}x - \tfrac{5}{6} \qquad \text{Divide by 6}$$

So the line has slope $m = -\tfrac{2}{3}$. Since the required line is parallel to the given line, it also has slope $m = -\tfrac{2}{3}$. From the point-slope form of the equation of a line, we get

$$y - 2 = -\tfrac{2}{3}(x - 5) \qquad \text{Slope } m = -\tfrac{2}{3}, \text{ point } (5, 2)$$

$$3y - 6 = -2x + 10 \qquad \text{Multiply by 3}$$

$$2x + 3y - 16 = 0 \qquad \text{Rearrange}$$

Thus, the equation of the required line is $2x + 3y - 16 = 0$.

NOW TRY EXERCISE 31

The condition for perpendicular lines is not as obvious as that for parallel lines.

PERPENDICULAR LINES

Two lines with slopes m_1 and m_2 are perpendicular if and only if $m_1 m_2 = -1$, that is, their slopes are negative reciprocals:

$$m_2 = -\frac{1}{m_1}$$

Also, a horizontal line (slope 0) is perpendicular to a vertical line (no slope).

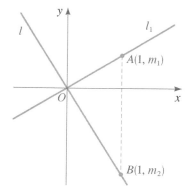

FIGURE 14

PROOF   In Figure 14 we show two lines intersecting at the origin. (If the lines intersect at some other point, we consider lines parallel to these that intersect at the origin. These lines have the same slopes as the original lines.)

If the lines l_1 and l_2 have slopes m_1 and m_2, then their equations are $y = m_1 x$ and $y = m_2 x$. Notice that $A(1, m_1)$ lies on l_1 and $B(1, m_2)$ lies on l_2. By the Pythagorean Theorem and its converse (see page 219), $OA \perp OB$ if and only if

$$[d(O, A)]^2 + [d(O, B)]^2 = [d(A, B)]^2$$

By the Distance Formula this becomes

$$(1^2 + m_1^2) + (1^2 + m_2^2) = (1 - 1)^2 + (m_2 - m_1)^2$$

$$2 + m_1^2 + m_2^2 = m_2^2 - 2m_1 m_2 + m_1^2$$

$$2 = -2m_1 m_2$$

$$m_1 m_2 = -1$$

EXAMPLE 8 | Perpendicular Lines

Show that the points $P(3, 3)$, $Q(8, 17)$, and $R(11, 5)$ are the vertices of a right triangle.

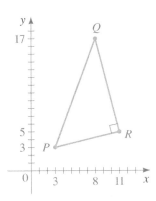

FIGURE 15

SOLUTION The slopes of the lines containing *PR* and *QR* are, respectively,

$$m_1 = \frac{5-3}{11-3} = \frac{1}{4} \quad \text{and} \quad m_2 = \frac{5-17}{11-8} = -4$$

Since $m_1m_2 = -1$, these lines are perpendicular, so *PQR* is a right triangle. It is sketched in Figure 15.

✎. NOW TRY EXERCISE **57**

EXAMPLE 9 | Finding an Equation of a Line Perpendicular to a Given Line

Find an equation of the line that is perpendicular to the line $4x + 6y + 5 = 0$ and passes through the origin.

SOLUTION In Example 7 we found that the slope of the line $4x + 6y + 5 = 0$ is $-\frac{2}{3}$. Thus, the slope of a perpendicular line is the negative reciprocal, that is, $\frac{3}{2}$. Since the required line passes through $(0, 0)$, the point-slope form gives

$$y - 0 = \tfrac{3}{2}(x - 0) \qquad \text{Slope } m = \tfrac{3}{2}, \text{ point } (0,0)$$
$$y = \tfrac{3}{2}x \qquad \text{Simplify}$$

✎. NOW TRY EXERCISE **35**

EXAMPLE 10 | Graphing a Family of Lines

Use a graphing calculator to graph the family of lines

$$y = 0.5x + b$$

for $b = -2, -1, 0, 1, 2$. What property do the lines share?

SOLUTION The lines are graphed in Figure 16 in the viewing rectangle $[-6, 6]$ by $[-6, 6]$. The lines all have the same slope, so they are parallel.

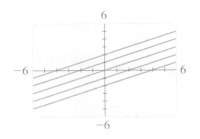

FIGURE 16 $y = 0.5x + b$

✎. NOW TRY EXERCISE **41**

▼ Modeling with Linear Equations: Slope as Rate of Change

When a line is used to model the relationship between two quantities, the slope of the line is the **rate of change** of one quantity with respect to the other. For example, the graph in Figure 17(a) on the next page gives the amount of gas in a tank that is being filled. The slope between the indicated points is

$$m = \frac{6 \text{ gallons}}{3 \text{ minutes}} = 2 \text{ gal/min}$$

The slope is the *rate* at which the tank is being filled, 2 gallons per minute. In Figure 17(b) the tank is being drained at the *rate* of 0.03 gallon per minute, and the slope is −0.03.

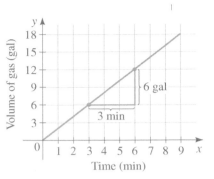

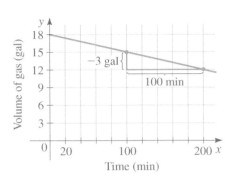

(a) Tank filled at 2 gal/min
Slope of line is 2

(b) Tank drained at 0.03 gal/min
Slope of line is −0.03

FIGURE 17

The next two examples give other situations in which the slope of a line is a rate of change.

EXAMPLE 11 | Slope as Rate of Change

A dam is built on a river to create a reservoir. The water level w in the reservoir is given by the equation

$$w = 4.5t + 28$$

where t is the number of years since the dam was constructed and w is measured in feet.

(a) Sketch a graph of this equation.

(b) What do the slope and w-intercept of this graph represent?

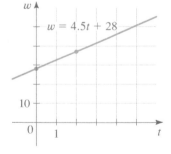

FIGURE 18

SOLUTION

(a) This equation is linear, so its graph is a line. Since two points determine a line, we plot two points that lie on the graph and draw a line through them.

> When $t = 0$, then $w = 4.5(0) + 28 = 28$, so $(0, 28)$ is on the line.
>
> When $t = 2$, then $w = 4.5(2) + 28 = 37$, so $(2, 37)$ is on the line.

The line that is determined by these points is shown in Figure 18.

(b) The slope is $m = 4.5$; it represents the rate of change of water level with respect to time. This means that the water level *increases* 4.5 ft per year. The w-intercept is 28 and occurs when $t = 0$, so it represents the water level when the dam was constructed.

✎. NOW TRY EXERCISE **69**

EXAMPLE 12 | Linear Relationship Between Temperature and Elevation

(a) As dry air moves upward, it expands and cools. If the ground temperature is 20°C and the temperature at a height of 1 km is 10°C, express the temperature T (in °C) in terms of the height h (in km). (Assume that the relationship between T and h is linear.)

(b) Draw the graph of the linear equation. What does its slope represent?

(c) What is the temperature at a height of 2.5 km?

SOLUTION

(a) Because we are assuming a linear relationship between T and h, the equation must be of the form

$$T = mh + b$$

where m and b are constants. When $h = 0$, we are given that $T = 20$, so

$$20 = m(0) + b$$

$$b = 20$$

Thus, we have

$$T = mh + 20$$

When $h = 1$, we have $T = 10$, so

$$10 = m(1) + 20$$

$$m = 10 - 20 = -10$$

The required expression is

$$T = -10h + 20$$

(b) The graph is sketched in Figure 19. The slope is $m = -10°C/km$, and this represents the rate of change of temperature with respect to distance above the ground. So the temperature *decreases* 10°C per kilometer of height.

(c) At a height of $h = 2.5$ km the temperature is

$$T = -10(2.5) + 20 = -25 + 20 = -5°C$$

NOW TRY EXERCISE **73**

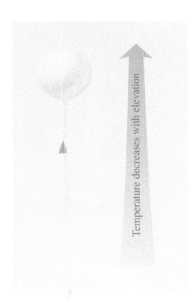

Temperature decreases with elevation

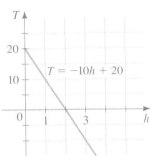

$T = -10h + 20$

FIGURE 19

1.10 EXERCISES

CONCEPTS

1. We find the "steepness," or slope, of a line passing through two points by dividing the difference in the _____-coordinates of these points by the difference in the _____-coordinates. So the line passing through the points $(0, 1)$ and $(2, 5)$ has slope _____.

2. A line has the equation $y = 3x + 2$.

　(a) This line has slope _____.

　(b) Any line parallel to this line has slope _____.

　(c) Any line perpendicular to this line has slope _____.

3. The point-slope form of the equation of the line with slope 3 passing through the point $(1, 2)$ is _____.

4. (a) The slope of a horizontal line is _____. The equation of the horizontal line passing through $(2, 3)$ is _____.

　(b) The slope of a vertical line is _____. The equation of the vertical line passing through $(2, 3)$ is _____.

SKILLS

5–12 ■ Find the slope of the line through P and Q.

5. $P(0, 0), Q(4, 2)$ 　　　 **6.** $P(0, 0), Q(2, -6)$

7. $P(2, 2), Q(-10, 0)$ 　 **8.** $P(1, 2), Q(3, 3)$

9. $P(2, 4), Q(4, 3)$ 　　 **10.** $P(2, -5), Q(-4, 3)$

11. $P(1, -3), Q(-1, 6)$ 　 **12.** $P(-1, -4), Q(6, 0)$

13. Find the slopes of the lines l_1, l_2, l_3, and l_4 in the figure below.

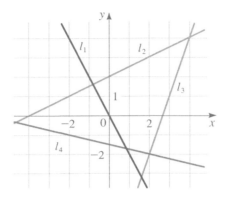

14. (a) Sketch lines through $(0, 0)$ with slopes $1, 0, \frac{1}{2}, 2$, and -1.

(b) Sketch lines through $(0, 0)$ with slopes $\frac{1}{3}, \frac{1}{2}, -\frac{1}{3}$, and 3.

15–18 ■ Find an equation for the line whose graph is sketched.

15.

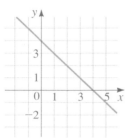

16.

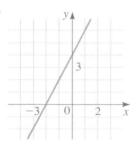

17.

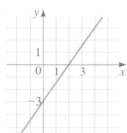

18.

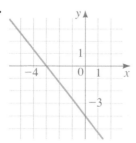

19–38 ■ Find an equation of the line that satisfies the given conditions.

19. Through $(2, 3)$; slope 5

20. Through $(-2, 4)$; slope -1

21. Through $(1, 7)$; slope $\frac{2}{3}$

22. Through $(-3, -5)$; slope $-\frac{7}{2}$

23. Through $(2, 1)$ and $(1, 6)$

24. Through $(-1, -2)$ and $(4, 3)$

25. Slope 3; y-intercept -2

26. Slope $\frac{2}{5}$; y-intercept 4

27. x-intercept 1; y-intercept -3

28. x-intercept -8; y-intercept 6

29. Through $(4, 5)$; parallel to the x-axis

30. Through $(4, 5)$; parallel to the y-axis

31. Through $(1, -6)$; parallel to the line $x + 2y = 6$

32. y-intercept 6; parallel to the line $2x + 3y + 4 = 0$

33. Through $(-1, 2)$; parallel to the line $x = 5$

34. Through $(2, 6)$; perpendicular to the line $y = 1$

35. Through $(-1, -2)$; perpendicular to the line $2x + 5y + 8 = 0$

36. Through $\left(\frac{1}{2}, -\frac{2}{3}\right)$; perpendicular to the line $4x - 8y = 1$

37. Through $(1, 7)$; parallel to the line passing through $(2, 5)$ and $(-2, 1)$

38. Through $(-2, -11)$; perpendicular to the line passing through $(1, 1)$ and $(5, -1)$

39. (a) Sketch the line with slope $\frac{3}{2}$ that passes through the point $(-2, 1)$.

(b) Find an equation for this line.

40. (a) Sketch the line with slope -2 that passes through the point $(4, -1)$.

(b) Find an equation for this line.

41–44 ■ Use a graphing device to graph the given family of lines in the same viewing rectangle. What do the lines have in common?

41. $y = -2x + b$ for $b = 0, \pm 1, \pm 3, \pm 6$

42. $y = mx - 3$ for $m = 0, \pm 0.25, \pm 0.75, \pm 1.5$

43. $y = m(x - 3)$ for $m = 0, \pm 0.25, \pm 0.75, \pm 1.5$

44. $y = 2 + m(x + 3)$ for $m = 0, \pm 0.5, \pm 1, \pm 2, \pm 6$

45–56 ■ Find the slope and y-intercept of the line and draw its graph.

45. $x + y = 3$ **46.** $3x - 2y = 12$

47. $x + 3y = 0$ **48.** $2x - 5y = 0$

49. $\frac{1}{2}x - \frac{1}{3}y + 1 = 0$ **50.** $-3x - 5y + 30 = 0$

51. $y = 4$ **52.** $x = -5$

53. $3x - 4y = 12$ **54.** $4y + 8 = 0$

55. $3x + 4y - 1 = 0$ **56.** $4x + 5y = 10$

57. Use slopes to show that $A(1, 1)$, $B(7, 4)$, $C(5, 10)$, and $D(-1, 7)$ are vertices of a parallelogram.

58. Use slopes to show that $A(-3, -1)$, $B(3, 3)$, and $C(-9, 8)$ are vertices of a right triangle.

59. Use slopes to show that $A(1, 1)$, $B(11, 3)$, $C(10, 8)$, and $D(0, 6)$ are vertices of a rectangle.

60. Use slopes to determine whether the given points are collinear (lie on a line).

(a) $(1, 1), (3, 9), (6, 21)$

(b) $(-1, 3), (1, 7), (4, 15)$

61. Find an equation of the perpendicular bisector of the line segment joining the points $A(1, 4)$ and $B(7, -2)$.

62. Find the area of the triangle formed by the coordinate axes and the line

$$2y + 3x - 6 = 0$$

63. (a) Show that if the x- and y-intercepts of a line are nonzero numbers a and b, then the equation of the line can be written in the form

$$\frac{x}{a} + \frac{y}{b} = 1$$

This is called the **two-intercept form** of the equation of a line.

(b) Use part (a) to find an equation of the line whose x-intercept is 6 and whose y-intercept is -8.

64. (a) Find an equation for the line tangent to the circle $x^2 + y^2 = 25$ at the point $(3, -4)$. (See the figure.)

(b) At what other point on the circle will a tangent line be parallel to the tangent line in part (a)?

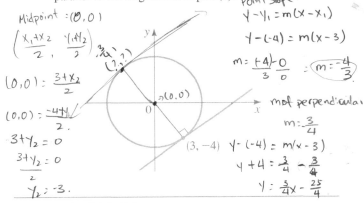

APPLICATIONS

65. Grade of a Road   West of Albuquerque, New Mexico, Route 40 eastbound is straight and makes a steep descent toward the city. The highway has a 6% grade, which means that its slope is $-\frac{6}{100}$. Driving on this road, you notice from elevation signs that you have descended a distance of 1000 ft. What is the change in your horizontal distance?

6% grade

1000 ft

66. Global Warming   Some scientists believe that the average surface temperature of the world has been rising steadily. The average surface temperature can be modeled by

$$T = 0.02t + 15.0$$

where T is temperature in °C and t is years since 1950.

(a) What do the slope and T-intercept represent?

(b) Use the equation to predict the average global surface temperature in 2050.

67. Drug Dosages   If the recommended adult dosage for a drug is D (in mg), then to determine the appropriate dosage c for a child of age a, pharmacists use the equation

$$c = 0.0417D(a + 1)$$

Suppose the dosage for an adult is 200 mg.

(a) Find the slope. What does it represent?

(b) What is the dosage for a newborn?

68. Flea Market   The manager of a weekend flea market knows from past experience that if she charges x dollars for a rental space at the flea market, then the number y of spaces she can rent is given by the equation $y = 200 - 4x$.

(a) Sketch a graph of this linear equation. (Remember that the rental charge per space and the number of spaces rented must both be nonnegative quantities.)

(b) What do the slope, the y-intercept, and the x-intercept of the graph represent?

69. Production Cost   A small-appliance manufacturer finds that if he produces x toaster ovens in a month, his production cost is given by the equation

$$y = 6x + 3000$$

(where y is measured in dollars).

(a) Sketch a graph of this linear equation.

(b) What do the slope and y-intercept of the graph represent?

70. Temperature Scales   The relationship between the Fahrenheit (F) and Celsius (C) temperature scales is given by the equation $F = \frac{9}{5}C + 32$.

(a) Complete the table to compare the two scales at the given values.

(b) Find the temperature at which the scales agree. [*Hint:* Suppose that a is the temperature at which the scales agree. Set $F = a$ and $C = a$. Then solve for a.]

C	F
$-30°$	
$-20°$	
$-10°$	
$0°$	
	$50°$
	$68°$
	$86°$

71. Crickets and Temperature   Biologists have observed that the chirping rate of crickets of a certain species is related to temperature, and the relationship appears to be very nearly linear. A cricket produces 120 chirps per minute at 70°F and 168 chirps per minute at 80°F.

(a) Find the linear equation that relates the temperature t and the number of chirps per minute n.

(b) If the crickets are chirping at 150 chirps per minute, estimate the temperature.

72. Depreciation   A small business buys a computer for $4000. After 4 years the value of the computer is expected to be $200. For accounting purposes the business uses *linear depreciation* to assess the value of the computer at a given time.

This means that if V is the value of the computer at time t, then a linear equation is used to relate V and t.

(a) Find a linear equation that relates V and t.

(b) Sketch a graph of this linear equation.

(c) What do the slope and V-intercept of the graph represent?

(d) Find the depreciated value of the computer 3 years from the date of purchase.

73. Pressure and Depth   At the surface of the ocean the water pressure is the same as the air pressure above the water, 15 lb/in^2. Below the surface the water pressure increases by 4.34 lb/in^2 for every 10 ft of descent.

(a) Find an equation for the relationship between pressure and depth below the ocean surface.

(b) Sketch a graph of this linear equation.

(c) What do the slope and y-intercept of the graph represent?

(d) At what depth is the pressure 100 lb/in^2?

Water pressure increases with depth

74. Distance, Speed, and Time   Jason and Debbie leave Detroit at 2:00 P.M. and drive at a constant speed, traveling west on I-90. They pass Ann Arbor, 40 mi from Detroit, at 2:50 P.M.

(a) Express the distance traveled in terms of the time elapsed.

(b) Draw the graph of the equation in part (a).

(c) What is the slope of this line? What does it represent?

75. Cost of Driving   The monthly cost of driving a car depends on the number of miles driven. Lynn found that in May her driving cost was $380 for 480 mi and in June her cost was $460 for 800 mi. Assume that there is a linear relationship between the monthly cost C of driving a car and the distance driven d.

(a) Find a linear equation that relates C and d.

(b) Use part (a) to predict the cost of driving 1500 mi per month.

(c) Draw the graph of the linear equation. What does the slope of the line represent?

(d) What does the y-intercept of the graph represent?

(e) Why is a linear relationship a suitable model for this situation?

76. Manufacturing Cost   The manager of a furniture factory finds that it costs $2200 to manufacture 100 chairs in one day and $4800 to produce 300 chairs in one day.

(a) Assuming that the relationship between cost and the number of chairs produced is linear, find an equation that expresses this relationship. Then graph the equation.

(b) What is the slope of the line in part (a), and what does it represent?

(c) What is the y-intercept of this line, and what does it represent?

DISCOVERY ▪ DISCUSSION ▪ WRITING

77. What Does the Slope Mean?   Suppose that the graph of the outdoor temperature over a certain period of time is a line. How is the weather changing if the slope of the line is positive? If it is negative? If it is zero?

78. Collinear Points   Suppose that you are given the coordinates of three points in the plane and you want to see whether they lie on the same line. How can you do this using slopes? Using the Distance Formula? Can you think of another method?

1.11 MAKING MODELS USING VARIATION

| Direct Variation ▶ Inverse Variation ▶ Joint Variation

When scientists talk about a mathematical model for a real-world phenomenon, they often mean an equation that describes the relationship between two quantities. For instance, the model might describe how the population of an animal species varies with time or how the pressure of a gas varies as its temperature changes. In this section we study a kind of modeling called *variation*.

▼ Direct Variation

Two types of mathematical models occur so often that they are given special names. The first is called *direct variation* and occurs when one quantity is a constant multiple of the other, so we use an equation of the form $y = kx$ to model this dependence.

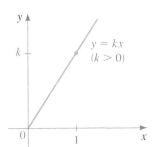

FIGURE 1

DIRECT VARIATION

If the quantities x and y are related by an equation

$$y = kx$$

for some constant $k \neq 0$, we say that y **varies directly as** x, or y is **directly proportional to** x, or simply y **is proportional to** x. The constant k is called the **constant of proportionality**.

Recall that the graph of an equation of the form $y = mx + b$ is a line with slope m and y-intercept b. So the graph of an equation $y = kx$ that describes direct variation is a line with slope k and y-intercept 0 (see Figure 1).

EXAMPLE 1 | Direct Variation

During a thunderstorm you see the lightning before you hear the thunder because light travels much faster than sound. The distance between you and the storm varies directly as the time interval between the lightning and the thunder.

(a) Suppose that the thunder from a storm 5400 ft away takes 5 s to reach you. Determine the constant of proportionality, and write the equation for the variation.

(b) Sketch the graph of this equation. What does the constant of proportionality represent?

(c) If the time interval between the lightning and thunder is now 8 s, how far away is the storm?

SOLUTION

(a) Let d be the distance from you to the storm, and let t be the length of the time interval. We are given that d varies directly as t, so

$$d = kt$$

where k is a constant. To find k, we use the fact that $t = 5$ when $d = 5400$. Substituting these values in the equation, we get

$$5400 = k(5) \qquad \text{Substitute}$$

$$k = \frac{5400}{5} = 1080 \qquad \text{Solve for } k$$

Substituting this value of k in the equation for d, we obtain

$$d = 1080t$$

as the equation for d as a function of t.

FIGURE 2

(b) The graph of the equation $d = 1080t$ is a line through the origin with slope 1080 and is shown in Figure 2. The constant $k = 1080$ is the approximate speed of sound (in ft/s).

(c) When $t = 8$, we have

$$d = 1080 \cdot 8 = 8640$$

So the storm is 8640 ft $\approx$ 1.6 mi away.

✎. NOW TRY EXERCISES **17** AND **29**

▼ Inverse Variation

Another equation that is frequently used in mathematical modeling is $y = k/x$, where k is a constant.

INVERSE VARIATION

If the quantities x and y are related by the equation

$$y = \frac{k}{x}$$

for some constant $k \neq 0$, we say that y **is inversely proportional to** x or y **varies inversely as** x. The constant k is called the **constant of proportionality**.

$y = \dfrac{k}{x}$
$(k > 0)$

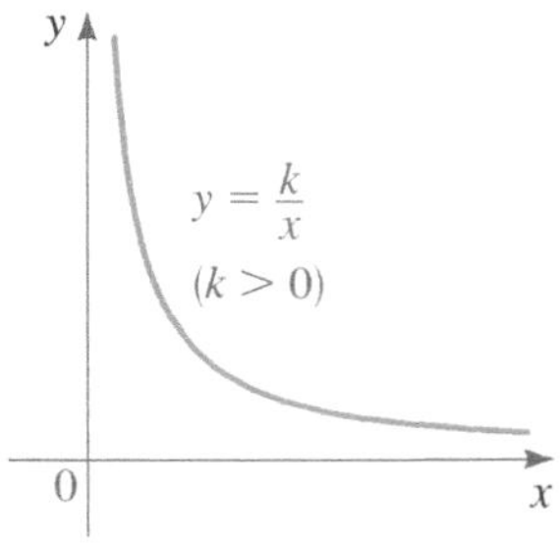

FIGURE 3 Inverse variation

The graph of $y = k/x$ for $x > 0$ is shown in Figure 3 for the case $k > 0$. It gives a picture of what happens when y is inversely proportional to x.

EXAMPLE 2 | Inverse Variation

Boyle's Law states that when a sample of gas is compressed at a constant temperature, the pressure of the gas is inversely proportional to the volume of the gas.

(a) Suppose the pressure of a sample of air that occupies 0.106 m³ at 25°C is 50 kPa. Find the constant of proportionality, and write the equation that expresses the inverse proportionality.

(b) If the sample expands to a volume of 0.3 m³, find the new pressure.

SOLUTION

(a) Let P be the pressure of the sample of gas, and let V be its volume. Then, by the definition of inverse proportionality, we have

$$P = \frac{k}{V}$$

where k is a constant. To find k, we use the fact that $P = 50$ when $V = 0.106$. Substituting these values in the equation, we get

$$50 = \frac{k}{0.106} \qquad \text{Substitute}$$

$$k = (50)(0.106) = 5.3 \qquad \text{Solve for } k$$

Putting this value of k in the equation for P, we have

$$P = \frac{5.3}{V}$$

(b) When $V = 0.3$, we have

$$P = \frac{5.3}{0.3} \approx 17.7$$

So the new pressure is about 17.7 kPa.

✎. NOW TRY EXERCISES **19** AND **35**

▼ Joint Variation

A physical quantity often depends on more than one other quantity. If one quantity is proportional to two or more other quantities, we call this relationship *joint variation*.

> **JOINT VARIATION**
>
> If the quantities x, y, and z are related by the equation
>
> $$z = kxy$$
>
> where k is a nonzero constant, we say that z **varies jointly as** x and y or z **is jointly proportional to** x and y.

In the sciences, relationships between three or more variables are common, and any combination of the different types of proportionality that we have discussed is possible. For example, if

$$z = k\frac{x}{y}$$

we say that z **is proportional to** x and **inversely proportional to** y.

EXAMPLE 3 | Newton's Law of Gravitation

Newton's Law of Gravitation says that two objects with masses m_1 and m_2 attract each other with a force F that is jointly proportional to their masses and inversely proportional to the square of the distance r between the objects. Express Newton's Law of Gravitation as an equation.

SOLUTION   Using the definitions of joint and inverse variation and the traditional notation G for the gravitational constant of proportionality, we have

$$F = G\frac{m_1 m_2}{r^2}$$

✎ . NOW TRY EXERCISES **21** AND **41**   ■

If m_1 and m_2 are fixed masses, then the gravitational force between them is $F = C/r^2$ (where $C = Gm_1 m_2$ is a constant). Figure 4 shows the graph of this equation for $r > 0$ with $C = 1$. Observe how the gravitational attraction decreases with increasing distance.

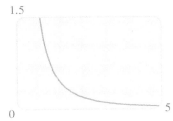

1.5

0   5

FIGURE 4 Graph of $F = \dfrac{1}{r^2}$

1.11 EXERCISES

CONCEPTS

1. If the quantities x and y are related by the equation $y = 3x$, then we say that y is _____ _____ to x and the constant of _____ is 3.

2. If the quantities x and y are related by the equation $y = \dfrac{3}{x}$, then we say that y is _____ _____ to x and the constant of _____ is 3.

3. If the quantities x, y, and z are related by the equation $z = 3\dfrac{x}{y}$, then we say that z is _____ _____ to x and _____ _____ to y.

4. If z is jointly proportional to x and y and if z is 10 when x is 4 and y is 5, then x, y, and z are related by the equation

$$z = \text{_____}.$$

SKILLS

5–16 ■ Write an equation that expresses the statement.

5. T varies directly as x.

6. P is directly proportional to w.

7. v is inversely proportional to z.

8. w is jointly proportional to m and n.

9. y is proportional to s and inversely proportional to t.

10. P varies inversely as T.

11. z is proportional to the square root of y.

12. A is proportional to the square of t and inversely proportional to the cube of x.

13. V is jointly proportional to l, w, and h.

14. S is jointly proportional to the squares of r and θ.

15. R is proportional to i and inversely proportional to P and t.

16. A is jointly proportional to the square roots of x and y.

17–28 ■ Express the statement as an equation. Use the given information to find the constant of proportionality.

17. y is directly proportional to x. If $x = 6$, then $y = 42$.

18. z varies inversely as t. If $t = 3$, then $z = 5$.

19. R is inversely proportional to s. If $s = 4$, then $R = 3$.

20. P is directly proportional to T. If $T = 300$, then $P = 20$.

21. M varies directly as x and inversely as y. If $x = 2$ and $y = 6$, then $M = 5$.

22. S varies jointly as p and q. If $p = 4$ and $q = 5$, then $S = 180$.

23. W is inversely proportional to the square of r. If $r = 6$, then $W = 10$.

24. t is jointly proportional to x and y, and inversely proportional to r. If $x = 2$, $y = 3$, and $r = 12$, then $t = 25$.

25. C is jointly proportional to l, w, and h. If $l = w = h = 2$, then $C = 128$.

26. H is jointly proportional to the squares of l and w. If $l = 2$ and $w = \frac{1}{3}$, then $H = 36$.

27. s is inversely proportional to the square root of t. If $s = 100$, then $t = 25$.

28. M is jointly proportional to a, b, and c and inversely proportional to d. If a and d have the same value and if b and c are both 2, then $M = 128$.

APPLICATIONS

29. Hooke's Law Hooke's Law states that the force needed to keep a spring stretched x units beyond its natural length is directly proportional to x. Here the constant of proportionality is called the **spring constant**.

(a) Write Hooke's Law as an equation.

(b) If a spring has a natural length of 10 cm and a force of 40 N is required to maintain the spring stretched to a length of 15 cm, find the spring constant.

(c) What force is needed to keep the spring stretched to a length of 14 cm?

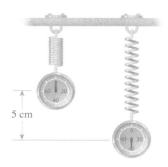

5 cm

30. Law of the Pendulum The period of a pendulum (the time elapsed during one complete swing of the pendulum) varies directly with the square root of the length of the pendulum.

(a) Express this relationship by writing an equation.

(b) To double the period, how would we have to change the length l?

31. Printing Costs The cost C of printing a magazine is jointly proportional to the number of pages p in the magazine and the number of magazines printed m.

(a) Write an equation that expresses this joint variation.

(b) Find the constant of proportionality if the printing cost is $60,000 for 4000 copies of a 120-page magazine.

(c) How much would the printing cost be for 5000 copies of a 92-page magazine?

32. Boyle's Law The pressure P of a sample of gas is directly proportional to the temperature T and inversely proportional to the volume V.

(a) Write an equation that expresses this variation.

(b) Find the constant of proportionality if 100 L of gas exerts a pressure of 33.2 kPa at a temperature of 400 K (absolute temperature measured on the Kelvin scale).

(c) If the temperature is increased to 500 K and the volume is decreased to 80 L, what is the pressure of the gas?

33. Power from a Windmill The power P that can be obtained from a windmill is directly proportional to the cube of the wind speed s.

(a) Write an equation that expresses this variation.

(b) Find the constant of proportionality for a windmill that produces 96 watts of power when the wind is blowing at 20 mi/h.

(c) How much power will this windmill produce if the wind speed increases to 30 mi/h?

34. Power Needed to Propel a Boat The power P (measured in horse power, hp) needed to propel a boat is directly proportional to the cube of the speed s. An 80-hp engine is needed to propel a certain boat at 10 knots. Find the power needed to drive the boat at 15 knots.

35. Loudness of Sound   The loudness L of a sound (measured in decibels, dB) is inversely proportional to the square of the distance d from the source of the sound. A person who is 10 ft from a lawn mower experiences a sound level of 70 dB. How loud is the lawn mower when the person is 100 ft away?

36. Stopping Distance   The stopping distance D of a car after the brakes have been applied varies directly as the square of the speed s. A certain car traveling at 50 mi/h can stop in 240 ft. What is the maximum speed it can be traveling if it needs to stop in 160 ft?

37. A Jet of Water   The power P of a jet of water is jointly proportional to the cross-sectional area A of the jet and to the cube of the velocity v. If the velocity is doubled and the cross-sectional area is halved, by what factor will the power increase?

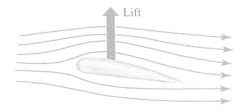

38. Aerodynamic Lift   The lift L on an airplane wing at take-off varies jointly as the square of the speed s of the plane and the area A of its wings. A plane with a wing area of 500 ft^2 traveling at 50 mi/h experiences a lift of 1700 lb. How much lift would a plane with a wing area of 600 ft^2 traveling at 40 mi/h experience?

39. Drag Force on a Boat   The drag force F on a boat is jointly proportional to the wetted surface area A on the hull and the square of the speed s of the boat. A boat experiences a drag force of 220 lb when traveling at 5 mi/h with a wetted surface area of 40 ft^2. How fast must a boat be traveling if it has 28 ft^2 of wetted surface area and is experiencing a drag force of 175 lb?

40. Skidding in a Curve   A car is traveling on a curve that forms a circular arc. The force F needed to keep the car from skidding is jointly proportional to the weight w of the car and the square of its speed s, and is inversely proportional to the radius r of the curve.

   (a) Write an equation that expresses this variation.

   (b) A car weighing 1600 lb travels around a curve at 60 mi/h. The next car to round this curve weighs 2500 lb and requires the same force as the first car to keep from skidding. How fast is the second car traveling?

41. Electrical Resistance   The resistance R of a wire varies directly as its length L and inversely as the square of its diameter d.

   (a) Write an equation that expresses this joint variation.

   (b) Find the constant of proportionality if a wire 1.2 m long and 0.005 m in diameter has a resistance of 140 ohms.

   (c) Find the resistance of a wire made of the same material that is 3 m long and has a diameter of 0.008 m.

42. Kepler's Third Law   Kepler's Third Law of planetary motion states that the square of the period T of a planet (the time it takes for the planet to make a complete revolution about the sun) is directly proportional to the cube of its average distance d from the sun.

   (a) Express Kepler's Third Law as an equation.

   (b) Find the constant of proportionality by using the fact that for our planet the period is about 365 days and the average distance is about 93 million miles.

   (c) The planet Neptune is about 2.79×10^9 mi from the sun. Find the period of Neptune.

43. Radiation Energy   The total radiation energy E emitted by a heated surface per unit area varies as the fourth power of its absolute temperature T. The temperature is 6000 K at the surface of the sun and 300 K at the surface of the earth.

   (a) How many times more radiation energy per unit area is produced by the sun than by the earth?

   (b) The radius of the earth is 3960 mi and the radius of the sun is 435,000 mi. How many times more total radiation does the sun emit than the earth?

44. Value of a Lot   The value of a building lot on Galiano Island is jointly proportional to its area and the quantity of water produced by a well on the property. A 200 ft by 300 ft lot has a well producing 10 gallons of water per minute, and is valued at $48,000. What is the value of a 400 ft by 400 ft lot if the well on the lot produces 4 gallons of water per minute?

45. Growing Cabbages   In the short growing season of the Canadian arctic territory of Nunavut, some gardeners find it possible to grow gigantic cabbages in the midnight sun.

Assume that the final size of a cabbage is proportional to the amount of nutrients it receives and inversely proportional to the number of other cabbages surrounding it. A cabbage that received 20 oz of nutrients and had 12 other cabbages around it grew to 30 lb. What size would it grow to if it received 10 oz of nutrients and had only 5 cabbage "neighbors"?

46. Heat of a Campfire The heat experienced by a hiker at a campfire is proportional to the amount of wood on the fire and inversely proportional to the cube of his distance from the fire. If the hiker is 20 ft from the fire and someone doubles the amount of wood burning, how far from the fire would he have to be so that he feels the same heat as before?

47. Frequency of Vibration The frequency f of vibration of a violin string is inversely proportional to its length L. The constant of proportionality k is positive and depends on the tension and density of the string.

(a) Write an equation that represents this variation.

(b) What effect does doubling the length of the string have on the frequency of its vibration?

48. Spread of a Disease The rate r at which a disease spreads in a population of size P is jointly proportional to the number x of infected people and the number $P - x$ who are not infected. An infection erupts in a small town that has population $P = 5000$.

(a) Write an equation that expresses r as a function of x.

(b) Compare the rate of spread of this infection when 10 people are infected to the rate of spread when 1000 people are infected. Which rate is larger? By what factor?

(c) Calculate the rate of spread when the entire population is infected. Why does this answer make intuitive sense?

DISCOVERY ■ DISCUSSION ■ WRITING

49. Is Proportionality Everything? A great many laws of physics and chemistry are expressible as proportionalities. Give at least one example of a function that occurs in the sciences that is *not* a proportionality.

CHAPTER 1 | REVIEW

■ CONCEPT CHECK

1. Define each term in your own words. (Check by referring to the definition in the text.)

(a) An integer   (b) A rational number

(c) An irrational number   (d) A real number

2. State each of these properties of real numbers.

(a) Commutative Property

(b) Associative Property

(c) Distributive Property

3. What is an open interval? What is a closed interval? What notation is used for these intervals?

4. What is the absolute value of a number?

5. (a) In the expression a^x, which is the base and which is the exponent?

(b) What does a^x mean if $x = n$, a positive integer?

(c) What if $x = 0$?

(d) What if x is a negative integer: $x = -n$, where n is a positive integer?

(e) What if $x = m/n$, a rational number?

(f) State the Laws of Exponents.

6. (a) What does $\sqrt[n]{a} = b$ mean?

(b) Why is $\sqrt{a^2} = |a|$?

(c) How many real nth roots does a positive real number have if n is odd? If n is even?

7. Explain how the procedure of rationalizing the denominator works.

8. State the Special Product Formulas for $(a + b)^2$, $(a - b)^2$, $(a + b)^3$, and $(a - b)^3$.

9. State each Special Factoring Formula.

(a) Difference of squares   (b) Difference of cubes

(c) Sum of cubes

10. What is a solution of an equation?

11. How do you solve an equation involving radicals? Why is it important to check your answers when solving equations of this type?

12. How do you solve an equation

(a) algebraically?   (b) graphically?

13. Write the general form of each type of equation.

(a) A linear equation   (b) A quadratic equation

14. What are the three ways to solve a quadratic equation?

15. State the Zero-Product Property.

16. Describe the process of completing the square.

17. State the quadratic formula.

18. What is the discriminant of a quadratic equation?

19. State the rules for working with inequalities.

20. How do you solve

    (a) a linear inequality?

    (b) a nonlinear inequality?

21. (a) How do you solve an equation involving an absolute value?

    (b) How do you solve an inequality involving an absolute value?

22. (a) Describe the coordinate plane.

    (b) How do you locate points in the coordinate plane?

23. State each formula.

    (a) The Distance Formula

    (b) The Midpoint Formula

24. Given an equation, what is its graph?

25. How do you find the x-intercepts and y-intercepts of a graph?

26. Write an equation of the circle with center (h, k) and radius r.

27. Explain the meaning of each type of symmetry. How do you test for it?

    (a) Symmetry with respect to the x-axis

    (b) Symmetry with respect to the y-axis

    (c) Symmetry with respect to the origin

28. Define the slope of a line.

29. Write each form of the equation of a line.

    (a) The point-slope form

    (b) The slope-intercept form

30. (a) What is the equation of a vertical line?

    (b) What is the equation of a horizontal line?

31. What is the general equation of a line?

32. Given lines with slopes m_1 and m_2, explain how you can tell if the lines are

    (a) parallel   **(b)** perpendicular

33. Write an equation that expresses each relationship.

    (a) y is directly proportional to x.

    (b) y is inversely proportional to x.

    (c) z is jointly proportional to x and y.

■ EXERCISES

1–4 ■ State the property of real numbers being used.

1. $3x + 2y = 2y + 3x$

2. $(a + b)(a - b) = (a - b)(a + b)$

3. $4(a + b) = 4a + 4b$

4. $(A + 1)(x + y) = (A + 1)x + (A + 1)y$

5–6 ■ Express the interval in terms of inequalities, and then graph the interval.

5. $[-2, 6)$

6. $(-\infty, 4]$

7–8 ■ Express the inequality in interval notation, and then graph the corresponding interval.

7. $x \geq 5$

8. $-1 < x \leq 5$

9–18 ■ Evaluate the expression.

9. $|3 - |-9||$

10. $1 - |1 - |-1||$

11. $2^{-3} - 3^{-2}$

12. $\sqrt[3]{-125}$

13. $216^{-1/3}$

14. $64^{2/3}$

15. $\dfrac{\sqrt{242}}{\sqrt{2}}$

16. $\sqrt[4]{4}\,\sqrt[4]{324}$

17. $2^{1/2}8^{1/2}$

18. $\sqrt{2}\,\sqrt{50}$

19–28 ■ Simplify the expression.

19. $\dfrac{x^2(2x)^4}{x^3}$

20. $(a^2)^{-3}(a^3b)^2(b^3)^4$

21. $(3xy^2)^3(\tfrac{2}{3}x^{-1}y)^2$

22. $\left(\dfrac{r^2s^{4/3}}{r^{1/3}s}\right)^6$

23. $\sqrt[3]{(x^3y)^2y^4}$

24. $\sqrt{x^2y^4}$

25. $\left(\dfrac{9x^3y}{y^{-3}}\right)^{1/2}$

26. $\left(\dfrac{x^{-2}y^3}{x^2y}\right)^{-1/2}\left(\dfrac{x^3y}{y^{1/2}}\right)^2$

27. $\dfrac{8r^{1/2}s^{-3}}{2r^{-2}s^4}$

28. $\left(\dfrac{ab^2c^{-3}}{2a^3b^{-4}}\right)^{-2}$

29. Write the number 78,250,000,000 in scientific notation.

30. Write the number 2.08×10^{-8} in ordinary decimal notation.

31. If $a \approx 0.00000293$, $b \approx 1.582 \times 10^{-14}$, and $c \approx 2.8064 \times 10^{12}$, use a calculator to approximate the number ab/c.

32. If your heart beats 80 times per minute and you live to be 90 years old, estimate the number of times your heart beats during your lifetime. State your answer in scientific notation.

33–48 ■ Factor the expression completely.

33. $12x^2y^4 - 3xy^5 + 9x^3y^2$

34. $x^2 - 9x + 18$

35. $x^2 + 3x - 10$

36. $6x^2 + x - 12$

37. $4t^2 - 13t - 12$

38. $x^4 - 2x^2 + 1$

39. $25 - 16t^2$

40. $2y^6 - 32y^2$

41. $x^6 - 1$

42. $y^3 - 2y^2 - y + 2$

43. $x^{-1/2} - 2x^{1/2} + x^{3/2}$

44. $a^4b^2 + ab^5$

45. $4x^3 - 8x^2 + 3x - 6$

46. $8x^3 + y^6$

47. $(x^2 + 2)^{5/2} + 2x(x^2 + 2)^{3/2} + x^2\sqrt{x^2 + 2}$

48. $3x^3 - 2x^2 + 18x - 12$

49–64 ■ Perform the indicated operations and simplify.

49. $(2x + 1)(3x - 2) - 5(4x - 1)$

50. $(2y - 7)(2y + 7)$

51. $(1 + x)(2 - x) - (3 - x)(3 + x)$

52. $\sqrt{x}(\sqrt{x} + 1)(2\sqrt{x} - 1)$

53. $x^2(x - 2) + x(x - 2)^2$

54. $\dfrac{x^2 - 2x - 3}{2x^2 + 5x + 3}$

55. $\dfrac{x^2 + 2x - 3}{x^2 + 8x + 16} \cdot \dfrac{3x + 12}{x - 1}$ **56.** $\dfrac{t^3 - 1}{t^2 - 1}$

57. $\dfrac{x^2 - 2x - 15}{x^2 - 6x + 5} \div \dfrac{x^2 - x - 12}{x^2 - 1}$

58. $\dfrac{2}{x} + \dfrac{1}{x - 2} + \dfrac{3}{(x - 2)^2}$ **59.** $\dfrac{1}{x - 1} - \dfrac{2}{x^2 - 1}$

60. $\dfrac{1}{x + 2} + \dfrac{1}{x^2 - 4} - \dfrac{2}{x^2 - x - 2}$

61. $\dfrac{\dfrac{1}{x} - \dfrac{1}{2}}{x - 2}$ **62.** $\dfrac{\dfrac{1}{x} - \dfrac{1}{x + 1}}{\dfrac{1}{x} + \dfrac{1}{x + 1}}$

63. $\dfrac{\sqrt{6}}{\sqrt{3} + \sqrt{2}}$ (rationalize the denominator)

64. $\dfrac{\sqrt{x + h} - \sqrt{x}}{h}$ (rationalize the numerator)

65–80 ■ Find all real solutions of the equation.

65. $7x - 6 = 4x + 9$ **66.** $8 - 2x = 14 + x$

67. $\dfrac{x + 1}{x - 1} = \dfrac{3x}{3x - 6}$ **68.** $(x + 2)^2 = (x - 4)^2$

69. $x^2 - 9x + 14 = 0$ **70.** $x^2 + 24x + 144 = 0$

71. $2x^2 + x = 1$ **72.** $3x^2 + 5x - 2 = 0$

73. $4x^3 - 25x = 0$ **74.** $x^3 - 2x^2 - 5x + 10 = 0$

75. $3x^2 + 4x - 1 = 0$ **76.** $\dfrac{1}{x} + \dfrac{2}{x - 1} = 3$

77. $\dfrac{x}{x - 2} + \dfrac{1}{x + 2} = \dfrac{8}{x^2 - 4}$

78. $x^4 - 8x^2 - 9 = 0$

79. $|x - 7| = 4$ **80.** $|2x - 5| = 9$

81. The owner of a store sells raisins for $3.20 per pound and nuts for $2.40 per pound. He decides to mix the raisins and nuts and sell 50 lb of the mixture for $2.72 per pound. What quantities of raisins and nuts should he use?

82. Anthony leaves Kingstown at 2:00 P.M. and drives to Queensville, 160 mi distant, at 45 mi/h. At 2:15 P.M. Helen leaves Queensville and drives to Kingstown at 40 mi/h. At what time do they pass each other on the road?

83. A woman cycles 8 mi/h faster than she runs. Every morning she cycles 4 mi and runs $2\frac{1}{2}$ mi, for a total of one hour of exercise. How fast does she run?

84. The hypotenuse of a right triangle has length 20 cm. The sum of the lengths of the other two sides is 28 cm. Find the lengths of the other two sides of the triangle.

85. Abbie paints twice as fast as Beth and three times as fast as Cathie. If it takes them 60 min to paint a living room with all three working together, how long would it take Abbie if she works alone?

86. A homeowner wishes to fence in three adjoining garden plots, one for each of her children, as shown in the figure. If each

plot is to be 80 ft² in area and she has 88 ft of fencing material at hand, what dimensions should each plot have?

87–94 ■ Solve the inequality. Express the solution using interval notation and graph the solution set on the real number line.

87. $3x - 2 > -11$ **88.** $-1 < 2x + 5 \le 3$

89. $x^2 + 4x - 12 > 0$ **90.** $x^2 \le 1$

91. $\dfrac{x - 4}{x^2 - 4} \le 0$ **92.** $\dfrac{5}{x^3 - x^2 - 4x + 4} < 0$

93. $|x - 5| \le 3$ **94.** $|x - 4| < 0.02$

 95–98 ■ Solve the equation or inequality graphically.

95. $x^2 - 4x = 2x + 7$ **96.** $\sqrt{x + 4} = x^2 - 5$

97. $4x - 3 \ge x^2$ **98.** $x^3 - 4x^2 - 5x > 2$

99–100 ■ Two points P and Q are given.
   (a) Plot P and Q on a coordinate plane.
   (b) Find the distance from P to Q.
   (c) Find the midpoint of the segment PQ.
   (d) Sketch the line determined by P and Q, and find its equation in slope-intercept form.
   (e) Sketch the circle that passes through Q and has center P, and find the equation of this circle.

99. $P(2, 0)$, $Q(-5, 12)$ **100.** $P(7, -1)$, $Q(2, -11)$

101–102 ■ Sketch the region given by the set.

101. $\{(x, y) \mid -4 < x < 4 \text{ and } -2 < y < 2\}$

102. $\{(x, y) \mid x \ge 4 \text{ or } y \ge 2\}$

103. Which of the points $A(4, 4)$ or $B(5, 3)$ is closer to the point $C(-1, -3)$?

104. Find an equation of the circle that has center $(2, -5)$ and radius $\sqrt{2}$.

105. Find an equation of the circle that has center $(-5, -1)$ and passes through the origin.

106. Find an equation of the circle that contains the points $P(2, 3)$ and $Q(-1, 8)$ and has the midpoint of the segment PQ as its center.

107–110 ■ Determine whether the equation represents a circle, represents a point, or has no graph. If the equation is that of a circle, find its center and radius.

107. $x^2 + y^2 + 2x - 6y + 9 = 0$

108. $2x^2 + 2y^2 - 2x + 8y = \frac{1}{2}$

109. $x^2 + y^2 + 72 = 12x$

110. $x^2 + y^2 - 6x - 10y + 34 = 0$

111–118 ■ Test the equation for symmetry, and sketch its graph.

111. $y = 2 - 3x$

112. $2x - y + 1 = 0$

113. $x + 3y = 21$

114. $x = 2y + 12$

115. $y = 16 - x^2$

116. $8x + y^2 = 0$

117. $x = \sqrt{y}$

118. $y = -\sqrt{1 - x^2}$

119–122 ■ Use a graphing device to graph the equation in an appropriate viewing rectangle.

119. $y = x^2 - 6x$

120. $y = \sqrt{5 - x}$

121. $y = x^3 - 4x^2 - 5x$

122. $\dfrac{x^2}{4} + y^2 = 1$

123. Find an equation for the line that passes through the points $(-1, -6)$ and $(2, -4)$.

124. Find an equation for the line that passes through the point $(6, -3)$ and has slope $-\frac{1}{2}$.

125. Find an equation for the line that has x-intercept 4 and y-intercept 12.

126. Find an equation for the line that passes through the point $(1, 7)$ and is perpendicular to the line $x - 3y + 16 = 0$.

127. Find an equation for the line that passes through the origin and is parallel to the line $3x + 15y = 22$.

128. Find an equation for the line that passes through the point $(5, 2)$ and is parallel to the line passing through $(-1, -3)$ and $(3, 2)$.

129–130 ■ Find equations for the circle and the line in the figure.

129.

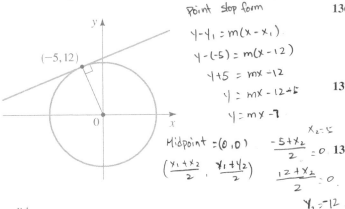

Point slop form

$y - y_1 = m(x - x_1)$

$y - (-5) = m(x - 12)$

$y + 5 = mx - 12$

$y = mx - 12 + 5$

$y = mx - 7$

Midpoint $= (0, 0)$

$\left(\dfrac{y_1 + x_2}{2}, \dfrac{y_1 + y_2}{2}\right)$

$x_2 = 5$

$\dfrac{-5 + x_2}{2} = 0$

$\dfrac{12 + x_2}{2} = 0$

$y_2 = -12$

130.

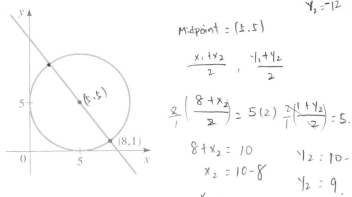

Midpoint $= (5, 5)$

$\dfrac{x_1 + x_2}{2}, \quad \dfrac{y_1 + y_2}{2}$

$\dfrac{2}{1}\left(\dfrac{8 + x_2}{2}\right) = 5(2) \quad \dfrac{2}{1}\left(\dfrac{1 + y_2}{2}\right) = 5.$

$8 + x_2 = 10 \qquad y_2 = 10 - 1$

$x_2 = 10 - 8 \qquad y_2 = 9.$

$x_2 = 2.$

131. Hooke's Law states that if a weight w is attached to a hanging spring, then the stretched length s of the spring is linearly related to w. For a particular spring we have

$$s = 0.3w + 2.5$$

where s is measured in inches and w in pounds.

(a) What do the slope and s-intercept in this equation represent?

(b) How long is the spring when a 5-lb weight is attached?

132. Margarita is hired by an accounting firm at a salary of $60,000 per year. Three years later her annual salary has increased to $70,500. Assume that her salary increases linearly.

(a) Find an equation that relates her annual salary S and the number of years t that she has worked for the firm.

(b) What do the slope and S-intercept of her salary equation represent?

(c) What will her salary be after 12 years with the firm?

133. Suppose that M varies directly as z, and $M = 120$ when $z = 15$. Write an equation that expresses this variation.

134. Suppose that z is inversely proportional to y, and that $z = 12$ when $y = 16$. Write an equation that expresses z in terms of y.

135. The intensity of illumination I from a light varies inversely as the square of the distance d from the light.

(a) Write this statement as an equation.

(b) Determine the constant of proportionality if it is known that a lamp has an intensity of 1000 candles at a distance of 8 m.

(c) What is the intensity of this lamp at a distance of 20 m?

136. The frequency of a vibrating string under constant tension is inversely proportional to its length. If a violin string 12 inches long vibrates 440 times per second, to what length must it be shortened to vibrate 660 times per second?

137. The terminal velocity of a parachutist is directly proportional to the square root of his weight. A 160-lb parachutist attains a terminal velocity of 9 mi/h. What is the terminal velocity for a parachutist weighing 240 lb?

138. The maximum range of a projectile is directly proportional to the square of its velocity. A baseball pitcher throws a ball at 60 mi/h, with a maximum range of 242 ft. What is his maximum range if he throws the ball at 70 mi/h?

test the point

$x_1 = 8 \quad x_2 = 2$

$y_1 = 1 \quad y_2 = 9$.

$\left(\dfrac{8 + 2}{2}\right) = \dfrac{10}{2} = 5 \checkmark$

$\left(\dfrac{1 + 9}{2}\right) = \dfrac{10}{2} = 5 \checkmark$.

1. **(a)** Graph the intervals $(-5, 3]$ and $(2, \infty)$ on the real number line.
   (b) Express the inequalities $x \le 3$ and $-1 \le x < 4$ in interval notation.
   (c) Find the distance between -7 and 9 on the real number line.

2. Evaluate each expression.
   (a) $(-3)^4$ **(b)** -3^4 **(c)** 3^{-4} **(d)** $\dfrac{5^{23}}{5^{21}}$ **(e)** $\left(\dfrac{2}{3}\right)^{-2}$ **(f)** $16^{-3/4}$

3. Write each number in scientific notation.
   (a) $186,000,000,000$ **(b)** 0.0000003965

4. Simplify each expression. Write your final answer without negative exponents.
   (a) $\sqrt{200} - \sqrt{32}$ **(b)** $(3a^3b^3)(4ab^2)^2$ **(c)** $\left(\dfrac{3x^{3/2}y^3}{x^2y^{-1/2}}\right)^{-2}$

   (d) $\dfrac{x^2 + 3x + 2}{x^2 - x - 2}$ **(e)** $\dfrac{x^2}{x^2 - 4} - \dfrac{x+1}{x+2}$ **(f)** $\dfrac{\dfrac{y}{x} - \dfrac{x}{y}}{\dfrac{1}{y} - \dfrac{1}{x}}$

5. Rationalize the denominator and simplify: $\dfrac{\sqrt{10}}{\sqrt{5} - 2}$

6. Perform the indicated operations and simplify.
   (a) $3(x + 6) + 4(2x - 5)$ **(b)** $(x + 3)(4x - 5)$ **(c)** $(\sqrt{a} + \sqrt{b})(\sqrt{a} - \sqrt{b})$
   (d) $(2x + 3)^2$ **(e)** $(x + 2)^3$

7. Factor each expression completely.
   (a) $4x^2 - 25$ **(b)** $2x^2 + 5x - 12$ **(c)** $x^3 - 3x^2 - 4x + 12$
   (d) $x^4 + 27x$ **(e)** $3x^{3/2} - 9x^{1/2} + 6x^{-1/2}$ **(f)** $x^3y - 4xy$

8. Find all real solutions.
   (a) $x + 5 = 14 - \frac{1}{2}x$ **(b)** $\dfrac{2x}{x+1} = \dfrac{2x-1}{x}$ **(c)** $x^2 - x - 12 = 0$
   (d) $2x^2 + 4x + 1 = 0$ **(e)** $\sqrt{3 - \sqrt{x+5}} = 2$ **(f)** $x^4 - 3x^2 + 2 = 0$
   (g) $3|x - 4| = 10$

9. Mary drove from Amity to Belleville at a speed of 50 mi/h. On the way back, she drove at 60 mi/h. The total trip took $4\frac{2}{5}$ h of driving time. Find the distance between these two cities.

10. A rectangular parcel of land is 70 ft longer than it is wide. Each diagonal between opposite corners is 130 ft. What are the dimensions of the parcel?

11. Solve each inequality. Write the answer using interval notation, and sketch the solution on the real number line.
    (a) $-4 < 5 - 3x \le 17$ **(b)** $x(x - 1)(x + 2) > 0$
    (c) $|x - 4| < 3$ **(d)** $\dfrac{2x - 3}{x + 1} \le 1$

12. A bottle of medicine is to be stored at a temperature between 5°C and 10°C. What range does this correspond to on the Fahrenheit scale? [*Note:* Fahrenheit (F) and Celsius (C) temperatures satisfy the relation $C = \frac{5}{9}(F - 32)$.]

13. For what values of x is the expression $\sqrt{6x - x^2}$ defined as a real number?

14. Solve the equation and the inequality graphically.
    (a) $x^3 - 9x - 1 = 0$ **(b)** $x^2 - 1 \le |x + 1|$

15. **(a)** Plot the points $P(0, 3)$, $Q(3, 0)$, and $R(6, 3)$ in the coordinate plane. Where must the point S be located so that $PQRS$ is a square?
    (b) Find the area of $PQRS$.

16. **(a)** Sketch the graph of $y = x^2 - 4$.
    (b) Find the x- and y-intercepts of the graph.
    (c) Is the graph symmetric about the x-axis, the y-axis, or the origin?

17. Let $P(-3,1)$ and $Q(5,6)$ be two points in the coordinate plane.

(a) Plot P and Q in the coordinate plane.

(b) Find the distance between P and Q.

(c) Find the midpoint of the segment PQ.

(d) Find the slope of the line that contains P and Q.

(e) Find the perpendicular bisector of the line that contains P and Q.

(f) Find an equation for the circle for which the segment PQ is a diameter.

18. Find the center and radius of each circle and sketch its graph.

(a) $x^2 + y^2 = 25$ (b) $(x - 2)^2 + (y + 1)^2 = 9$ (c) $x^2 + 6x + y^2 - 2y + 6 = 0$

19. Write the linear equation $2x - 3y = 15$ in slope-intercept form, and sketch its graph. What are the slope and y-intercept?

20. Find an equation for the line with the given property.

(a) It passes through the point $(3, -6)$ and is parallel to the line $3x + y - 10 = 0$.

(b) It has x-intercept 6 and y-intercept 4.

21. A geologist uses a probe to measure the temperature T (in °C) of the soil at various depths below the surface, and finds that at a depth of x cm, the temperature is given by the linear equation $T = 0.08x - 4$.

(a) What is the temperature at a depth of one meter (100 cm)?

(b) Sketch a graph of the linear equation.

(c) What do the slope, the x-intercept, and T-intercept of the graph of this equation represent?

22. The maximum weight M that can be supported by a beam is jointly proportional to its width w and the square of its height h, and inversely proportional to its length L.

(a) Write an equation that expresses this proportionality.

(b) Determine the constant of proportionality if a beam 4 in. wide, 6 in. high, and 12 ft long can support a weight of 4800 lb.

(c) If a 10-ft beam made of the same material is 3 in. wide and 10 in. high, what is the maximum weight it can support?

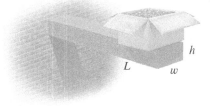

If you had difficulty with any of these problems, you may wish to review the section of this chapter indicated below.

If you had trouble with this test problem	Review this section
1	Section 1.1
2, 3, 4(a), 4(b), 4(c)	Section 1.2
4(d), 4(e), 4(f), 5	Section 1.4
6, 7	Section 1.3
8	Section 1.5
9, 10	Section 1.6
11, 12, 13	Section 1.7
14	Section 1.9
15, 16, 17(a), 17(b)	Section 1.8
17(c), 17(d)	Section 1.10
17(e), 17(f), 18	Section 1.8
19, 20, 21	Section 1.10
22	Section 1.11

A model is a representation of an object or process. For example, a toy Ferrari is a model of the actual car; a road map is a model of the streets in a city. A **mathematical model** is a mathematical representation (usually an equation) of an object or process. Once a mathematical model is made it can be used to obtain useful information or make predictions about the thing being modeled. In these *Focus on Modeling* sections we explore different ways in which mathematics is used to model real-world phenomena.

▼ The Line That Best Fits the Data

In Section 1.10 we used linear equations to model relationships between varying quantities. In practice, such relationships are discovered by collecting data. But real-world data seldom fall into a precise line. The **scatter plot** in Figure 1(a) shows the result of a study on childhood obesity. The graph plots the body mass index (BMI) versus the number of hours of television watched per day for 25 adolescent subjects. Of course, we would not expect the data to be exactly linear as in Figure 1(b). But there is a linear *trend* indicated by the blue line in Figure 1(a): The more hours a subject watches TV the higher the BMI. In this section we learn how to find the line that best fits the data.

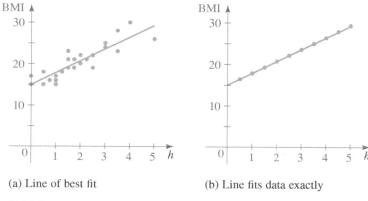

(a) Line of best fit   (b) Line fits data exactly

FIGURE 1

Table 1 gives the nationwide infant mortality rate for the period from 1950 to 2000. The *rate* is the number of infants who die before reaching their first birthday, out of every 1000 live births.

TABLE 1
U.S. Infant Mortality

Year	Rate
1950	29.2
1960	26.0
1970	20.0
1980	12.6
1990	9.2
2000	6.9

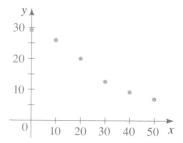

FIGURE 2   U.S. infant mortality rate

The scatter plot in Figure 2 shows that the data lie roughly on a straight line. We can try to fit a line visually to approximate the data points, but since the data aren't *exactly* linear, there are many lines that might seem to work. Figure 3 shows two attempts at "eye-balling" a line to fit the data.

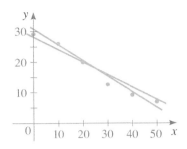

FIGURE 3 Visual attempts to fit line to data

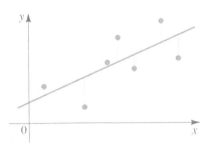

FIGURE 4 Distance from the data points to the line

Of all the lines that run through these data points, there is one that "best" fits the data, in the sense that it provides the most accurate linear model for the data. We now describe how to find this line.

It seems reasonable that the line of best fit is the line that is as close as possible to all the data points. This is the line for which the sum of the vertical distances from the data points to the line is as small as possible (see Figure 4). For technical reasons it is better to use the line where the sum of the squares of these distances is smallest. This is called the **regression line**. The formula for the regression line is found by using calculus, but fortunately, the formula is programmed into most graphing calculators. In Example 1 we see how to use a TI-83 calculator to find the regression line for the infant mortality data described above. (The process for other calculators is similar.)

EXAMPLE 1 | Regression Line for U.S. Infant Mortality Rates

(a) Find the regression line for the infant mortality data in Table 1.

(b) Graph the regression line on a scatter plot of the data.

(c) Use the regression line to estimate the infant mortality rates in 1995 and 2006.

SOLUTION

(a) To find the regression line using a TI-83 calculator, we must first enter the data into the lists L_1 and L_2, which are accessed by pressing the STAT key and selecting Edit. Figure 5 shows the calculator screen after the data have been entered. (Note that we are letting $x = 0$ correspond to the year 1950, so that $x = 50$ corresponds to 2000. This makes the equations easier to work with.) We then press the STAT key again and select Calc, then 4:LinReg(ax+b), which provides the output shown in Figure 6(a). This tells us that the regression line is

$$y = -0.48x + 29.4$$

Here x represents the number of years since 1950, and y represents the corresponding infant mortality rate.

(b) The scatter plot and the regression line have been plotted on a graphing calculator screen in Figure 6(b).

FIGURE 5 Entering the data

(a) Output of the LinReg command

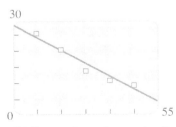

(b) Scatter plot and regression line

FIGURE 6

(c) The year 1995 is 45 years after 1950, so substituting 45 for x, we find that $y = -0.48(45) + 29.4 = 7.8$. So the infant mortality rate in 1995 was about 7.8. Similarly, substituting 56 for x, we find that the infant mortality rate predicted for 2006 was about $-0.48(56) + 29.4 \approx 2.5$.

An Internet search shows that the actual infant mortality rate was 7.6 in 1995 and 6.4 in 2006. So the regression line is fairly accurate for 1995 (the actual rate was slightly lower than the predicted rate), but it is considerably off for 2006 (the actual rate was more than twice the predicted rate). The reason is that infant mortality in the United States stopped declining and actually started rising in 2002, for the first time in more than a century. This shows that we have to be very careful about extrapolating linear models outside the domain over which the data are spread.

▼ Examples of Regression Analysis

Since the modern Olympic Games began in 1896, achievements in track and field events have been improving steadily. One example in which the winning records have shown an upward linear trend is the pole vault. Pole vaulting began in the northern Netherlands as a practical activity: When traveling from village to village, people would vault across the many canals that crisscrossed the area to avoid having to go out of their way to find a bridge. Households maintained a supply of wooden poles of lengths appropriate for each member of the family. Pole vaulting for height rather than distance became a collegiate track and field event in the mid-1800s and was one of the events in the first modern Olympics. In the next example we find a linear model for the gold-medal-winning records in the men's Olympic pole vault.

Steven Hooker, 2008 Olympic gold medal winner, men's pole vault

EXAMPLE 2 | Regression Line for Olympic Pole Vault Records

Table 2 gives the men's Olympic pole vault records up to 2004.

(a) Find the regression line for the data.

(b) Make a scatter plot of the data, and graph the regression line. Does the regression line appear to be a suitable model for the data?

(c) What does the slope of the regression line represent?

(d) Use the model to predict the winning pole vault height for the 2008 Olympics.

TABLE 2
Men's Olympic Pole Vault Records

Year	x	Gold medalist	Height (m)	Year	x	Gold medalist	Height (m)
1896	−4	William Hoyt, USA	3.30	1956	56	Robert Richards, USA	4.56
1900	0	Irving Baxter, USA	3.30	1960	60	Don Bragg, USA	4.70
1904	4	Charles Dvorak, USA	3.50	1964	64	Fred Hansen, USA	5.10
1906	6	Fernand Gonder, France	3.50	1968	68	Bob Seagren, USA	5.40
1908	8	A. Gilbert, E. Cook, USA	3.71	1972	72	W. Nordwig, E. Germany	5.64
1912	12	Harry Babcock, USA	3.95	1976	76	Tadeusz Slusarski, Poland	5.64
1920	20	Frank Foss, USA	4.09	1980	80	W. Kozakiewicz, Poland	5.78
1924	24	Lee Barnes, USA	3.95	1984	84	Pierre Quinon, France	5.75
1928	28	Sabin Can, USA	4.20	1988	88	Sergei Bubka, USSR	5.90
1932	32	William Miller, USA	4.31	1992	92	M. Tarassob, Unified Team	5.87
1936	36	Earle Meadows, USA	4.35	1996	96	Jean Jaffione, France	5.92
1948	48	Guinn Smith, USA	4.30	2000	100	Nick Hysong, USA	5.90
1952	52	Robert Richards, USA	4.55	2004	104	Timothy Mack, USA	5.95

LinReg
 y=ax+b
 a=.0265652857
 b=3.400989881

Output of the `LinReg`
function on the TI-83

SOLUTION

(a) Let $x =$ year $- 1900$, so 1896 corresponds to $x = -4$, 1900 to $x = 0$, and so on. Using a calculator, we find the following regression line:

$$y = 0.0266x + 3.40$$

(b) The scatter plot and the regression line are shown in Figure 7. The regression line appears to be a good model for the data.

(c) The slope is the average rate of increase in the pole vault record per year. So on average, the pole vault record increased by 0.0266 m/yr.

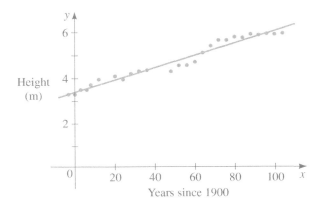

FIGURE 7 Scatter plot and regression line for pole vault data

(d) The year 2008 corresponds to $x = 108$ in our model. The model gives

$$y = 0.0266(108) + 3.40$$

$$\approx 6.27$$

So the model predicts that in 2008 the winning pole vault will be 6.27 m.

At the 2008 Olympics in Beijing, China, the men's Olympic gold medal in the pole vault was won by Steven Hooker of Australia, with a vault of 5.96 m. Although this height set an Olympic record, it was considerably lower than the 6.27 m predicted by the model of Example 2. In Problem 10 we find a regression line for the pole vault data from 1972 to 2004. Do the problem to see whether this restricted set of more recent data provides a better predictor for the 2008 record.

Is a linear model really appropriate for the data of Example 2? In subsequent *Focus on Modeling* sections, we study regression models that use other types of functions, and we learn how to choose the best model for a given set of data.

In the next example we see how linear regression is used in medical research to investigate potential causes of diseases such as cancer.

EXAMPLE 3 | Regression Line for Links Between Asbestos and Cancer

When laboratory rats are exposed to asbestos fibers, some of the rats develop lung tumors. Table 3 lists the results of several experiments by different scientists.

(a) Find the regression line for the data.

(b) Make a scatter plot and graph the regression line. Does the regression line appear to be a suitable model for the data?

(c) What does the y-intercept of the regression line represent?

TABLE 3
Asbestos–Tumor Data

Asbestos exposure (fibers/mL)	Percent that develop lung tumors
50	2
400	6
500	5
900	10
1100	26
1600	42
1800	37
2000	28
3000	50

SOLUTION

(a) Using a calculator, we find the following regression line (see Figure 8(a)):

$$y = 0.0177x + 0.5405$$

(b) The scatter plot and regression line are graphed in Figure 8(b). The regression line appears to be a reasonable model for the data.

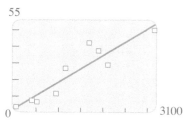

(a) Output of the LinReg command

(b) Scatter plot and regression line

FIGURE 8 Linear regression for the asbestos–tumor data

(c) The y-intercept is the percentage of rats that develop tumors when no asbestos fibers are present. In other words, this is the percentage that normally develop lung tumors (for reasons other than asbestos).

▼ How Good Is the Fit? The Correlation Coefficient

For any given set of two-variable data it is always possible to find a regression line, even if the data points do not tend to lie on a line and even if the variables don't seem to be related at all. Look at the three scatter plots in Figure 9. In the first scatter plot, the data points lie close to a line. In the second plot, there is still a linear trend but the points are more scattered. In the third plot there doesn't seem to be any trend at all, linear or otherwise.

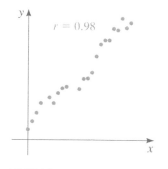

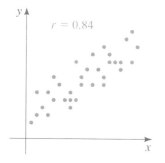

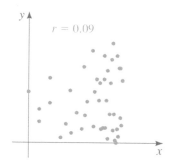

FIGURE 9

A graphing calculator can give us a regression line for each of these scatter plots. But how well do these lines represent or "fit" the data? To answer this question, statisticians have invented the **correlation coefficient**, usually denoted r. The correlation coefficient is a number between -1 and 1 that measures how closely the data follow the regression line—or, in other words, how strongly the variables are **correlated**. Many graphing calculators give the value of r when they compute a regression line. If r is close to -1

or 1, then the variables are strongly correlated—that is, the scatter plot follows the regression line closely. If r is close to 0, then the variables are weakly correlated or not correlated at all. (The sign of r depends on the slope of the regression line.) The correlation coefficients of the scatter plots in Figure 9 are indicated on the graphs. For the first plot, r is close to 1 because the data are very close to linear. The second plot also has a relatively large r, but it is not as large as the first, because the data, while fairly linear, are more diffuse. The third plot has an r close to 0, since there is virtually no linear trend in the data.

There are no hard and fast rules for deciding what values of r are sufficient for deciding that a linear correlation is "significant." The correlation coefficient is only a rough guide in helping us decide how much faith to put into a given regression line. In Example 1 the correlation coefficient is -0.99, indicating a very high level of correlation, so we can safely say that the drop in infant mortality rates from 1950 to 2000 was strongly linear. (The value of r is negative, since infant mortality trended *down* over this period.) In Example 3 the correlation coefficient is 0.92, which also indicates a strong correlation between the variables. So exposure to asbestos is clearly associated with the growth of lung tumors in rats. Does this mean that asbestos *causes* lung cancer?

If two variables are correlated, it does not necessarily mean that a change in one variable *causes* a change in the other. For example, the mathematician John Allen Paulos points out that shoe size is strongly correlated to mathematics scores among schoolchildren. Does this mean that big feet cause high math scores? Certainly not—both shoe size and math skills increase independently as children get older. So it is important not to jump to conclusions: Correlation and causation are not the same thing. Correlation is a useful tool in bringing important cause-and-effect relationships to light; but to prove causation, we must explain the mechanism by which one variable affects the other. For example, the link between smoking and lung cancer was observed as a correlation long before science found the mechanism through which smoking causes lung cancer.

PROBLEMS

1. **Femur Length and Height** Anthropologists use a linear model that relates femur length to height. The model allows an anthropologist to determine the height of an individual when only a partial skeleton (including the femur) is found. In this problem we find the model by analyzing the data on femur length and height for the eight males given in the table.

   (a) Make a scatter plot of the data.

   (b) Find and graph a linear function that models the data.

   (c) An anthropologist finds a femur of length 58 cm. How tall was the person?

Femur length (cm)	Height (cm)
50.1	178.5
48.3	173.6
45.2	164.8
44.7	163.7
44.5	168.3
42.7	165.0
39.5	155.4
38.0	155.8

Femur →

2. **Demand for Soft Drinks** A convenience store manager notices that sales of soft drinks are higher on hotter days, so he assembles the data in the table.

   (a) Make a scatter plot of the data.

   (b) Find and graph a linear function that models the data.

(c) Use the model to predict soft drink sales if the temperature is 95°F.

High temperature (°F)	Number of cans sold
55	340
58	335
64	410
68	460
70	450
75	610
80	735
84	780

3. **Tree Diameter and Age** To estimate ages of trees, forest rangers use a linear model that relates tree diameter to age. The model is useful because tree diameter is much easier to measure than tree age (which requires special tools for extracting a representative cross section of the tree and counting the rings). To find the model, use the data in the table, which were collected for a certain variety of oaks.

(a) Make a scatter plot of the data.

(b) Find and graph a linear function that models the data.

(c) Use the model to estimate the age of an oak whose diameter is 18 in.

Diameter (in.)	Age (years)
2.5	15
4.0	24
6.0	32
8.0	56
9.0	49
9.5	76
12.5	90
15.5	89

4. **Carbon Dioxide Levels** The Mauna Loa Observatory, located on the island of Hawaii, has been monitoring carbon dioxide (CO_2) levels in the atmosphere since 1958. The table lists the average annual CO_2 levels measured in parts per million (ppm) from 1984 to 2006.

(a) Make a scatter plot of the data.

(b) Find and graph the regression line.

(c) Use the linear model in part (b) to estimate the CO_2 level in the atmosphere in 2005. Compare your answer with the actual CO_2 level of 379.7 that was measured in 2005.

Year	CO_2 level (ppm)
1984	344.3
1986	347.0
1988	351.3
1990	354.0
1992	356.3
1994	358.9
1996	362.7
1998	366.5
2000	369.4
2002	372.0
2004	377.5
2006	380.9

Temperature (°F)	Chirping rate (chirps/min)
50	20
55	46
60	79
65	91
70	113
75	140
80	173
85	198
90	211

5. Temperature and Chirping Crickets   Biologists have observed that the chirping rate of crickets of a certain species appears to be related to temperature. The table shows the chirping rates for various temperatures.

(a) Make a scatter plot of the data.

(b) Find and graph the regression line.

(c) Use the linear model in part (b) to estimate the chirping rate at 100°F.

6. Extent of Arctic Sea Ice   The National Snow and Ice Data Center monitors the amount of ice in the Arctic year round. The table gives approximate values for the sea ice extent in millions of square kilometers from 1980 to 2006, in two-year intervals.

(a) Make a scatter plot of the data.

(b) Find and graph the regression line.

(c) Use the linear model in part (b) to estimate the ice extent in the year 2010.

Year	Ice extent (million km²)	Year	Ice extent (million km²)
1980	7.9	1994	7.1
1982	7.4	1996	7.9
1984	7.2	1998	6.6
1986	7.6	2000	6.3
1988	7.5	2002	6.0
1990	6.2	2004	6.1
1992	7.6	2006	5.7

Flow rate (%)	Mosquito positive rate (%)
0	22
10	16
40	12
60	11
90	6
100	2

7. Mosquito Prevalence   The table lists the relative abundance of mosquitoes (as measured by the mosquito positive rate) versus the flow rate (measured as a percentage of maximum flow) of canal networks in Saga City, Japan.

(a) Make a scatter plot of the data.

(b) Find and graph the regression line.

(c) Use the linear model in part (b) to estimate the mosquito positive rate if the canal flow is 70% of maximum.

8. Noise and Intelligibility   Audiologists study the intelligibility of spoken sentences under different noise levels. Intelligibility, the MRT score, is measured as the percent of a spoken sentence that the listener can decipher at a certain noise level in decibels (dB). The table shows the results of one such test.

(a) Make a scatter plot of the data.

(b) Find and graph the regression line.

(c) Find the correlation coefficient. Is a linear model appropriate?

(d) Use the linear model in part (b) to estimate the intelligibility of a sentence at a 94-dB noise level.

Noise level (dB)	MRT score (%)
80	99
84	91
88	84
92	70
96	47
100	23
104	11

9. **Life Expectancy**   The average life expectancy in the United States has been rising steadily over the past few decades, as shown in the table.

(a) Make a scatter plot of the data.

(b) Find and graph the regression line.

(c) Use the linear model you found in part (b) to predict the life expectancy in the year 2006.

(d) Search the Internet or your campus library to find the actual 2006 average life expectancy. Compare to your answer in part (c).

Year	Life expectancy
1920	54.1
1930	59.7
1940	62.9
1950	68.2
1960	69.7
1970	70.8
1980	73.7
1990	75.4
2000	76.9

10. **Olympic Pole Vault**   The graph in Figure 7 indicates that in recent years the winning Olympic men's pole vault height has fallen below the value predicted by the regression line in Example 2. This might have occurred because when the pole vault was a new event, there was much room for improvement in vaulters' performances, whereas now even the best training can produce only incremental advances. Let's see whether concentrating on more recent results gives a better predictor of future records.

(a) Use the data in Table 2 to complete the table of winning pole vault heights. (Note that we are using $x = 0$ to correspond to the year 1972, where this restricted data set begins.)

(b) Find the regression line for the data in part (a).

(c) Plot the data and the regression line on the same axes. Does the regression line seem to provide a good model for the data?

(d) What does the regression line predict as the winning pole vault height for the 2008 Olympics? Compare this predicted value to the actual 2008 winning height of 5.96 m, as described on page 133. Has this new regression line provided a better prediction than the line in Example 2?

Year	x	Height (m)
1972	0	5.64
1976	4	
1980	8	
1984		
1988		
1992		
1996		
2000		
2004		

11. **Olympic Swimming Records**   The tables give the gold medal times in the men's and women's 100-m freestyle Olympic swimming event.

    (a) Find the regression lines for the men's data and the women's data.

    (b) Sketch both regression lines on the same graph. When do these lines predict that the women will overtake the men in the event? Does this conclusion seem reasonable?

MEN

Year	Gold medalist	Time (s)
1908	C. Daniels, USA	65.6
1912	D. Kahanamoku, USA	63.4
1920	D. Kahanamoku, USA	61.4
1924	J. Weissmuller, USA	59.0
1928	J. Weissmuller, USA	58.6
1932	Y. Miyazaki, Japan	58.2
1936	F. Csik, Hungary	57.6
1948	W. Ris, USA	57.3
1952	C. Scholes, USA	57.4
1956	J. Henricks, Australia	55.4
1960	J. Devitt, Australia	55.2
1964	D. Schollander, USA	53.4
1968	M. Wenden, Australia	52.2
1972	M. Spitz, USA	51.22
1976	J. Montgomery, USA	49.99
1980	J. Woithe, E. Germany	50.40
1984	R. Gaines, USA	49.80
1988	M. Biondi, USA	48.63
1992	A. Popov, Russia	49.02
1996	A. Popov, Russia	48.74
2000	P. van den Hoogenband, Netherlands	48.30
2004	P. van den Hoogenband, Netherlands	48.17
2008	A. Bernard, France	47.21

WOMEN

Year	Gold medalist	Time (s)
1912	F. Durack, Australia	82.2
1920	E. Bleibtrey, USA	73.6
1924	E. Lackie, USA	72.4
1928	A. Osipowich, USA	71.0
1932	H. Madison, USA	66.8
1936	H. Mastenbroek, Holland	65.9
1948	G. Andersen, Denmark	66.3
1952	K. Szoke, Hungary	66.8
1956	D. Fraser, Australia	62.0
1960	D. Fraser, Australia	61.2
1964	D. Fraser, Australia	59.5
1968	J. Henne, USA	60.0
1972	S. Nielson, USA	58.59
1976	K. Ender, E. Germany	55.65
1980	B. Krause, E. Germany	54.79
1984	(Tie) C. Steinseifer, USA	55.92
	N. Hogshead, USA	55.92
1988	K. Otto, E. Germany	54.93
1992	Z. Yong, China	54.64
1996	L. Jingyi, China	54.50
2000	I. DeBruijn, Netherlands	53.83
2004	J. Henry, Australia	53.84
2008	B. Steffen, Germany	53.12

12. **Shoe Size and Height**   Do you think that shoe size and height are correlated? Find out by surveying the shoe sizes and heights of people in your class. (Of course, the data for men and women should be separate.) Find the correlation coefficient.

13. **Demand for Candy Bars**   In this problem you will determine a linear demand equation that describes the demand for candy bars in your class. Survey your classmates to determine what price they would be willing to pay for a candy bar. Your survey form might look like the sample to the left.

    (a) Make a table of the number of respondents who answered "yes" at each price level.

    (b) Make a scatter plot of your data.

    (c) Find and graph the regression line $y = mp + b$, which gives the number of responents y who would buy a candy bar if the price were p cents. This is the *demand equation*. Why is the slope m negative?

    (d) What is the p-intercept of the demand equation? What does this intercept tell you about pricing candy bars?

Would you buy a candy bar from the vending machine in the hallway if the price is as indicated?

Price	Yes or No
30¢	
40¢	
50¢	
60¢	
70¢	
80¢	
90¢	
$1.00	
$1.10	
$1.20	

FUNCTIONS

Perhaps the most useful idea for modeling the real world is the concept of *function*. Let's look at an example. If a rock climber drops a stone from a high cliff, we know that the stone will fall. But this general description doesn't help us figure out when the stone will hit the ground. To find out, we need a *rule* that relates the distance d the stone falls to the time it has been falling. Galileo was the first to discover the rule: In t seconds the stone falls $16t^2$ feet. This "rule" is called a *function;* we write this function as $d(t) = 16t^2$. Using this function model, we can *predict* when the stone will hit the ground. In this chapter we study properties of functions and how function models can help us to get precise information about the thing or process being modeled.

 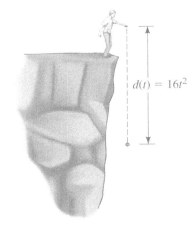

General description: The stone falls.   **Function:** In t seconds the stone falls $16t^2$ ft.

2.1 WHAT IS A FUNCTION?

Functions All Around Us ▶ Definition of Function ▶ Evaluating a Function
▶ Domain of a Function ▶ Four Ways to Represent a Function

In this section we explore the idea of a function and then give the mathematical definition of function.

▼ Functions All Around Us

In nearly every physical phenomenon we observe that one quantity depends on another. For example, your height depends on your age, the temperature depends on the date, the cost of mailing a package depends on its weight (see Figure 1). We use the term *function* to describe this dependence of one quantity on another. That is, we say the following:

- Height is a function of age.
- Temperature is a function of date.
- Cost of mailing a package is a function of weight.

The U.S. Post Office uses a simple rule to determine the cost of mailing a first-class parcel on the basis of its weight. But it's not so easy to describe the rule that relates height to age or the rule that relates temperature to date.

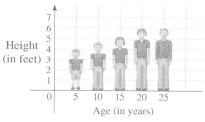

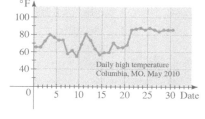

w (ounces)	Postage (dollars)
$0 < w \le 1$	1.22
$1 < w \le 2$	1.39
$2 < w \le 3$	1.56
$3 < w \le 4$	1.73
$4 < w \le 5$	1.90
$5 < w \le 6$	2.07

FIGURE 1

Height is a function of age.   Temperature is a function of date.   Postage is a function of weight.

Can you think of other functions? Here are some more examples:

- The area of a circle is a function of its radius.
- The number of bacteria in a culture is a function of time.
- The weight of an astronaut is a function of her elevation.
- The price of a commodity is a function of the demand for that commodity.

The rule that describes how the area A of a circle depends on its radius r is given by the formula $A = \pi r^2$. Even when a precise rule or formula describing a function is not available, we can still describe the function by a graph. For example, when you turn on a hot water faucet, the temperature of the water depends on how long the water has been running. So we can say:

- The temperature of water from the faucet is a function of time.

Figure 2 shows a rough graph of the temperature T of the water as a function of the time t that has elapsed since the faucet was turned on. The graph shows that the initial temperature of the water is close to room temperature. When the water from the hot water tank reaches the faucet, the water's temperature T increases quickly. In the next phase, T is constant at the temperature of the water in the tank. When the tank is drained, T decreases to the temperature of the cold water supply.

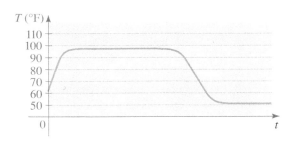

FIGURE 2 Graph of water temperature T as a function of time t

▼ Definition of Function

A function is a rule. To talk about a function, we need to give it a name. We will use letters such as $f, g, h, \ldots$ to represent functions. For example, we can use the letter f to represent a rule as follows:

$$\text{``}f\text{''} \qquad \text{is the rule} \qquad \text{``square the number''}$$

When we write $f(2)$, we mean "apply the rule f to the number 2." Applying the rule gives $f(2) = 2^2 = 4$. Similarly, $f(3) = 3^2 = 9$, $f(4) = 4^2 = 16$, and in general $f(x) = x^2$.

> **DEFINITION OF A FUNCTION**
>
> A **function** f is a rule that assigns to each element x in a set A exactly one element, called $f(x)$, in a set B.

We usually consider functions for which the sets A and B are sets of real numbers. The symbol $f(x)$ is read "f of x" or "f at x" and is called the **value of f at x**, or the **image of x under f**. The set A is called the **domain** of the function. The **range** of f is the set of all possible values of $f(x)$ as x varies throughout the domain, that is,

$$\text{range of } f = \{f(x) \mid x \in A\}$$

The symbol that represents an arbitrary number in the domain of a function f is called an **independent variable**. The symbol that represents a number in the range of f is called a **dependent variable**. So if we write $y = f(x)$, then x is the independent variable and y is the dependent variable.

It is helpful to think of a function as a **machine** (see Figure 3). If x is in the domain of the function f, then when x enters the machine, it is accepted as an **input** and the machine produces an **output** $f(x)$ according to the rule of the function. Thus, we can think of the domain as the set of all possible inputs and the range as the set of all possible outputs.

FIGURE 3 Machine diagram of f

Another way to picture a function is by an **arrow diagram** as in Figure 4. Each arrow connects an element of A to an element of B. The arrow indicates that $f(x)$ is associated with x, $f(a)$ is associated with a, and so on.

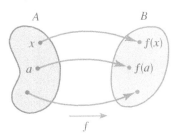

FIGURE 4 Arrow diagram of f

EXAMPLE 1 | Analyzing a Function

A function f is defined by the formula

$$f(x) = x^2 + 4$$

(a) Express in words how f acts on the input x to produce the output $f(x)$.
(b) Evaluate $f(3)$, $f(-2)$, and $f(\sqrt{5})$.
(c) Find the domain and range of f.
(d) Draw a machine diagram for f.

SOLUTION

(a) The formula tells us that f first squares the input x and then adds 4 to the result. So f is the function

"square, then add 4"

(b) The values of f are found by substituting for x in the formula $f(x) = x^2 + 4$.

$$f(3) = 3^2 + 4 = 13 \qquad \text{Replace } x \text{ by } 3$$

$$f(-2) = (-2)^2 + 4 = 8 \qquad \text{Replace } x \text{ by } -2$$

$$f(\sqrt{5}) = (\sqrt{5})^2 + 4 = 9 \qquad \text{Replace } x \text{ by } \sqrt{5}$$

(c) The domain of f consists of all possible inputs for f. Since we can evaluate the formula $f(x) = x^2 + 4$ for every real number x, the domain of f is the set $\mathbb{R}$ of all real numbers.

The range of f consists of all possible outputs of f. Because $x^2 \geq 0$ for all real numbers x, we have $x^2 + 4 \geq 4$, so for every output of f we have $f(x) \geq 4$. Thus, the range of f is $\{y \mid y \geq 4\} = [4, \infty)$.

(d) A machine diagram for f is shown in Figure 5.

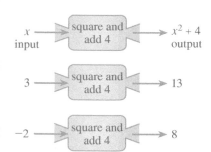

FIGURE 5 Machine diagram

NOW TRY EXERCISES **9**, **13**, **17**, AND **43**

▼ Evaluating a Function

In the definition of a function the independent variable x plays the role of a placeholder. For example, the function $f(x) = 3x^2 + x - 5$ can be thought of as

$$f(\quad) = 3 \cdot \quad^2 + \quad - 5$$

To evaluate f at a number, we substitute the number for the placeholder.

EXAMPLE 2 | Evaluating a Function

Let $f(x) = 3x^2 + x - 5$. Evaluate each function value.
(a) $f(-2)$ (b) $f(0)$ (c) $f(4)$ (d) $f(\tfrac{1}{2})$

SOLUTION   To evaluate f at a number, we substitute the number for x in the definition of f.

(a) $f(-2) = 3 \cdot (-2)^2 + (-2) - 5 = 5$

(b) $f(0) = 3 \cdot 0^2 + 0 - 5 = -5$

(c) $f(4) = 3 \cdot (4)^2 + 4 - 5 = 47$

(d) $f(\tfrac{1}{2}) = 3 \cdot (\tfrac{1}{2})^2 + \tfrac{1}{2} - 5 = -\tfrac{15}{4}$

NOW TRY EXERCISE **19**

EXAMPLE 3 | A Piecewise Defined Function

A cell phone plan costs $39 a month. The plan includes 400 free minutes and charges 20¢ for each additional minute of usage. The monthly charges are a function of the number of minutes used, given by

$$C(x) = \begin{cases} 39 & \text{if } 0 \le x \le 400 \\ 39 + 0.20(x - 400) & \text{if } x > 400 \end{cases}$$

Find $C(100)$, $C(400)$, and $C(480)$.

SOLUTION   Remember that a function is a rule. Here is how we apply the rule for this function. First we look at the value of the input x. If $0 \le x \le 400$, then the value of $C(x)$ is 39. On the other hand, if $x > 400$, then the value of $C(x)$ is $39 + 0.20(x - 400)$.

A **piecewise defined function** is defined by different formulas on different parts of its domain. The function C of Example 3 is piecewise defined.

Since $100 \le 400$, we have $C(100) = 39$.

Since $400 \le 400$, we have $C(400) = 39$.

Since $480 > 400$, we have $C(480) = 39 + 0.20(480 - 400) = 55$.

Thus, the plan charges $39 for 100 minutes, $39 for 400 minutes, and $55 for 480 minutes.

✎ . NOW TRY EXERCISE **27**

EXAMPLE 4 | Evaluating a Function

If $f(x) = 2x^2 + 3x - 1$, evaluate the following.

(a) $f(a)$ **(b)** $f(-a)$

(c) $f(a + h)$ **(d)** $\dfrac{f(a + h) - f(a)}{h}$, $h \ne 0$

Expressions like the one in part (d) of Example 4 occur frequently in calculus; they are called *difference quotients*, and they represent the average change in the value of f between $x = a$ and $x = a + h$.

SOLUTION

(a) $f(a) = 2a^2 + 3a - 1$

(b) $f(-a) = 2(-a)^2 + 3(-a) - 1 = 2a^2 - 3a - 1$

(c) $f(a + h) = 2(a + h)^2 + 3(a + h) - 1$

$$= 2(a^2 + 2ah + h^2) + 3(a + h) - 1$$

$$= 2a^2 + 4ah + 2h^2 + 3a + 3h - 1$$

(d) Using the results from parts (c) and (a), we have

$$\frac{f(a + h) - f(a)}{h} = \frac{(2a^2 + 4ah + 2h^2 + 3a + 3h - 1) - (2a^2 + 3a - 1)}{h}$$

$$= \frac{4ah + 2h^2 + 3h}{h} = 4a + 2h + 3$$

✎ . NOW TRY EXERCISE **35**

EXAMPLE 5 | The Weight of an Astronaut

If an astronaut weighs 130 pounds on the surface of the earth, then her weight when she is h miles above the earth is given by the function

$$w(h) = 130\left(\frac{3960}{3960 + h}\right)^2$$

(a) What is her weight when she is 100 mi above the earth?

The weight of an object on or near the earth is the gravitational force that the earth exerts on it. When in orbit around the earth, an astronaut experiences the sensation of "weightlessness" because the centripetal force that keeps her in orbit is exactly the same as the gravitational pull of the earth.

(b) Construct a table of values for the function w that gives her weight at heights from 0 to 500 mi. What do you conclude from the table?

SOLUTION

(a) We want the value of the function w when $h = 100$; that is, we must calculate $w(100)$.

$$w(100) = 130\left(\frac{3960}{3960 + 100}\right)^2 \approx 123.67$$

So at a height of 100 mi she weighs about 124 lb.

(b) The table gives the astronaut's weight, rounded to the nearest pound, at 100-mile increments. The values in the table are calculated as in part (a).

h	$w(h)$
0	130
100	124
200	118
300	112
400	107
500	102

The table indicates that the higher the astronaut travels, the less she weighs.

✎. NOW TRY EXERCISE **71**

▼ The Domain of a Function

Recall that the *domain* of a function is the set of all inputs for the function. The domain of a function may be stated explicitly. For example, if we write

$$f(x) = x^2 \qquad 0 \le x \le 5$$

then the domain is the set of all real numbers x for which $0 \le x \le 5$. If the function is given by an algebraic expression and the domain is not stated explicitly, then by convention *the domain of the function is the domain of the algebraic expression—that is, the set of all real numbers for which the expression is defined as a real number*. For example, consider the functions

Domains of algebraic expressions are discussed on page 35.

$$f(x) = \frac{1}{x - 4} \qquad g(x) = \sqrt{x}$$

The function f is not defined at $x = 4$, so its domain is $\{x \mid x \ne 4\}$. The function g is not defined for negative x, so its domain is $\{x \mid x \ge 0\}$.

EXAMPLE 6 | Finding Domains of Functions

Find the domain of each function.

(a) $f(x) = \dfrac{1}{x^2 - x}$ **(b)** $g(x) = \sqrt{9 - x^2}$ **(c)** $h(t) = \dfrac{t}{\sqrt{t + 1}}$

SECTION 2.1 | What Is a Function? **147**

SOLUTION

(a) A rational expression is not defined when the denominator is 0. Since

$$f(x) = \frac{1}{x^2 - x} = \frac{1}{x(x-1)}$$

we see that $f(x)$ is not defined when $x = 0$ or $x = 1$. Thus, the domain of f is

$$\{x \mid x \neq 0, x \neq 1\}$$

The domain may also be written in interval notation as

$$(\infty, 0) \cup (0, 1) \cup (1, \infty)$$

(b) We can't take the square root of a negative number, so we must have $9 - x^2 \geq 0$. Using the methods of Section 1.7, we can solve this inequality to find that $-3 \leq x \leq 3$. Thus, the domain of g is

$$\{x \mid -3 \leq x \leq 3\} = [-3, 3]$$

(c) We can't take the square root of a negative number, and we can't divide by 0, so we must have $t + 1 > 0$, that is, $t > -1$. So the domain of h is

$$\{t \mid t > -1\} = (-1, \infty)$$

NOW TRY EXERCISES 47 AND 51

▼ Four Ways to Represent a Function

To help us understand what a function is, we have used machine and arrow diagrams. We can describe a specific function in the following four ways:

- verbally (by a description in words)
- algebraically (by an explicit formula)
- visually (by a graph)
- numerically (by a table of values)

A single function may be represented in all four ways, and it is often useful to go from one representation to another to gain insight into the function. However, certain functions are described more naturally by one method than by the others. An example of a verbal description is the following rule for converting between temperature scales:

"To find the Fahrenheit equivalent of a Celsius temperature, multiply the Celsius temperature by $\frac{9}{5}$, then add 32."

In Example 7 we see how to describe this verbal rule or function algebraically, graphically, and numerically. A useful representation of the area of a circle as a function of its radius is the algebraic formula

$$A(r) = \pi r^2$$

The graph produced by a seismograph (see the box on the next page) is a visual representation of the vertical acceleration function $a(t)$ of the ground during an earthquake. As a final example, consider the function $C(w)$, which is described verbally as "the cost of mailing a first-class letter with weight w." The most convenient way of describing this function is numerically—that is, using a table of values.

We will be using all four representations of functions throughout this book. We summarize them in the following box.

FOUR WAYS TO REPRESENT A FUNCTION

Verbal

Using words:

"To convert from Celsius to Fahrenheit, multiply the Celsius temperature by $\frac{9}{5}$, then add 32."

Relation between Celsius and Fahrenheit temperature scales

Algebraic

Using a formula:

$$A(r) = \pi r^2$$

Area of a circle

Visual

Using a graph:

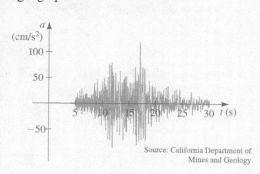

Source: California Department of Mines and Geology

Vertical acceleration during an earthquake

Numerical

Using a table of values:

w (ounces)	$C(w)$ (dollars)
$0 < w \le 1$	1.22
$1 < w \le 2$	1.39
$2 < w \le 3$	1.56
$3 < w \le 4$	1.73
$4 < w \le 5$	1.90
$\vdots$	$\vdots$

Cost of mailing a first-class parcel

EXAMPLE 7 | Representing a Function Verbally, Algebraically, Numerically, and Graphically

Let $F(C)$ be the Fahrenheit temperature corresponding to the Celsius temperature C. (Thus, F is the function that converts Celsius inputs to Fahrenheit outputs.) The box above gives a verbal description of this function. Find ways to represent this function

(a) Algebraically (using a formula)

(b) Numerically (using a table of values)

(c) Visually (using a graph)

SOLUTION

(a) The verbal description tells us that we should first multiply the input C by $\frac{9}{5}$ and then add 32 to the result. So we get

$$F(C) = \tfrac{9}{5}C + 32$$

(b) We use the algebraic formula for F that we found in part (a) to construct a table of values:

C (Celsius)	F (Fahrenheit)
-10	14
0	32
10	50
20	68
30	86
40	104

(c) We use the points tabulated in part (b) to help us draw the graph of this function in Figure 6.

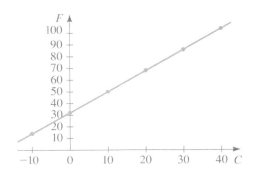

FIGURE 6 Celsius and Fahrenheit

NOW TRY EXERCISE **65**

2.1 EXERCISES

CONCEPTS

1. If a function f is given by the formula $y = f(x)$, then $f(a)$ is the _____ of f at $x = a$.

2. For a function f, the set of all possible inputs is called the _____ of f, and the set of all possible outputs is called the _____ of f.

3. (a) Which of the following functions have 5 in their domain?

$$f(x) = x^2 - 3x \qquad g(x) = \frac{x-5}{x} \qquad h(x) = \sqrt{x-10}$$

(b) For the functions from part (a) that *do* have 5 in their domain, find the value of the function at 5.

4. A function is given algebraically by the formula $f(x) = (x-4)^2 + 3$. Complete these other ways to represent f:

(a) *Verbal:* "Subtract 4, then ___square___ and ___add 3___."

(b) *Numerical:*

$y = 2$.

x	$f(x)$
0	19
2	7.
4	3.
6	7.

$(x-4)^2 + 3.$
$(2-4)^2 + 3.$
$(-2)^2 + 3 = 7.$

$4 + 3$

SKILLS

5–8 ■ Express the rule in function notation. (For example, the rule "square, then subtract 5" is expressed as the function $f(x) = x^2 - 5$.)

5. Add 3, then multiply by 2

6. Divide by 7, then subtract 4

7. Subtract 5, then square

8. Take the square root, add 8, then multiply by $\frac{1}{3}$

9–12 ■ Express the function (or rule) in words.

9. $h(x) = x^2 + 2$ Square add 2

10. $k(x) = \sqrt{x+2}$ take the square root of x+2.

11. $f(x) = \dfrac{x-4}{3}$ subtract by 4 divided by 3.

12. $g(x) = \dfrac{x}{3} - 4$ divided by 3 subtract by 4.

13–14 ■ Draw a machine diagram for the function.

13. $f(x) = \sqrt{x-1}$

14. $f(x) = \dfrac{3}{x-2}$

15–16 ■ Complete the table.

15. $f(x) = 2(x-1)^2$

16. $g(x) = |2x+3|$

x	$f(x)$
-1	
0	
1	
2	
3	

$2(-1-1)^2 = 8$
$2(0-1)^2 = 2$
$2(1-1)^2 = 0$
$2(3-1)^2 = 8$

x	$g(x)$
-3	$2(-3+3) = 2(0) = 0$
-2	$2(-2+3) = 2(-1)$
0	$2(0+3)$
1	$2(1+3)$
3	$2(3+3)$

17–26 ■ Evaluate the function at the indicated values.

17. $f(x) = x^2 - 6;$ $f(-3), f(3), f(0), f\left(\frac{1}{2}\right), f(10)$

18. $f(x) = x^3 + 2x;$ $f(-2), f(1), f(0), f\left(\frac{1}{3}\right), f(0.2)$

19. $f(x) = 2x + 1;$
$f(1), f(-2), f\left(\frac{1}{2}\right), f(a), f(-a), f(a+b)$

20. $f(x) = x^2 + 2x;$
$f(0), f(3), f(-3), f(a), f(-x), f\left(\dfrac{1}{a}\right)$

21. $g(x) = \dfrac{1-x}{1+x};$
$g(2), g(-2), g\left(\frac{1}{2}\right), g(a), g(a-1), g(-1)$

22. $h(t) = t + \dfrac{1}{t}$;

$h(1), h(-1), h(2), h(\tfrac{1}{2}), h(x), h\left(\dfrac{1}{x}\right)$

23. $f(x) = 2x^2 + 3x - 4$;

$f(0), f(2), f(-2), f(\sqrt{2}), f(x + 1), f(-x)$

24. $f(x) = x^3 - 4x^2$;

$f(0), f(1), f(-1), f(\tfrac{3}{2}), f\left(\dfrac{x}{2}\right), f(x^2)$

25. $f(x) = 2|x - 1|$;

$f(-2), f(0), f(\tfrac{1}{2}), f(2), f(x + 1), f(x^2 + 2)$

26. $f(x) = \dfrac{|x|}{x}$;

$f(-2), f(-1), f(0), f(5), f(x^2), f\left(\dfrac{1}{x}\right)$

27–30 ■ Evaluate the piecewise defined function at the indicated values.

27. $f(x) = \begin{cases} x^2 & \text{if } x < 0 \\ x + 1 & \text{if } x \geq 0 \end{cases}$

$f(-2), f(-1), f(0), f(1), f(2)$

28. $f(x) = \begin{cases} 5 & \text{if } x \leq 2 \\ 2x - 3 & \text{if } x > 2 \end{cases}$

$f(-3), f(0), f(2), f(3), f(5)$

29. $f(x) = \begin{cases} x^2 + 2x & \text{if } x \leq -1 \\ x & \text{if } -1 < x \leq 1 \\ -1 & \text{if } x > 1 \end{cases}$

$f(-4), f(-\tfrac{3}{2}), f(-1), f(0), f(25)$

30. $f(x) = \begin{cases} 3x & \text{if } x < 0 \\ x + 1 & \text{if } 0 \leq x \leq 2 \\ (x - 2)^2 & \text{if } x > 2 \end{cases}$

$f(-5), f(0), f(1), f(2), f(5)$

31–34 ■ Use the function to evaluate the indicated expressions and simplify.

31. $f(x) = x^2 + 1$; $f(x + 2), f(x) + f(2)$

32. $f(x) = 3x - 1$; $f(2x), 2f(x)$

33. $f(x) = x + 4$; $f(x^2), (f(x))^2$

34. $f(x) = 6x - 18$; $f\left(\dfrac{x}{3}\right), \dfrac{f(x)}{3}$

35–42 ■ Find $f(a)$, $f(a + h)$, and the difference quotient $\dfrac{f(a + h) - f(a)}{h}$, where $h \neq 0$.

35. $f(x) = 3x + 2$

36. $f(x) = x^2 + 1$

37. $f(x) = 5$

38. $f(x) = \dfrac{1}{x + 1}$

39. $f(x) = \dfrac{x}{x + 1}$

40. $f(x) = \dfrac{2x}{x - 1}$

41. $f(x) = 3 - 5x + 4x^2$

42. $f(x) = x^3$

43–64 ■ Find the domain of the function.

43. $f(x) = 2x$

44. $f(x) = x^2 + 1$

45. $f(x) = 2x, \quad -1 \leq x \leq 5$

46. $f(x) = x^2 + 1, \quad 0 \leq x \leq 5$

47. $f(x) = \dfrac{1}{x - 3}$

48. $f(x) = \dfrac{1}{3x - 6}$

49. $f(x) = \dfrac{x + 2}{x^2 - 1}$

50. $f(x) = \dfrac{x^4}{x^2 + x - 6}$

51. $f(x) = \sqrt{x - 5}$

52. $f(x) = \sqrt[4]{x + 9}$

53. $f(t) = \sqrt[3]{t - 1}$

54. $g(x) = \sqrt{7 - 3x}$

55. $h(x) = \sqrt{2x - 5}$

56. $G(x) = \sqrt{x^2 - 9}$

57. $g(x) = \dfrac{\sqrt{2 + x}}{3 - x}$

58. $g(x) = \dfrac{\sqrt{x}}{2x^2 + x - 1}$

59. $g(x) = \sqrt[4]{x^2 - 6x}$

60. $g(x) = \sqrt{x^2 - 2x - 8}$

61. $f(x) = \dfrac{3}{\sqrt{x - 4}}$

62. $f(x) = \dfrac{x^2}{\sqrt{6 - x}}$

63. $f(x) = \dfrac{(x + 1)^2}{\sqrt{2x - 1}}$

64. $f(x) = \dfrac{x}{\sqrt[4]{9 - x^2}}$

65–68 ■ A verbal description of a function is given. Find **(a)** algebraic, **(b)** numerical, and **(c)** graphical representations for the function.

65. To evaluate $f(x)$, divide the input by 3 and add $\tfrac{2}{3}$ to the result.

66. To evaluate $g(x)$, subtract 4 from the input and multiply the result by $\tfrac{3}{4}$.

67. Let $T(x)$ be the amount of sales tax charged in Lemon County on a purchase of x dollars. To find the tax, take 8% of the purchase price.

68. Let $V(d)$ be the volume of a sphere of diameter d. To find the volume, take the cube of the diameter, then multiply by π and divide by 6.

APPLICATIONS

69. Production Cost   The cost C in dollars of producing x yards of a certain fabric is given by the function

$$C(x) = 1500 + 3x + 0.02x^2 + 0.0001x^3$$

(a) Find $C(10)$ and $C(100)$.

(b) What do your answers in part (a) represent?

(c) Find $C(0)$. (This number represents the *fixed costs*.)

70. Area of a Sphere The surface area S of a sphere is a function of its radius r given by

$$S(r) = 4\pi r^2$$

(a) Find $S(2)$ and $S(3)$.
(b) What do your answers in part (a) represent?

71. Torricelli's Law A tank holds 50 gallons of water, which drains from a leak at the bottom, causing the tank to empty in 20 minutes. The tank drains faster when it is nearly full because the pressure on the leak is greater. **Torricelli's Law** gives the volume of water remaining in the tank after t minutes as

$$V(t) = 50\left(1 - \frac{t}{20}\right)^2 \qquad 0 \le t \le 20$$

(a) Find $V(0)$ and $V(20)$.
(b) What do your answers to part (a) represent?
(c) Make a table of values of $V(t)$ for $t = 0, 5, 10, 15, 20$.

72. How Far Can You See? Because of the curvature of the earth, the maximum distance D that you can see from the top of a tall building or from an airplane at height h is given by the function

$$D(h) = \sqrt{2rh + h^2}$$

where $r = 3960$ mi is the radius of the earth and D and h are measured in miles.
(a) Find $D(0.1)$ and $D(0.2)$.
(b) How far can you see from the observation deck of Toronto's CN Tower, 1135 ft above the ground?
(c) Commercial aircraft fly at an altitude of about 7 mi. How far can the pilot see?

73. Blood Flow As blood moves through a vein or an artery, its velocity v is greatest along the central axis and decreases as the distance r from the central axis increases (see the figure). The formula that gives v as a function of r is called the **law of laminar flow**. For an artery with radius 0.5 cm, the relationship between v (in cm/s) and r (in cm) is given by the function

$$v(r) = 18{,}500(0.25 - r^2) \qquad 0 \le r \le 0.5$$

(a) Find $v(0.1)$ and $v(0.4)$.
(b) What do your answers to part (a) tell you about the flow of blood in this artery?
(c) Make a table of values of $v(r)$ for $r = 0, 0.1, 0.2, 0.3, 0.4, 0.5$.

74. Pupil Size When the brightness x of a light source is increased, the eye reacts by decreasing the radius R of the pupil. The dependence of R on x is given by the function

$$R(x) = \sqrt{\frac{13 + 7x^{0.4}}{1 + 4x^{0.4}}}$$

where R is measured in millimeters and x is measured in appropriate units of brightness.
(a) Find $R(1)$, $R(10)$, and $R(100)$.
(b) Make a table of values of $R(x)$.

75. Relativity According to the Theory of Relativity, the length L of an object is a function of its velocity v with respect to an observer. For an object whose length at rest is 10 m, the function is given by

$$L(v) = 10\sqrt{1 - \frac{v^2}{c^2}}$$

where c is the speed of light (300,000 km/s).
(a) Find $L(0.5c)$, $L(0.75c)$, and $L(0.9c)$.
(b) How does the length of an object change as its velocity increases?

76. Income Tax In a certain country, income tax T is assessed according to the following function of income x:

$$T(x) = \begin{cases} 0 & \text{if } 0 \le x \le 10{,}000 \\ 0.08x & \text{if } 10{,}000 < x \le 20{,}000 \\ 1600 + 0.15x & \text{if } 20{,}000 < x \end{cases}$$

(a) Find $T(5{,}000)$, $T(12{,}000)$, and $T(25{,}000)$.
(b) What do your answers in part (a) represent?

77. Internet Purchases An Internet bookstore charges $15 shipping for orders under $100 but provides free shipping for orders of $100 or more. The cost C of an order is a function of the total price x of the books purchased, given by

$$C(x) = \begin{cases} x + 15 & \text{if } x < 100 \\ x & \text{if } x \ge 100 \end{cases}$$

(a) Find $C(75)$, $C(90)$, $C(100)$, and $C(105)$.
(b) What do your answers in part (a) represent?

78. Cost of a Hotel Stay A hotel chain charges $75 each night for the first two nights and $50 for each additional night's stay. The total cost T is a function of the number of nights x that a guest stays.

(a) Complete the expressions in the following piecewise defined function.

$$T(x) = \begin{cases} \rule{1cm}{0.4pt} & \text{if } 0 \le x \le 2 \\ \rule{1cm}{0.4pt} & \text{if } x > 2 \end{cases}$$

(b) Find $T(2)$, $T(3)$, and $T(5)$.

(c) What do your answers in part (b) represent?

79. Speeding Tickets In a certain state the maximum speed permitted on freeways is 65 mi/h, and the minimum is 40. The fine F for violating these limits is \$15 for every mile above the maximum or below the minimum.

(a) Complete the expressions in the following piecewise defined function, where x is the speed at which you are driving.

$$F(x) = \begin{cases} \rule{1cm}{0.4pt} & \text{if } 0 < x < 40 \\ \rule{1cm}{0.4pt} & \text{if } 40 \le x \le 65 \\ \rule{1cm}{0.4pt} & \text{if } x > 65 \end{cases}$$

(b) Find $F(30)$, $F(50)$, and $F(75)$.

(c) What do your answers in part (b) represent?

80. Height of Grass A home owner mows the lawn every Wednesday afternoon. Sketch a rough graph of the height of the grass as a function of time over the course of a four-week period beginning on a Sunday.

81. Temperature Change You place a frozen pie in an oven and bake it for an hour. Then you take the pie out and let it cool before eating it. Sketch a rough graph of the temperature of the pie as a function of time.

82. Daily Temperature Change Temperature readings T (in °F) were recorded every 2 hours from midnight to noon in Atlanta, Georgia, on March 18, 1996. The time t was measured in hours from midnight. Sketch a rough graph of T as a function of t.

t	0	2	4	6	8	10	12
T	58	57	53	50	51	57	61

83. Population Growth The population P (in thousands) of San Jose, California, from 1988 to 2000 is shown in the table. (Midyear estimates are given.) Draw a rough graph of P as a function of time t.

t	1988	1990	1992	1994	1996	1998	2000
P	733	782	800	817	838	861	895

DISCOVERY ▪ DISCUSSION ▪ WRITING

84. Examples of Functions At the beginning of this section we discussed three examples of everyday, ordinary functions: Height is a function of age, temperature is a function of date, and postage cost is a function of weight. Give three other examples of functions from everyday life.

85. Four Ways to Represent a Function In the box on page 148 we represented four different functions verbally, algebraically, visually, and numerically. Think of a function that can be represented in all four ways, and write the four representations.

2.2 GRAPHS OF FUNCTIONS

Graphing Functions by Plotting Points ▶ Graphing Functions with a Graphing Calculator ▶ Graphing Piecewise Defined Functions ▶ The Vertical Line Test ▶ Equations That Define Functions

The most important way to visualize a function is through its graph. In this section we investigate in more detail the concept of graphing functions.

▼ Graphing Functions by Plotting Points

To graph a function f, we plot the points $(x, f(x))$ in a coordinate plane. In other words, we plot the points (x, y) whose x-coordinate is an input and whose y-coordinate is the corresponding output of the function.

THE GRAPH OF A FUNCTION

If f is a function with domain A, then the **graph** of f is the set of ordered pairs

$$\{(x, f(x)) \mid x \in A\}$$

plotted in a coordinate plane. In other words, the graph of f is the set of all points (x, y) such that $y = f(x)$; that is, the graph of f is the graph of the equation $y = f(x)$.

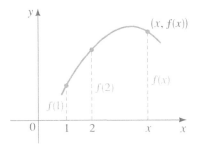

FIGURE 1 The height of the graph above the point x is the value of $f(x)$.

The graph of a function f gives a picture of the behavior or "life history" of the function. We can read the value of $f(x)$ from the graph as being the height of the graph above the point x (see Figure 1).

A function f of the form $f(x) = mx + b$ is called a **linear function** because its graph is the graph of the equation $y = mx + b$, which represents a line with slope m and y-intercept b. A special case of a linear function occurs when the slope is $m = 0$. The function $f(x) = b$, where b is a given number, is called a **constant function** because all its values are the same number, namely, b. Its graph is the horizontal line $y = b$. Figure 2 shows the graphs of the constant function $f(x) = 3$ and the linear function $f(x) = 2x + 1$.

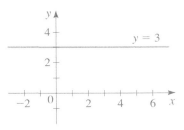

The constant function $f(x) = 3$

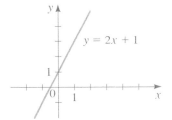

The linear function $f(x) = 2x + 1$

FIGURE 2

EXAMPLE 1 | Graphing Functions by Plotting Points

Sketch graphs of the following functions.

(a) $f(x) = x^2$ **(b)** $g(x) = x^3$ **(c)** $h(x) = \sqrt{x}$

SOLUTION   We first make a table of values. Then we plot the points given by the table and join them by a smooth curve to obtain the graph. The graphs are sketched in Figure 3 on the next page.

x	$f(x) = x^2$
0	0
$\pm\frac{1}{2}$	$\frac{1}{4}$
± 1	1
± 2	4
± 3	9

x	$g(x) = x^3$
0	0
$\frac{1}{2}$	$\frac{1}{8}$
1	1
2	8
$-\frac{1}{2}$	$-\frac{1}{8}$
-1	-1
-2	-8

x	$h(x) = \sqrt{x}$
0	0
1	1
2	$\sqrt{2}$
3	$\sqrt{3}$
4	2
5	$\sqrt{5}$

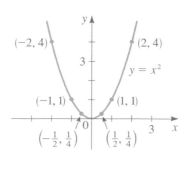

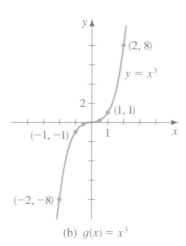

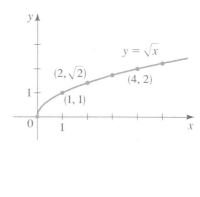

FIGURE 3   (a) $f(x) = x^2$ (b) $g(x) = x^3$ (c) $h(x) = \sqrt{x}$

✎ NOW TRY EXERCISES **11**, **15**, AND **19**

▼ Graphing Functions with a Graphing Calculator

A convenient way to graph a function is to use a graphing calculator. Because the graph of a function f is the graph of the equation $y = f(x)$, we can use the methods of Section 1.9 to graph functions on a graphing calculator.

EXAMPLE 2 | Graphing a Function with a Graphing Calculator

Use a graphing calculator to graph the function $f(x) = x^3 - 8x^2$ in an appropriate viewing rectangle.

SOLUTION   To graph the function $f(x) = x^3 - 8x^2$, we must graph the equation $y = x^3 - 8x^2$. On the TI-83 graphing calculator the default viewing rectangle gives the graph in Figure 4(a). But this graph appears to spill over the top and bottom of the screen. We need to expand the vertical axis to get a better representation of the graph. The viewing rectangle $[-4, 10]$ by $[-100, 100]$ gives a more complete picture of the graph, as shown in Figure 4(b).

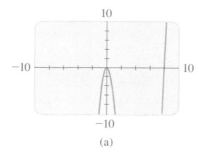

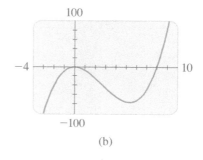

FIGURE 4 Graphing the function
$f(x) = x^3 - 8x^2$

(a)   (b)

✎ NOW TRY EXERCISE **29**

EXAMPLE 3 | A Family of Power Functions

(a) Graph the functions $f(x) = x^n$ for $n = 2$, 4, and 6 in the viewing rectangle $[-2, 2]$ by $[-1, 3]$.

(b) Graph the functions $f(x) = x^n$ for $n = 1$, 3, and 5 in the viewing rectangle $[-2, 2]$ by $[-2, 2]$.

(c) What conclusions can you draw from these graphs?

SOLUTION To graph the function $f(x) = x^n$, we graph the equation $y = x^n$. The graphs for parts (a) and (b) are shown in Figure 5.

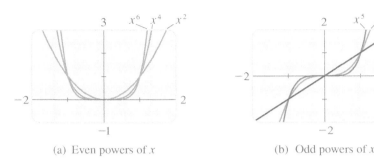

FIGURE 5 A family of power functions $f(x) = x^n$

(a) Even powers of x

(b) Odd powers of x

(c) We see that the general shape of the graph of $f(x) = x^n$ depends on whether n is even or odd.

If n is even, the graph of $f(x) = x^n$ is similar to the parabola $y = x^2$.

If n is odd, the graph of $f(x) = x^n$ is similar to that of $y = x^3$.

■ NOW TRY EXERCISE 69

Notice from Figure 5 that as n increases, the graph of $y = x^n$ becomes flatter near 0 and steeper when $x > 1$. When $0 < x < 1$, the lower powers of x are the "bigger" functions. But when $x > 1$, the higher powers of x are the dominant functions.

▼ Graphing Piecewise Defined Functions

A piecewise defined function is defined by different formulas on different parts of its domain. As you might expect, the graph of such a function consists of separate pieces.

EXAMPLE 4 | Graph of a Piecewise Defined Function

Sketch the graph of the function.

$$f(x) = \begin{cases} x^2 & \text{if } x \le 1 \\ 2x + 1 & \text{if } x > 1 \end{cases}$$

SOLUTION If $x \le 1$, then $f(x) = x^2$, so the part of the graph to the left of $x = 1$ coincides with the graph of $y = x^2$, which we sketched in Figure 3. If $x > 1$, then $f(x) = 2x + 1$, so the part of the graph to the right of $x = 1$ coincides with the line $y = 2x + 1$, which we graphed in Figure 2. This enables us to sketch the graph in Figure 6.

The solid dot at $(1, 1)$ indicates that this point is included in the graph; the open dot at $(1, 3)$ indicates that this point is excluded from the graph.

On many graphing calculators the graph in Figure 6 can be produced by using the logical functions in the calculator. For example, on the TI-83 the following equation gives the required graph:

$Y_1 = (X < 1)X^2 + (X > 1)(2X + 1)$

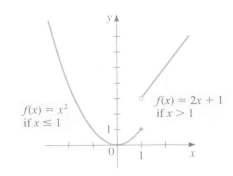

(To avoid the extraneous vertical line between the two parts of the graph, put the calculator in Dot mode.)

$f(x) = x^2$
if $x \le 1$

$f(x) = 2x + 1$
if $x > 1$

FIGURE 6

$$f(x) = \begin{cases} x^2 & \text{if } x \le 1 \\ 2x + 1 & \text{if } x > 1 \end{cases}$$

■ NOW TRY EXERCISE 35

EXAMPLE 5 | Graph of the Absolute Value Function

Sketch a graph of the absolute value function $f(x) = |x|$.

SOLUTION   Recall that

$$|x| = \begin{cases} x & \text{if } x \geq 0 \\ -x & \text{if } x < 0 \end{cases}$$

Using the same method as in Example 4, we note that the graph of f coincides with the line $y = x$ to the right of the y-axis and coincides with the line $y = -x$ to the left of the y-axis (see Figure 7).

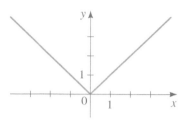

FIGURE 7 Graph of $f(x) = |x|$

✎. NOW TRY EXERCISE **23**

The **greatest integer function** is defined by

$$[\![x]\!] = \text{greatest integer less than or equal to } x$$

For example, $[\![2]\!] = 2$, $[\![2.3]\!] = 2$, $[\![1.999]\!] = 1$, $[\![0.002]\!] = 0$, $[\![-3.5]\!] = -4$, and $[\![-0.5]\!] = -1$.

EXAMPLE 6 | Graph of the Greatest Integer Function

Sketch a graph of $f(x) = [\![x]\!]$.

SOLUTION   The table shows the values of f for some values of x. Note that $f(x)$ is constant between consecutive integers, so the graph between integers is a horizontal line segment, as shown in Figure 8.

x	$[\![x]\!]$
⋮	⋮
$-2 \leq x < -1$	-2
$-1 \leq x < 0$	-1
$0 \leq x < 1$	0
$1 \leq x < 2$	1
$2 \leq x < 3$	2
⋮	⋮

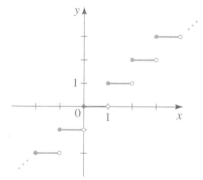

FIGURE 8 The greatest integer function, $y = [\![x]\!]$

The greatest integer function is an example of a **step function**. The next example gives a real-world example of a step function.

EXAMPLE 7 | The Cost Function for Long-Distance Phone Calls

The cost of a long-distance daytime phone call from Toronto, Canada, to Mumbai, India, is 69 cents for the first minute and 58 cents for each additional minute (or part of a minute). Draw the graph of the cost C (in dollars) of the phone call as a function of time t (in minutes).

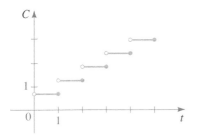

FIGURE 9 Cost of a long-distance call

Continuous functions are defined more precisely in Section 13.2, on page 851.

SOLUTION Let $C(t)$ be the cost for t minutes. Since $t > 0$, the domain of the function is $(0, \infty)$. From the given information we have

$$C(t) = 0.69 \qquad\qquad \text{if } 0 < t \le 1$$
$$C(t) = 0.69 + 0.58 = 1.27 \qquad \text{if } 1 < t \le 2$$
$$C(t) = 0.69 + 2(0.58) = 1.85 \quad \text{if } 2 < t \le 3$$
$$C(t) = 0.69 + 3(0.58) = 2.43 \quad \text{if } 3 < t \le 4$$

and so on. The graph is shown in Figure 9.

✎. NOW TRY EXERCISE **81**

A function is called **continuous** if its graph has no "breaks" or "holes." The functions in Examples 1, 2, 3, and 5 are continuous; the functions in Examples 4, 6, and 7 are not continuous.

▼ The Vertical Line Test

The graph of a function is a curve in the xy-plane. But the question arises: Which curves in the xy-plane are graphs of functions? This is answered by the following test.

> **THE VERTICAL LINE TEST**
>
> A curve in the coordinate plane is the graph of a function if and only if no vertical line intersects the curve more than once.

We can see from Figure 10 why the Vertical Line Test is true. If each vertical line $x = a$ intersects a curve only once at (a, b), then exactly one functional value is defined by $f(a) = b$. But if a line $x = a$ intersects the curve twice, at (a, b) and at (a, c), then the curve cannot represent a function because a function cannot assign two different values to a.

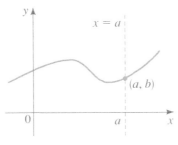

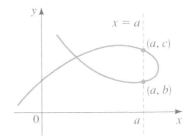

FIGURE 10 Vertical Line Test

Graph of a function

Not a graph of a function

EXAMPLE 8 | Using the Vertical Line Test

Using the Vertical Line Test, we see that the curves in parts (b) and (c) of Figure 11 represent functions, whereas those in parts (a) and (d) do not.

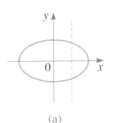

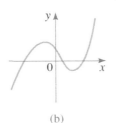

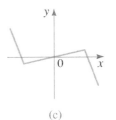

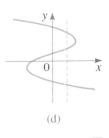

FIGURE 11   (a)   (b)   (c)   (d)

✎. NOW TRY EXERCISE **51**

▼ Equations That Define Functions

Any equation in the variables x and y defines a relationship between these variables. For example, the equation

$$y - x^2 = 0$$

defines a relationship between y and x. Does this equation define y as a *function* of x? To find out, we solve for y and get

$$y = x^2$$

We see that the equation defines a rule, or function, that gives one value of y for each value of x. We can express this rule in function notation as

$$f(x) = x^2$$

But not every equation defines y as a function of x, as the following example shows.

EXAMPLE 9 | Equations That Define Functions

Does the equation define y as a function of x?

(a) $y - x^2 = 2$ **(b)** $x^2 + y^2 = 4$

SOLUTION

(a) Solving for y in terms of x gives

$$y - x^2 = 2$$
$$y = x^2 + 2 \qquad \text{Add } x^2$$

The last equation is a rule that gives one value of y for each value of x, so it defines y as a function of x. We can write the function as $f(x) = x^2 + 2$.

(b) We try to solve for y in terms of x:

$$x^2 + y^2 = 4$$
$$y^2 = 4 - x^2 \qquad \text{Subtract } x^2$$
$$y = \pm\sqrt{4 - x^2} \qquad \text{Take square roots}$$

The last equation gives two values of y for a given value of x. Thus, the equation does not define y as a function of x.

✎. NOW TRY EXERCISES **57** AND **61**

The graphs of the equations in Example 9 are shown in Figure 12. The Vertical Line Test shows graphically that the equation in Example 9(a) defines a function but the equation in Example 9(b) does not.

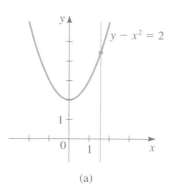

(a)

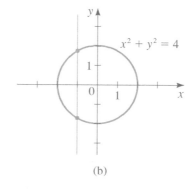

(b)

FIGURE 12

DONALD KNUTH was born in Milwaukee in 1938 and is Professor Emeritus of Computer Science at Stanford University. When Knuth was a high school student, he became fascinated with graphs of functions and laboriously drew many hundreds of them because he wanted to see the behavior of a great variety of functions. (Today, of course, it is far easier to use computers and graphing calculators to do this.) While still a graduate student at Caltech, he started writing a monumental series of books entitled *The Art of Computer Programming*.

Knuth is famous for his invention of T$_E$X, a system of computer-assisted typesetting. This system was used in the preparation of the manuscript for this textbook.

Knuth has received numerous honors, among them election as an associate of the French Academy of Sciences, and as a Fellow of the Royal Society. President Carter awarded him the National Medal of Science in 1979.

The following table shows the graphs of some functions that you will see frequently in this book.

SOME FUNCTIONS AND THEIR GRAPHS

Linear functions
$f(x) = mx + b$

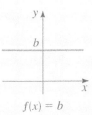

$f(x) = b$ $\qquad$ $f(x) = mx + b$

Power functions
$f(x) = x^n$

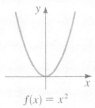 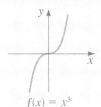 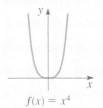 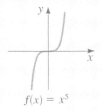

$f(x) = x^2$ $\qquad$ $f(x) = x^3$ $\qquad$ $f(x) = x^4$ $\qquad$ $f(x) = x^5$

Root functions
$f(x) = \sqrt[n]{x}$

   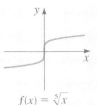

$f(x) = \sqrt{x}$ $\qquad$ $f(x) = \sqrt[3]{x}$ $\qquad$ $f(x) = \sqrt[4]{x}$ $\qquad$ $f(x) = \sqrt[5]{x}$

Reciprocal functions
$f(x) = \dfrac{1}{x^n}$

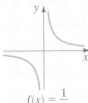 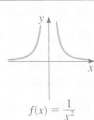

$f(x) = \dfrac{1}{x}$ $\qquad$ $f(x) = \dfrac{1}{x^2}$

Absolute value function
$f(x) = |x|$

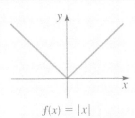

$f(x) = |x|$

Greatest integer function
$f(x) = [\![x]\!]$

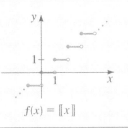

$f(x) = [\![x]\!]$

2.2 EXERCISES

CONCEPTS

1. To graph the function f, we plot the points $(x, \underline{\hspace{1cm}})$ in a coordinate plane. To graph $f(x) = x^3 + 2$, we plot the points $(x, \underline{\hspace{1cm}})$. So the point $(2, \underline{\hspace{1cm}})$ is on the graph of f.

The height of the graph of f above the x-axis when $x = 2$ is

$\underline{\hspace{1cm}}$.

2. If $f(2) = 3$, then the point $(2, \underline{\hspace{1cm}})$ is on the graph of f.

3. If the point $(2, 3)$ is on the graph of f, then $f(2) = $ _____.

4. Match the function with its graph.

   (a) $f(x) = x^2$ **(b)** $f(x) = x^3$

   (c) $f(x) = \sqrt{x}$ **(d)** $f(x) = |x|$

I
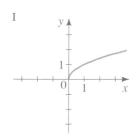

II
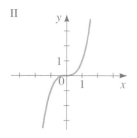

III
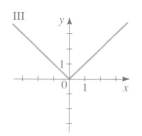

IV
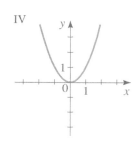

SKILLS

5–28 ■ Sketch the graph of the function by first making a table of values.

5. $f(x) = 2$ **6.** $f(x) = -3$

7. $f(x) = 2x - 4$ **8.** $f(x) = 6 - 3x$

9. $f(x) = -x + 3, \quad -3 \le x \le 3$

10. $f(x) = \dfrac{x - 3}{2}, \quad 0 \le x \le 5$

11. $f(x) = -x^2$ **12.** $f(x) = x^2 - 4$

13. $h(x) = 16 - x^2$ **14.** $g(x) = (x - 3)^2$

15. $g(x) = x^3 - 8$ **16.** $g(x) = (x + 2)^3$

17. $g(x) = x^2 - 2x$ **18.** $h(x) = 4x^2 - x^4$

19. $f(x) = 1 + \sqrt{x}$ **20.** $f(x) = \sqrt{x + 4}$

21. $g(x) = -\sqrt{x}$ **22.** $g(x) = \sqrt{-x}$

23. $H(x) = |2x|$ **24.** $H(x) = |x + 1|$

25. $G(x) = |x| + x$ **26.** $G(x) = |x| - x$

27. $f(x) = |2x - 2|$ **28.** $f(x) = \dfrac{x}{|x|}$

29–32 ■ Graph the function in each of the given viewing rectangles, and select the one that produces the most appropriate graph of the function.

29. $f(x) = 8x - x^2$

   (a) $[-5, 5]$ by $[-5, 5]$

   (b) $[-10, 10]$ by $[-10, 10]$

   (c) $[-2, 10]$ by $[-5, 20]$

   (d) $[-10, 10]$ by $[-100, 100]$

30. $g(x) = x^2 - x - 20$

   (a) $[-2, 2]$ by $[-5, 5]$

   (b) $[-10, 10]$ by $[-10, 10]$

   (c) $[-7, 7]$ by $[-25, 20]$

   (d) $[-10, 10]$ by $[-100, 100]$

31. $h(x) = x^3 - 5x - 4$

   (a) $[-2, 2]$ by $[-2, 2]$

   (b) $[-3, 3]$ by $[-10, 10]$

   (c) $[-3, 3]$ by $[-10, 5]$

   (d) $[-10, 10]$ by $[-10, 10]$

32. $k(x) = \frac{1}{32}x^4 - x^2 + 2$

   (a) $[-1, 1]$ by $[-1, 1]$

   (b) $[-2, 2]$ by $[-2, 2]$

   (c) $[-5, 5]$ by $[-5, 5]$

   (d) $[-10, 10]$ by $[-10, 10]$

33–46 ■ Sketch the graph of the piecewise defined function.

33. $f(x) = \begin{cases} 0 & \text{if } x < 2 \\ 1 & \text{if } x \ge 2 \end{cases}$

34. $f(x) = \begin{cases} 1 & \text{if } x \le 1 \\ x + 1 & \text{if } x > 1 \end{cases}$

35. $f(x) = \begin{cases} 3 & \text{if } x < 2 \\ x - 1 & \text{if } x \ge 2 \end{cases}$

36. $f(x) = \begin{cases} 1 - x & \text{if } x < -2 \\ 5 & \text{if } x \ge -2 \end{cases}$

37. $f(x) = \begin{cases} x & \text{if } x \le 0 \\ x + 1 & \text{if } x > 0 \end{cases}$

38. $f(x) = \begin{cases} 2x + 3 & \text{if } x < -1 \\ 3 - x & \text{if } x \ge -1 \end{cases}$

39. $f(x) = \begin{cases} -1 & \text{if } x < -1 \\ 1 & \text{if } -1 \le x \le 1 \\ -1 & \text{if } x > 1 \end{cases}$

40. $f(x) = \begin{cases} -1 & \text{if } x < -1 \\ x & \text{if } -1 \le x \le 1 \\ 1 & \text{if } x > 1 \end{cases}$

41. $f(x) = \begin{cases} 2 & \text{if } x \le -1 \\ x^2 & \text{if } x > -1 \end{cases}$

42. $f(x) = \begin{cases} 1 - x^2 & \text{if } x \le 2 \\ x & \text{if } x > 2 \end{cases}$

43. $f(x) = \begin{cases} 0 & \text{if } |x| \le 2 \\ 3 & \text{if } |x| > 2 \end{cases}$

44. $f(x) = \begin{cases} x^2 & \text{if } |x| \le 1 \\ 1 & \text{if } |x| > 1 \end{cases}$

45. $f(x) = \begin{cases} 4 & \text{if } x < -2 \\ x^2 & \text{if } -2 \le x \le 2 \\ -x + 6 & \text{if } x > 2 \end{cases}$

46. $f(x) = \begin{cases} -x & \text{if } x \le 0 \\ 9 - x^2 & \text{if } 0 < x \le 3 \\ x - 3 & \text{if } x > 3 \end{cases}$

47–48 ■ Use a graphing device to draw the graph of the piecewise defined function. (See the margin note on page 155.)

47. $f(x) = \begin{cases} x + 2 & \text{if } x \leq -1 \\ x^2 & \text{if } x > -1 \end{cases}$

48. $f(x) = \begin{cases} 2x - x^2 & \text{if } x > 1 \\ (x - 1)^3 & \text{if } x \leq 1 \end{cases}$

49–50 ■ The graph of a piecewise defined function is given. Find a formula for the function in the indicated form.

49.

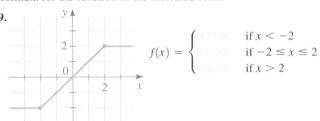

$f(x) = \begin{cases} \underline{\quad} & \text{if } x < -2 \\ \underline{\quad} & \text{if } -2 \leq x \leq 2 \\ \underline{\quad} & \text{if } x > 2 \end{cases}$

50.

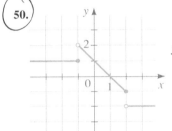

$f(x) = \begin{cases} \underline{\quad} & \text{if } x \leq -1 \\ \underline{\quad} & \text{if } -1 < x \leq 2 \\ \underline{\quad} & \text{if } x > 2 \end{cases}$

51–52 ■ Use the Vertical Line Test to determine whether the curve is the graph of a function of x.

51. (a)

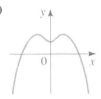

(b)

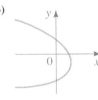

(c)

(d)

52. (a)

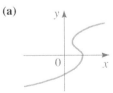

(b)

(c)

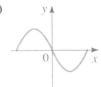

(d)

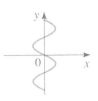

53–56 ■ Use the Vertical Line Test to determine whether the curve is the graph of a function of x. If it is, state the domain and range of the function.

53.

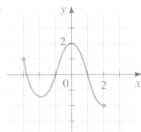

54.

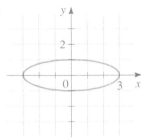

55.

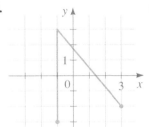

56.

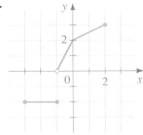

57–68 ■ Determine whether the equation defines y as a function of x. (See Example 9.)

57. $x^2 + 2y = 4$

58. $3x + 7y = 21$

59. $x = y^2$

60. $x^2 + (y - 1)^2 = 4$

61. $x + y^2 = 9$

62. $x^2 + y = 9$

63. $x^2y + y = 1$

64. $\sqrt{x} + y = 12$

65. $2|x| + y = 0$

66. $2x + |y| = 0$

67. $x = y^3$

68. $x = y^4$

69–74 ■ A family of functions is given. In parts (a) and (b) graph all the given members of the family in the viewing rectangle indicated. In part (c) state the conclusions that you can make from your graphs.

69. $f(x) = x^2 + c$
  (a) $c = 0, 2, 4, 6;$ $[-5, 5]$ by $[-10, 10]$
  (b) $c = 0, -2, -4, -6;$ $[-5, 5]$ by $[-10, 10]$
  (c) How does the value of c affect the graph?

70. $f(x) = (x - c)^2$
  (a) $c = 0, 1, 2, 3;$ $[-5, 5]$ by $[-10, 10]$
  (b) $c = 0, -1, -2, -3;$ $[-5, 5]$ by $[-10, 10]$
  (c) How does the value of c affect the graph?

71. $f(x) = (x - c)^3$
  (a) $c = 0, 2, 4, 6;$ $[-10, 10]$ by $[-10, 10]$
  (b) $c = 0, -2, -4, -6;$ $[-10, 10]$ by $[-10, 10]$
  (c) How does the value of c affect the graph?

72. $f(x) = cx^2$
  (a) $c = 1, \frac{1}{2}, 2, 4;$ $[-5, 5]$ by $[-10, 10]$
  (b) $c = 1, -1, -\frac{1}{2}, -2;$ $[-5, 5]$ by $[-10, 10]$
  (c) How does the value of c affect the graph?

73. $f(x) = x^c$
  (a) $c = \frac{1}{2}, \frac{1}{4}, \frac{1}{6};$ $[-1, 4]$ by $[-1, 3]$
  (b) $c = 1, \frac{1}{3}, \frac{1}{5};$ $[-3, 3]$ by $[-2, 2]$
  (c) How does the value of c affect the graph?

74. $f(x) = \dfrac{1}{x^n}$

(a) $n = 1, 3$; $[-3, 3]$ by $[-3, 3]$
(b) $n = 2, 4$; $[-3, 3]$ by $[-3, 3]$
(c) How does the value of n affect the graph?

75–78 ■ Find a function whose graph is the given curve.

75. The line segment joining the points $(-2, 1)$ and $(4, -6)$

76. The line segment joining the points $(-3, -2)$ and $(6, 3)$

77. The top half of the circle $x^2 + y^2 = 9$

78. The bottom half of the circle $x^2 + y^2 = 9$

APPLICATIONS

79. Weather Balloon As a weather balloon is inflated, the thickness T of its rubber skin is related to the radius of the balloon by

$$T(r) = \frac{0.5}{r^2}$$

where T and r are measured in centimeters. Graph the function T for values of r between 10 and 100.

80. Power from a Wind Turbine The power produced by a wind turbine depends on the speed of the wind. If a windmill has blades 3 meters long, then the power P produced by the turbine is modeled by

$$P(v) = 14.1v^3$$

where P is measured in watts (W) and v is measured in meters per second (m/s). Graph the function P for wind speeds between 1 m/s and 10 m/s.

81. Utility Rates Westside Energy charges its electric customers a base rate of $6.00 per month, plus 10¢ per kilowatt-hour (kWh) for the first 300 kWh used and 6¢ per kWh for all usage over 300 kWh. Suppose a customer uses x kWh of electricity in one month.

(a) Express the monthly cost E as a piecewise-defined function of x.
(b) Graph the function E for $0 \le x \le 600$.

82. Taxicab Function A taxi company charges $2.00 for the first mile (or part of a mile) and 20 cents for each succeeding tenth of a mile (or part). Express the cost C (in dollars) of a ride as a piecewise-defined function of the distance x traveled (in miles) for $0 < x < 2$, and sketch the graph of this function.

83. Postage Rates The domestic postage rate for first-class letters weighing 3.5 oz or less is 44 cents for the first ounce (or less), plus 17 cents for each additional ounce (or part of an ounce). Express the postage P as a piecewise-defined function of the weight x of a letter, with $0 < x \le 3.5$, and sketch the graph of this function.

DISCOVERY ■ DISCUSSION ■ WRITING

84. When Does a Graph Represent a Function? For every integer n, the graph of the equation $y = x^n$ is the graph of a function, namely $f(x) = x^n$. Explain why the graph of $x = y^2$ is *not* the graph of a function of x. Is the graph of $x = y^3$ the graph of a function of x? If so, of what function of x is it the graph? Determine for what integers n the graph of $x = y^n$ is the graph of a function of x.

85. Step Functions In Example 7 and Exercises 82 and 83 we are given functions whose graphs consist of horizontal line segments. Such functions are often called *step functions*, because their graphs look like stairs. Give some other examples of step functions that arise in everyday life.

86. Stretched Step Functions Sketch graphs of the functions $f(x) = [\![x]\!]$, $g(x) = [\![2x]\!]$, and $h(x) = [\![3x]\!]$ on separate graphs. How are the graphs related? If n is a positive integer, what does the graph of $k(x) = [\![nx]\!]$ look like?

87. Graph of the Absolute Value of a Function

(a) Draw the graphs of the functions

$$f(x) = x^2 + x - 6$$
$$\text{and} \qquad g(x) = |x^2 + x - 6|$$

How are the graphs of f and g related?

(b) Draw the graphs of the functions $f(x) = x^4 - 6x^2$ and $g(x) = |x^4 - 6x^2|$. How are the graphs of f and g related?

(c) In general, if $g(x) = |f(x)|$, how are the graphs of f and g related? Draw graphs to illustrate your answer.

◯ **DISCOVERY PROJECT** Relations and Functions

In this project we explore the concept of function by comparing it with the concept of a *relation*. You can find the project at the book companion website:
www.stewartmath.com

2.3 GETTING INFORMATION FROM THE GRAPH OF A FUNCTION

| Values of a Function; Domain and Range ▶ Increasing and Decreasing
Functions ▶ Local Maximum and Minimum Values of a Function

Many properties of a function are more easily obtained from a graph than from the rule
that describes the function. We will see in this section how a graph tells us whether the
values of a function are increasing or decreasing and also where the maximum and minimum values of a function are.

▼ Values of a Function; Domain and Range

A complete graph of a function contains all the information about a function, because the
graph tells us which input values correspond to which output values. To analyze the graph
of a function, we must keep in mind that *the height of the graph is the value of the function.* So we can read off the values of a function from its graph.

EXAMPLE 1 | Finding the Values of a Function from a Graph

The function T graphed in Figure 1 gives the temperature between noon and 6:00 P.M. at
a certain weather station.

(a) Find $T(1)$, $T(3)$, and $T(5)$.

(b) Which is larger, $T(2)$ or $T(4)$?

(c) Find the value(s) of x for which $T(x) = 25$.

(d) Find the value(s) of x for which $T(x) \geq 25$.

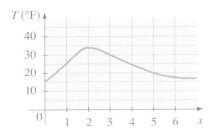

FIGURE 1 Temperature function

SOLUTION

(a) $T(1)$ is the temperature at 1:00 P.M. It is represented by the height of the graph
above the x-axis at $x = 1$. Thus, $T(1) = 25$. Similarly, $T(3) = 30$ and $T(5) = 20$.

(b) Since the graph is higher at $x = 2$ than at $x = 4$, it follows that $T(2)$ is larger than $T(4)$.

(c) The height of the graph is 25 when x is 1 and when x is 4. In other words, the temperature is 25 at 1:00 P.M. and 4:00 P.M.

(d) The graph is higher than 25 for x between 1 and 4. In other words, the temperature
was 25 or greater between 1:00 P.M. and 4:00 P.M.

✎ NOW TRY EXERCISE **5**

The graph of a function helps us to picture the domain and range of the function on the
x-axis and y-axis, as shown in Figure 2.

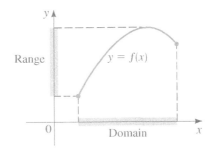

FIGURE 2 Domain and range of f

EXAMPLE 2 | Finding the Domain and Range from a Graph

(a) Use a graphing calculator to draw the graph of $f(x) = \sqrt{4 - x^2}$.

(b) Find the domain and range of f.

SOLUTION

(a) The graph is shown in Figure 3.

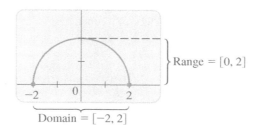

FIGURE 3 Graph of $f(x) = \sqrt{4 - x^2}$

(b) From the graph in Figure 3 we see that the domain is $[-2, 2]$ and the range is $[0, 2]$.

✎. NOW TRY EXERCISE **15**

▼ Increasing and Decreasing Functions

It is very useful to know where the graph of a function rises and where it falls. The graph shown in Figure 4 rises, falls, then rises again as we move from left to right: It rises from A to B, falls from B to C, and rises again from C to D. The function f is said to be *increasing* when its graph rises and *decreasing* when its graph falls.

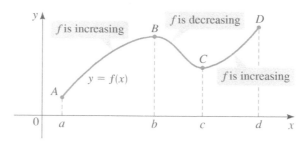

FIGURE 4 f is increasing on $[a, b]$ and $[c, d]$. f is decreasing on $[b, c]$.

We have the following definition.

DEFINITION OF INCREASING AND DECREASING FUNCTIONS

f is **increasing** on an interval I if $f(x_1) < f(x_2)$ whenever $x_1 < x_2$ in I.

f is **decreasing** on an interval I if $f(x_1) > f(x_2)$ whenever $x_1 < x_2$ in I.

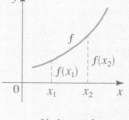

f is increasing

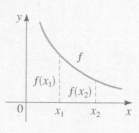

f is decreasing

EXAMPLE 3 | **Intervals on Which a Function Increases and Decreases**

The graph in Figure 5 gives the weight W of a person at age x. Determine the intervals on which the function W is increasing and on which it is decreasing.

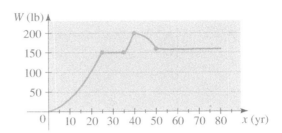

FIGURE 5 Weight as a function of age

SOLUTION The function W is increasing on $[0, 25]$ and $[35, 40]$. It is decreasing on $[40, 50]$. The function W is constant (neither increasing nor decreasing) on $[25, 30]$ and $[50, 80]$. This means that the person gained weight until age 25, then gained weight again between ages 35 and 40. He lost weight between ages 40 and 50.

✎ . NOW TRY EXERCISE **45**

EXAMPLE 4 | **Finding Intervals Where a Function Increases and Decreases**

(a) Sketch a graph of the function $f(x) = 12x^2 + 4x^3 - 3x^4$.

(b) Find the domain and range of f.

(c) Find the intervals on which f increases and decreases.

SOLUTION

(a) We use a graphing calculator to sketch the graph in Figure 6.

(b) The domain of f is $\mathbb{R}$ because f is defined for all real numbers. Using the $\boxed{\text{TRACE}}$ feature on the calculator, we find that the highest value is $f(2) = 32$. So the range of f is $(-\infty, 32]$.

(c) From the graph we see that f is increasing on the intervals $(-\infty, -1]$ and $[0, 2]$ and is decreasing on $[-1, 0]$ and $[2, \infty)$.

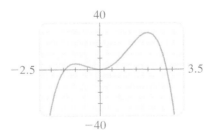

FIGURE 6 Graph of
$f(x) = 12x^2 + 4x^3 - 3x^4$

✎ . NOW TRY EXERCISE **23**

EXAMPLE 5 | Finding Intervals Where a Function Increases and Decreases

(a) Sketch the graph of the function $f(x) = x^{2/3}$.

(b) Find the domain and range of the function.

(c) Find the intervals on which f increases and decreases.

SOLUTION

(a) We use a graphing calculator to sketch the graph in Figure 7.

(b) From the graph we observe that the domain of f is $\mathbb{R}$ and the range is $[0, \infty)$.

(c) From the graph we see that f is decreasing on $(-\infty, 0]$ and increasing on $[0, \infty)$.

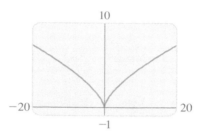

FIGURE 7 Graph of $f(x) = x^{2/3}$

✎. NOW TRY EXERCISE **29**

▼ Local Maximum and Minimum Values of a Function

Finding the largest or smallest values of a function is important in many applications. For example, if a function represents revenue or profit, then we are interested in its maximum value. For a function that represents cost, we would want to find its minimum value. (See *Focus on Modeling: Modeling with Functions* on pages 213–222 for many such examples.) We can easily find these values from the graph of a function. We first define what we mean by a local maximum or minimum.

LOCAL MAXIMA AND MINIMA OF A FUNCTION

1. The function value $f(a)$ is a **local maximum value** of f if

$$f(a) \geq f(x) \quad \text{when } x \text{ is near } a$$

(This means that $f(a) \geq f(x)$ for all x in some open interval containing a.)
In this case we say that f has a **local maximum** at $x = a$.

2. The function value $f(a)$ is a **local minimum** of f if

$$f(a) \leq f(x) \quad \text{when } x \text{ is near } a$$

(This means that $f(a) \leq f(x)$ for all x in some open interval containing a.)
In this case we say that f has a **local minimum** at $x = a$.

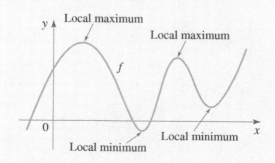

We can find the local maximum and minimum values of a function using a graphing calculator.

If there is a viewing rectangle such that the point $(a, f(a))$ is the highest point on the graph of f *within* the viewing rectangle (not on the edge), then the number $f(a)$ is a local maximum value of f (see Figure 8). Notice that $f(a) \geq f(x)$ for all numbers x that are close to a.

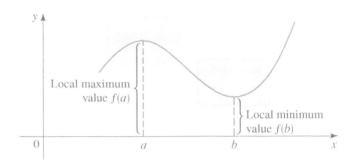

FIGURE 8

Similarly, if there is a viewing rectangle such that the point $(b, f(b))$ is the lowest point on the graph of f within the viewing rectangle, then the number $f(b)$ is a local minimum value of f. In this case, $f(b) \leq f(x)$ for all numbers x that are close to b.

EXAMPLE 6 | Finding Local Maxima and Minima from a Graph

Find the local maximum and minimum values of the function $f(x) = x^3 - 8x + 1$, correct to three decimal places.

SOLUTION   The graph of f is shown in Figure 9. There appears to be one local maximum between $x = -2$ and $x = -1$, and one local minimum between $x = 1$ and $x = 2$.

Let's find the coordinates of the local maximum point first. We zoom in to enlarge the area near this point, as shown in Figure 10. Using the TRACE feature on the graphing device, we move the cursor along the curve and observe how the y-coordinates change. The local maximum value of y is 9.709, and this value occurs when x is -1.633, correct to three decimal places.

We locate the minimum value in a similar fashion. By zooming in to the viewing rectangle shown in Figure 11, we find that the local minimum value is about -7.709, and this value occurs when $x \approx 1.633$.

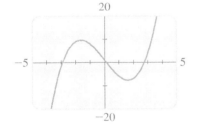

FIGURE 9 Graph of
$f(x) = x^3 - 8x + 1$

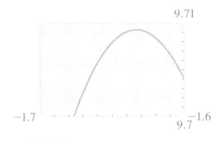

FIGURE 10

FIGURE 11

NOW TRY EXERCISE **35**

The `maximum` and `minimum` commands on a TI-83 or TI-84 calculator provide another method for finding extreme values of functions. We use this method in the next example.

EXAMPLE 7 | A Model for the Food Price Index

A model for the food price index (the price of a representative "basket" of foods) between 1990 and 2000 is given by the function

$$I(t) = -0.0113t^3 + 0.0681t^2 + 0.198t + 99.1$$

where t is measured in years since midyear 1990, so $0 \le t \le 10$, and $I(t)$ is scaled so that $I(3) = 100$. Estimate the time when food was most expensive during the period 1990–2000.

SOLUTION The graph of I as a function of t is shown in Figure 12(a). There appears to be a maximum between $t = 4$ and $t = 7$. Using the `maximum` command, as shown in Figure 12(b), we see that the maximum value of I is about 100.38, and it occurs when $t \approx 5.15$, which corresponds to August 1995.

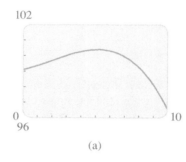

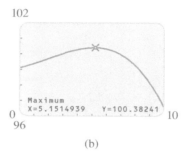

FIGURE 12

(a)   (b)

✎. NOW TRY EXERCISE **53**

2.3 EXERCISES

CONCEPTS

1–4 ■ These exercises refer to the graph of the function f shown below.

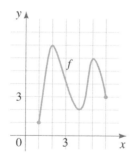

1. To find a function value $f(a)$ from the graph of f, we find the height of the graph above the x-axis at $x =$ _____ . From the graph of f we see that $f(3) =$ _____ .

2. The domain of the function f is all the _____ -values of the points on the graph, and the range is all the corresponding _____ -values. From the graph of f we see that the domain of f is the interval _____ and the range of f is the interval _____ .

3. (a) If f is increasing on an interval, then the y-values of the points on the graph _____ as the x-values increase. From the graph of f we see that f is increasing on the intervals _____ and _____ .

(b) If f is decreasing on an interval, then y-values of the points on the graph _____ as the x-values increase. From the graph of f we see that f is decreasing on the intervals _____ and _____ .

4. (a) A function value $f(a)$ is a local maximum value of f if $f(a)$ is the _____ value of f on some interval containing a. From the graph of f we see that one local maximum value of f is _____ and that this value occurs when x is _____ .

(b) The function value $f(a)$ is a local minimum value of f if $f(a)$ is the _____ value of f on some interval containing a. From the graph of f we see that one local minimum value of f is _____ and that this value occurs when x is _____ .

SKILLS

5. The graph of a function h is given.
    (a) Find $h(-2)$, $h(0)$, $h(2)$, and $h(3)$.
    (b) Find the domain and range of h.
    (c) Find the values of x for which $h(x) = 3$.
    (d) Find the values of x for which $h(x) \le 3$.

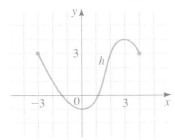

6. The graph of a function g is given.
    (a) Find $g(-2)$, $g(0)$, and $g(7)$.
    (b) Find the domain and range of g.
    (c) Find the values of x for which $g(x) = 4$.
    (d) Find the values of x for which $g(x) > 4$.

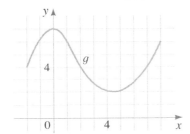

7. The graph of a function g is given.
    (a) Find $g(-4)$, $g(-2)$, $g(0)$, $g(2)$, and $g(4)$.
    (b) Find the domain and range of g.

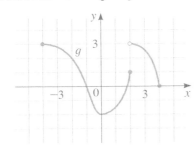

8. Graphs of the functions f and g are given.
    (a) Which is larger, $f(0)$ or $g(0)$?
    (b) Which is larger, $f(-3)$ or $g(-3)$?
    (c) For which values of x is $f(x) = g(x)$?

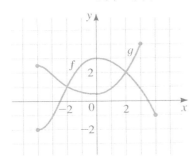

9–18 ■ A function f is given. **(a)** Use a graphing calculator to draw the graph of f. **(b)** Find the domain and range of f from the graph.

9. $f(x) = x - 1$ **10.** $f(x) = 2(x + 1)$

11. $f(x) = 4$, $1 \le x \le 3$ **12.** $f(x) = x^2$, $-2 \le x \le 5$

13. $f(x) = 4 - x^2$ **14.** $f(x) = x^2 + 4$

15. $f(x) = \sqrt{16 - x^2}$ **16.** $f(x) = -\sqrt{25 - x^2}$

17. $f(x) = \sqrt{x - 1}$ **18.** $f(x) = \sqrt{x + 2}$

19–22 ■ The graph of a function is given. Determine the intervals on which the function is **(a)** increasing and **(b)** decreasing.

19. 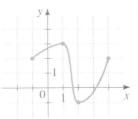   **20.**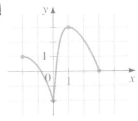

21. 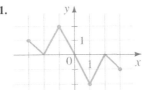   **22.**

23–30 ■ A function f is given. **(a)** Use a graphing device to draw the graph of f. **(b)** State approximately the intervals on which f is increasing and on which f is decreasing.

23. $f(x) = x^2 - 5x$ **24.** $f(x) = x^3 - 4x$

25. $f(x) = 2x^3 - 3x^2 - 12x$ **26.** $f(x) = x^4 - 16x^2$

27. $f(x) = x^3 + 2x^2 - x - 2$

28. $f(x) = x^4 - 4x^3 + 2x^2 + 4x - 3$

29. $f(x) = x^{2/5}$ **30.** $f(x) = 4 - x^{2/3}$

31–34 ■ The graph of a function is given. **(a)** Find all the local maximum and minimum values of the function and the value of x at which each occurs. **(b)** Find the intervals on which the function is increasing and on which the function is decreasing.

31. 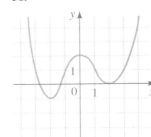   **32.**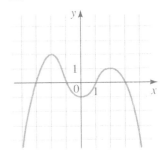

33.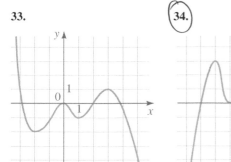

34.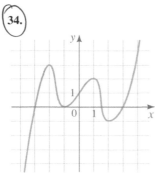

35–42 ■ A function is given. **(a)** Find all the local maximum and minimum values of the function and the value of x at which each occurs. State each answer correct to two decimal places. **(b)** Find the intervals on which the function is increasing and on which the function is decreasing. State each answer correct to two decimal places.

35. $f(x) = x^3 - x$

36. $f(x) = 3 + x + x^2 - x^3$

37. $g(x) = x^4 - 2x^3 - 11x^2$

38. $g(x) = x^5 - 8x^3 + 20x$

39. $U(x) = x\sqrt{6 - x}$

40. $U(x) = x\sqrt{x - x^2}$

41. $V(x) = \dfrac{1 - x^2}{x^3}$

42. $V(x) = \dfrac{1}{x^2 + x + 1}$

APPLICATIONS

43. Power Consumption The figure shows the power consumption in San Francisco for September 19, 1996 (P is measured in megawatts; t is measured in hours starting at midnight).

(a) What was the power consumption at 6:00 A.M.? At 6:00 P.M.?

(b) When was the power consumption the lowest?

(c) When was the power consumption the highest?

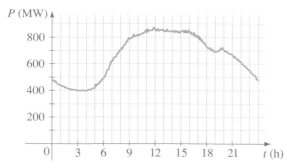

Source: Pacific Gas & Electric

44. Earthquake The graph shows the vertical acceleration of the ground from the 1994 Northridge earthquake in Los Angeles, as measured by a seismograph. (Here t represents the time in seconds.)

(a) At what time t did the earthquake first make noticeable movements of the earth?

(b) At what time t did the earthquake seem to end?

(c) At what time t was the maximum intensity of the earthquake reached?

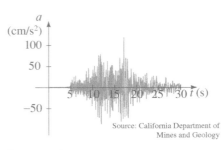

Source: California Department of Mines and Geology

45. Weight Function The graph gives the weight W of a person at age x.

(a) Determine the intervals on which the function W is increasing and those on which it is decreasing.

(b) What do you think happened when this person was 30 years old?

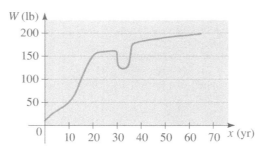

46. Distance Function The graph gives a sales representative's distance from his home as a function of time on a certain day.

(a) Determine the time intervals on which his distance from home was increasing and those on which it was decreasing.

(b) Describe in words what the graph indicates about his travels on this day.

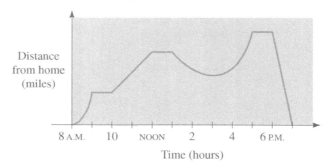

47. Changing Water Levels The graph shows the depth of water W in a reservoir over a one-year period as a function of the number of days x since the beginning of the year.

(a) Determine the intervals on which the function W is increasing and on which it is decreasing.

(b) At what value of x does W achieve a local maximum? A local minimum?

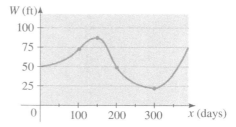

48. Population Growth and Decline   The graph shows the population P in a small industrial city from 1950 to 2000. The variable x represents the number of years since 1950.
   (a) Determine the intervals on which the function P is increasing and on which it is decreasing.
   (b) What was the maximum population, and in what year was it attained?

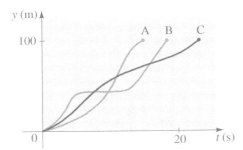

49. Hurdle Race   Three runners compete in a 100-meter hurdle race. The graph depicts the distance run as a function of time for each runner. Describe in words what the graph tells you about this race. Who won the race? Did each runner finish the race? What do you think happened to runner B?

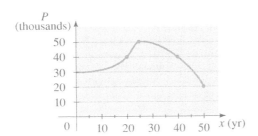

 50. Gravity Near the Moon   We can use Newton's Law of Gravity to measure the gravitational attraction between the moon and an algebra student in a space ship located a distance x above the moon's surface:

$$F(x) = \frac{350}{x^2}$$

Here F is measured in newtons (N), and x is measured in millions of meters.
   (a) Graph the function F for values of x between 0 and 10.
   (b) Use the graph to describe the behavior of the gravitational attraction F as the distance x increases.

 51. Radii of Stars   Astronomers infer the radii of stars using the Stefan Boltzmann Law:

$$E(T) = (5.67 \times 10^{-8})T^4$$

where E is the energy radiated per unit of surface area

measured in watts (W) and T is the absolute temperature measured in kelvins (K).
   (a) Graph the function E for temperatures T between 100 K and 300 K.
   (b) Use the graph to describe the change in energy E as the temperature T increases.

 52. Migrating Fish   A fish swims at a speed v relative to the water, against a current of 5 mi/h. Using a mathematical model of energy expenditure, it can be shown that the total energy E required to swim a distance of 10 mi is given by

$$E(v) = 2.73v^3 \frac{10}{v - 5}$$

Biologists believe that migrating fish try to minimize the total energy required to swim a fixed distance. Find the value of v that minimizes energy required.

NOTE: This result has been verified; migrating fish swim against a current at a speed 50% greater than the speed of the current.

 53. Highway Engineering   A highway engineer wants to estimate the maximum number of cars that can safely travel a particular highway at a given speed. She assumes that each car is 17 ft long, travels at a speed s, and follows the car in front of it at the "safe following distance" for that speed. She finds that the number N of cars that can pass a given point per minute is modeled by the function

$$N(s) = \frac{88s}{17 + 17\left(\dfrac{s}{20}\right)^2}$$

At what speed can the greatest number of cars travel the highway safely?

 54. Volume of Water   Between 0°C and 30°C, the volume V (in cubic centimeters) of 1 kg of water at a temperature T is given by the formula

$$V = 999.87 - 0.06426T + 0.0085043T^2 - 0.0000679T^3$$

Find the temperature at which the volume of 1 kg of water is a minimum.

 55. Coughing   When a foreign object that is lodged in the trachea (windpipe) forces a person to cough, the diaphragm thrusts upward, causing an increase in pressure in the lungs. At the same time, the trachea contracts, causing the expelled air to move faster and increasing the pressure on the foreign object. According to a mathematical model of coughing, the velocity v of the airstream through an average-sized person's trachea is related to the radius r of the trachea (in centimeters) by the function

$$v(r) = 3.2(1 - r)r^2 \qquad \tfrac{1}{2} \le r \le 1$$

Determine the value of r for which v is a maximum.

DISCOVERY ▪ DISCUSSION ▪ WRITING

56. Functions That Are Always Increasing or Decreasing   Sketch rough graphs of functions that are defined for all real numbers and that exhibit the indicated behavior (or explain why the behavior is impossible).
(a) f is always increasing, and $f(x) > 0$ for all x
(b) f is always decreasing, and $f(x) > 0$ for all x
(c) f is always increasing, and $f(x) < 0$ for all x
(d) f is always decreasing, and $f(x) < 0$ for all x

57. Maxima and Minima   In Example 7 we saw a real-world situation in which the maximum value of a function is important. Name several other everyday situations in which a maximum or minimum value is important.

58. Minimizing a Distance   When we seek a minimum or maximum value of a function, it is sometimes easier to work with a simpler function instead.
(a) Suppose

$$g(x) = \sqrt{f(x)}$$

where $f(x) \geq 0$ for all x. Explain why the local minima and maxima of f and g occur at the same values of x.
(b) Let $g(x)$ be the distance between the point $(3, 0)$ and the point (x, x^2) on the graph of the parabola $y = x^2$. Express g as a function of x.
(c) Find the minimum value of the function g that you found in part (b). Use the principle described in part (a) to simplify your work.

2.4 AVERAGE RATE OF CHANGE OF A FUNCTION

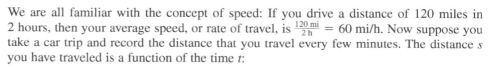

| Average Rate of Change ▶ Linear Functions Have Constant Rate of Change

Functions are often used to model changing quantities. In this section we learn how to find the rate at which the values of a function change as the input variable changes.

▼ Average Rate of Change

We are all familiar with the concept of speed: If you drive a distance of 120 miles in 2 hours, then your average speed, or rate of travel, is $\frac{120 \text{ mi}}{2 \text{ h}} = 60$ mi/h. Now suppose you take a car trip and record the distance that you travel every few minutes. The distance s you have traveled is a function of the time t:

$$s(t) = \text{total distance traveled at time } t$$

We graph the function s as shown in Figure 1. The graph shows that you have traveled a total of 50 miles after 1 hour, 75 miles after 2 hours, 140 miles after 3 hours, and so on. To find your *average* speed between any two points on the trip, we divide the distance traveled by the time elapsed.

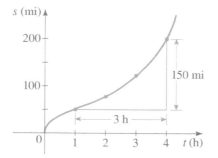

FIGURE 1
Average speed

Let's calculate your average speed between 1:00 P.M. and 4:00 P.M. The time elapsed is $4 - 1 = 3$ hours. To find the distance you traveled, we subtract the distance at 1:00 P.M. from the distance at 4:00 P.M., that is, $200 - 50 = 150$ mi. Thus, your average speed is

$$\text{average speed} = \frac{\text{distance traveled}}{\text{time elapsed}} = \frac{150 \text{ mi}}{3 \text{ h}} = 50 \text{ mi/h}$$

The average speed that we have just calculated can be expressed by using function notation:

$$\text{average speed} = \frac{s(4) - s(1)}{4 - 1} = \frac{200 - 50}{3} = 50 \text{ mi/h}$$

Note that the average speed is different over different time intervals. For example, between 2:00 P.M. and 3:00 P.M. we find that

$$\text{average speed} = \frac{s(3) - s(2)}{3 - 2} = \frac{140 - 75}{1} = 65 \text{ mi/h}$$

Finding average rates of change is important in many contexts. For instance, we might be interested in knowing how quickly the air temperature is dropping as a storm approaches or how fast revenues are increasing from the sale of a new product. So we need to know how to determine the average rate of change of the functions that model these quantities. In fact, the concept of average rate of change can be defined for any function.

AVERAGE RATE OF CHANGE

The **average rate of change** of the function $y = f(x)$ between $x = a$ and $x = b$ is

$$\text{average rate of change} = \frac{\text{change in } y}{\text{change in } x} = \frac{f(b) - f(a)}{b - a}$$

The average rate of change is the slope of the **secant line** between $x = a$ and $x = b$ on the graph of f, that is, the line that passes through $(a, f(a))$ and $(b, f(b))$.

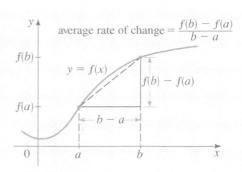

EXAMPLE 1 | Calculating the Average Rate of Change

For the function $f(x) = (x - 3)^2$, whose graph is shown in Figure 2, find the average rate of change between the following points:

(a) $x = 1$ and $x = 3$ **(b)** $x = 4$ and $x = 7$

SOLUTION

(a) Average rate of change $= \dfrac{f(3) - f(1)}{3 - 1}$ Definition

$$= \frac{(3 - 3)^2 - (1 - 3)^2}{3 - 1} \qquad \text{Use } f(x) = (x - 3)^2$$

$$= \frac{0 - 4}{2} = -2$$

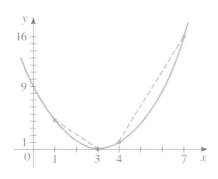

FIGURE 2 $f(x) = (x - 3)^2$

(b) Average rate of change $= \dfrac{f(7) - f(4)}{7 - 4}$ Definition

$= \dfrac{(7 - 3)^2 - (4 - 3)^2}{7 - 4}$ Use $f(x) = (x - 3)^2$

$= \dfrac{16 - 1}{3} = 5$

◆ NOW TRY EXERCISE **11**

EXAMPLE 2 | Average Speed of a Falling Object

If an object is dropped from a high cliff or a tall building, then the distance it has fallen after t seconds is given by the function $d(t) = 16t^2$. Find its average speed (average rate of change) over the following intervals:

(a) Between 1 s and 5 s   **(b)** Between $t = a$ and $t = a + h$

SOLUTION

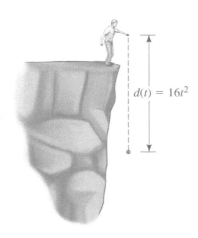

$d(t) = 16t^2$

Function: In t seconds the stone falls $16t^2$ ft.

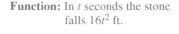

(a) Average rate of change $= \dfrac{d(5) - d(1)}{5 - 1}$ Definition

$= \dfrac{16(5)^2 - 16(1)^2}{5 - 1}$ Use $d(t) = 16t^2$

$= \dfrac{400 - 16}{4}$

$= 96 \text{ ft/s}$

(b) Average rate of change $= \dfrac{d(a + h) - d(a)}{(a + h) - a}$ Definition

$= \dfrac{16(a + h)^2 - 16(a)^2}{(a + h) - a}$ Use $d(t) = 16t^2$

$= \dfrac{16(a^2 + 2ah + h^2 - a^2)}{h}$ Expand and factor 16

$= \dfrac{16(2ah + h^2)}{h}$ Simplify numerator

$= \dfrac{16h(2a + h)}{h}$ Factor h

$= 16(2a + h)$ Simplify

◆ NOW TRY EXERCISE **15**

The average rate of change calculated in Example 2(b) is known as a *difference quotient*. In calculus we use difference quotients to calculate *instantaneous* rates of change. An example of an instantaneous rate of change is the speed shown on the speedometer of your car. This changes from one instant to the next as your car's speed changes.

The graphs in Figure 3 show that if a function is increasing on an interval, then the average rate of change between any two points is positive, whereas if a function is decreasing on an interval, then the average rate of change between any two points is negative.

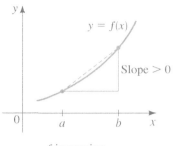 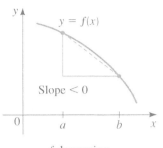

f increasing
Average rate of change positive

f decreasing
Average rate of change negative

FIGURE 3

EXAMPLE 3 | Average Rate of Temperature Change

The table gives the outdoor temperatures observed by a science student on a spring day. Draw a graph of the data, and find the average rate of change of temperature between the following times:

(a) 8:00 A.M. and 9:00 A.M.

(b) 1:00 P.M. and 3:00 P.M.

(c) 4:00 P.M. and 7:00 P.M.

Time	Temperature (°F)
8:00 A.M.	38
9:00 A.M.	40
10:00 A.M.	44
11:00 A.M.	50
12:00 NOON	56
1:00 P.M.	62
2:00 P.M.	66
3:00 P.M.	67
4:00 P.M.	64
5:00 P.M.	58
6:00 P.M.	55
7:00 P.M.	51

SOLUTION A graph of the temperature data is shown in Figure 4. Let *t* represent time, measured in hours since midnight (so, for example, 2:00 P.M. corresponds to $t = 14$). Define the function *F* by

$$F(t) = \text{temperature at time } t$$

(a) Average rate of change $= \dfrac{\text{temperature at 9 A.M.} - \text{temperature at 8 A.M.}}{9 - 8}$

$$= \frac{F(9) - F(8)}{9 - 8} = \frac{40 - 38}{9 - 8} = 2$$

The average rate of change was 2°F per hour.

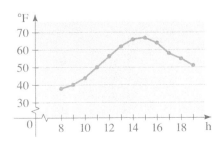

FIGURE 4

(b) Average rate of change $= \dfrac{\text{temperature at 3 P.M.} - \text{temperature at 1 P.M.}}{15 - 13}$

$$= \frac{F(15) - F(13)}{15 - 13} = \frac{67 - 62}{2} = 2.5$$

The average rate of change was 2.5°F per hour.

(c) Average rate of change $= \dfrac{\text{temperature at 7 P.M.} - \text{temperature at 4 P.M.}}{19 - 16}$

$$= \frac{F(19) - F(16)}{19 - 16} = \frac{51 - 64}{3} \approx -4.3$$

The average rate of change was about −4.3°F per hour during this time interval. The negative sign indicates that the temperature was dropping.

✎. NOW TRY EXERCISE **25**

▼ Linear Functions Have Constant Rate of Change

For a linear function $f(x) = mx + b$ the average rate of change between any two points is the same constant m. This agrees with what we learned in Section 1.10: that the slope of a line $y = mx + b$ is the average rate of change of y with respect to x. On the other hand, if a function f has constant average rate of change, then it must be a linear function. You are asked to prove this fact in Exercise 33. In the next example we find the average rate of change for a particular linear function.

EXAMPLE 4 | Linear Functions Have Constant Rate of Change

Let $f(x) = 3x - 5$. Find the average rate of change of f between the following points.
(a) $x = 0$ and $x = 1$
(b) $x = 3$ and $x = 7$
(c) $x = a$ and $x = a + h$

What conclusion can you draw from your answers?

SOLUTION

(a) Average rate of change $= \dfrac{f(1) - f(0)}{1 - 0} = \dfrac{(3 \cdot 1 - 5) - (3 \cdot 0 - 5)}{1}$

$$= \frac{(-2) - (-5)}{1} = 3$$

(b) Average rate of change $= \dfrac{f(7) - f(3)}{7 - 3} = \dfrac{(3 \cdot 7 - 5) - (3 \cdot 3 - 5)}{4}$

$$= \frac{16 - 4}{4} = 3$$

(c) Average rate of change $= \dfrac{f(a + h) - f(a)}{(a + h) - a} = \dfrac{[3(a + h) - 5] - [3a - 5]}{h}$

$$= \frac{3a + 3h - 5 - 3a + 5}{h} = \frac{3h}{h} = 3$$

It appears that the average rate of change is always 3 for this function. In fact, part (c) proves that the rate of change between any two arbitrary points $x = a$ and $x = a + h$ is 3.

✎. NOW TRY EXERCISE **21**

2.4 EXERCISES

CONCEPTS

1. If you travel 100 miles in two hours, then your average speed for the trip is

$$\text{average speed} = \frac{\qquad}{\qquad} = \underline{\qquad}$$

2. The average rate of change of a function f between $x = a$ and $x = b$ is

$$\text{average rate of change} = \frac{\qquad}{\qquad}$$

3. The average rate of change of the function $f(x) = x^2$ between $x = 1$ and $x = 5$ is

$$\text{average rate of change} = \frac{\qquad}{\qquad} = \underline{\qquad}$$

4. **(a)** The average rate of change of a function f between $x = a$ and $x = b$ is the slope of the _____ line between $(a, f(a))$ and $(b, f(b))$.
   (b) The average rate of change of the linear function

   $f(x) = 3x + 5$ between any two points is _____.

SKILLS

5–8 ■ The graph of a function is given. Determine the average rate of change of the function between the indicated points on the graph.

5.
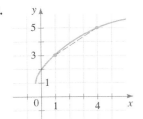

6.
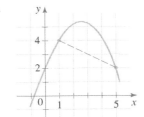

7.
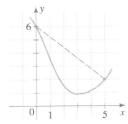

8.
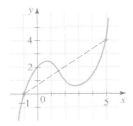

9–20 ■ A function is given. Determine the average rate of change of the function between the given values of the variable.

9. $f(x) = 3x - 2; \quad x = 2, x = 3$

10. $g(x) = 5 + \frac{1}{2}x; \quad x = 1, x = 5$

11. $h(t) = t^2 + 2t; \quad t = -1, t = 4$

12. $f(z) = 1 - 3z^2; \quad z = -2, z = 0$

13. $f(x) = x^3 - 4x^2; \quad x = 0, x = 10$

14. $f(x) = x + x^4; \quad x = -1, x = 3$

15. $f(x) = 3x^2; \quad x = 2, x = 2 + h$

16. $f(x) = 4 - x^2; \quad x = 1, x = 1 + h$

17. $g(x) = \frac{1}{x}; \quad x = 1, x = a$

18. $g(x) = \frac{2}{x + 1}; \quad x = 0, x = h$

19. $f(t) = \frac{2}{t}; \quad t = a, t = a + h$

20. $f(t) = \sqrt{t}; \quad t = a, t = a + h$

21–22 ■ A linear function is given. **(a)** Find the average rate of change of the function between $x = a$ and $x = a + h$. **(b)** Show that the average rate of change is the same as the slope of the line.

21. $f(x) = \frac{1}{2}x + 3$

22. $g(x) = -4x + 2$

APPLICATIONS

23. **Changing Water Levels**   The graph shows the depth of water W in a reservoir over a one-year period as a function of the number of days x since the beginning of the year. What was the average rate of change of W between $x = 100$ and $x = 200$?

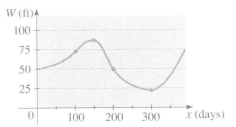

24. **Population Growth and Decline**   The graph shows the population P in a small industrial city from 1950 to 2000. The variable x represents the number of years since 1950.
   (a) What was the average rate of change of P between $x = 20$ and $x = 40$?
   (b) Interpret the value of the average rate of change that you found in part (a).

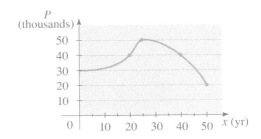

25. Population Growth and Decline The table gives the population in a small coastal community for the period 1997–2006. Figures shown are for January 1 in each year.
(a) What was the average rate of change of population between 1998 and 2001?
(b) What was the average rate of change of population between 2002 and 2004?
(c) For what period of time was the population increasing?
(d) For what period of time was the population decreasing?

Year	Population
1997	624
1998	856
1999	1,336
2000	1,578
2001	1,591
2002	1,483
2003	994
2004	826
2005	801
2006	745

26. Running Speed A man is running around a circular track that is 200 m in circumference. An observer uses a stopwatch to record the runner's time at the end of each lap, obtaining the data in the following table.
(a) What was the man's average speed (rate) between 68 s and 152 s?
(b) What was the man's average speed between 263 s and 412 s?
(c) Calculate the man's speed for each lap. Is he slowing down, speeding up, or neither?

Time (s)	Distance (m)
32	200
68	400
108	600
152	800
203	1000
263	1200
335	1400
412	1600

27. CD Player Sales The table shows the number of CD players sold in a small electronics store in the years 1993–2003.
(a) What was the average rate of change of sales between 1993 and 2003?
(b) What was the average rate of change of sales between 1993 and 1994?
(c) What was the average rate of change of sales between 1994 and 1996?

(d) Between which two successive years did CD player sales *increase* most quickly? *Decrease* most quickly?

Year	CD players sold
1993	512
1994	520
1995	413
1996	410
1997	468
1998	510
1999	590
2000	607
2001	732
2002	612
2003	584

28. Book Collection Between 1980 and 2000, a rare book collector purchased books for his collection at the rate of 40 books per year. Use this information to complete the following table. (Note that not every year is given in the table.)

Year	Number of books
1980	420
1981	460
1982	
1985	
1990	
1992	
1995	
1997	
1998	
1999	
2000	1220

29. Cooling Soup When a bowl of hot soup is left in a room, the soup eventually cools down to room temperature. The temperature T of the soup is a function of time t. The table below gives the temperature (in °F) of a bowl of soup t minutes after it was set on the table. Find the average rate of change of the temperature of the soup over the first 20 minutes and over the next 20 minutes. During which interval did the soup cool off more quickly?

t (min)	T (°F)	t (min)	T (°F)
0	200	35	94
5	172	40	89
10	150	50	81
15	133	60	77
20	119	90	72
25	108	120	70
30	100	150	70

30. Farms in the United States The graph gives the number of farms in the United States from 1850 to 2000.

(a) Estimate the average rate of change in the number of farms between (i) 1860 and 1890 and (ii) 1950 and 1970.

(b) In which decade did the number of farms experience the greatest average rate of decline?

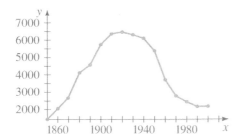

DISCOVERY ▪ DISCUSSION ▪ WRITING

31. 100-Meter Race A 100-m race ends in a three-way tie for first place. The graph at the top of the next column shows distance as a function of time for each of the three winners.

(a) Find the average speed for each winner.

(b) Describe the differences between the ways in which the three runners ran the race.

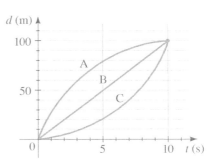

32. Linear Functions Have Constant Rate of Change

If $f(x) = mx + b$ is a linear function, then the average rate of change of f between any two real numbers x_1 and x_2 is

$$\text{average rate of change} = \frac{f(x_2) - f(x_1)}{x_2 - x_1}$$

Calculate this average rate of change to show that it is the same as the slope m.

33. Functions with Constant Rate of Change Are Linear

If the function f has the same average rate of change c between any two points, then for the points a and x we have

$$c = \frac{f(x) - f(a)}{x - a}$$

Rearrange this expression to show that

$$f(x) = cx + (f(a) - ca)$$

and conclude that f is a linear function.

2.5 TRANSFORMATIONS OF FUNCTIONS

Vertical Shifting ▶ Horizontal Shifting ▶ Reflecting Graphs ▶ Vertical Stretching and Shrinking ▶ Horizontal Stretching and Shrinking ▶ Even and Odd Functions

In this section we study how certain transformations of a function affect its graph. This will give us a better understanding of how to graph functions. The transformations that we study are shifting, reflecting, and stretching.

▼ Vertical Shifting

Adding a constant to a function shifts its graph vertically: upward if the constant is positive and downward if it is negative.

In general, suppose we know the graph of $y = f(x)$. How do we obtain from it the graphs of

$$y = f(x) + c \qquad \text{and} \qquad y = f(x) - c \qquad (c > 0)$$

The y-coordinate of each point on the graph of $y = f(x) + c$ is c units above the y-coordinate of the corresponding point on the graph of $y = f(x)$. So we obtain the graph of $y = f(x) + c$ simply by shifting the graph of $y = f(x)$ upward c units. Similarly, we obtain the graph of $y = f(x) - c$ by shifting the graph of $y = f(x)$ downward c units.

Recall that the graph of the function f is the same as the graph of the equation $y = f(x)$.

VERTICAL SHIFTS OF GRAPHS

Suppose $c > 0$.

To graph $y = f(x) + c$, shift the graph of $y = f(x)$ upward c units.

To graph $y = f(x) - c$, shift the graph of $y = f(x)$ downward c units.

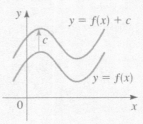 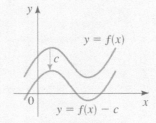

EXAMPLE 1 | Vertical Shifts of Graphs

Use the graph of $f(x) = x^2$ to sketch the graph of each function.

(a) $g(x) = x^2 + 3$ **(b)** $h(x) = x^2 - 2$

SOLUTION The function $f(x) = x^2$ was graphed in Example 1(a), Section 2.2. It is sketched again in Figure 1.

(a) Observe that

$$g(x) = x^2 + 3 = f(x) + 3$$

So the y-coordinate of each point on the graph of g is 3 units above the corresponding point on the graph of f. This means that to graph g, we shift the graph of f upward 3 units, as in Figure 1.

(b) Similarly, to graph h, we shift the graph of f downward 2 units, as shown in Figure 1.

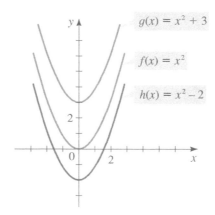

FIGURE 1

✎. NOW TRY EXERCISES **21** AND **23**

▼ Horizontal Shifting

Suppose that we know the graph of $y = f(x)$. How do we use it to obtain the graphs of

$$y = f(x + c) \qquad \text{and} \qquad y = f(x - c) \qquad (c > 0)$$

The value of $f(x - c)$ at x is the same as the value of $f(x)$ at $x - c$. Since $x - c$ is c units to the left of x, it follows that the graph of $y = f(x - c)$ is just the graph of $y = f(x)$

shifted to the right c units. Similar reasoning shows that the graph of $y = f(x + c)$ is the graph of $y = f(x)$ shifted to the left c units. The following box summarizes these facts.

HORIZONTAL SHIFTS OF GRAPHS

Suppose $c > 0$.

To graph $y = f(x - c)$, shift the graph of $y = f(x)$ to the right c units.
To graph $y = f(x + c)$, shift the graph of $y = f(x)$ to the left c units.

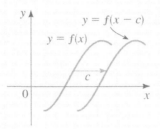 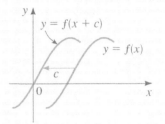

EXAMPLE 2 | Horizontal Shifts of Graphs

Use the graph of $f(x) = x^2$ to sketch the graph of each function.

(a) $g(x) = (x + 4)^2$ **(b)** $h(x) = (x - 2)^2$

SOLUTION

(a) To graph g, we shift the graph of f to the left 4 units.

(b) To graph h, we shift the graph of f to the right 2 units.

The graphs of g and h are sketched in Figure 2.

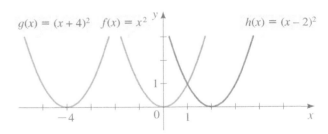

FIGURE 2

NOW TRY EXERCISE **25** AND **27**

RENÉ DESCARTES (1596–1650) was born in the town of La Haye in southern France. From an early age Descartes liked mathematics because of "the certainty of its results and the clarity of its reasoning." He believed that to arrive at truth, one must begin by doubting everything, including one's own existence; this led him to formulate perhaps the best-known sentence in all of philosophy: "I think, therefore I am." In his book *Discourse on Method* he described what is now called the Cartesian plane. This idea of combining algebra and geometry enabled mathematicians for the first time to graph functions and thus "see" the equations they were studying. The philosopher John Stuart Mill called this invention "the greatest single step ever made in the progress of the exact sciences." Descartes liked to get up late and spend the morning in bed thinking and writing. He invented the coordinate plane while lying in bed watching a fly crawl on the ceiling, reasoning that he could describe the exact location of the fly by knowing its distance from two perpendicular walls. In 1649 Descartes became the tutor of Queen Christina of Sweden. She liked her lessons at 5 o'clock in the morning, when, she said, her mind was sharpest. However, the change from his usual habits and the ice-cold library where they studied proved too much for Descartes. In February 1650, after just two months of this, he caught pneumonia and died.

EXAMPLE 3 | Combining Horizontal and Vertical Shifts

Sketch the graph of $f(x) = \sqrt{x - 3} + 4$.

SOLUTION We start with the graph of $y = \sqrt{x}$ (Example 1(c), Section 2.2) and shift it to the right 3 units to obtain the graph of $y = \sqrt{x - 3}$. Then we shift the resulting graph upward 4 units to obtain the graph of $f(x) = \sqrt{x - 3} + 4$ shown in Figure 3.

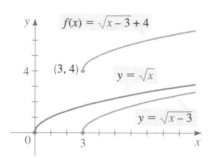

FIGURE 3

✎ NOW TRY EXERCISE **37**

▼ Reflecting Graphs

Suppose we know the graph of $y = f(x)$. How do we use it to obtain the graphs of $y = -f(x)$ and $y = f(-x)$? The y-coordinate of each point on the graph of $y = -f(x)$ is simply the negative of the y-coordinate of the corresponding point on the graph of $y = f(x)$. So the desired graph is the reflection of the graph of $y = f(x)$ in the x-axis. On the other hand, the value of $y = f(-x)$ at x is the same as the value of $y = f(x)$ at $-x$, so the desired graph here is the reflection of the graph of $y = f(x)$ in the y-axis. The fol-lowing box summarizes these observations.

REFLECTING GRAPHS

To graph $y = -f(x)$, reflect the graph of $y = f(x)$ in the x-axis.
To graph $y = f(-x)$, reflect the graph of $y = f(x)$ in the y-axis.

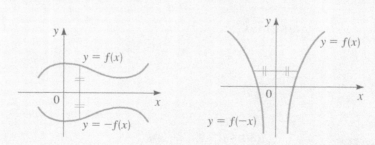

EXAMPLE 4 | Reflecting Graphs

Sketch the graph of each function.

(a) $f(x) = -x^2$ **(b)** $g(x) = \sqrt{-x}$

SOLUTION

(a) We start with the graph of $y = x^2$. The graph of $f(x) = -x^2$ is the graph of $y = x^2$ reflected in the x-axis (see Figure 4).

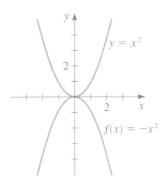

FIGURE 4

(b) We start with the graph of $y = \sqrt{x}$ (Example 1(c) in Section 2.2). The graph of $g(x) = \sqrt{-x}$ is the graph of $y = \sqrt{x}$ reflected in the y-axis (see Figure 5). Note that the domain of the function $g(x) = \sqrt{-x}$ is $\{x \mid x \leq 0\}$.

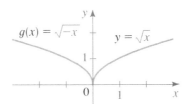

FIGURE 5

◆ . NOW TRY EXERCISES **29** AND **31**

▼ Vertical Stretching and Shrinking

Suppose we know the graph of $y = f(x)$. How do we use it to obtain the graph of $y = cf(x)$? The y-coordinate of $y = cf(x)$ at x is the same as the corresponding y-coordinate of $y = f(x)$ multiplied by c. Multiplying the y-coordinates by c has the effect of vertically stretching or shrinking the graph by a factor of c.

VERTICAL STRETCHING AND SHRINKING OF GRAPHS

To graph $y = cf(x)$:

If $c > 1$, stretch the graph of $y = f(x)$ vertically by a factor of c.

If $0 < c < 1$, shrink the graph of $y = f(x)$ vertically by a factor of c.

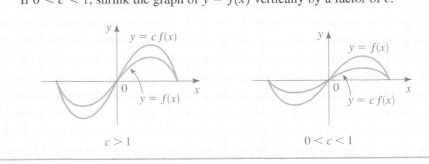

EXAMPLE 5 | Vertical Stretching and Shrinking of Graphs

Use the graph of $f(x) = x^2$ to sketch the graph of each function.

(a) $g(x) = 3x^2$ **(b)** $h(x) = \frac{1}{3}x^2$

SOLUTION

(a) The graph of g is obtained by multiplying the y-coordinate of each point on the graph of f by 3. That is, to obtain the graph of g, we stretch the graph of f vertically by a factor of 3. The result is the narrower parabola in Figure 6.

(b) The graph of h is obtained by multiplying the y-coordinate of each point on the graph of f by $\frac{1}{3}$. That is, to obtain the graph of h, we shrink the graph of f vertically by a factor of $\frac{1}{3}$. The result is the wider parabola in Figure 6.

◆ . NOW TRY EXERCISES **33** AND **35**

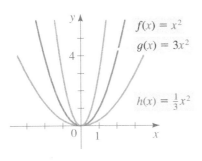

FIGURE 6

We illustrate the effect of combining shifts, reflections, and stretching in the following example.

EXAMPLE 6 | Combining Shifting, Stretching, and Reflecting

Sketch the graph of the function $f(x) = 1 - 2(x - 3)^2$.

SOLUTION Starting with the graph of $y = x^2$, we first shift to the right 3 units to get the graph of $y = (x - 3)^2$. Then we reflect in the x-axis and stretch by a factor of 2 to get the graph of $y = -2(x - 3)^2$. Finally, we shift upward 1 unit to get the graph of $f(x) = 1 - 2(x - 3)^2$ shown in Figure 7.

FIGURE 7

NOW TRY EXERCISE **39**

▼ Horizontal Stretching and Shrinking

Now we consider horizontal shrinking and stretching of graphs. If we know the graph of $y = f(x)$, then how is the graph of $y = f(cx)$ related to it? The y-coordinate of $y = f(cx)$ at x is the same as the y-coordinate of $y = f(x)$ at cx. Thus, the x-coordinates in the graph of $y = f(x)$ correspond to the x-coordinates in the graph of $y = f(cx)$ multiplied by c. Looking at this the other way around, we see that the x-coordinates in the graph of $y = f(cx)$ are the x-coordinates in the graph of $y = f(x)$ multiplied by $1/c$. In other words, to change the graph of $y = f(x)$ to the graph of $y = f(cx)$, we must shrink (or stretch) the graph horizontally by a factor of $1/c$, as summarized in the following box.

HORIZONTAL SHRINKING AND STRETCHING OF GRAPHS

To graph $y = f(cx)$:

If $c > 1$, shrink the graph of $y = f(x)$ horizontally by a factor of $1/c$.

If $0 < c < 1$, stretch the graph of $y = f(x)$ horizontally by a factor of $1/c$.

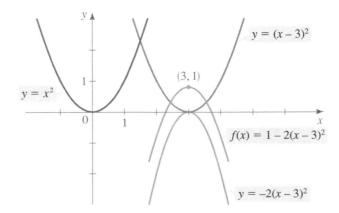

EXAMPLE 7 | Horizontal Stretching and Shrinking of Graphs

The graph of $y = f(x)$ is shown in Figure 8 on the next page. Sketch the graph of each function.

(a) $y = f(2x)$ **(b)** $y = f\left(\frac{1}{2}x\right)$

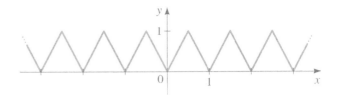

FIGURE 8 $y = f(x)$

SOLUTION   Using the principles described in the preceding box, we obtain the graphs shown in Figures 9 and 10.

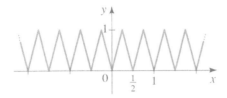

FIGURE 9 $y = f(2x)$

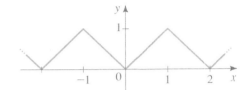

FIGURE 10 $y = f(\frac{1}{2}x)$

✎ NOW TRY EXERCISE **63**

▼ Even and Odd Functions

If a function f satisfies $f(-x) = f(x)$ for every number x in its domain, then f is called an **even function**. For instance, the function $f(x) = x^2$ is even because

$$f(-x) = (-x)^2 = (-1)^2 x^2 = x^2 = f(x)$$

The graph of an even function is symmetric with respect to the y-axis (see Figure 11). This means that if we have plotted the graph of f for $x \geq 0$, then we can obtain the entire graph simply by reflecting this portion in the y-axis.

If f satisfies $f(-x) = -f(x)$ for every number x in its domain, then f is called an **odd function**. For example, the function $f(x) = x^3$ is odd because

$$f(-x) = (-x)^3 = (-1)^3 x^3 = -x^3 = -f(x)$$

The graph of an odd function is symmetric about the origin (see Figure 12). If we have plotted the graph of f for $x \geq 0$, then we can obtain the entire graph by rotating this portion through 180° about the origin. (This is equivalent to reflecting first in the x-axis and then in the y-axis.)

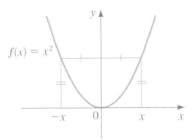

FIGURE 11 $f(x) = x^2$ is an even function.

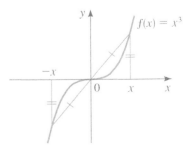

FIGURE 12 $f(x) = x^3$ is an odd function.

EVEN AND ODD FUNCTIONS

Let f be a function.

f is **even** if $f(-x) = f(x)$ for all x in the domain of f.

f is **odd** if $f(-x) = -f(x)$ for all x in the domain of f.

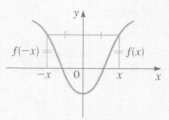

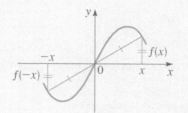

The graph of an even function is symmetric with respect to the y-axis.

The graph of an odd function is symmetric with respect to the origin.

EXAMPLE 8 | Even and Odd Functions

Determine whether the functions are even, odd, or neither even nor odd.

(a) $f(x) = x^5 + x$

(b) $g(x) = 1 - x^4$

(c) $h(x) = 2x - x^2$

SOLUTION

(a)
$$f(-x) = (-x)^5 + (-x)$$
$$= -x^5 - x = -(x^5 + x)$$
$$= -f(x)$$

Therefore, f is an odd function.

(b) $g(-x) = 1 - (-x)^4 = 1 - x^4 = g(x)$

So g is even.

(c) $h(-x) = 2(-x) - (-x)^2 = -2x - x^2$

Since $h(-x) \neq h(x)$ and $h(-x) \neq -h(x)$, we conclude that h is neither even nor odd.

NOW TRY EXERCISES **75, 77,** AND **79**

The graphs of the functions in Example 8 are shown in Figure 13. The graph of f is symmetric about the origin, and the graph of g is symmetric about the y-axis. The graph of h is not symmetric either about the y-axis or the origin.

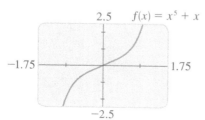

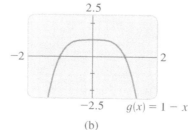

FIGURE 13

(a)

(b)

(c)

2.5 EXERCISES

CONCEPTS

1–2 ■ Fill in the blank with the appropriate direction (left, right, up, or down).

1. (a) The graph of $y = f(x) + 3$ is obtained from the graph of

$y = f(x)$ by shifting _____ 3 units.

(b) The graph of $y = f(x + 3)$ is obtained from the graph of

$y = f(x)$ by shifting _____ 3 units.

2. (a) The graph of $y = f(x) - 3$ is obtained from the graph of

$y = f(x)$ by shifting _____ 3 units.

(b) The graph of $y = f(x - 3)$ is obtained from the graph of

$y = f(x)$ by shifting _____ 3 units.

3. Fill in the blank with the appropriate axis (x-axis or y-axis).

(a) The graph of $y = -f(x)$ is obtained from the graph of

$y = f(x)$ by reflecting in the _____.

(b) The graph of $y = f(-x)$ is obtained from the graph of

$y = f(x)$ by reflecting in the _____.

4. Match the graph with the function.

(a) $y = |x + 1|$ **(b)** $y = |x - 1|$

(c) $y = |x| - 1$ **(d)** $y = -|x|$

I
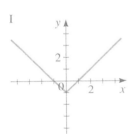

II
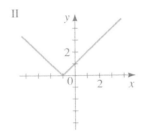

III
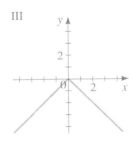

IV
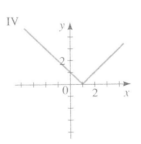

SKILLS

5–14 ■ Suppose the graph of f is given. Describe how the graph of each function can be obtained from the graph of f.

5. (a) $y = f(x) - 5$ **(b)** $y = f(x - 5)$

6. (a) $y = f(x + 7)$ **(b)** $y = f(x) + 7$

7. (a) $y = -f(x)$ **(b)** $y = f(-x)$

8. (a) $y = -2f(x)$ **(b)** $y = -\frac{1}{2}f(x)$

9. (a) $y = -f(x) + 5$ **(b)** $y = 3f(x) - 5$

10. (a) $y = f(x - 4) + \frac{3}{4}$ **(b)** $y = f(x + 4) - \frac{3}{4}$

11. (a) $y = 2f(x + 1) - 3$ **(b)** $y = 2f(x - 1) + 3$

12. (a) $y = 3 - 2f(x)$ **(b)** $y = 2 - f(-x)$

13. (a) $y = f(4x)$ **(b)** $y = f(\frac{1}{4}x)$

14. (a) $y = f(2x) - 1$ **(b)** $y = 2f(\frac{1}{2}x)$

15–18 ■ Explain how the graph of g is obtained from the graph of f.

15. (a) $f(x) = x^2$, $g(x) = (x + 2)^2$
    (b) $f(x) = x^2$, $g(x) = x^2 + 2$

16. (a) $f(x) = x^3$, $g(x) = (x - 4)^3$
    (b) $f(x) = x^3$, $g(x) = x^3 - 4$

17. (a) $f(x) = |x|$, $g(x) = |x + 2| - 2$
    (b) $f(x) = |x|$, $g(x) = |x - 2| + 2$

18. (a) $f(x) = \sqrt{x}$, $g(x) = -\sqrt{x} + 1$
    (b) $f(x) = \sqrt{x}$, $g(x) = \sqrt{-x} + 1$

19. Use the graph of $y = x^2$ in Figure 4 to graph the following.
    (a) $g(x) = x^2 + 1$
    (b) $g(x) = (x - 1)^2$
    (c) $g(x) = -x^2$
    (d) $g(x) = (x - 1)^2 + 3$

20. Use the graph of $y = \sqrt{x}$ in Figure 5 to graph the following.
    (a) $g(x) = \sqrt{x - 2}$
    (b) $g(x) = \sqrt{x} + 1$
    (c) $g(x) = \sqrt{x + 2} + 2$
    (d) $g(x) = -\sqrt{x} + 1$

21–44 ■ Sketch the graph of the function, not by plotting points, but by starting with the graph of a standard function and applying transformations.

21. $f(x) = x^2 - 1$

22. $f(x) = x^2 + 5$

23. $f(x) = \sqrt{x} + 1$

24. $f(x) = |x| - 1$

25. $f(x) = (x - 5)^2$

26. $f(x) = (x + 1)^2$

27. $f(x) = \sqrt{x + 4}$

28. $f(x) = |x - 3|$

29. $f(x) = -x^3$

30. $f(x) = -|x|$

31. $y = \sqrt[4]{-x}$

32. $y = \sqrt[3]{-x}$

33. $y = \frac{1}{4}x^2$

34. $y = -5\sqrt{x}$

35. $y = 3|x|$

36. $y = \frac{1}{2}|x|$

37. $y = (x - 3)^2 + 5$

38. $y = \sqrt{x + 4} - 3$

39. $y = 3 - \frac{1}{2}(x - 1)^2$

40. $y = 2 - \sqrt{x + 1}$

41. $y = |x + 2| + 2$

42. $y = 2 - |x|$

43. $y = \frac{1}{2}\sqrt{x + 4} - 3$

44. $y = 3 - 2(x - 1)^2$

45–54 ■ A function f is given, and the indicated transformations are applied to its graph (in the given order). Write the equation for the final transformed graph.

45. $f(x) = x^2$; shift upward 3 units

46. $f(x) = x^3$; shift downward 1 unit

47. $f(x) = \sqrt{x}$; shift 2 units to the left

48. $f(x) = \sqrt[3]{x}$; shift 1 unit to the right

49. $f(x) = |x|$; shift 3 units to the right and shift upward 1 unit

50. $f(x) = |x|$; shift 4 units to the left and shift downward 2 units

51. $f(x) = \sqrt[4]{x}$; reflect in the y-axis and shift upward 1 unit

52. $f(x) = x^2$; shift 2 units to the left and reflect in the x-axis

53. $f(x) = x^2$; stretch vertically by a factor of 2, shift downward 2 units, and shift 3 units to the right

54. $f(x) = |x|$; shrink vertically by a factor of $\frac{1}{2}$, shift to the left 1 unit, and shift upward 3 units

55–60 ■ The graphs of f and g are given. Find a formula for the function g.

55.

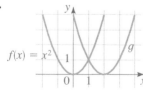

56.

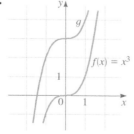

57.

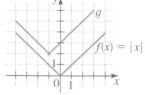

58.

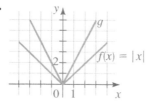

59.

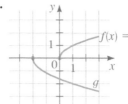

60.

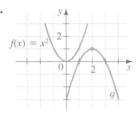

61–62 ■ The graph of $y = f(x)$ is given. Match each equation with its graph.

61. (a) $y = f(x - 4)$ **(b)** $y = f(x) + 3$
   (c) $y = 2f(x + 6)$ **(d)** $y = -f(2x)$

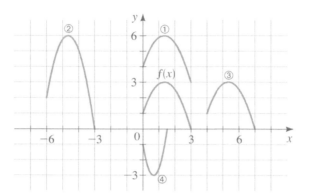

62. (a) $y = \frac{1}{3}f(x)$ **(b)** $y = -f(x + 4)$
   (c) $y = f(x - 4) + 3$ **(d)** $y = f(-x)$

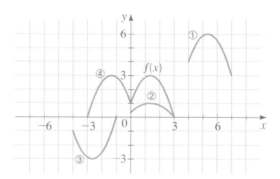

63. The graph of f is given. Sketch the graphs of the following functions.
   (a) $y = f(x - 2)$ **(b)** $y = f(x) - 2$
   (c) $y = 2f(x)$ **(d)** $y = -f(x) + 3$
   (e) $y = f(-x)$ **(f)** $y = \frac{1}{2}f(x - 1)$

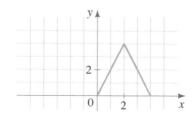

64. The graph of g is given. Sketch the graphs of the following functions.

(a) $y = g(x + 1)$ (b) $y = g(-x)$
(c) $y = g(x - 2)$ (d) $y = g(x) - 2$
(e) $y = -g(x)$ (f) $y = 2g(x)$

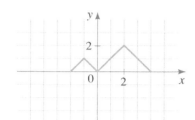

65. The graph of g is given. Use it to graph each of the following functions.

(a) $y = g(2x)$ (b) $y = g\left(\frac{1}{2}x\right)$

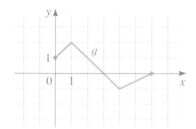

66. The graph of h is given. Use it to graph each of the following functions.

(a) $y = h(3x)$ (b) $y = h\left(\frac{1}{3}x\right)$

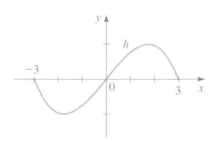

67–68 ■ Use the graph of $f(x) = [\![x]\!]$ described on page 156 to graph the indicated function.

67. $y = [\![2x]\!]$ **68.** $y = [\![\frac{1}{4}x]\!]$

69–72 ■ Graph the functions on the same screen using the given viewing rectangle. How is each graph related to the graph in part (a)?

69. Viewing rectangle $[-8, 8]$ by $[-2, 8]$
(a) $y = \sqrt[4]{x}$ (b) $y = \sqrt[4]{x + 5}$
(c) $y = 2\sqrt[4]{x + 5}$ (d) $y = 4 + 2\sqrt[4]{x + 5}$

70. Viewing rectangle $[-8, 8]$ by $[-6, 6]$
(a) $y = |x|$ (b) $y = -|x|$
(c) $y = -3|x|$ (d) $y = -3|x - 5|$

71. Viewing rectangle $[-4, 6]$ by $[-4, 4]$
(a) $y = x^6$ (b) $y = \frac{1}{3}x^6$
(c) $y = -\frac{1}{3}x^6$ (d) $y = -\frac{1}{3}(x - 4)^6$

72. Viewing rectangle $[-6, 6]$ by $[-4, 4]$
(a) $y = \dfrac{1}{\sqrt{x}}$ (b) $y = \dfrac{1}{\sqrt{x + 3}}$
(c) $y = \dfrac{1}{2\sqrt{x + 3}}$ (d) $y = \dfrac{1}{2\sqrt{x + 3}} - 3$

73. If $f(x) = \sqrt{2x - x^2}$, graph the following functions in the viewing rectangle $[-5, 5]$ by $[-4, 4]$. How is each graph related to the graph in part (a)?
(a) $y = f(x)$ (b) $y = f(2x)$ (c) $y = f\left(\frac{1}{2}x\right)$

74. If $f(x) = \sqrt{2x - x^2}$, graph the following functions in the viewing rectangle $[-5, 5]$ by $[-4, 4]$. How is each graph related to the graph in part (a)?
(a) $y = f(x)$ (b) $y = f(-x)$
(c) $y = -f(-x)$ (d) $y = f(-2x)$
(e) $y = f\left(-\frac{1}{2}x\right)$

75–82 ■ Determine whether the function f is even, odd, or neither. If f is even or odd, use symmetry to sketch its graph.

75. $f(x) = x^4$ **76.** $f(x) = x^3$

77. $f(x) = x^2 + x$ **78.** $f(x) = x^4 - 4x^2$

79. $f(x) = x^3 - x$ **80.** $f(x) = 3x^3 + 2x^2 + 1$

81. $f(x) = 1 - \sqrt[3]{x}$ **82.** $f(x) = x + \dfrac{1}{x}$

83–84 ■ The graph of a function defined for $x \geq 0$ is given. Complete the graph for $x < 0$ to make (a) an even function and (b) an odd function.

83.   **84.**

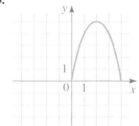 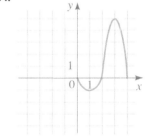

85–86 ■ These exercises show how the graph of $y = |f(x)|$ is obtained from the graph of $y = f(x)$.

85. The graphs of $f(x) = x^2 - 4$ and $g(x) = |x^2 - 4|$ are shown. Explain how the graph of g is obtained from the graph of f.

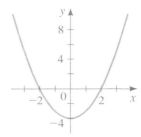 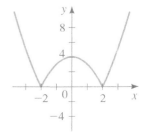

$f(x) = x^2 - 4$ $g(x) = |x^2 - 4|$

86. The graph of $f(x) = x^4 - 4x^2$ is shown. Use this graph to sketch the graph of $g(x) = |x^4 - 4x^2|$.

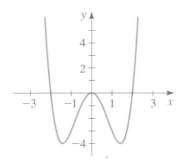

87–88 ■ Sketch the graph of each function.

87. (a) $f(x) = 4x - x^2$ **(b)** $g(x) = |4x - x^2|$

88. (a) $f(x) = x^3$ **(b)** $g(x) = |x^3|$

APPLICATIONS

89. Sales Growth The annual sales of a certain company can be modeled by the function $f(t) = 4 + 0.01t^2$, where t represents years since 1990 and $f(t)$ is measured in millions of dollars.
(a) What shifting and shrinking operations must be performed on the function $y = t^2$ to obtain the function $y = f(t)$?
(b) Suppose you want t to represent years since 2000 instead of 1990. What transformation would you have to apply to the function $y = f(t)$ to accomplish this? Write the new function $y = g(t)$ that results from this transformation.

90. Changing Temperature Scales The temperature on a certain afternoon is modeled by the function

$$C(t) = \tfrac{1}{2}t^2 + 2$$

where t represents hours after 12 noon $(0 \le t \le 6)$ and C is measured in °C.
(a) What shifting and shrinking operations must be performed on the function $y = t^2$ to obtain the function $y = C(t)$?
(b) Suppose you want to measure the temperature in °F instead. What transformation would you have to apply to the function $y = C(t)$ to accomplish this? (Use the fact that the relationship between Celsius and Fahrenheit degrees is given by $F = \tfrac{9}{5}C + 32$.) Write the new function $y = F(t)$ that results from this transformation.

DISCOVERY ▪ DISCUSSION ▪ WRITING

91. Sums of Even and Odd Functions If f and g are both even functions, is $f + g$ necessarily even? If both are odd, is their sum necessarily odd? What can you say about the sum if one is odd and one is even? In each case, prove your answer.

92. Products of Even and Odd Functions Answer the same questions as in Exercise 91, except this time consider the product of f and g instead of the sum.

93. Even and Odd Power Functions What must be true about the integer n if the function

$$f(x) = x^n$$

is an even function? If it is an odd function? Why do you think the names "even" and "odd" were chosen for these function properties?

2.6 COMBINING FUNCTIONS

| Sums, Differences, Products, and Quotients ▶ Composition of Functions

In this section we study different ways to combine functions to make new functions.

▼ Sums, Differences, Products, and Quotients

The sum of f and g is defined by

$(f + g)(x) = f(x) + g(x)$

The name of the new function is "$f + g$." So this $+$ sign stands for the operation of addition of *functions*. The $+$ sign on the right side, however, stands for addition of the *numbers* $f(x)$ and $g(x)$.

Two functions f and g can be combined to form new functions $f + g$, $f - g$, fg, and f/g in a manner similar to the way we add, subtract, multiply, and divide real numbers. For example, we define the function $f + g$ by

$$(f + g)(x) = f(x) + g(x)$$

The new function $f + g$ is called the **sum** of the functions f and g; its value at x is $f(x) + g(x)$. Of course, the sum on the right-hand side makes sense only if both $f(x)$ and $g(x)$ are defined, that is, if x belongs to the domain of f and also to the domain of g. So if the domain of f is A and the domain of g is B, then the domain of $f + g$ is the intersection of these domains, that is, $A \cap B$. Similarly, we can define the **difference** $f - g$, the **product** fg, and the **quotient** f/g of the functions f and g. Their domains are $A \cap B$, but in the case of the quotient we must remember not to divide by 0.

> **ALGEBRA OF FUNCTIONS**
>
> Let f and g be functions with domains A and B. Then the functions $f + g$, $f - g$, fg, and f/g are defined as follows.
>
> $$(f + g)(x) = f(x) + g(x) \qquad \text{Domain } A \cap B$$
>
> $$(f - g)(x) = f(x) - g(x) \qquad \text{Domain } A \cap B$$
>
> $$(fg)(x) = f(x)g(x) \qquad \text{Domain } A \cap B$$
>
> $$\left(\frac{f}{g}\right)(x) = \frac{f(x)}{g(x)} \qquad \text{Domain } \{x \in A \cap B \mid g(x) \neq 0\}$$

EXAMPLE 1 | Combinations of Functions and Their Domains

Let $f(x) = \dfrac{1}{x - 2}$ and $g(x) = \sqrt{x}$.

(a) Find the functions $f + g$, $f - g$, fg, and f/g and their domains.

(b) Find $(f + g)(4)$, $(f - g)(4)$, $(fg)(4)$, and $(f/g)(4)$.

SOLUTION

(a) The domain of f is $\{x \mid x \neq 2\}$, and the domain of g is $\{x \mid x \geq 0\}$. The intersection of the domains of f and g is

$$\{x \mid x \geq 0 \text{ and } x \neq 2\} = [0, 2) \cup (2, \infty)$$

Thus, we have

$$(f + g)(x) = f(x) + g(x) = \frac{1}{x - 2} + \sqrt{x} \qquad \text{Domain } \{x \mid x \geq 0 \text{ and } x \neq 2\}$$

$$(f - g)(x) = f(x) - g(x) = \frac{1}{x - 2} - \sqrt{x} \qquad \text{Domain } \{x \mid x \geq 0 \text{ and } x \neq 2\}$$

$$(fg)(x) = f(x)g(x) = \frac{\sqrt{x}}{x - 2} \qquad \text{Domain } \{x \mid x \geq 0 \text{ and } x \neq 2\}$$

$$\left(\frac{f}{g}\right)(x) = \frac{f(x)}{g(x)} = \frac{1}{(x - 2)\sqrt{x}} \qquad \text{Domain } \{x \mid x > 0 \text{ and } x \neq 2\}$$

To divide fractions, invert the denominator and multiply:

$$\frac{1/(x - 2)}{\sqrt{x}} = \frac{1/(x - 2)}{\sqrt{x}/1}$$

$$= \frac{1}{x - 2} \cdot \frac{1}{\sqrt{x}}$$

$$= \frac{1}{(x - 2)\sqrt{x}}$$

Note that in the domain of f/g we exclude 0 because $g(0) = 0$.

(b) Each of these values exist because $x = 4$ is in the domain of each function.

$$(f + g)(4) = f(4) + g(4) = \frac{1}{4 - 2} + \sqrt{4} = \frac{5}{2}$$

$$(f - g)(4) = f(4) - g(4) = \frac{1}{4 - 2} - \sqrt{4} = -\frac{3}{2}$$

$$(fg)(4) = f(4)g(4) = \left(\frac{1}{4 - 2}\right)\sqrt{4} = 1$$

$$\left(\frac{f}{g}\right)(4) = \frac{f(4)}{g(4)} = \frac{1}{(4 - 2)\sqrt{4}} = \frac{1}{4}$$

NOW TRY EXERCISE **5**

The graph of the function $f + g$ can be obtained from the graphs of f and g by **graphical addition**. This means that we add corresponding y-coordinates, as illustrated in the next example.

EXAMPLE 2 | Using Graphical Addition

The graphs of f and g are shown in Figure 1. Use graphical addition to graph the function $f + g$.

SOLUTION We obtain the graph of $f + g$ by "graphically adding" the value of $f(x)$ to $g(x)$ as shown in Figure 2. This is implemented by copying the line segment PQ on top of PR to obtain the point S on the graph of $f + g$.

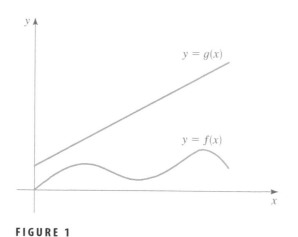

FIGURE 1

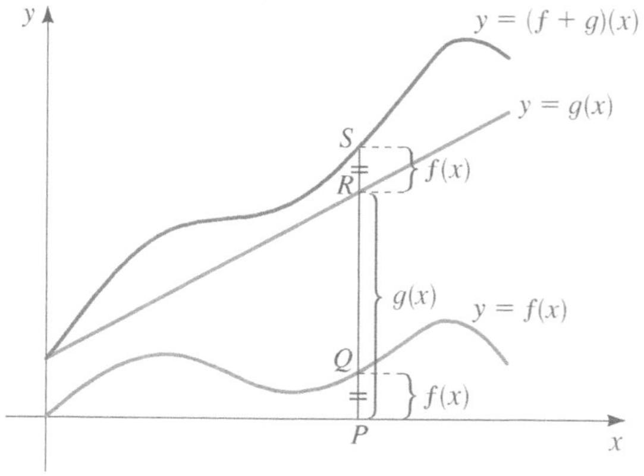

FIGURE 2 Graphical addition

NOW TRY EXERCISE **15**

▼ Composition of Functions

Now let's consider a very important way of combining two functions to get a new function. Suppose $f(x) = \sqrt{x}$ and $g(x) = x^2 + 1$. We may define a new function h as

$$h(x) = f(g(x)) = f(x^2 + 1) = \sqrt{x^2 + 1}$$

The function h is made up of the functions f and g in an interesting way: Given a number x, we first apply the function g to it, then apply f to the result. In this case, f is the rule "take the square root," g is the rule "square, then add 1," and h is the rule "square, then add 1, then take the square root." In other words, we get the rule h by applying the rule g and then the rule f. Figure 3 shows a machine diagram for h.

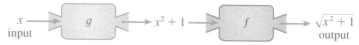

FIGURE 3 The h machine is composed of the g machine (first) and then the f machine.

In general, given any two functions f and g, we start with a number x in the domain of g and find its image $g(x)$. If this number $g(x)$ is in the domain of f, we can then calculate the value of $f(g(x))$. The result is a new function $h(x) = f(g(x))$ that is obtained by substituting g into f. It is called the *composition* (or *composite*) of f and g and is denoted by $f \circ g$ ("f composed with g").

> **COMPOSITION OF FUNCTIONS**
>
> Given two functions f and g, the **composite function** $f \circ g$ (also called the **composition** of f and g) is defined by
>
> $$(f \circ g)(x) = f(g(x))$$

The domain of $f \circ g$ is the set of all x in the domain of g such that $g(x)$ is in the domain of f. In other words, $(f \circ g)(x)$ is defined whenever both $g(x)$ and $f(g(x))$ are defined. We can picture $f \circ g$ using an arrow diagram (Figure 4).

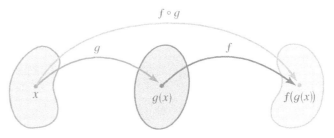

FIGURE 4   Arrow diagram for $f \circ g$

EXAMPLE 3 | Finding the Composition of Functions

Let $f(x) = x^2$ and $g(x) = x - 3$.

(a) Find the functions $f \circ g$ and $g \circ f$ and their domains.

(b) Find $(f \circ g)(5)$ and $(g \circ f)(7)$.

SOLUTION

In Example 3, f is the rule "square" and g is the rule "subtract 3." The function $f \circ g$ *first* subtracts 3 and *then* squares; the function $g \circ f$ *first* squares and *then* subtracts 3.

(a) We have

$$
\begin{aligned}
(f \circ g)(x) &= f(g(x)) && \text{Definition of } f \circ g \\
&= f(x - 3) && \text{Definition of } g \\
&= (x - 3)^2 && \text{Definition of } f
\end{aligned}
$$

and

$$
\begin{aligned}
(g \circ f)(x) &= g(f(x)) && \text{Definition of } g \circ f \\
&= g(x^2) && \text{Definition of } f \\
&= x^2 - 3 && \text{Definition of } g
\end{aligned}
$$

The domains of both $f \circ g$ and $g \circ f$ are $\mathbb{R}$.

(b) We have

$$(f \circ g)(5) = f(g(5)) = f(2) = 2^2 = 4$$

$$(g \circ f)(7) = g(f(7)) = g(49) = 49 - 3 = 46$$

. NOW TRY EXERCISES **21** AND **35**

You can see from Example 3 that, in general, $f \circ g \neq g \circ f$. Remember that the notation $f \circ g$ means that the function g is applied first and then f is applied second.

The graphs of f and g of Example 4, as well as those of $f \circ g$, $g \circ f$, $f \circ f$, and $g \circ g$, are shown below. These graphs indicate that the operation of composition can produce functions that are quite different from the original functions.

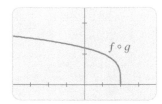

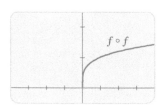

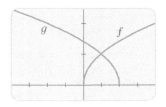

EXAMPLE 4 | Finding the Composition of Functions

If $f(x) = \sqrt{x}$ and $g(x) = \sqrt{2 - x}$, find the following functions and their domains.

(a) $f \circ g$ **(b)** $g \circ f$ **(c)** $f \circ f$ **(d)** $g \circ g$

SOLUTION

(a)
$$
\begin{aligned}
(f \circ g)(x) &= f(g(x)) &&\text{Definition of } f \circ g \\
&= f(\sqrt{2 - x}) &&\text{Definition of } g \\
&= \sqrt{\sqrt{2 - x}} &&\text{Definition of } f \\
&= \sqrt[4]{2 - x}
\end{aligned}
$$

The domain of $f \circ g$ is $\{x \mid 2 - x \geq 0\} = \{x \mid x \leq 2\} = (-\infty, 2]$.

(b)
$$
\begin{aligned}
(g \circ f)(x) &= g(f(x)) &&\text{Definition of } g \circ f \\
&= g(\sqrt{x}) &&\text{Definition of } f \\
&= \sqrt{2 - \sqrt{x}} &&\text{Definition of } g
\end{aligned}
$$

For $\sqrt{x}$ to be defined, we must have $x \geq 0$. For $\sqrt{2 - \sqrt{x}}$ to be defined, we must have $2 - \sqrt{x} \geq 0$, that is, $\sqrt{x} \leq 2$, or $x \leq 4$. Thus, we have $0 \leq x \leq 4$, so the domain of $g \circ f$ is the closed interval $[0, 4]$.

(c)
$$
\begin{aligned}
(f \circ f)(x) &= f(f(x)) &&\text{Definition of } f \circ f \\
&= f(\sqrt{x}) &&\text{Definition of } f \\
&= \sqrt{\sqrt{x}} &&\text{Definition of } f \\
&= \sqrt[4]{x}
\end{aligned}
$$

The domain of $f \circ f$ is $[0, \infty)$.

(d)
$$
\begin{aligned}
(g \circ g)(x) &= g(g(x)) &&\text{Definition of } g \circ g \\
&= g(\sqrt{2 - x}) &&\text{Definition of } g \\
&= \sqrt{2 - \sqrt{2 - x}} &&\text{Definition of } g
\end{aligned}
$$

This expression is defined when both $2 - x \geq 0$ and $2 - \sqrt{2 - x} \geq 0$. The first inequality means $x \leq 2$, and the second is equivalent to $\sqrt{2 - x} \leq 2$, or $2 - x \leq 4$, or $x \geq -2$. Thus, $-2 \leq x \leq 2$, so the domain of $g \circ g$ is $[-2, 2]$.

NOW TRY EXERCISE 41

It is possible to take the composition of three or more functions. For instance, the composite function $f \circ g \circ h$ is found by first applying h, then g, and then f as follows:

$$(f \circ g \circ h)(x) = f(g(h(x)))$$

EXAMPLE 5 | A Composition of Three Functions

Find $f \circ g \circ h$ if $f(x) = x/(x + 1)$, $g(x) = x^{10}$, and $h(x) = x + 3$.

SOLUTION

$$
\begin{aligned}
(f \circ g \circ h)(x) &= f(g(h(x))) &&\text{Definition of } f \circ g \circ h \\
&= f(g(x + 3)) &&\text{Definition of } h \\
&= f((x + 3)^{10}) &&\text{Definition of } g \\
&= \frac{(x + 3)^{10}}{(x + 3)^{10} + 1} &&\text{Definition of } f
\end{aligned}
$$

NOW TRY EXERCISE 45

So far, we have used composition to build complicated functions from simpler ones. But in calculus it is useful to be able to "decompose" a complicated function into simpler ones, as shown in the following example.

EXAMPLE 6 | Recognizing a Composition of Functions

Given $F(x) = \sqrt[4]{x + 9}$, find functions f and g such that $F = f \circ g$.

SOLUTION Since the formula for F says to first add 9 and then take the fourth root, we let

$$g(x) = x + 9 \qquad \text{and} \qquad f(x) = \sqrt[4]{x}$$

Then

$$
\begin{aligned}
(f \circ g)(x) &= f(g(x)) && \text{Definition of } f \circ g\\
&= f(x + 9) && \text{Definition of } g\\
&= \sqrt[4]{x + 9} && \text{Definition of } f\\
&= F(x)
\end{aligned}
$$

◆. NOW TRY EXERCISE **49**

EXAMPLE 7 | An Application of Composition of Functions

A ship is traveling at 20 mi/h parallel to a straight shoreline. The ship is 5 mi from shore. It passes a lighthouse at noon.

(a) Express the distance s between the lighthouse and the ship as a function of d, the distance the ship has traveled since noon; that is, find f so that $s = f(d)$.

(b) Express d as a function of t, the time elapsed since noon; that is, find g so that $d = g(t)$.

(c) Find $f \circ g$. What does this function represent?

SOLUTION We first draw a diagram as in Figure 5.

(a) We can relate the distances s and d by the Pythagorean Theorem. Thus, s can be expressed as a function of d by

$$s = f(d) = \sqrt{25 + d^2}$$

(b) Since the ship is traveling at 20 mi/h, the distance d it has traveled is a function of t as follows:

$$d = g(t) = 20t$$

(c) We have

$$
\begin{aligned}
(f \circ g)(t) &= f(g(t)) && \text{Definition of } f \circ g\\
&= f(20t) && \text{Definition of } g\\
&= \sqrt{25 + (20t)^2} && \text{Definition of } f
\end{aligned}
$$

The function $f \circ g$ gives the distance of the ship from the lighthouse as a function of time.

◆. NOW TRY EXERCISE **63**

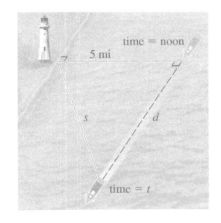

time = noon

5 mi

s

d

time = t

FIGURE 5

distance = rate × time

2.6 EXERCISES

CONCEPTS

1. From the graphs of f and g in the figure, we find

$(f + g)(2) =$ _____ $(f - g)(2) =$ _____

$(fg)(2) =$ _____ $\left(\dfrac{f}{g}\right)(2) =$ _____

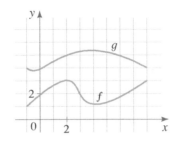

2. By definition, $f \circ g(x) =$ _____. So if $g(2) = 5$ and

$f(5) = 12$, then $f \circ g(2) =$ _____.

3. If the rule of the function f is "add one" and the rule of the function g is "multiply by 2," then the rule of $f \circ g$ is

"_____,"

and the rule of $g \circ f$ is

"_____."

4. We can express the functions in Exercise 3 algebraically as

$f(x) =$ _____ $g(x) =$ _____

$f \circ g(x) =$ _____ $g \circ f(x) =$ _____

SKILLS

5–10 ■ Find $f + g$, $f - g$, fg, and f/g and their domains.

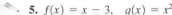

5. $f(x) = x - 3$, $g(x) = x^2$

6. $f(x) = x^2 + 2x$, $g(x) = 3x^2 - 1$

7. $f(x) = \sqrt{4 - x^2}$, $g(x) = \sqrt{1 + x}$

8. $f(x) = \sqrt{9 - x^2}$, $g(x) = \sqrt{x^2 - 4}$

9. $f(x) = \dfrac{2}{x}$, $g(x) = \dfrac{4}{x + 4}$

10. $f(x) = \dfrac{2}{x + 1}$, $g(x) = \dfrac{x}{x + 1}$

11–14 ■ Find the domain of the function.

11. $f(x) = \sqrt{x} + \sqrt{1 - x}$ **12.** $g(x) = \sqrt{x + 1} - \dfrac{1}{x}$

13. $h(x) = (x - 3)^{-1/4}$ **14.** $k(x) = \dfrac{\sqrt{x + 3}}{x - 1}$

15–16 ■ Use graphical addition to sketch the graph of $f + g$.

15. 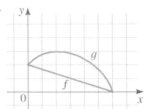   **16.**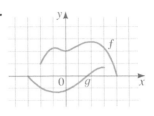

17–20 ■ Draw the graphs of f, g, and $f + g$ on a common screen to illustrate graphical addition.

17. $f(x) = \sqrt{1 + x}$, $g(x) = \sqrt{1 - x}$

18. $f(x) = x^2$, $g(x) = \sqrt{x}$

19. $f(x) = x^2$, $g(x) = \frac{1}{3}x^3$

20. $f(x) = \sqrt[4]{1 - x}$, $g(x) = \sqrt{1 - \dfrac{x^2}{9}}$

21–26 ■ Use $f(x) = 3x - 5$ and $g(x) = 2 - x^2$ to evaluate the expression.

21. (a) $f(g(0))$ (b) $g(f(0))$

22. (a) $f(f(4))$ (b) $g(g(3))$

23. (a) $(f \circ g)(-2)$ (b) $(g \circ f)(-2)$

24. (a) $(f \circ f)(-1)$ (b) $(g \circ g)(2)$

25. (a) $(f \circ g)(x)$ (b) $(g \circ f)(x)$

26. (a) $(f \circ f)(x)$ (b) $(g \circ g)(x)$

27–32 ■ Use the given graphs of f and g to evaluate the expression.

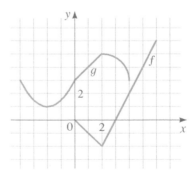

27. $f(g(2))$

28. $g(f(0))$

29. $(g \circ f)(4)$

30. $(f \circ g)(0)$

31. $(g \circ g)(-2)$

32. $(f \circ f)(4)$

33–44 ■ Find the functions $f \circ g$, $g \circ f$, $f \circ f$, and $g \circ g$ and their domains.

33. $f(x) = 2x + 3$, $g(x) = 4x - 1$

34. $f(x) = 6x - 5$, $g(x) = \dfrac{x}{2}$

35. $f(x) = x^2$, $g(x) = x + 1$

36. $f(x) = x^3 + 2$, $g(x) = \sqrt[3]{x}$

37. $f(x) = \dfrac{1}{x}$, $g(x) = 2x + 4$

38. $f(x) = x^2$, $g(x) = \sqrt{x - 3}$

39. $f(x) = |x|$, $g(x) = 2x + 3$

40. $f(x) = x - 4$, $g(x) = |x + 4|$

41. $f(x) = \dfrac{x}{x + 1}$, $g(x) = 2x - 1$

42. $f(x) = \dfrac{1}{\sqrt{x}}$, $g(x) = x^2 - 4x$

43. $f(x) = \dfrac{x}{x + 1}$, $g(x) = \dfrac{1}{x}$

44. $f(x) = \dfrac{2}{x}$, $g(x) = \dfrac{x}{x + 2}$

45–48 ■ Find $f \circ g \circ h$.

45. $f(x) = x - 1$, $g(x) = \sqrt{x}$, $h(x) = x - 1$

46. $f(x) = \dfrac{1}{x}$, $g(x) = x^3$, $h(x) = x^2 + 2$

47. $f(x) = x^4 + 1$, $g(x) = x - 5$, $h(x) = \sqrt{x}$

48. $f(x) = \sqrt{x}$, $g(x) = \dfrac{x}{x - 1}$, $h(x) = \sqrt[3]{x}$

49–54 ■ Express the function in the form $f \circ g$.

49. $F(x) = (x - 9)^5$

50. $F(x) = \sqrt{x} + 1$

51. $G(x) = \dfrac{x^2}{x^2 + 4}$

52. $G(x) = \dfrac{1}{x + 3}$

53. $H(x) = |1 - x^3|$

54. $H(x) = \sqrt{1 + \sqrt{x}}$

55–58 ■ Express the function in the form $f \circ g \circ h$.

55. $F(x) = \dfrac{1}{x^2 + 1}$

56. $F(x) = \sqrt[3]{\sqrt{x} - 1}$

57. $G(x) = (4 + \sqrt[3]{x})^9$

58. $G(x) = \dfrac{2}{(3 + \sqrt{x})^2}$

APPLICATIONS

59–60 ■ **Revenue, Cost, and Profit**   A print shop makes bumper stickers for election campaigns. If x stickers are ordered (where $x < 10{,}000$), then the price per bumper sticker is $0.15 - 0.000002x$ dollars, and the total cost of producing the order is $0.095x - 0.0000005x^2$ dollars.

59. Use the fact that

$$\text{revenue} \;=\; \text{price per item} \;\times\; \text{number of items sold}$$

to express $R(x)$, the revenue from an order of x stickers, as a product of two functions of x.

60. Use the fact that

$$\text{profit} \;=\; \text{revenue} \;-\; \text{cost}$$

to express $P(x)$, the profit on an order of x stickers, as a difference of two functions of x.

61. Area of a Ripple   A stone is dropped in a lake, creating a circular ripple that travels outward at a speed of 60 cm/s.
 (a) Find a function g that models the radius as a function of time.
 (b) Find a function f that models the area of the circle as a function of the radius.
 (c) Find $f \circ g$. What does this function represent?

62. Inflating a Balloon   A spherical balloon is being inflated. The radius of the balloon is increasing at the rate of 1 cm/s.
 (a) Find a function f that models the radius as a function of time.
 (b) Find a function g that models the volume as a function of the radius.
 (c) Find $g \circ f$. What does this function represent?

63. Area of a Balloon   A spherical weather balloon is being inflated. The radius of the balloon is increasing at the rate of 2 cm/s. Express the surface area of the balloon as a function of time t (in seconds).

64. Multiple Discounts   You have a $50 coupon from the manufacturer good for the purchase of a cell phone. The store where you are purchasing your cell phone is offering a 20% discount on all cell phones. Let x represent the regular price of the cell phone.
 (a) Suppose only the 20% discount applies. Find a function f that models the purchase price of the cell phone as a function of the regular price x.

(b) Suppose only the $50 coupon applies. Find a function g that models the purchase price of the cell phone as a function of the sticker price x.

(c) If you can use the coupon and the discount, then the purchase price is either $f \circ g(x)$ or $g \circ f(x)$, depending on the order in which they are applied to the price. Find both $f \circ g(x)$ and $g \circ f(x)$. Which composition gives the lower price?

65. Multiple Discounts An appliance dealer advertises a 10% discount on all his washing machines. In addition, the manufacturer offers a $100 rebate on the purchase of a washing machine. Let x represent the sticker price of the washing machine.

(a) Suppose only the 10% discount applies. Find a function f that models the purchase price of the washer as a function of the sticker price x.

(b) Suppose only the $100 rebate applies. Find a function g that models the purchase price of the washer as a function of the sticker price x.

(c) Find $f \circ g$ and $g \circ f$. What do these functions represent? Which is the better deal?

66. Airplane Trajectory An airplane is flying at a speed of 350 mi/h at an altitude of one mile. The plane passes directly above a radar station at time $t = 0$.

(a) Express the distance s (in miles) between the plane and the radar station as a function of the horizontal distance d (in miles) that the plane has flown.

(b) Express d as a function of the time t (in hours) that the plane has flown.

(c) Use composition to express s as a function of t.

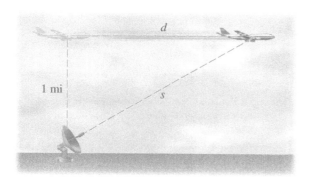

Find

$$A \circ A$$

$$A \circ A \circ A$$

$$A \circ A \circ A \circ A$$

What do these compositions represent? Find a formula for what you get when you compose n copies of A.

68. Composing Linear Functions The graphs of the functions

$$f(x) = m_1 x + b_1$$

$$g(x) = m_2 x + b_2$$

are lines with slopes m_1 and m_2, respectively. Is the graph of $f \circ g$ a line? If so, what is its slope?

69. Solving an Equation for an Unknown Function Suppose that

$$g(x) = 2x + 1$$

$$h(x) = 4x^2 + 4x + 7$$

Find a function f such that $f \circ g = h$. (Think about what operations you would have to perform on the formula for g to end up with the formula for h.) Now suppose that

$$f(x) = 3x + 5$$

$$h(x) = 3x^2 + 3x + 2$$

Use the same sort of reasoning to find a function g such that $f \circ g = h$.

70. Compositions of Odd and Even Functions Suppose that

$$h = f \circ g$$

If g is an even function, is h necessarily even? If g is odd, is h odd? What if g is odd and f is odd? What if g is odd and f is even?

DISCOVERY ▪ DISCUSSION ▪ WRITING

67. Compound Interest A savings account earns 5% interest compounded annually. If you invest x dollars in such an account, then the amount $A(x)$ of the investment after one year is the initial investment plus 5%; that is,

$$A(x) = x + 0.05x = 1.05x$$

2.7 ONE-TO-ONE FUNCTIONS AND THEIR INVERSES

One-to-One Functions ▶ The Inverse of a Function ▶ Graphing the Inverse of a Function

The *inverse* of a function is a rule that acts on the output of the function and produces the corresponding input. So the inverse "undoes" or reverses what the function has done. Not all functions have inverses; those that do are called *one-to-one*.

▼ One-to-One Functions

Let's compare the functions f and g whose arrow diagrams are shown in Figure 1. Note that f never takes on the same value twice (any two numbers in A have different images), whereas g does take on the same value twice (both 2 and 3 have the same image, 4). In symbols, $g(2) = g(3)$ but $f(x_1) \neq f(x_2)$ whenever $x_1 \neq x_2$. Functions that have this latter property are called *one-to-one*.

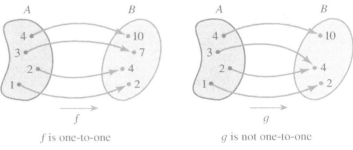

f is one-to-one g is not one-to-one

FIGURE 1

DEFINITION OF A ONE-TO-ONE FUNCTION

A function with domain A is called a **one-to-one function** if no two elements of A have the same image, that is,

$$f(x_1) \neq f(x_2) \quad \text{whenever } x_1 \neq x_2$$

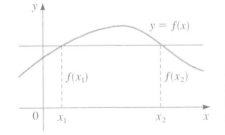

FIGURE 2 This function is not one-to-one because $f(x_1) = f(x_2)$.

An equivalent way of writing the condition for a one-to-one function is this:

$$\text{If } f(x_1) = f(x_2), \text{ then } x_1 = x_2.$$

If a horizontal line intersects the graph of f at more than one point, then we see from Figure 2 that there are numbers $x_1 \neq x_2$ such that $f(x_1) = f(x_2)$. This means that f is not one-to-one. Therefore, we have the following geometric method for determining whether a function is one-to-one.

HORIZONTAL LINE TEST

A function is one-to-one if and only if no horizontal line intersects its graph more than once.

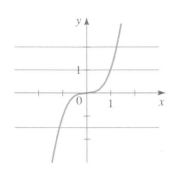

FIGURE 3 $f(x) = x^3$ is one-to-one.

EXAMPLE 1 | Deciding Whether a Function Is One-to-One

Is the function $f(x) = x^3$ one-to-one?

SOLUTION 1   If $x_1 \neq x_2$, then $x_1^3 \neq x_2^3$ (two different numbers cannot have the same cube). Therefore, $f(x) = x^3$ is one-to-one.

SOLUTION 2   From Figure 3 we see that no horizontal line intersects the graph of $f(x) = x^3$ more than once. Therefore, by the Horizontal Line Test, f is one-to-one.

✎ NOW TRY EXERCISE 13

Notice that the function f of Example 1 is increasing and is also one-to-one. In fact, it can be proved that *every increasing function and every decreasing function is one-to-one.*

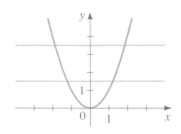

FIGURE 4 $f(x) = x^2$ is not one-to-one.

EXAMPLE 2 | Deciding Whether a Function Is One-to-One

Is the function $g(x) = x^2$ one-to-one?

SOLUTION 1   This function is not one-to-one because, for instance,

$$g(1) = 1 \quad \text{and} \quad g(-1) = 1$$

so 1 and -1 have the same image.

SOLUTION 2   From Figure 4 we see that there are horizontal lines that intersect the graph of g more than once. Therefore, by the Horizontal Line Test, g is not one-to-one.

✎ NOW TRY EXERCISE 15

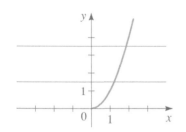

FIGURE 5 $f(x) = x^2$ ($x \geq 0$) is one-to-one.

Although the function g in Example 2 is not one-to-one, it is possible to restrict its domain so that the resulting function is one-to-one. In fact, if we define

$$h(x) = x^2 \qquad x \geq 0$$

then h is one-to-one, as you can see from Figure 5 and the Horizontal Line Test.

EXAMPLE 3 | Showing That a Function Is One-to-One

Show that the function $f(x) = 3x + 4$ is one-to-one.

SOLUTION   Suppose there are numbers x_1 and x_2 such that $f(x_1) = f(x_2)$. Then

$$3x_1 + 4 = 3x_2 + 4 \qquad \text{Suppose } f(x_1) = f(x_2)$$
$$3x_1 = 3x_2 \qquad \text{Subtract 4}$$
$$x_1 = x_2 \qquad \text{Divide by 3}$$

Therefore, f is one-to-one.

✎ NOW TRY EXERCISE 11

▼ The Inverse of a Function

One-to-one functions are important because they are precisely the functions that possess inverse functions according to the following definition.

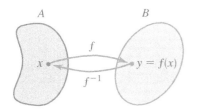

FIGURE 6

Don't mistake the −1 in f^{-1} for an exponent.

$f^{-1}(x)$ *does not mean* $\dfrac{1}{f(x)}$

The reciprocal $1/f(x)$ is written as $(f(x))^{-1}$.

DEFINITION OF THE INVERSE OF A FUNCTION

Let f be a one-to-one function with domain A and range B. Then its **inverse function** f^{-1} has domain B and range A and is defined by

$$f^{-1}(y) = x \quad \Leftrightarrow \quad f(x) = y$$

for any y in B.

This definition says that if f takes x to y, then f^{-1} takes y back to x. (If f were not one-to-one, then f^{-1} would not be defined uniquely.) The arrow diagram in Figure 6 indicates that f^{-1} reverses the effect of f. From the definition we have

$$\text{domain of } f^{-1} = \text{range of } f$$
$$\text{range of } f^{-1} = \text{domain of } f$$

EXAMPLE 4 | Finding f^{-1} for Specific Values

If $f(1) = 5$, $f(3) = 7$, and $f(8) = -10$, find $f^{-1}(5)$, $f^{-1}(7)$, and $f^{-1}(-10)$.

SOLUTION From the definition of f^{-1} we have

$$f^{-1}(5) = 1 \quad \text{because} \quad f(1) = 5$$
$$f^{-1}(7) = 3 \quad \text{because} \quad f(3) = 7$$
$$f^{-1}(-10) = 8 \quad \text{because} \quad f(8) = -10$$

Figure 7 shows how f^{-1} reverses the effect of f in this case.

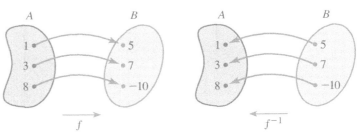

FIGURE 7

NOW TRY EXERCISE **21**

By definition the inverse function f^{-1} undoes what f does: If we start with x, apply f, and then apply f^{-1}, we arrive back at x, where we started. Similarly, f undoes what f^{-1} does. In general, any function that reverses the effect of f in this way must be the inverse of f. These observations are expressed precisely as follows.

INVERSE FUNCTION PROPERTY

Let f be a one-to-one function with domain A and range B. The inverse function f^{-1} satisfies the following cancellation properties:

$$f^{-1}(f(x)) = x \quad \text{for every } x \text{ in } A$$
$$f(f^{-1}(x)) = x \quad \text{for every } x \text{ in } B$$

Conversely, any function f^{-1} satisfying these equations is the inverse of f.

These properties indicate that f is the inverse function of f^{-1}, so we say that f and f^{-1} are *inverses of each other*.

EXAMPLE 5 | Verifying That Two Functions Are Inverses

Show that $f(x) = x^3$ and $g(x) = x^{1/3}$ are inverses of each other.

SOLUTION Note that the domain and range of both f and g is $\mathbb{R}$. We have

$$g(f(x)) = g(x^3) = (x^3)^{1/3} = x$$
$$f(g(x)) = f(x^{1/3}) = (x^{1/3})^3 = x$$

So by the Property of Inverse Functions, f and g are inverses of each other. These equations simply say that the cube function and the cube root function, when composed, cancel each other.

✎. NOW TRY EXERCISE **27**

Now let's examine how we compute inverse functions. We first observe from the definition of f^{-1} that

$$y = f(x) \quad \Leftrightarrow \quad f^{-1}(y) = x$$

So if $y = f(x)$ and if we are able to solve this equation for x in terms of y, then we must have $x = f^{-1}(y)$. If we then interchange x and y, we have $y = f^{-1}(x)$, which is the desired equation.

HOW TO FIND THE INVERSE OF A ONE-TO-ONE FUNCTION

1. Write $y = f(x)$.

2. Solve this equation for x in terms of y (if possible).

3. Interchange x and y. The resulting equation is $y = f^{-1}(x)$.

In Example 6 note how f^{-1} reverses the effect of f. The function f is the rule "Multiply by 3, then subtract 2," whereas f^{-1} is the rule "Add 2, then divide by 3."

Note that Steps 2 and 3 can be reversed. In other words, we can interchange x and y first and then solve for y in terms of x.

EXAMPLE 6 | Finding the Inverse of a Function

Find the inverse of the function $f(x) = 3x - 2$.

SOLUTION First we write $y = f(x)$.

$$y = 3x - 2$$

Then we solve this equation for x.

$$3x = y + 2 \qquad \text{Add 2}$$
$$x = \frac{y + 2}{3} \qquad \text{Divide by 3}$$

Finally, we interchange x and y.

$$y = \frac{x + 2}{3}$$

Therefore, the inverse function is $f^{-1}(x) = \dfrac{x + 2}{3}$.

✎. NOW TRY EXERCISE **37**

CHECK YOUR ANSWER

We use the Inverse Function Property.

$$f^{-1}(f(x)) = f^{-1}(3x - 2)$$
$$= \frac{(3x - 2) + 2}{3}$$
$$= \frac{3x}{3} = x$$

$$f(f^{-1}(x)) = f\left(\frac{x + 2}{3}\right)$$
$$= 3\left(\frac{x + 2}{3}\right) - 2$$
$$= x + 2 - 2 = x \quad ✔$$

EXAMPLE 7 | Finding the Inverse of a Function

Find the inverse of the function $f(x) = \dfrac{x^5 - 3}{2}$.

In Example 7 note how f^{-1} reverses the effect of f. The function f is the rule "Take the fifth power, subtract 3, then divide by 2," whereas f^{-1} is the rule "Multiply by 2, add 3, then take the fifth root."

SOLUTION   We first write $y = (x^5 - 3)/2$ and solve for x.

$$y = \frac{x^5 - 3}{2} \qquad \text{Equation defining function}$$

$$2y = x^5 - 3 \qquad \text{Multiply by 2}$$

$$x^5 = 2y + 3 \qquad \text{Add 3 (and switch sides)}$$

$$x = (2y + 3)^{1/5} \qquad \text{Take fifth root of each side}$$

Then we interchange x and y to get $y = (2x + 3)^{1/5}$. Therefore, the inverse function is $f^{-1}(x) = (2x + 3)^{1/5}$.

◈ . NOW TRY EXERCISE **53**

CHECK YOUR ANSWER

We use the Inverse Function Property.

$$f^{-1}(f(x)) = f^{-1}\left(\frac{x^5 - 3}{2}\right)$$

$$= \left[2\left(\frac{x^5 - 3}{2}\right) + 3\right]^{1/5}$$

$$= (x^5 - 3 + 3)^{1/5}$$

$$= (x^5)^{1/5} = x$$

$$f(f^{-1}(x)) = f((2x + 3)^{1/5})$$

$$= \frac{[(2x + 3)^{1/5}]^5 - 3}{2}$$

$$= \frac{2x + 3 - 3}{2}$$

$$= \frac{2x}{2} = x \quad ✔$$

A **rational function** is a function defined by a rational expression. In the next example we find the inverse of a rational function.

EXAMPLE 8 | Finding the Inverse of a Rational Function

Find the inverse of the function $f(x) = \dfrac{2x + 3}{x - 1}$.

Rational functions are studied in Section 3.7.

SOLUTION   We first write $y = (2x + 3)/(x - 1)$ and solve for x.

$$y = \frac{2x + 3}{x - 1} \qquad \text{Equation defining function}$$

$$y(x - 1) = 2x + 3 \qquad \text{Multiply by } x - 1$$

$$yx - y = 2x + 3 \qquad \text{Expand}$$

$$yx - 2x = y + 3 \qquad \text{Bring } x\text{-terms to LHS}$$

$$x(y - 2) = y + 3 \qquad \text{Factor } x$$

$$x = \frac{y + 3}{y - 2} \qquad \text{Divide by } y - 2$$

Therefore the inverse function is $f^{-1}(x) = \dfrac{x + 3}{x - 2}$.

◈ . NOW TRY EXERCISE **45**

▼ Graphing the Inverse of a Function

The principle of interchanging x and y to find the inverse function also gives us a method for obtaining the graph of f^{-1} from the graph of f. If $f(a) = b$, then $f^{-1}(b) = a$. Thus, the point (a, b) is on the graph of f if and only if the point (b, a) is on the graph of f^{-1}. But we get the point (b, a) from the point (a, b) by reflecting in the line $y = x$ (see Figure 8 on the next page). Therefore, as Figure 9 on the next page illustrates, the following is true.

> The graph of f^{-1} is obtained by reflecting the graph of f in the line $y = x$.

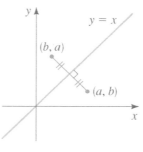

FIGURE 8

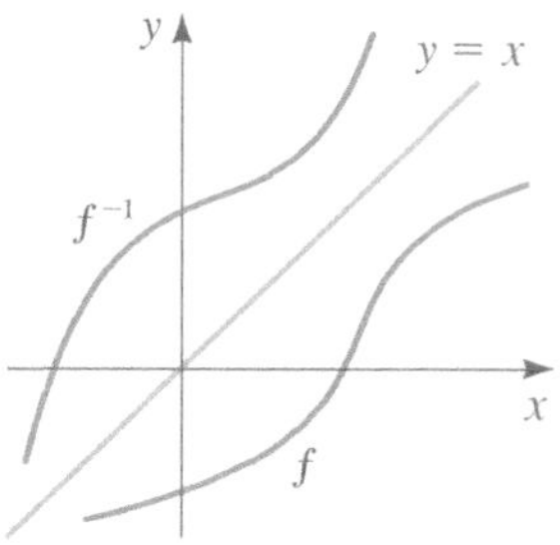

FIGURE 9

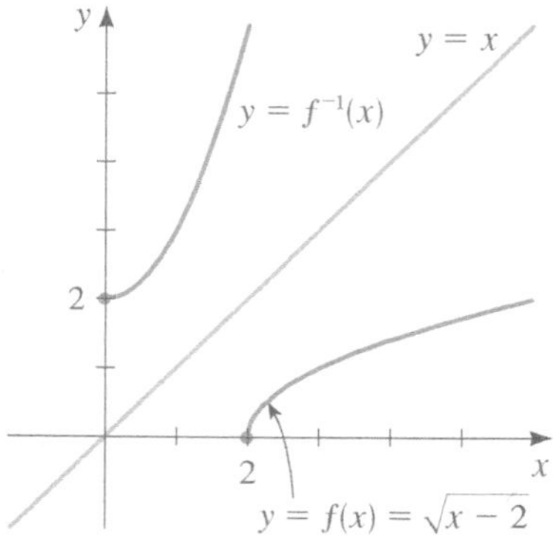

FIGURE 10

In Example 9 note how f^{-1} reverses the effect of f. The function f is the rule "Subtract 2, then take the square root," whereas f^{-1} is the rule "Square, then add 2."

EXAMPLE 9 | Graphing the Inverse of a Function

(a) Sketch the graph of $f(x) = \sqrt{x - 2}$.

(b) Use the graph of f to sketch the graph of f^{-1}.

(c) Find an equation for f^{-1}.

SOLUTION

(a) Using the transformations from Section 2.5, we sketch the graph of $y = \sqrt{x - 2}$ by plotting the graph of the function $y = \sqrt{x}$ (Example 1(c) in Section 2.2) and moving it to the right 2 units.

(b) The graph of f^{-1} is obtained from the graph of f in part (a) by reflecting it in the line $y = x$, as shown in Figure 10.

(c) Solve $y = \sqrt{x - 2}$ for x, noting that $y \geq 0$.

$$\sqrt{x - 2} = y$$
$$x - 2 = y^2 \qquad \text{Square each side}$$
$$x = y^2 + 2 \qquad y \geq 0 \qquad \text{Add 2}$$

Interchange x and y:

$$y = x^2 + 2 \qquad x \geq 0$$

Thus

$$f^{-1}(x) = x^2 + 2 \qquad x \geq 0$$

This expression shows that the graph of f^{-1} is the right half of the parabola $y = x^2 + 2$, and from the graph shown in Figure 10, this seems reasonable.

NOW TRY EXERCISE **63**

2.7 EXERCISES

CONCEPTS

1. A function f is one-to-one if different inputs produce

_____ outputs. You can tell from the graph that a function

is one-to-one by using the _____ Test.

2. (a) For a function to have an inverse, it must be _____.
So which one of the following functions has an inverse?

$$f(x) = x^2 \qquad g(x) = x^3$$

(b) What is the inverse of the function that you chose in part (a)?

3. A function f has the following verbal description: "Multiply by 3, add 5, and then take the third power of the result."

(a) Write a verbal description for f^{-1}.

(b) Find algebraic formulas that express f and f^{-1} in terms of the input x.

4. *True or false?*

(a) If f has an inverse, then $f^{-1}(x)$ is the same as $\dfrac{1}{f(x)}$.

(b) If f has an inverse, then $f^{-1}(f(x)) = x$.

SKILLS

5–10 ■ The graph of a function f is given. Determine whether f is one-to-one.

5.
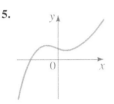

6.

7.
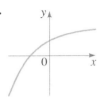

8.

9.

10.
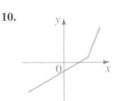

11–20 ■ Determine whether the function is one-to-one.

11. $f(x) = -2x + 4$

12. $f(x) = 3x - 2$

13. $g(x) = \sqrt{x}$

14. $g(x) = |x|$

15. $h(x) = x^2 - 2x$

16. $h(x) = x^3 + 8$

17. $f(x) = x^4 + 5$

18. $f(x) = x^4 + 5, \quad 0 \le x \le 2$

19. $f(x) = \dfrac{1}{x^2}$

20. $f(x) = \dfrac{1}{x}$

21–22 ■ Assume that f is a one-to-one function.

21. (a) If $f(2) = 7$, find $f^{-1}(7)$.
   (b) If $f^{-1}(3) = -1$, find $f(-1)$.

22. (a) If $f(5) = 18$, find $f^{-1}(18)$.
   (b) If $f^{-1}(4) = 2$, find $f(2)$.

23. If $f(x) = 5 - 2x$, find $f^{-1}(3)$.

24. If $g(x) = x^2 + 4x$ with $x \ge -2$, find $g^{-1}(5)$.

25–36 ■ Use the Inverse Function Property to show that f and g are inverses of each other.

25. $f(x) = x - 6; \quad g(x) = x + 6$ $f^{-1} = (x-6)+6$

26. $f(x) = 3x; \quad g(x) = \dfrac{x}{3}$ $3\left(\frac{x}{3}\right) = \frac{3x}{3}$.

27. $f(x) = 2x - 5; \quad g(x) = \dfrac{x + 5}{2}$ $2\left(\frac{x+5}{2}\right) - 5$

28. $f(x) = \dfrac{3 - x}{4}; \quad g(x) = 3 - 4x$

$3 - \left(\frac{3-x}{4}\right) - 4 \cdot 3 - 4\left(\frac{3-x}{4}\right).$

$3 - \left(\frac{3-x}{4}\right)$

29. $f(x) = \dfrac{1}{x}; \quad g(x) = \dfrac{1}{x}$

30. $f(x) = x^5; \quad g(x) = \sqrt[5]{x}$

31. $f(x) = x^2 - 4, \quad x \ge 0;$
   $g(x) = \sqrt{x + 4}, \quad x \ge -4$

32. $f(x) = x^3 + 1; \quad g(x) = (x - 1)^{1/3}$

33. $f(x) = \dfrac{1}{x - 1}, \quad x \ne 1; \quad g(x) = \dfrac{1}{x} + 1, \quad x \ne 0$

34. $f(x) = \sqrt{4 - x^2}, \quad 0 \le x \le 2;$
   $g(x) = \sqrt{4 - x^2}, \quad 0 \le x \le 2$

35. $f(x) = \dfrac{x + 2}{x - 2}; \quad g(x) = \dfrac{2x + 2}{x - 1}$

36. $f(x) = \dfrac{x - 5}{3x + 4}; \quad g(x) = \dfrac{5 + 4x}{1 - 3x}$

37–60 ■ Find the inverse function of f.

37. $f(x) = 2x + 1$

38. $f(x) = 6 - x$

39. $f(x) = 4x + 7$

40. $f(x) = 3 - 5x$

41. $f(x) = 5 - 4x^3$

42. $f(x) = \dfrac{1}{x^2}, \quad x > 0$ $f^{-1} = x^2 - 1$

43. $f(x) = \dfrac{1}{x + 2}$

44. $f(x) = \dfrac{x - 2}{x + 2}$

45. $f(x) = \dfrac{x}{x + 4}$

46. $f(x) = \dfrac{3x}{x - 2}$

47. $f(x) = \dfrac{2x + 5}{x - 7}$

48. $f(x) = \dfrac{4x - 2}{3x + 1}$

49. $f(x) = \dfrac{1 + 3x}{5 - 2x}$

50. $f(x) = \dfrac{2x - 1}{x - 3}$

51. $f(x) = \sqrt{2 + 5x}$

52. $f(x) = x^2 + x, \quad x \ge -\frac{1}{2}$

53. $f(x) = 4 - x^2, \quad x \ge 0$

54. $f(x) = \sqrt{2x - 1}$

55. $f(x) = 4 + \sqrt[3]{x}$

56. $f(x) = (2 - x^3)^5$

57. $f(x) = 1 + \sqrt{1 + x}$

58. $f(x) = \sqrt{9 - x^2}, \quad 0 \le x \le 3$

59. $f(x) = x^4, \quad x \ge 0$

60. $f(x) = 1 - x^3$

61–64 ■ A function f is given. (a) Sketch the graph of f. (b) Use the graph of f to sketch the graph of f^{-1}. (c) Find f^{-1}.

61. $f(x) = 3x - 6$

62. $f(x) = 16 - x^2, \quad x \ge 0$

63. $f(x) = \sqrt{x + 1}$

64. $f(x) = x^3 - 1$

65–70 ■ Draw the graph of f and use it to determine whether the function is one-to-one.

65. $f(x) = x^3 - x$

66. $f(x) = x^3 + x$

67. $f(x) = \dfrac{x + 12}{x - 6}$

68. $f(x) = \sqrt{x^3 - 4x + 1}$

69. $f(x) = |x| - |x - 6|$

70. $f(x) = x \cdot |x|$

71–74 ■ A one-to-one function is given. **(a)** Find the inverse of the function. **(b)** Graph both the function and its inverse on the same screen to verify that the graphs are reflections of each other in the line $y = x$.

71. $f(x) = 2 + x$ **72.** $f(x) = 2 - \frac{1}{2}x$

73. $g(x) = \sqrt{x + 3}$ **74.** $g(x) = x^2 + 1, \quad x \geq 0$

75–78 ■ The given function is not one-to-one. Restrict its domain so that the resulting function *is* one-to-one. Find the inverse of the function with the restricted domain. (There is more than one correct answer.)

75. $f(x) = 4 - x^2$ **76.** $g(x) = (x - 1)^2$

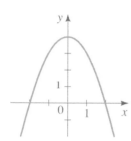
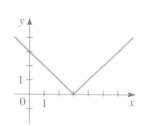

77. $h(x) = (x + 2)^2$ **78.** $k(x) = |x - 3|$

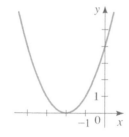
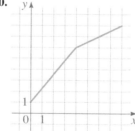

79–80 ■ Use the graph of f to sketch the graph of f^{-1}.

79.   **80.**

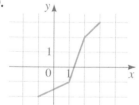

APPLICATIONS

81. Fee for Service   For his services, a private investigator requires a $500 retention fee plus $80 per hour. Let x represent the number of hours the investigator spends working on a case.
   (a) Find a function f that models the investigator's fee as a function of x.
   (b) Find f^{-1}. What does f^{-1} represent?
   (c) Find $f^{-1}(1220)$. What does your answer represent?

82. Toricelli's Law   A tank holds 100 gallons of water, which drains from a leak at the bottom, causing the tank to empty in 40 minutes. Toricelli's Law gives the volume of water remaining in the tank after t minutes as

$$V(t) = 100\left(1 - \frac{t}{40}\right)^2$$

   (a) Find V^{-1}. What does V^{-1} represent?
   (b) Find $V^{-1}(15)$. What does your answer represent?

83. Blood Flow   As blood moves through a vein or artery, its velocity v is greatest along the central axis and decreases as the distance r from the central axis increases (see the figure below). For an artery with radius 0.5 cm, v (in cm/s) is given as a function of r (in cm) by

$$v(r) = 18{,}500(0.25 - r^2)$$

   (a) Find v^{-1}. What does v^{-1} represent?
   (b) Find $v^{-1}(30)$. What does your answer represent?

84. Demand Function   The amount of a commodity that is sold is called the *demand* for the commodity. The demand D for a certain commodity is a function of the price given by

$$D(p) = -3p + 150$$

   (a) Find D^{-1}. What does D^{-1} represent?
   (b) Find $D^{-1}(30)$. What does your answer represent?

85. Temperature Scales   The relationship between the Fahrenheit (F) and Celsius (C) scales is given by

$$F(C) = \frac{9}{5}C + 32$$

   (a) Find F^{-1}. What does F^{-1} represent?
   (b) Find $F^{-1}(86)$. What does your answer represent?

86. Exchange Rates   The relative value of currencies fluctuates every day. When this problem was written, one Canadian dollar was worth 1.0573 U.S. dollar.
   (a) Find a function f that gives the U.S. dollar value $f(x)$ of x Canadian dollars.
   (b) Find f^{-1}. What does f^{-1} represent?
   (c) How much Canadian money would $12,250 in U.S. currency be worth?

87. Income Tax   In a certain country, the tax on incomes less than or equal to €20,000 is 10%. For incomes that are more than €20,000, the tax is €2000 plus 20% of the amount over €20,000.
   (a) Find a function f that gives the income tax on an income x. Express f as a piecewise defined function.
   (b) Find f^{-1}. What does f^{-1} represent?
   (c) How much income would require paying a tax of €10,000?

88. Multiple Discounts   A car dealership advertises a 15% discount on all its new cars. In addition, the manufacturer offers a $1000 rebate on the purchase of a new car. Let x represent the sticker price of the car.
   (a) Suppose only the 15% discount applies. Find a function f that models the purchase price of the car as a function of the sticker price x.

(b) Suppose only the $1000 rebate applies. Find a function g that models the purchase price of the car as a function of the sticker price x.

(c) Find a formula for $H = f \circ g$.

(d) Find H^{-1}. What does H^{-1} represent?

(e) Find $H^{-1}(13,000)$. What does your answer represent?

89. Pizza Cost Marcello's Pizza charges a base price of $7 for a large pizza plus $2 for each topping. Thus, if you order a large pizza with x toppings, the price of your pizza is given by the function $f(x) = 7 + 2x$. Find f^{-1}. What does the function f^{-1} represent?

DISCOVERY ▪ DISCUSSION ▪ WRITING

90. Determining When a Linear Function Has an Inverse For the linear function $f(x) = mx + b$ to be one-to-one, what must be true about its slope? If it is one-to-one, find its inverse. Is the inverse linear? If so, what is its slope?

91. Finding an Inverse "in Your Head" In the margin notes in this section we pointed out that the inverse of a function can be found by simply reversing the operations that make up the function. For instance, in Example 6 we saw that the inverse of

$$f(x) = 3x - 2 \quad \text{is} \quad f^{-1}(x) = \frac{x + 2}{3}$$

because the "reverse" of "Multiply by 3 and subtract 2" is "Add 2 and divide by 3." Use the same procedure to find the inverse of the following functions.

(a) $f(x) = \dfrac{2x + 1}{5}$ **(b)** $f(x) = 3 - \dfrac{1}{x}$

(c) $f(x) = \sqrt{x^3 + 2}$ **(d)** $f(x) = (2x - 5)^3$

Now consider another function:

$$f(x) = x^3 + 2x + 6$$

Is it possible to use the same sort of simple reversal of operations to find the inverse of this function? If so, do it. If not, explain what is different about this function that makes this task difficult.

92. The Identity Function The function $I(x) = x$ is called the **identity function**. Show that for any function f we have $f \circ I = f$, $I \circ f = f$, and $f \circ f^{-1} = f^{-1} \circ f = I$. (This means that the identity function I behaves for functions and composition just the way the number 1 behaves for real numbers and multiplication.)

93. Solving an Equation for an Unknown Function In Exercise 69 of Section 2.6 you were asked to solve equations in which the unknowns were functions. Now that we know about inverses and the identity function (see Exercise 92), we can use algebra to solve such equations. For instance, to solve $f \circ g = h$ for the unknown function f, we perform the following steps:

$$\begin{array}{ll} f \circ g = h & \text{Problem: Solve for } f \\ f \circ g \circ g^{-1} = h \circ g^{-1} & \text{Compose with } g^{-1} \text{ on the right} \\ f \circ I = h \circ g^{-1} & \text{Because } g \circ g^{-1} = I \\ f = h \circ g^{-1} & \text{Because } f \circ I = f \end{array}$$

So the solution is $f = h \circ g^{-1}$. Use this technique to solve the equation $f \circ g = h$ for the indicated unknown function.

(a) Solve for f, where $g(x) = 2x + 1$ and $h(x) = 4x^2 + 4x + 7$.

(b) Solve for g, where $f(x) = 3x + 5$ and $h(x) = 3x^2 + 3x + 2$.

CHAPTER 2 | REVIEW

■ CONCEPT CHECK

1. Define each concept in your own words. (Check by referring to the definition in the text.)
 (a) Function
 (b) Domain and range of a function
 (c) Graph of a function
 (d) Independent and dependent variables

2. Sketch by hand, on the same axes, the graphs of the following functions.
 (a) $f(x) = x$ **(b)** $g(x) = x^2$
 (c) $h(x) = x^3$ **(d)** $j(x) = x^4$

3. (a) State the Vertical Line Test.
 (b) State the Horizontal Line Test.

4. How is the average rate of change of the function f between two points defined?

5. What can you say about the average rate of change of a linear function?

6. Define each concept in your own words.
 (a) Increasing function
 (b) Decreasing function
 (c) Constant function

7. Suppose the graph of f is given. Write an equation for each graph that is obtained from the graph of f as follows.
 (a) Shift 3 units upward.
 (b) Shift 3 units downward.
 (c) Shift 3 units to the right.
 (d) Shift 3 units to the left.
 (e) Reflect in the x-axis.
 (f) Reflect in the y-axis.
 (g) Stretch vertically by a factor of 3.
 (h) Shrink vertically by a factor of $\frac{1}{3}$.
 (i) Stretch horizontally by a factor of 2.
 (j) Shrink horizontally by a factor of $\frac{1}{2}$.

8. (a) What is an even function? What symmetry does its graph possess? Give an example of an even function.

(b) What is an odd function? What symmetry does its graph possess? Give an example of an odd function.

9. What does it mean to say that $f(3)$ is a local maximum value of f?

10. Suppose that f has domain A and g has domain B.

(a) What is the domain of $f + g$?

(b) What is the domain of fg?

(c) What is the domain of f/g?

11. How is the composite function $f \circ g$ defined?

12. (a) What is a one-to-one function?

(b) How can you tell from the graph of a function whether it is one-to-one?

(c) Suppose f is a one-to-one function with domain A and range B. How is the inverse function f^{-1} defined? What is the domain of f^{-1}? What is the range of f^{-1}?

(d) If you are given a formula for f, how do you find a formula for f^{-1}?

(e) If you are given the graph of f, how do you find the graph of f^{-1}?

■ EXERCISES

1–2 ■ A verbal description of a function f is given. Find a formula that expresses f in function notation.

1. "Square, then subtract 5."

2. "Divide by 2, then add 9."

3–4 ■ A formula for a function f is given. Give a verbal description of the function.

3. $f(x) = 3(x + 10)$

4. $f(x) = \sqrt{6x - 10}$

5–6 ■ Complete the table of values for the given function.

5. $g(x) = x^2 - 4x$ **6.** $h(x) = 3x^2 + 2x - 5$

x	$g(x)$
-1	
0	
1	
2	
3	

x	$h(x)$
-2	
-1	
0	
1	
2	

7. A publisher estimates that the cost $C(x)$ of printing a run of x copies of a certain mathematics textbook is given by the function $C(x) = 5000 + 30x - 0.001x^2$.

(a) Find $C(1000)$ and $C(10,000)$.

(b) What do your answers in part (a) represent?

(c) Find $C(0)$. What does this number represent?

8. Reynalda works as a salesperson in the electronics division of a department store. She earns a base weekly salary plus a commission based on the retail price of the goods she has sold. If she sells x dollars worth of goods in a week, her earnings for that week are given by the function $E(x) = 400 + 0.03x$.

(a) Find $E(2000)$ and $E(15,000)$.

(b) What do your answers in part (a) represent?

(c) Find $E(0)$. What does this number represent?

(d) From the formula for E, determine what percentage Reynalda earns on the goods that she sells.

9. If $f(x) = x^2 - 4x + 6$, find $f(0)$, $f(2)$, $f(-2)$, $f(a)$, $f(-a)$, $f(x + 1)$, $f(2x)$, and $2f(x) - 2$.

10. If $f(x) = 4 - \sqrt{3x - 6}$, find $f(5)$, $f(9)$, $f(a + 2)$, $f(-x)$, $f(x^2)$, and $[f(x)]^2$.

11. Which of the following figures are graphs of functions? Which of the functions are one-to-one?

(a) 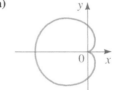   **(b)**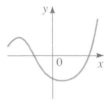

(c) 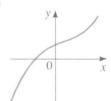   **(d)**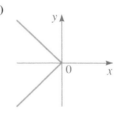

12. The graph of a function f is given.

(a) Find $f(-2)$ and $f(2)$.

(b) Find the domain of f.

(c) Find the range of f.

(d) On what intervals is f increasing? On what intervals is f decreasing?

(e) What are the local maximum values of f?

(f) Is f one-to-one?

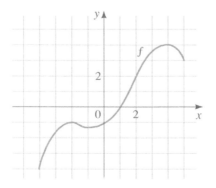

13–14 ■ Find the domain and range of the function.

13. $f(x) = \sqrt{x + 3}$ **14.** $F(t) = t^2 + 2t + 5$

15–22 ■ Find the domain of the function.

15. $f(x) = 7x + 15$

16. $f(x) = \dfrac{2x + 1}{2x - 1}$

17. $f(x) = \sqrt{x + 4}$

18. $f(x) = 3x - \dfrac{2}{\sqrt{x + 1}}$

19. $f(x) = \dfrac{1}{x} + \dfrac{1}{x + 1} + \dfrac{1}{x + 2}$

20. $g(x) = \dfrac{2x^2 + 5x + 3}{2x^2 - 5x - 3}$

21. $h(x) = \sqrt{4 - x} + \sqrt{x^2 - 1}$

22. $f(x) = \dfrac{\sqrt[3]{2x + 1}}{\sqrt[3]{2x + 2}}$

23–40 ■ Sketch the graph of the function.

23. $f(x) = 1 - 2x$

24. $f(x) = \frac{1}{3}(x - 5),\ 2 \le x \le 8$

25. $f(t) = 1 - \frac{1}{2}t^2$

26. $g(t) = t^2 - 2t$

27. $f(x) = x^2 - 6x + 6$

28. $f(x) = 3 - 8x - 2x^2$

29. $g(x) = 1 - \sqrt{x}$

30. $g(x) = -|x|$

31. $h(x) = \frac{1}{2}x^3$

32. $h(x) = \sqrt{x + 3}$

33. $h(x) = \sqrt[3]{x}$

34. $H(x) = x^3 - 3x^2$

35. $g(x) = \dfrac{1}{x^2}$

36. $G(x) = \dfrac{1}{(x - 3)^2}$

37. $f(x) = \begin{cases} 1 - x & \text{if } x < 0 \\ 1 & \text{if } x \ge 0 \end{cases}$

38. $f(x) = \begin{cases} 1 - 2x & \text{if } x \le 0 \\ 2x - 1 & \text{if } x > 0 \end{cases}$

39. $f(x) = \begin{cases} x + 6 & \text{if } x < -2 \\ x^2 & \text{if } x \ge -2 \end{cases}$

40. $f(x) = \begin{cases} -x & \text{if } x < 0 \\ x^2 & \text{if } 0 \le x < 2 \\ 1 & \text{if } x \ge 2 \end{cases}$

41–44 ■ Determine whether the equation defines y as a function of x.

41. $x + y^2 = 14$

42. $3x - \sqrt{y} = 8$

43. $x^3 - y^3 = 27$

44. $2x = y^4 - 16$

 45. Determine which viewing rectangle produces the most appropriate graph of the function
$$f(x) = 6x^3 - 15x^2 + 4x - 1$$

    (i) $[-2, 2]$ by $[-2, 2]$ (ii) $[-8, 8]$ by $[-8, 8]$

    (iii) $[-4, 4]$ by $[-12, 12]$ (iv) $[-100, 100]$ by $[-100, 100]$

 46. Determine which viewing rectangle produces the most appropriate graph of the function $f(x) = \sqrt{100 - x^3}$.
    (i) $[-4, 4]$ by $[-4, 4]$
    (ii) $[-10, 10]$ by $[-10, 10]$
    (iii) $[-10, 10]$ by $[-10, 40]$
    (iv) $[-100, 100]$ by $[-100, 100]$

47–50 ■ Draw the graph of the function in an appropriate viewing rectangle.

47. $f(x) = x^2 + 25x + 173$

48. $f(x) = 1.1x^3 - 9.6x^2 - 1.4x + 3.2$

49. $f(x) = \dfrac{x}{\sqrt{x^2 + 16}}$

50. $f(x) = |x(x + 2)(x + 4)|$

 51. Find, approximately, the domain of the function
$$f(x) = \sqrt{x^3 - 4x + 1}$$

 52. Find, approximately, the range of the function
$$f(x) = x^4 - x^3 + x^2 + 3x - 6$$

 53–54 ■ Draw a graph of the function f, and determine the intervals on which f is increasing and on which f is decreasing.

53. $f(x) = x^3 - 4x^2$

54. $f(x) = |x^4 - 16|$

55–58 ■ Find the average rate of change of the function between the given points.

55. $f(x) = x^2 + 3x;\quad x = 0, x = 2$

56. $f(x) = \dfrac{1}{x - 2};\quad x = 4, x = 8$

57. $f(x) = \dfrac{1}{x};\quad x = 3, x = 3 + h$

58. $f(x) = (x + 1)^2;\quad x = a, x = a + h$

59. The population of a planned seaside community in Florida is given by the function $P(t) = 3000 + 200t + 0.1t^2$, where t represents the number of years since the community was incorporated in 1985.
    (a) Find $P(10)$ and $P(20)$. What do these values represent?
    (b) Find the average rate of change of P between $t = 10$ and $t = 20$. What does this number represent?

60. Ella is saving for her retirement by making regular deposits into a 401(k) plan. As her salary rises, she finds that she can deposit increasing amounts each year. Between 1995 and 2008, the annual amount (in dollars) that she deposited was given by the function $D(t) = 3500 + 15t^2$, where t represents the year of the deposit measured from the start of the plan (so 1995 corresponds to $t = 0$ and 1996 corresponds to $t = 1$, and so on).
    (a) Find $D(0)$ and $D(15)$. What do these values represent?
    (b) Assuming that her deposits continue to be modeled by the function D, in what year will she deposit \$17,000?
    (c) Find the average rate of change of D between $t = 0$ and $t = 15$. What does this number represent?

61–62 ■ A function f is given. **(a)** Find the average rate of change of f between $x = 0$ and $x = 2$, and the average rate of change of f between $x = 15$ and $x = 50$. **(b)** Were the two average rates of change that you found in part (a) the same? Explain why or why not.

61. $f(x) = \frac{1}{2}x - 6$

62. $f(x) = 8 - 3x$

63. Suppose the graph of f is given. Describe how the graphs of the following functions can be obtained from the graph of f.
    (a) $y = f(x) + 8$ **(b)** $y = f(x + 8)$
    (c) $y = 1 + 2f(x)$ **(d)** $y = f(x - 2) - 2$
    (e) $y = f(-x)$ **(f)** $y = -f(-x)$
    (g) $y = -f(x)$ **(h)** $y = f^{-1}(x)$

64. The graph of f is given. Draw the graphs of the following functions.

(a) $y = f(x - 2)$ (b) $y = -f(x)$

(c) $y = 3 - f(x)$ (d) $y = \frac{1}{2}f(x) - 1$

(e) $y = f^{-1}(x)$ (f) $y = f(-x)$

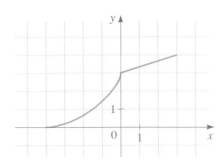

65. Determine whether f is even, odd, or neither.

(a) $f(x) = 2x^5 - 3x^2 + 2$ (b) $f(x) = x^3 - x^7$

(c) $f(x) = \dfrac{1 - x^2}{1 + x^2}$ (d) $f(x) = \dfrac{1}{x + 2}$

66. Determine whether the function in the figure is even, odd, or neither.

(a)    (b)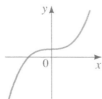

(c) 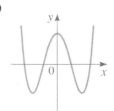   (d)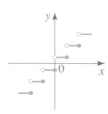

 67. Find the minimum value of the function $g(x) = 2x^2 + 4x - 5$.

68. Find the maximum value of the function $f(x) = 1 - x - x^2$.

69. A stone is thrown upward from the top of a building. Its height (in feet) above the ground after t seconds is given by

$$h(t) = -16t^2 + 48t + 32$$

What maximum height does it reach?

70. The profit P (in dollars) generated by selling x units of a certain commodity is given by

$$P(x) = -1500 + 12x - 0.0004x^2$$

What is the maximum profit, and how many units must be sold to generate it?

71–72 ■ Find the local maximum and minimum values of the function and the values of x at which they occur. State each answer correct to two decimal places.

71. $f(x) = 3.3 + 1.6x - 2.5x^3$ **72.** $f(x) = x^{2/3}(6 - x)^{1/3}$

73–74 ■ Two functions, f and g, are given. Draw graphs of f, g, and $f + g$ on the same graphing calculator screen to illustrate the concept of graphical addition.

73. $f(x) = x + 2$, $g(x) = x^2$

74. $f(x) = x^2 + 1$, $g(x) = 3 - x^2$

75. If $f(x) = x^2 - 3x + 2$ and $g(x) = 4 - 3x$, find the following functions.

(a) $f + g$ (b) $f - g$ (c) fg

(d) f/g (e) $f \circ g$ (f) $g \circ f$

76. If $f(x) = 1 + x^2$ and $g(x) = \sqrt{x - 1}$, find the following.

(a) $f \circ g$ (b) $g \circ f$ (c) $(f \circ g)(2)$

(d) $(f \circ f)(2)$ (e) $f \circ g \circ f$ (f) $g \circ f \circ g$

77–78 ■ Find the functions $f \circ g$, $g \circ f$, $f \circ f$, and $g \circ g$ and their domains.

77. $f(x) = 3x - 1$, $g(x) = 2x - x^2$

78. $f(x) = \sqrt{x}$, $g(x) = \dfrac{2}{x - 4}$

79. Find $f \circ g \circ h$, where $f(x) = \sqrt{1 - x}$, $g(x) = 1 - x^2$, and $h(x) = 1 + \sqrt{x}$.

80. If $T(x) = \dfrac{1}{\sqrt{1 + \sqrt{x}}}$, find functions f, g, and h such that $f \circ g \circ h = T$.

81–86 ■ Determine whether the function is one-to-one.

81. $f(x) = 3 + x^3$

82. $g(x) = 2 - 2x + x^2$

83. $h(x) = \dfrac{1}{x^4}$

84. $r(x) = 2 + \sqrt{x + 3}$

85. $p(x) = 3.3 + 1.6x - 2.5x^3$

86. $q(x) = 3.3 + 1.6x + 2.5x^3$

87–90 ■ Find the inverse of the function.

87. $f(x) = 3x - 2$ **88.** $f(x) = \dfrac{2x + 1}{3}$

89. $f(x) = (x + 1)^3$ **90.** $f(x) = 1 + \sqrt[5]{x - 2}$

91. (a) Sketch the graph of the function

$$f(x) = x^2 - 4 \qquad x \geq 0$$

(b) Use part (a) to sketch the graph of f^{-1}.

(c) Find an equation for f^{-1}.

92. (a) Show that the function $f(x) = 1 + \sqrt[4]{x}$ is one-to-one.

(b) Sketch the graph of f.

(c) Use part (b) to sketch the graph of f^{-1}.

(d) Find an equation for f^{-1}.

1. Which of the following are graphs of functions? If the graph is that of a function, is it one-to-one?

(a)

(b)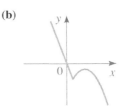

(c)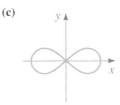

(d)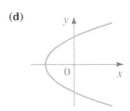

2. Let $f(x) = \dfrac{\sqrt{x+1}}{x}$.

   (a) Evaluate $f(3)$, $f(5)$, and $f(a-1)$.

   (b) Find the domain of f.

3. A function f has the following verbal description: "Subtract 2, then cube the result."

   (a) Find a formula that expresses f algebraically.

   (b) Make a table of values of f, for the inputs -1, 0, 1, 2, 3, and 4.

   (c) Sketch a graph of f, using the table of values from part (b) to help you.

   (d) How do we know that f has an inverse? Give a verbal description for f^{-1}.

   (e) Find a formula that expresses f^{-1} algebraically.

 4. A school fund-raising group sells chocolate bars to help finance a swimming pool for their physical education program. The group finds that when they set their price at x dollars per bar (where $0 < x \le 5$), their total sales revenue (in dollars) is given by the function $R(x) = -500x^2 + 3000x$.

   (a) Evaluate $R(2)$ and $R(4)$. What do these values represent?

   (b) Use a graphing calculator to draw a graph of R. What does the graph tell us about what happens to revenue as the price increases from 0 to 5 dollars?

   (c) What is the maximum revenue, and at what price is it achieved?

5. Determine the average rate of change for the function $f(t) = t^2 - 2t$ between $t = 2$ and $t = 5$.

6. (a) Sketch the graph of the function $f(x) = x^3$.

   (b) Use part (a) to graph the function $g(x) = (x-1)^3 - 2$.

7. (a) How is the graph of $y = f(x-3) + 2$ obtained from the graph of f?

   (b) How is the graph of $y = f(-x)$ obtained from the graph of f?

8. Let $f(x) = \begin{cases} 1 - x & \text{if } x \le 1 \\ 2x + 1 & \text{if } x > 1 \end{cases}$

   (a) Evaluate $f(-2)$ and $f(1)$.

   (b) Sketch the graph of f.

9. If $f(x) = x^2 + 1$ and $g(x) = x - 3$, find the following.

   (a) $f \circ g$ (b) $g \circ f$

   (c) $f(g(2))$ (d) $g(f(2))$

   (e) $g \circ g \circ g$

10. **(a)** If $f(x) = \sqrt{3 - x}$, find the inverse function f^{-1}.

(b) Sketch the graphs of f and f^{-1} on the same coordinate axes.

11. The graph of a function f is given.

(a) Find the domain and range of f.

(b) Sketch the graph of f^{-1}.

(c) Find the average rate of change of f between $x = 2$ and $x = 6$.

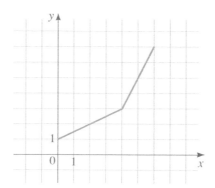

12. Let $f(x) = 3x^4 - 14x^2 + 5x - 3$.

(a) Draw the graph of f in an appropriate viewing rectangle.

(b) Is f one-to-one?

(c) Find the local maximum and minimum values of f and the values of x at which they occur. State each answer correct to two decimal places.

(d) Use the graph to determine the range of f.

(e) Find the intervals on which f is increasing and on which f is decreasing.

Modeling with Functions

Many of the processes that are studied in the physical and social sciences involve understanding how one quantity varies with respect to another. Finding a function that describes the dependence of one quantity on another is called *modeling*. For example, a biologist observes that the number of bacteria in a certain culture increases with time. He tries to model this phenomenon by finding the precise function (or rule) that relates the bacteria population to the elapsed time.

In this *Focus* we will learn how to find models that can be constructed using geometric or algebraic properties of the object under study. Once the model is found, we use it to analyze and predict properties of the object or process being studied.

▼ Modeling with Functions

We begin with a simple real-life situation that illustrates the modeling process.

EXAMPLE 1 | Modeling the Volume of a Box

A breakfast cereal company manufactures boxes to package their product. For aesthetic reasons, the box must have the following proportions: Its width is 3 times its depth, and its height is 5 times its depth.

(a) Find a function that models the volume of the box in terms of its depth.

(b) Find the volume of the box if the depth is 1.5 in.

(c) For what depth is the volume 90 in^3?

(d) For what depth is the volume greater than 60 in^3?

THINKING ABOUT THE PROBLEM

Let's experiment with the problem. If the depth is 1 in., then the width is 3 in. and the height is 5 in. So in this case, the volume is $V = 1 \times 3 \times 5 = 15$ in^3. The table gives other values. Notice that all the boxes have the same shape, and the greater the depth, the greater the volume.

Depth	Volume
1	$1 \times 3 \times 5 = 15$
2	$2 \times 6 \times 10 = 120$
3	$3 \times 9 \times 15 = 405$
4	$4 \times 12 \times 20 = 96$

SOLUTION

(a) To find the function that models the volume of the box, we use the following steps.

▶ **Express the Model in Words**

We know that the volume of a rectangular box is

$$\boxed{\text{volume}} \; = \; \boxed{\text{depth}} \; \times \; \boxed{\text{width}} \; \times \; \boxed{\text{height}}$$

▶ **Choose the Variable**

There are three varying quantities: width, depth, and height. Because the function we want depends on the depth, we let

$$x = \text{depth of the box}$$

Then we express the other dimensions of the box in terms of x.

In Words	In Algebra
Depth	x
Width	$3x$
Height	$5x$

▶ **Set Up the Model**

The model is the function V that gives the volume of the box in terms of the depth x.

$$\boxed{\text{volume}} \; = \; \boxed{\text{depth}} \; \times \; \boxed{\text{width}} \; \times \; \boxed{\text{height}}$$

$$V(x) = x \cdot 3x \cdot 5x$$

$$V(x) = 15x^3$$

The volume of the box is modeled by the function $V(x) = 15x^3$. The function V is graphed in Figure 1.

▶ **Use the Model**

We use the model to answer the questions in parts (b), (c), and (d).

(b) If the depth is 1.5 in., the volume is $V(1.5) = 15(1.5)^3 = 50.625 \text{ in}^3$.

(c) We need to solve the equation $V(x) = 90$ or

$$15x^3 = 90$$

$$x^3 = 6$$

$$x = \sqrt[3]{6} \approx 1.82 \text{ in.}$$

The volume is 90 in^3 when the depth is about 1.82 in. (We can also solve this equation graphically, as shown in Figure 2.)

(d) We need to solve the inequality $V(x) \geq 60$ or

$$15x^3 \geq 60$$

$$x^3 \geq 4$$

$$x \geq \sqrt[3]{4} \approx 1.59$$

The volume will be greater than 60 in^3 if the depth is greater than 1.59 in. (We can also solve this inequality graphically, as shown in Figure 3.)

400

0   3

FIGURE 1

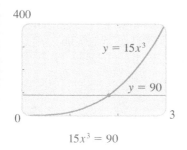

400

$y = 15x^3$

$y = 90$

0   3

$15x^3 = 90$

FIGURE 2

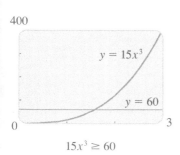

400

$y = 15x^3$

$y = 60$

0   3

$15x^3 \geq 60$

FIGURE 3

The steps in Example 1 are typical of how we model with functions. They are summarized in the following box.

GUIDELINES FOR MODELING WITH FUNCTIONS

1. **Express the Model in Words.**   Identify the quantity you want to model, and express it, in words, as a function of the other quantities in the problem.

2. **Choose the Variable.**   Identify all the variables that are used to express the function in Step 1. Assign a symbol, such as x, to one variable, and express the other variables in terms of this symbol.

3. **Set up the Model.**   Express the function in the language of algebra by writing it as a function of the single variable chosen in Step 2.

4. **Use the Model.**   Use the function to answer the questions posed in the problem. (To find a maximum or a minimum, use the methods described in Section 3.3.)

EXAMPLE 2 | Fencing a Garden

A gardener has 140 feet of fencing to fence in a rectangular vegetable garden.

(a) Find a function that models the area of the garden she can fence.

(b) For what range of widths is the area greater than 825 ft^2?

(c) Can she fence a garden with area 1250 ft^2?

(d) Find the dimensions of the largest area she can fence.

> **THINKING ABOUT THE PROBLEM**

If the gardener fences a plot with width 10 ft, then the length must be 60 ft, because $10 + 10 + 60 + 60 = 140$. So the area is

$$A = \text{width} \times \text{length} = 10 \cdot 60 = 600 \text{ ft}^2$$

The table shows various choices for fencing the garden. We see that as the width increases, the fenced area increases, then decreases.

Width	Length	Area
10	60	600
20	50	1000
30	40	1200
40	30	1200
50	20	1000
60	10	600

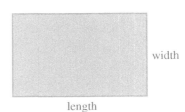

SOLUTION

(a) The model that we want is a function that gives the area she can fence.

▶ **Express the Model in Words**

We know that the area of a rectangular garden is

$$\text{area} \quad = \quad \text{width} \quad \times \quad \text{length}$$

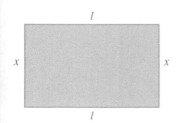

FIGURE 4

▶ **Choose the Variable**

There are two varying quantities: width and length. Because the function we want depends on only one variable, we let

$$x = \text{width of the garden}$$

Then we must express the length in terms of x. The perimeter is fixed at 140 ft, so the length is determined once we choose the width. If we let the length be l, as in Figure 4, then $2x + 2l = 140$, so $l = 70 - x$. We summarize these facts.

In Words	In Algebra
Width	x
Length	$70 - x$

▶ **Set Up the Model**

The model is the function A that gives the area of the garden for any width x.

$$\boxed{\text{area}} = \boxed{\text{width}} \times \boxed{\text{length}}$$

$$A(x) = x(70 - x)$$
$$A(x) = 70x - x^2$$

The area that she can fence is modeled by the function $A(x) = 70x - x^2$.

▶ **Use the Model**

We use the model to answer the questions in parts (b)–(d).

(b) We need to solve the inequality $A(x) \geq 825$. To solve graphically, we graph $y = 70x - x^2$ and $y = 825$ in the same viewing rectangle (see Figure 5). We see that $15 \leq x \leq 55$.

(c) From Figure 6 we see that the graph of $A(x)$ always lies below the line $y = 1250$, so an area of 1250 ft^2 is never attained.

Maximum values of functions are discussed on page 166.

(d) We need to find where the maximum value of the function $A(x) = 70x - x^2$ occurs. The function is graphed in Figure 7. Using the [TRACE] feature on a graphing calculator, we find that the function achieves its maximum value at $x = 35$. So the maximum area that she can fence is that when the garden's width is 35 ft and its length is $70 - 35 = 35$ ft. The maximum area then is $35 \times 35 = 1225$ ft^2.

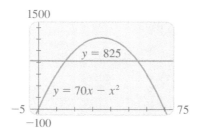

FIGURE 5

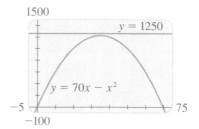

FIGURE 6

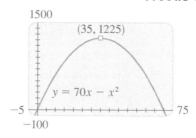

FIGURE 7

EXAMPLE 3 | Minimizing the Metal in a Can

A manufacturer makes a metal can that holds 1 L (liter) of oil. What radius minimizes the amount of metal in the can?

THINKING ABOUT THE PROBLEM

To use the least amount of metal, we must minimize the surface area of the can, that is, the area of the top, bottom, and the sides. The area of the top and bottom is $2\pi r^2$ and the area of the sides is $2\pi rh$ (see Figure 8), so the surface area of the can is

$$S = 2\pi r^2 + 2\pi rh$$

The radius and height of the can must be chosen so that the volume is exactly 1 L, or 1000 cm³. If we want a small radius, say $r = 3$, then the height must be just tall enough to make the total volume 1000 cm³. In other words, we must have

$$\pi(3)^2 h = 1000 \qquad \text{Volume of the can is } \pi r^2 h$$

$$h = \frac{1000}{9\pi} \approx 35.4 \text{ cm} \qquad \text{Solve for } h$$

Now that we know the radius and height, we can find the surface area of the can:

$$\text{surface area} = 2\pi(3)^2 + 2\pi(3)(35.4) \approx 723.8 \text{ cm}^3$$

If we want a different radius, we can find the corresponding height and surface area in a similar fashion.

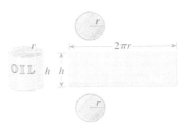

FIGURE 8

SOLUTION   The model that we want is a function that gives the surface area of the can.

▶ **Express the Model in Words**

We know that for a cylindrical can

$$\text{surface area} \quad = \quad \text{area of top and bottom} \quad + \quad \text{area of sides}$$

▶ **Choose the Variable**

There are two varying quantities: radius and height. Because the function we want depends on the radius, we let

$$r = \text{radius of can}$$

Next, we must express the height in terms of the radius r. Because the volume of a cylindrical can is $V = \pi r^2 h$ and the volume must be 1000 cm³, we have

$$\pi r^2 h = 1000 \qquad \text{Volume of can is 1000 cm}^3$$

$$h = \frac{1000}{\pi r^2} \qquad \text{Solve for } h$$

We can now express the areas of the top, bottom, and sides in terms of r only.

In Words	In Algebra
Radius of can	r
Height of can	$\dfrac{1000}{\pi r^2}$
Area of top and bottom	$2\pi r^2$
Area of sides ($2\pi rh$)	$2\pi r \left(\dfrac{1000}{\pi r^2}\right)$

▶ **Set Up the Model**

The model is the function S that gives the surface area of the can as a function of the radius r.

$$\boxed{\text{surface area}} \; = \; \boxed{\text{area of top and bottom}} \; + \; \boxed{\text{area of sides}}$$

$$S(r) = 2\pi r^2 + 2\pi r \left(\frac{1000}{\pi r^2}\right)$$

$$S(r) = 2\pi r^2 + \frac{2000}{r}$$

▶ **Use the Model**

We use the model to find the minimum surface area of the can. We graph S in Figure 9 and zoom in on the minimum point to find that the minimum value of S is about 554 cm² and occurs when the radius is about 5.4 cm.

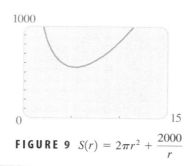

FIGURE 9 $S(r) = 2\pi r^2 + \dfrac{2000}{r}$

PROBLEMS

1–18 ■ In these problems you are asked to find a function that models a real-life situation. Use the principles of modeling described in this *Focus* to help you.

1. Area   A rectangular building lot is three times as long as it is wide. Find a function that models its area A in terms of its width w.

2. Area   A poster is 10 inches longer than it is wide. Find a function that models its area A in terms of its width w.

3. Volume   A rectangular box has a square base. Its height is half the width of the base. Find a function that models its volume V in terms of its width w.

4. Volume   The height of a cylinder is four times its radius. Find a function that models the volume V of the cylinder in terms of its radius r.

5. Area   A rectangle has a perimeter of 20 ft. Find a function that models its area A in terms of the length x of one of its sides.

6. Perimeter   A rectangle has an area of 16 m². Find a function that models its perimeter P in terms of the length x of one of its sides.

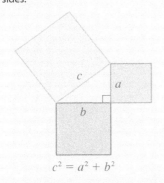
7. Area   Find a function that models the area A of an equilateral triangle in terms of the length x of one of its sides.

8. Area   Find a function that models the surface area S of a cube in terms of its volume V.

9. Radius   Find a function that models the radius r of a circle in terms of its area A.

10. Area   Find a function that models the area A of a circle in terms of its circumference C.

11. Area   A rectangular box with a volume of 60 ft^3 has a square base. Find a function that models its surface area S in terms of the length x of one side of its base.

12. Length   A woman 5 ft tall is standing near a street lamp that is 12 ft tall, as shown in the figure. Find a function that models the length L of her shadow in terms of her distance d from the base of the lamp.

13. Distance   Two ships leave port at the same time. One sails south at 15 mi/h, and the other sails east at 20 mi/h. Find a function that models the distance D between the ships in terms of the time t (in hours) elapsed since their departure.

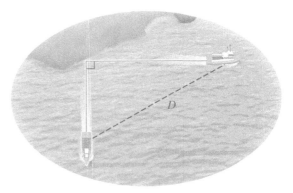

14. Product   The sum of two positive numbers is 60. Find a function that models their product P in terms of x, one of the numbers.

15. Area   An isosceles triangle has a perimeter of 8 cm. Find a function that models its area A in terms of the length of its base b.

16. Perimeter   A right triangle has one leg twice as long as the other. Find a function that models its perimeter P in terms of the length x of the shorter leg.

17. Area   A rectangle is inscribed in a semicircle of radius 10, as shown in the figure. Find a function that models the area A of the rectangle in terms of its height h.

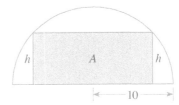

18. Height   The volume of a cone is 100 in^3. Find a function that models the height h of the cone in terms of its radius r.

19–32 ■ In these problems you are asked to find a function that models a real-life situation, and then use the model to answer questions about the situation. Use the guidelines on page 215 to help you.

 19. Maximizing a Product   Consider the following problem: Find two numbers whose sum is 19 and whose product is as large as possible.

(a) Experiment with the problem by making a table like the one following, showing the product of different pairs of numbers that add up to 19. On the basis of the evidence in your table, estimate the answer to the problem.

(b) Find a function that models the product in terms of one of the two numbers.

(c) Use your model to solve the problem, and compare with your answer to part (a).

 20. Minimizing a Sum   Find two positive numbers whose sum is 100 and the sum of whose squares is a minimum.

21. Fencing a Field   Consider the following problem: A farmer has 2400 ft of fencing and wants to fence off a rectangular field that borders a straight river. He does not need a fence along the river (see the figure). What are the dimensions of the field of largest area that he can fence?

(a) Experiment with the problem by drawing several diagrams illustrating the situation. Calculate the area of each configuration, and use your results to estimate the dimensions of the largest possible field.

First number	Second number	Product
1	18	18
2	17	34
3	16	48
⋮	⋮	⋮

(b) Find a function that models the area of the field in terms of one of its sides.

(c) Use your model to solve the problem, and compare with your answer to part (a).

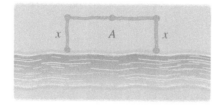

 **22. Dividing a Pen**   A rancher with 750 ft of fencing wants to enclose a rectangular area and then divide it into four pens with fencing parallel to one side of the rectangle (see the figure).

(a) Find a function that models the total area of the four pens.

(b) Find the largest possible total area of the four pens.

 23. Fencing a Garden Plot   A property owner wants to fence a garden plot adjacent to a road, as shown in the figure. The fencing next to the road must be sturdier and costs $5 per foot, but the other fencing costs just $3 per foot. The garden is to have an area of 1200 ft^2.

(a) Find a function that models the cost of fencing the garden.

(b) Find the garden dimensions that minimize the cost of fencing.

(c) If the owner has at most $600 to spend on fencing, find the range of lengths he can fence along the road.

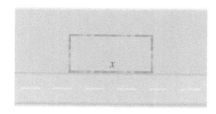

24. Maximizing Area A wire 10 cm long is cut into two pieces, one of length x and the other of length $10 - x$, as shown in the figure. Each piece is bent into the shape of a square.

(a) Find a function that models the total area enclosed by the two squares.

(b) Find the value of x that minimizes the total area of the two squares.

 25. Light from a Window A Norman window has the shape of a rectangle surmounted by a semicircle, as shown in the figure to the left. A Norman window with perimeter 30 ft is to be constructed.

(a) Find a function that models the area of the window.

(b) Find the dimensions of the window that admits the greatest amount of light.

 26. Volume of a Box A box with an open top is to be constructed from a rectangular piece of cardboard with dimensions 12 in. by 20 in. by cutting out equal squares of side x at each corner and then folding up the sides (see the figure).

(a) Find a function that models the volume of the box.

(b) Find the values of x for which the volume is greater than 200 in^3.

(c) Find the largest volume that such a box can have.

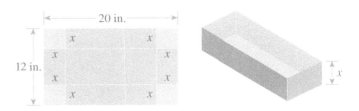

 27. Area of a Box An open box with a square base is to have a volume of 12 ft^3.

(a) Find a function that models the surface area of the box.

(b) Find the box dimensions that minimize the amount of material used.

 **28. Inscribed Rectangle** Find the dimensions that give the largest area for the rectangle shown in the figure. Its base is on the x-axis and its other two vertices are above the x-axis, lying on the parabola $y = 8 - x^2$.

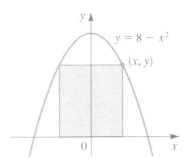

 29. Minimizing Costs A rancher wants to build a rectangular pen with an area of 100 m^2.

(a) Find a function that models the length of fencing required.

(b) Find the pen dimensions that require the minimum amount of fencing.

30. **Minimizing Time** A man stands at a point A on the bank of a straight river, 2 mi wide. To reach point B, 7 mi downstream on the opposite bank, he first rows his boat to point P on the opposite bank and then walks the remaining distance x to B, as shown in the figure. He can row at a speed of 2 mi/h and walk at a speed of 5 mi/h.

    (a) Find a function that models the time needed for the trip.

    (b) Where should he land so that he reaches B as soon as possible?

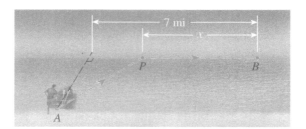

31. **Bird Flight** A bird is released from point A on an island, 5 mi from the nearest point B on a straight shoreline. The bird flies to a point C on the shoreline and then flies along the shoreline to its nesting area D (see the figure). Suppose the bird requires 10 kcal/mi of energy to fly over land and 14 kcal/mi to fly over water.

    (a) Use the fact that

    $$\text{energy used} = \text{energy per mile} \times \text{miles flown}$$

    to show that the total energy used by the bird is modeled by the function

    $$E(x) = 14\sqrt{x^2 + 25} + 10(12 - x)$$

    (b) If the bird instinctively chooses a path that minimizes its energy expenditure, to what point does it fly?

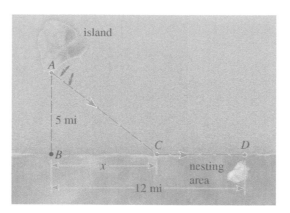

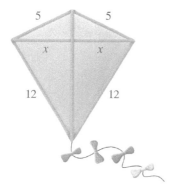

32. **Area of a Kite** A kite frame is to be made from six pieces of wood. The four pieces that form its border have been cut to the lengths indicated in the figure. Let x be as shown in the figure.

    (a) Show that the area of the kite is given by the function

    $$A(x) = x\left(\sqrt{25 - x^2} + \sqrt{144 - x^2}\right)$$

    (b) How long should each of the two crosspieces be to maximize the area of the kite?

Image 100/Corbis

POLYNOMIAL AND RATIONAL FUNCTIONS

Functions defined by polynomial expressions are called polynomial functions. The graphs of polynomial functions can have many peaks and valleys; this makes them suitable models for many real-world situations. For example, a factory owner notices that if she increases the number of workers, productivity increases, but if there are too many workers, productivity begins to decrease. This situation is modeled by a polynomial function of degree 2 (a quadratic function). As another example, when a volleyball is hit, it goes up and then down, following a path that is also modeled by a quadratic function. The graphs of polynomial functions are smooth curves that are used in designing many things. For example, sailboat designers put together portions of the graphs of different cubic functions (called cubic splines) to make the curves of the hull of a sailboat.

3.1 QUADRATIC FUNCTIONS AND MODELS

Graphing Quadratic Functions Using the Standard Form ▶ Maximum and Minimum Values of Quadratic Functions ▶ Modeling with Quadratic Functions

A polynomial function is a function that is defined by a polynomial expression. So a **polynomial function of degree *n*** is a function of the form

$$P(x) = a_n x^n + a_{n-1} x^{n-1} + \cdots + a_1 x + a_0$$

Polynomial expressions are defined in Section 1.3.

We have already studied polynomial functions of degree 0 and 1. These are functions of the form $P(x) = a_0$ and $P(x) = a_1 x + a_0$, respectively, whose graphs are lines. In this section we study polynomial functions of degree 2. These are called quadratic functions.

QUADRATIC FUNCTIONS

A **quadratic function** is a polynomial function of degree 2. So a quadratic function is a function of the form

$$f(x) = ax^2 + bx + c, \qquad a \neq 0$$

We see in this section how quadratic functions model many real-world phenomena. We begin by analyzing the graphs of quadratic functions.

▼ Graphing Quadratic Functions Using the Standard Form

For a geometric definition of parabolas, see Section 11.1.

If we take $a = 1$ and $b = c = 0$ in the quadratic function $f(x) = ax^2 + bx + c$, we get the quadratic function $f(x) = x^2$, whose graph is the parabola graphed in Example 1 of Section 2.2. In fact, the graph of any quadratic function is a **parabola**; it can be obtained from the graph of $f(x) = x^2$ by the transformations given in Section 2.5.

STANDARD FORM OF A QUADRATIC FUNCTION

A quadratic function $f(x) = ax^2 + bx + c$ can be expressed in the **standard form**

$$f(x) = a(x - h)^2 + k$$

by completing the square. The graph of f is a parabola with **vertex** (h, k); the parabola opens upward if $a > 0$ or downward if $a < 0$.

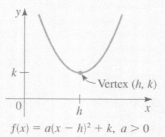

$f(x) = a(x - h)^2 + k, \ a > 0$

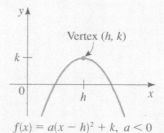

$f(x) = a(x - h)^2 + k, \ a < 0$

EXAMPLE 1 | Standard Form of a Quadratic Function

Let $f(x) = 2x^2 - 12x + 23$.

(a) Express f in standard form.

(b) Sketch the graph of f.

Completing the square is discussed
in Section 1.5.

$$f(x) = 2(x - 3)^2 + 5$$

Vertex is $(3, 5)$

SOLUTION

(a) Since the coefficient of x^2 is not 1, we must factor this coefficient from the terms involving x before we complete the square.

$$f(x) = 2x^2 - 12x + 23$$

$$= 2(x^2 - 6x) + 23 \qquad \text{Factor 2 from the } x\text{-terms}$$

$$= 2(x^2 - 6x + 9) + 23 - 2 \cdot 9 \qquad \begin{array}{l}\text{Complete the square: Add 9 inside} \\ \text{parentheses. subtract } 2 \cdot 9 \text{ outside}\end{array}$$

$$= 2(x - 3)^2 + 5 \qquad \text{Factor and simplify}$$

The standard form is $f(x) = 2(x - 3)^2 + 5$.

(b) The standard form tells us that we get the graph of f by taking the parabola $y = x^2$, shifting it to the right 3 units, stretching it by a factor of 2, and moving it upward 5 units. The vertex of the parabola is at $(3, 5)$, and the parabola opens upward. We sketch the graph in Figure 1 after noting that the y-intercept is $f(0) = 23$.

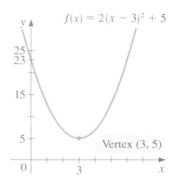

FIGURE 1

🔖 ⌐ NOW TRY EXERCISE **13**

▼ Maximum and Minimum Values of Quadratic Functions

If a quadratic function has vertex (h, k), then the function has a minimum value at the vertex if its graph opens upward and a maximum value at the vertex if its graph opens downward. For example, the function graphed in Figure 1 has minimum value 5 when $x = 3$, since the vertex $(3, 5)$ is the lowest point on the graph.

MAXIMUM OR MINIMUM VALUE OF A QUADRATIC FUNCTION

Let f be a quadratic function with standard form $f(x) = a(x - h)^2 + k$. The maximum or minimum value of f occurs at $x = h$.

If $a > 0$, then the **minimum value** of f is $f(h) = k$.

If $a < 0$, then the **maximum value** of f is $f(h) = k$.

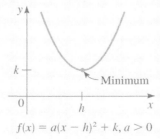

$$f(x) = a(x - h)^2 + k, a > 0$$

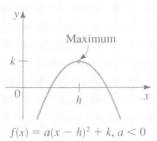

$$f(x) = a(x - h)^2 + k, a < 0$$

EXAMPLE 2 | Minimum Value of a Quadratic Function

Consider the quadratic function $f(x) = 5x^2 - 30x + 49$.

(a) Express f in standard form.

(b) Sketch the graph of f.

(c) Find the minimum value of f.

SOLUTION

(a) To express this quadratic function in standard form, we complete the square.

$$f(x) = 5x^2 - 30x + 49$$

$$= 5(x^2 - 6x) + 49 \qquad \text{Factor 5 from the } x\text{-terms}$$

$$= 5(x^2 - 6x + 9) + 49 - 5 \cdot 9 \qquad \begin{array}{l}\text{Complete the square: Add 9 inside} \\ \text{parentheses, subtract } 5 \cdot 9 \text{ outside}\end{array}$$

$$= 5(x - 3)^2 + 4 \qquad \text{Factor and simplify}$$

(b) The graph is a parabola that has its vertex at $(3, 4)$ and opens upward, as sketched in Figure 2.

(c) Since the coefficient of x^2 is positive, f has a minimum value. The minimum value is $f(3) = 4$.

✎. NOW TRY EXERCISE **25**

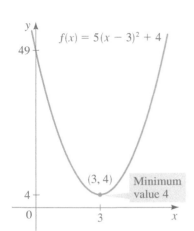

$f(x) = 5(x - 3)^2 + 4$

$(3, 4)$ Minimum value 4

FIGURE 2

EXAMPLE 3 | Maximum Value of a Quadratic Function

Consider the quadratic function $f(x) = -x^2 + x + 2$.

(a) Express f in standard form.

(b) Sketch the graph of f.

(c) Find the maximum value of f.

SOLUTION

(a) To express this quadratic function in standard form, we complete the square.

$$y = -x^2 + x + 2$$

$$= -(x^2 - x) + 2 \qquad \text{Factor } -1 \text{ from the } x\text{-terms}$$

$$= -\left(x^2 - x + \tfrac{1}{4}\right) + 2 - (-1)\tfrac{1}{4} \qquad \begin{array}{l}\text{Complete the square: Add } \tfrac{1}{4} \text{ inside} \\ \text{parentheses, subtract } (-1)\tfrac{1}{4} \text{ outside}\end{array}$$

$$= -\left(x - \tfrac{1}{2}\right)^2 + \tfrac{9}{4} \qquad \text{Factor and simplify}$$

(b) From the standard form we see that the graph is a parabola that opens downward and has vertex $\left(\tfrac{1}{2}, \tfrac{9}{4}\right)$. As an aid to sketching the graph, we find the intercepts. The y-intercept is $f(0) = 2$. To find the x-intercepts, we set $f(x) = 0$ and factor the resulting equation.

$$-x^2 + x + 2 = 0 \qquad \text{Set } y = 0$$

$$x^2 - x - 2 = 0 \qquad \text{Multiply by } -1$$

$$(x - 2)(x + 1) = 0 \qquad \text{Factor}$$

Thus the x-intercepts are $x = 2$ and $x = -1$. The graph of f is sketched in Figure 3.

(c) Since the coefficient of x^2 is negative, f has a maximum value, which is $f\left(\tfrac{1}{2}\right) = \tfrac{9}{4}$.

✎. NOW TRY EXERCISE **27**

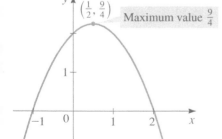

$\left(\tfrac{1}{2}, \tfrac{9}{4}\right)$ Maximum value $\tfrac{9}{4}$

FIGURE 3 Graph of $f(x) = -x^2 + x + 2$

Expressing a quadratic function in standard form helps us to sketch its graph as well as to find its maximum or minimum value. If we are interested only in finding the maximum or minimum value, then a formula is available for doing so. This formula is obtained by completing the square for the general quadratic function as follows:

$$f(x) = ax^2 + bx + c$$

$$= a\left(x^2 + \frac{b}{a}x\right) + c \qquad \text{Factor } a \text{ from the } x\text{-terms}$$

$$= a\left(x^2 + \frac{b}{a}x + \frac{b^2}{4a^2}\right) + c - a\left(\frac{b^2}{4a^2}\right) \qquad \begin{array}{l}\text{Complete the square: Add } \frac{b^2}{4a^2} \\ \text{inside parentheses, subtract} \\ a\left(\frac{b^2}{4a^2}\right) \text{ outside}\end{array}$$

$$= a\left(x + \frac{b}{2a}\right)^2 + c - \frac{b^2}{4a} \qquad \text{Factor}$$

This equation is in standard form with $h = -b/(2a)$ and $k = c - b^2/(4a)$. Since the maximum or minimum value occurs at $x = h$, we have the following result.

MAXIMUM OR MINIMUM VALUE OF A QUADRATIC FUNCTION

The maximum or minimum value of a quadratic function $f(x) = ax^2 + bx + c$ occurs at

$$x = -\frac{b}{2a}$$

If $a > 0$, then the **minimum value** is $f\left(-\dfrac{b}{2a}\right)$.

If $a < 0$, then the **maximum value** is $f\left(-\dfrac{b}{2a}\right)$.

EXAMPLE 4 | Finding Maximum and Minimum Values of Quadratic Functions

Find the maximum or minimum value of each quadratic function.

(a) $f(x) = x^2 + 4x$ **(b)** $g(x) = -2x^2 + 4x - 5$

SOLUTION

(a) This is a quadratic function with $a = 1$ and $b = 4$. Thus, the maximum or minimum value occurs at

$$x = -\frac{b}{2a} = -\frac{4}{2 \cdot 1} = -2$$

Since $a > 0$, the function has the *minimum* value

$$f(-2) = (-2)^2 + 4(-2) = -4$$

(b) This is a quadratic function with $a = -2$ and $b = 4$. Thus, the maximum or minimum value occurs at

$$x = -\frac{b}{2a} = -\frac{4}{2 \cdot (-2)} = 1$$

Since $a < 0$, the function has the *maximum* value

$$f(1) = -2(1)^2 + 4(1) - 5 = -3$$

NOW TRY EXERCISES **33** AND **35**

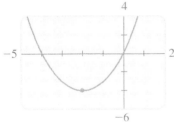

The minimum value occurs at $x = -2$.

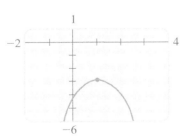

The maximum value occurs at $x = 1$.

▼ Modeling with Quadratic Functions

We study some examples of real-world phenomena that are modeled by quadratic functions. These examples and the *Application* exercises for this section show some of the variety of situations that are naturally modeled by quadratic functions.

EXAMPLE 5 | Maximum Gas Mileage for a Car

Most cars get their best gas mileage when traveling at a relatively modest speed. The gas mileage M for a certain new car is modeled by the function

$$M(s) = -\frac{1}{28}s^2 + 3s - 31, \qquad 15 \le s \le 70$$

where s is the speed in mi/h and M is measured in mi/gal. What is the car's best gas mileage, and at what speed is it attained?

SOLUTION The function M is a quadratic function with $a = -\frac{1}{28}$ and $b = 3$. Thus, its maximum value occurs when

$$s = -\frac{b}{2a} = -\frac{3}{2\left(-\frac{1}{28}\right)} = 42$$

The maximum gas mileage occurs at 42 mi/h.

The maximum is $M(42) = -\frac{1}{28}(42)^2 + 3(42) - 31 = 32$. So the car's best gas mileage is 32 mi/gal, when it is traveling at 42 mi/h.

✎ NOW TRY EXERCISE **67**

EXAMPLE 6 | Maximizing Revenue from Ticket Sales

A hockey team plays in an arena that has a seating capacity of 15,000 spectators. With the ticket price set at $14, average attendance at recent games has been 9500. A market survey indicates that for each dollar the ticket price is lowered, the average attendance increases by 1000.

(a) Find a function that models the revenue in terms of ticket price.

(b) Find the price that maximizes revenue from ticket sales.

(c) What ticket price is so high that no one attends and so no revenue is generated?

SOLUTION

(a) Express the model in words. The model that we want is a function that gives the revenue for any ticket price.

$$\text{revenue} = \text{ticket price} \times \text{attendance}$$

Choose the variable. There are two varying quantities: ticket price and attendance. Since the function we want depends on price, we let

$$x = \text{ticket price}$$

Next, we express attendance in terms of x.

In Words	In Algebra
Ticket price	x
Amount ticket price is lowered	$14 - x$
Increase in attendance	$1000(14 - x)$
Attendance	$9500 + 1000(14 - x)$

Set up the model. The model that we want is the function R that gives the revenue for a given ticket price x.

$$\text{revenue} = \text{ticket price} \times \text{attendance}$$

$$R(x) = x \times [9500 + 1000(14 - x)]$$
$$R(x) = x(23,500 - 1000x)$$
$$R(x) = 23,500x - 1000x^2$$

(b) Use the model. Since R is a quadratic function with $a = -1000$ and $b = 23,500$, the maximum occurs at

$$x = -\frac{b}{2a} = -\frac{23,500}{2(-1000)} = 11.75$$

So a ticket price of $11.75 gives the maximum revenue.

(c) Use the model. We want to find the ticket price for which $R(x) = 0$.

$$23,500x - 1000x^2 = 0 \qquad \text{Set } R(x) = 0$$
$$23.5x - x^2 = 0 \qquad \text{Divide by } 1000$$
$$x(23.5 - x) = 0 \qquad \text{Factor}$$
$$x = 0 \quad \text{or} \quad x = 23.5 \qquad \text{Solve for } x$$

So according to this model, a ticket price of $23.50 is just too high; at that price, no one attends to watch this team play. (Of course, revenue is also zero if the ticket price is zero.)

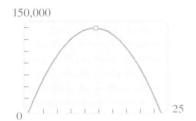

150,000

25

0

Maximum attendance occurs when ticket price is $11.75.

NOW TRY EXERCISE **77**

3.1 EXERCISES

CONCEPTS

1. To put the quadratic function $f(x) = ax^2 + bx + c$ in standard form, we complete the _____.

2. The quadratic function $f(x) = a(x - h)^2 + k$ is in standard form.
   (a) The graph of f is a parabola with vertex (____ , ____).
   (b) If $a > 0$, the graph of f opens _____. In this case
   $f(h) = k$ is the _____ value of f.
   (c) If $a < 0$, the graph of f opens _____. In this case
   $f(h) = k$ is the _____ value of f.

3. The graph of $f(x) = 2(x - 3)^2 + 5$ is a parabola that opens _____, with its vertex at (____ , ____), and
   $f(3) =$ _____ is the (minimum/maximum) _____ value of f.

4. The graph of $f(x) = -2(x - 3)^2 + 5$ is a parabola that opens _____, with its vertex at (____ , ____), and

$f(3) =$ _____ is the (minimum/maximum) _____ value of f.

SKILLS

5–8 ■ The graph of a quadratic function f is given. **(a)** Find the coordinates of the vertex. **(b)** Find the maximum or minimum value of f. **(c)** Find the domain and range of f.

5. $f(x) = -x^2 + 6x - 5$ **6.** $f(x) = -\frac{1}{2}x^2 - 2x + 6$

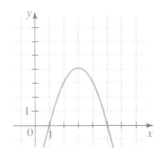

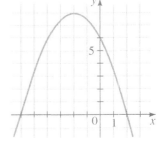

7. $f(x) = 2x^2 - 4x - 1$ **8.** $f(x) = 3x^2 + 6x - 1$

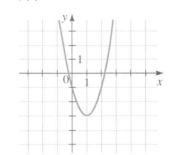

9–22 ■ A quadratic function is given. **(a)** Express the quadratic function in standard form. **(b)** Find its vertex and its x- and y-intercept(s). **(c)** Sketch its graph.

9. $f(x) = x^2 - 6x$ **10.** $f(x) = x^2 + 8x$

11. $f(x) = 2x^2 + 6x$ **12.** $f(x) = -x^2 + 10x$

13. $f(x) = x^2 + 4x + 3$ **14.** $f(x) = x^2 - 2x + 2$

15. $f(x) = -x^2 + 6x + 4$ **16.** $f(x) = -x^2 - 4x + 4$

17. $f(x) = 2x^2 + 4x + 3$ **18.** $f(x) = -3x^2 + 6x - 2$

19. $f(x) = 2x^2 - 20x + 57$ **20.** $f(x) = 2x^2 + x - 6$

21. $f(x) = -4x^2 - 16x + 3$ **22.** $f(x) = 6x^2 + 12x - 5$

23–32 ■ A quadratic function is given. **(a)** Express the quadratic function in standard form. **(b)** Sketch its graph. **(c)** Find its maximum or minimum value.

23. $f(x) = x^2 + 2x - 1$ **24.** $f(x) = x^2 - 8x + 8$

25. $f(x) = 3x^2 - 6x + 1$ **26.** $f(x) = 5x^2 + 30x + 4$

27. $f(x) = -x^2 - 3x + 3$ **28.** $f(x) = 1 - 6x - x^2$

29. $g(x) = 3x^2 - 12x + 13$ **30.** $g(x) = 2x^2 + 8x + 11$

31. $h(x) = 1 - x - x^2$ **32.** $h(x) = 3 - 4x - 4x^2$

33–42 ■ Find the maximum or minimum value of the function.

33. $f(x) = x^2 + x + 1$ **34.** $f(x) = 1 + 3x - x^2$

35. $f(t) = 100 - 49t - 7t^2$ **36.** $f(t) = 10t^2 + 40t + 113$

37. $f(s) = s^2 - 1.2s + 16$ **38.** $g(x) = 100x^2 - 1500x$

39. $h(x) = \frac{1}{2}x^2 + 2x - 6$ **40.** $f(x) = -\frac{x^2}{3} + 2x + 7$

41. $f(x) = 3 - x - \frac{1}{2}x^2$ **42.** $g(x) = 2x(x - 4) + 7$

43. Find a function whose graph is a parabola with vertex $(1, -2)$ and that passes through the point $(4, 16)$.

44. Find a function whose graph is a parabola with vertex $(3, 4)$ and that passes through the point $(1, -8)$.

45–48 ■ Find the domain and range of the function.

45. $f(x) = -x^2 + 4x - 3$ **46.** $f(x) = x^2 - 2x - 3$

47. $f(x) = 2x^2 + 6x - 7$ **48.** $f(x) = -3x^2 + 6x + 4$

49–50 ■ A quadratic function is given. **(a)** Use a graphing device to find the maximum or minimum value of the quadratic function f, correct to two decimal places. **(b)** Find the exact maximum or minimum value of f, and compare it with your answer to part (a).

49. $f(x) = x^2 + 1.79x - 3.21$

50. $f(x) = 1 + x - \sqrt{2}x^2$

51–54 ■ Find all local maximum and minimum values of the function whose graph is shown.

51.

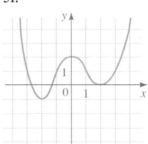

52.

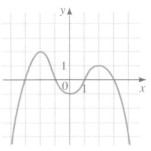

53.

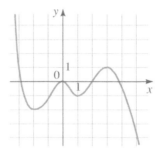

54.

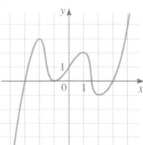

55–62 ■ Find the local maximum and minimum values of the function and the value of x at which each occurs. State each answer correct to two decimal places.

55. $f(x) = x^3 - x$

56. $f(x) = 3 + x + x^2 - x^3$

57. $g(x) = x^4 - 2x^3 - 11x^2$

58. $g(x) = x^5 - 8x^3 + 20x$

59. $U(x) = x\sqrt{6 - x}$

60. $U(x) = x\sqrt{x - x^2}$

61. $V(x) = \dfrac{1 - x^2}{x^3}$

62. $V(x) = \dfrac{1}{x^2 + x + 1}$

APPLICATIONS

63. Height of a Ball If a ball is thrown directly upward with a velocity of 40 ft/s, its height (in feet) after t seconds is given by $y = 40t - 16t^2$. What is the maximum height attained by the ball?

64. Path of a Ball A ball is thrown across a playing field from a height of 5 ft above the ground at an angle of 45° to the horizontal at a speed of 20 ft/s. It can be deduced from physical principles that the path of the ball is modeled by the function

$$y = -\frac{32}{(20)^2}x^2 + x + 5$$

where x is the distance in feet that the ball has traveled horizontally.

(a) Find the maximum height attained by the ball.

(b) Find the horizontal distance the ball has traveled when it hits the ground.

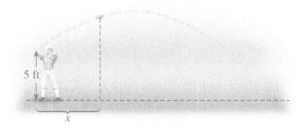

65. Revenue A manufacturer finds that the revenue generated by selling x units of a certain commodity is given by the function $R(x) = 80x - 0.4x^2$, where the revenue $R(x)$ is measured in dollars. What is the maximum revenue, and how many units should be manufactured to obtain this maximum?

66. Sales A soft-drink vendor at a popular beach analyzes his sales records and finds that if he sells x cans of soda pop in one day, his profit (in dollars) is given by

$$P(x) = -0.001x^2 + 3x - 1800$$

What is his maximum profit per day, and how many cans must he sell for maximum profit?

67. Advertising The effectiveness of a television commercial depends on how many times a viewer watches it. After some experiments an advertising agency found that if the effectiveness E is measured on a scale of 0 to 10, then

$$E(n) = \tfrac{2}{3}n - \tfrac{1}{90}n^2$$

where n is the number of times a viewer watches a given commercial. For a commercial to have maximum effectiveness, how many times should a viewer watch it?

68. Pharmaceuticals When a certain drug is taken orally, the concentration of the drug in the patient's bloodstream after t minutes is given by $C(t) = 0.06t - 0.0002t^2$, where $0 \le t \le 240$ and the concentration is measured in mg/L. When is the maximum serum concentration reached, and what is that maximum concentration?

69. Agriculture The number of apples produced by each tree in an apple orchard depends on how densely the trees are planted. If n trees are planted on an acre of land, then each tree produces $900 - 9n$ apples. So the number of apples produced per acre is

$$A(n) = n(900 - 9n)$$

How many trees should be planted per acre to obtain the maximum yield of apples?

70. Agriculture At a certain vineyard it is found that each grape vine produces about 10 pounds of grapes in a season when about 700 vines are planted per acre. For each additional vine that is planted, the production of each vine decreases by about 1 percent. So the number of pounds of grapes produced per acre is modeled by

$$A(n) = (700 + n)(10 - 0.01n)$$

where n is the number of additional vines planted. Find the number of vines that should be planted to maximize grape production.

71–74 ■ Use the formulas of this section to give an alternative solution to the indicated problem in *Focus on Modeling: Modeling with Functions* on pages 220–221.

71. Problem 21   **72.** Problem 22

73. Problem 25   **74.** Problem 24

75. Fencing a Horse Corral Carol has 2400 ft of fencing to fence in a rectangular horse corral.

(a) Find a function that models the area of the corral in terms of the width x of the corral.

(b) Find the dimensions of the rectangle that maximize the area of the corral.

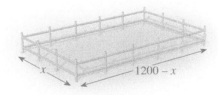

76. Making a Rain Gutter A rain gutter is formed by bending up the sides of a 30-inch-wide rectangular metal sheet as shown in the figure.

(a) Find a function that models the cross-sectional area of the gutter in terms of x.

(b) Find the value of x that maximizes the cross-sectional area of the gutter.

(c) What is the maximum cross-sectional area for the gutter?

77. Stadium Revenue A baseball team plays in a stadium that holds 55,000 spectators. With the ticket price at $10, the average attendance at recent games has been 27,000. A market survey indicates that for every dollar the ticket price is lowered, attendance increases by 3000.

(a) Find a function that models the revenue in terms of ticket price.

(b) Find the price that maximizes revenue from ticket sales.

(c) What ticket price is so high that no revenue is generated?

78. Maximizing Profit A community bird-watching society makes and sells simple bird feeders to raise money for its conservation activities. The materials for each feeder cost $6, and the society sells an average of 20 per week at a price of $10 each. The society has been considering raising the price, so it conducts a survey and finds that for every dollar increase, it loses 2 sales per week.

(a) Find a function that models weekly profit in terms of price per feeder.

(b) What price should the society charge for each feeder to maximize profits? What is the maximum weekly profit?

DISCOVERY ▪ DISCUSSION ▪ WRITING

79. Vertex and x-Intercepts We know that the graph of the quadratic function $f(x) = (x - m)(x - n)$ is a parabola. Sketch a rough graph of what such a parabola would look like. What are the x-intercepts of the graph of f? Can you tell from your graph the x-coordinate of the vertex in terms of m and n? (Use the symmetry of the parabola.) Confirm your answer by expanding and using the formulas of this section.

80. Maximum of a Fourth-Degree Polynomial Find the maximum value of the function

$$f(x) = 3 + 4x^2 - x^4$$

[*Hint:* Let $t = x^2$.]

3.2 POLYNOMIAL FUNCTIONS AND THEIR GRAPHS

Graphing Basic Polynomial Functions ▶ End Behavior and the Leading Term ▶ Using Zeros to Graph Polynomials ▶ Shape of the Graph Near a Zero ▶ Local Maxima and Minima of Polynomials

In this section we study polynomial functions of any degree. But before we work with polynomial functions, we must agree on some terminology.

POLYNOMIAL FUNCTIONS

A **polynomial function of degree n** is a function of the form

$$P(x) = a_n x^n + a_{n-1} x^{n-1} + \cdots + a_1 x + a_0$$

where n is a nonnegative integer and $a_n \neq 0$.

The numbers $a_0, a_1, a_2, \ldots, a_n$ are called the **coefficients** of the polynomial.

The number a_0 is the **constant coefficient** or **constant term**.

The number a_n, the coefficient of the highest power, is the **leading coefficient**, and the term $a_n x^n$ is the **leading term**.

We often refer to polynomial functions simply as *polynomials*. The following polynomial has degree 5, leading coefficient 3, and constant term -6.

Leading coefficient 3   Degree 5   Constant term -6

$$3x^5 + 6x^4 - 2x^3 + x^2 + 7x - 6$$

Leading term $3x^5$

Coefficients 3, 6, -2, 1, 7, and -6

Here are some more examples of polynomials.

$$P(x) = 3 \qquad \text{Degree 0}$$
$$Q(x) = 4x - 7 \qquad \text{Degree 1}$$
$$R(x) = x^2 + x \qquad \text{Degree 2}$$
$$S(x) = 2x^3 - 6x^2 - 10 \qquad \text{Degree 3}$$

If a polynomial consists of just a single term, then it is called a **monomial**. For example, $P(x) = x^3$ and $Q(x) = -6x^5$ are monomials.

▼ Graphing Basic Polynomial Functions

The graphs of polynomials of degree 0 or 1 are lines (Section 1.10), and the graphs of polynomials of degree 2 are parabolas (Section 3.1). The greater the degree of a polynomial, the more complicated its graph can be. However, the graph of a polynomial function is **continuous**. This means that the graph has no breaks or holes (see Figure 1). Moreover, the graph of a polynomial function is a smooth curve; that is, it has no corners or sharp points (cusps) as shown in Figure 1.

Continuous functions are studied in Section 13.2, page 851.

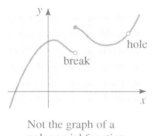
Not the graph of a polynomial function

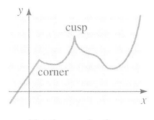
Not the graph of a polynomial function

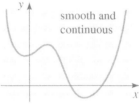
Graph of a polynomial function

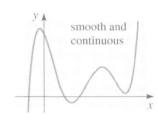
Graph of a polynomial function

FIGURE 1

The simplest polynomial functions are the monomials $P(x) = x^n$, whose graphs are shown in Figure 2. As the figure suggests, the graph of $P(x) = x^n$ has the same general shape as the graph of $y = x^2$ when n is even and the same general shape as the graph of $y = x^3$ when n is odd. However, as the degree n becomes larger, the graphs become flatter around the origin and steeper elsewhere.

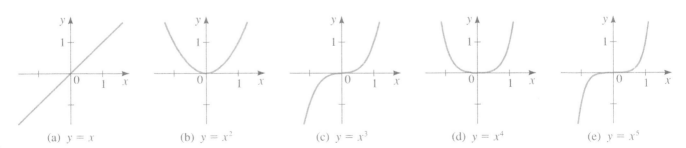
(a) $y = x$ (b) $y = x^2$ (c) $y = x^3$ (d) $y = x^4$ (e) $y = x^5$

FIGURE 2 Graphs of monomials

EXAMPLE 1 | Transformations of Monomials

Sketch the graphs of the following functions.

(a) $P(x) = -x^3$ **(b)** $Q(x) = (x - 2)^4$
(c) $R(x) = -2x^5 + 4$

SOLUTION We use the graphs in Figure 2 and transform them using the techniques of Section 2.5.

(a) The graph of $P(x) = -x^3$ is the reflection of the graph of $y = x^3$ in the x-axis, as shown in Figure 3(a) below.

(b) The graph of $Q(x) = (x - 2)^4$ is the graph of $y = x^4$ shifted to the right 2 units, as shown in Figure 3(b).

(c) We begin with the graph of $y = x^5$. The graph of $y = -2x^5$ is obtained by stretching the graph vertically and reflecting it in the x-axis (see the dashed blue graph in Figure 3(c)). Finally, the graph of $R(x) = -2x^5 + 4$ is obtained by shifting upward 4 units (see the red graph in Figure 3(c)).

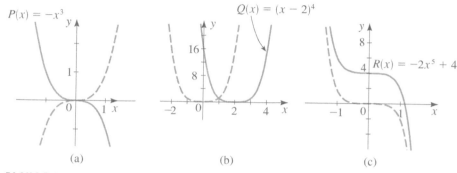

FIGURE 3

✎. NOW TRY EXERCISE **5**

▼ End Behavior and the Leading Term

The **end behavior** of a polynomial is a description of what happens as x becomes large in the positive or negative direction. To describe end behavior, we use the following notation:

$$x \to \infty \quad \text{means} \quad \text{"}x \text{ becomes large in the positive direction"}$$

$$x \to -\infty \quad \text{means} \quad \text{"}x \text{ becomes large in the negative direction"}$$

For example, the monomial $y = x^2$ in Figure 2(b) has the following end behavior:

$$y \to \infty \quad \text{as} \quad x \to \infty \quad \text{and} \quad y \to \infty \quad \text{as} \quad x \to -\infty$$

The monomial $y = x^3$ in Figure 2(c) has the following end behavior:

$$y \to \infty \quad \text{as} \quad x \to \infty \quad \text{and} \quad y \to -\infty \quad \text{as} \quad x \to -\infty$$

For any polynomial *the end behavior is determined by the term that contains the highest power of x*, because when x is large, the other terms are relatively insignificant in size. The following box shows the four possible types of end behavior, based on the highest power and the sign of its coefficient.

END BEHAVIOR OF POLYNOMIALS

The end behavior of the polynomial $P(x) = a_n x^n + a_{n-1} x^{n-1} + \cdots + a_1 x + a_0$ is determined by the degree n and the sign of the leading coefficient a_n, as indicated in the following graphs.

| *P* has odd degree | | *P* has even degree | |

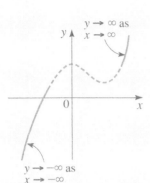

$y \to \infty$ as $x \to \infty$

$y \to -\infty$ as $x \to -\infty$

Leading coefficient positive

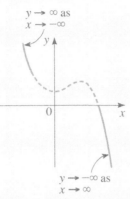

$y \to \infty$ as $x \to -\infty$

$y \to -\infty$ as $x \to \infty$

Leading coefficient negative

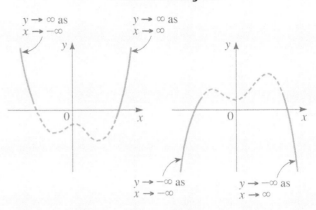

$y \to \infty$ as $x \to -\infty$

$y \to \infty$ as $x \to \infty$

$y \to -\infty$ as $x \to -\infty$

Leading coefficient positive

$y \to -\infty$ as $x \to \infty$

Leading coefficient negative

EXAMPLE 2 | End Behavior of a Polynomial

Determine the end behavior of the polynomial

$$P(x) = -2x^4 + 5x^3 + 4x - 7$$

SOLUTION   The polynomial P has degree 4 and leading coefficient -2. Thus, P has *even* degree and *negative* leading coefficient, so it has the following end behavior:

$$y \to -\infty \quad \text{as} \quad x \to \infty \qquad \text{and} \qquad y \to -\infty \quad \text{as} \quad x \to -\infty$$

The graph in Figure 4 illustrates the end behavior of P.

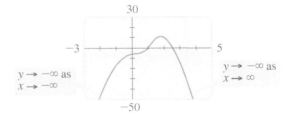

$y \to -\infty$ as $x \to -\infty$

$y \to -\infty$ as $x \to \infty$

FIGURE 4
$P(x) = -2x^4 + 5x^3 + 4x - 7$

✎ NOW TRY EXERCISE **11**

EXAMPLE 3 | End Behavior of a Polynomial

(a) Determine the end behavior of the polynomial $P(x) = 3x^5 - 5x^3 + 2x$.

(b) Confirm that P and its leading term $Q(x) = 3x^5$ have the same end behavior by graphing them together.

SOLUTION

(a) Since P has odd degree and positive leading coefficient, it has the following end behavior:

$$y \to \infty \quad \text{as} \quad x \to \infty \qquad \text{and} \qquad y \to -\infty \quad \text{as} \quad x \to -\infty$$

(b) Figure 5 shows the graphs of P and Q in progressively larger viewing rectangles. The larger the viewing rectangle, the more the graphs look alike. This confirms that they have the same end behavior.

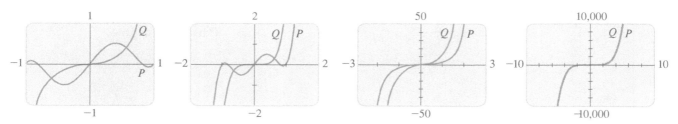

FIGURE 5

$P(x) = 3x^5 - 5x^3 + 2x$

$Q(x) = 3x^5$

✎ NOW TRY EXERCISE **41**

To see algebraically why P and Q in Example 3 have the same end behavior, factor P as follows and compare with Q.

$$P(x) = 3x^5\left(1 - \frac{5}{3x^2} + \frac{2}{3x^4}\right) \qquad Q(x) = 3x^5$$

When x is large, the terms $5/3x^2$ and $2/3x^4$ are close to 0 (see Exercise 83 on page 12). So for large x, we have

$$P(x) \approx 3x^5(1 - 0 - 0) = 3x^5 = Q(x)$$

So when x is large, P and Q have approximately the same values. We can also see this numerically by making a table like the one shown below.

x	$P(x)$	$Q(x)$
15	2,261,280	2,278,125
30	72,765,060	72,900,000
50	936,875,100	937,500,000

By the same reasoning we can show that the end behavior of *any* polynomial is determined by its leading term.

▼ Using Zeros to Graph Polynomials

If P is a polynomial function, then c is called a **zero** of P if $P(c) = 0$. In other words, the zeros of P are the solutions of the polynomial equation $P(x) = 0$. Note that if $P(c) = 0$, then the graph of P has an x-intercept at $x = c$, so the x-intercepts of the graph are the zeros of the function.

REAL ZEROS OF POLYNOMIALS

If P is a polynomial and c is a real number, then the following are equivalent:

1. c is a zero of P.

2. $x = c$ is a solution of the equation $P(x) = 0$.

3. $x - c$ is a factor of $P(x)$.

4. c is an x-intercept of the graph of P.

To find the zeros of a polynomial P, we factor and then use the Zero-Product Property (see page 47). For example, to find the zeros of $P(x) = x^2 + x - 6$, we factor P to get

$$P(x) = (x - 2)(x + 3)$$

From this factored form we easily see that

1. 2 is a zero of P.

2. $x = 2$ is a solution of the equation $x^2 + x - 6 = 0$.

3. $x - 2$ is a factor of $x^2 + x - 6$.

4. 2 is an x-intercept of the graph of P.

The same facts are true for the other zero, -3.

The following theorem has many important consequences. (See, for instance, the *Discovery Project* referenced on page 263.) Here we use it to help us graph polynomial functions.

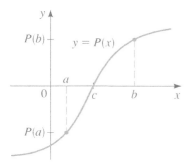

FIGURE 6

INTERMEDIATE VALUE THEOREM FOR POLYNOMIALS

If P is a polynomial function and $P(a)$ and $P(b)$ have opposite signs, then there exists at least one value c between a and b for which $P(c) = 0$.

We will not prove this theorem, but Figure 6 shows why it is intuitively plausible.

One important consequence of this theorem is that between any two successive zeros the values of a polynomial are either all positive or all negative. That is, between two successive zeros the graph of a polynomial lies *entirely above* or *entirely below* the x-axis. To see why, suppose c_1 and c_2 are successive zeros of P. If P has both positive and negative values between c_1 and c_2, then by the Intermediate Value Theorem P must have another zero between c_1 and c_2. But that's not possible because c_1 and c_2 are successive zeros. This observation allows us to use the following guidelines to graph polynomial functions.

GUIDELINES FOR GRAPHING POLYNOMIAL FUNCTIONS

1. Zeros.   Factor the polynomial to find all its real zeros; these are the x-intercepts of the graph.

2. Test Points.   Make a table of values for the polynomial. Include test points to determine whether the graph of the polynomial lies above or below the x-axis on the intervals determined by the zeros. Include the y-intercept in the table.

3. End Behavior.   Determine the end behavior of the polynomial.

4. Graph.   Plot the intercepts and other points you found in the table. Sketch a smooth curve that passes through these points and exhibits the required end behavior.

EXAMPLE 4 | Using Zeros to Graph a Polynomial Function

Sketch the graph of the polynomial function $P(x) = (x + 2)(x - 1)(x - 3)$.

SOLUTION   The zeros are $x = -2$, 1, and 3. These determine the intervals $(-\infty, -2)$, $(-2, 1)$, $(1, 3)$, and $(3, \infty)$. Using test points in these intervals, we get the information in the following sign diagram (see Section 1.7).

	Test point $x = -3$ $P(-3) < 0$	Test point $x = -1$ $P(-1) > 0$	Test point $x = 2$ $P(2) < 0$	Test point $x = 4$ $P(3) > 0$
		-2	1	3
Sign of $P(x) = (x + 2)(x - 1)(x - 3)$	$-$	$+$	$-$	$+$
Graph of P	below x-axis	above x-axis	below x-axis	above x-axis

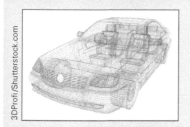
Plotting a few additional points and connecting them with a smooth curve helps us to complete the graph in Figure 7.

	x	$P(x)$
Test point →	-3	-24
	-2	0
Test point →	-1	8
	0	6
	1	0
Test point →	2	-4
	3	0
Test point →	4	18

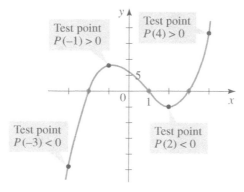

FIGURE 7 $P(x) = (x + 2)(x - 1)(x - 3)$

✎. NOW TRY EXERCISE **17**

EXAMPLE 5 | Finding Zeros and Graphing a Polynomial Function

Let $P(x) = x^3 - 2x^2 - 3x$.

(a) Find the zeros of P.

(b) Sketch a graph of P.

SOLUTION

(a) To find the zeros, we factor completely.

$$P(x) = x^3 - 2x^2 - 3x$$
$$= x(x^2 - 2x - 3) \qquad \text{Factor } x$$
$$= x(x - 3)(x + 1) \qquad \text{Factor quadratic}$$

Thus, the zeros are $x = 0$, $x = 3$, and $x = -1$.

(b) The x-intercepts are $x = 0$, $x = 3$, and $x = -1$. The y-intercept is $P(0) = 0$. We make a table of values of $P(x)$, making sure that we choose test points between (and to the right and left of) successive zeros.

Since P is of odd degree and its leading coefficient is positive, it has the following end behavior:

$$y \to \infty \quad \text{as} \quad x \to \infty \qquad \text{and} \qquad y \to -\infty \quad \text{as} \quad x \to -\infty$$

We plot the points in the table and connect them by a smooth curve to complete the graph, as shown in Figure 8.

	x	$P(x)$
Test point →	-2	-10
	-1	0
Test point →	$-\frac{1}{2}$	$\frac{7}{8}$
	0	0
Test point →	1	-4
	2	-6
	3	0
Test point →	4	20

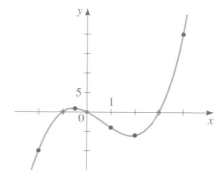

FIGURE 8 $P(x) = x^3 - 2x^2 - 3x$

✎. NOW TRY EXERCISE **27**

EXAMPLE 6 | Finding Zeros and Graphing a Polynomial Function

Let $P(x) = -2x^4 - x^3 + 3x^2$.

(a) Find the zeros of P. **(b)** Sketch a graph of P.

SOLUTION

(a) To find the zeros, we factor completely.

$$\begin{aligned} P(x) &= -2x^4 - x^3 + 3x^2 \\ &= -x^2(2x^2 + x - 3) && \text{Factor } -x^2 \\ &= -x^2(2x + 3)(x - 1) && \text{Factor quadratic} \end{aligned}$$

Thus, the zeros are $x = 0$, $x = -\frac{3}{2}$, and $x = 1$.

(b) The x-intercepts are $x = 0$, $x = -\frac{3}{2}$, and $x = 1$. The y-intercept is $P(0) = 0$. We make a table of values of $P(x)$, making sure that we choose test points between (and to the right and left of) successive zeros.

Since P is of even degree and its leading coefficient is negative, it has the following end behavior:

$$y \to -\infty \quad \text{as} \quad x \to \infty \qquad \text{and} \qquad y \to -\infty \quad \text{as} \quad x \to -\infty$$

We plot the points from the table and connect the points by a smooth curve to complete the graph in Figure 9.

A table of values is most easily calculated by using a programmable calculator or a graphing calculator.

x	$P(x)$
-2	-12
-1.5	0
-1	2
-0.5	0.75
0	0
0.5	0.5
1	0
1.5	-6.75

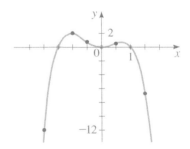

FIGURE 9 $P(x) = -2x^4 - x^3 + 3x^2$

NOW TRY EXERCISE 31

EXAMPLE 7 | Finding Zeros and Graphing a Polynomial Function

Let $P(x) = x^3 - 2x^2 - 4x + 8$.

(a) Find the zeros of P. **(b)** Sketch a graph of P.

SOLUTION

(a) To find the zeros, we factor completely.

$$\begin{aligned} P(x) &= x^3 - 2x^2 - 4x + 8 \\ &= x^2(x - 2) - 4(x - 2) && \text{Group and factor} \\ &= (x^2 - 4)(x - 2) && \text{Factor } x - 2 \\ &= (x + 2)(x - 2)(x - 2) && \text{Difference of squares} \\ &= (x + 2)(x - 2)^2 && \text{Simplify} \end{aligned}$$

Thus the zeros are $x = -2$ and $x = 2$.

(b) The x-intercepts are $x = -2$ and $x = 2$. The y-intercept is $P(0) = 8$. The table gives additional values of $P(x)$.

Since P is of odd degree and its leading coefficient is positive, it has the following end behavior:

$$y \to \infty \quad \text{as} \quad x \to \infty \qquad \text{and} \qquad y \to -\infty \quad \text{as} \quad x \to -\infty$$

We connect the points by a smooth curve to complete the graph in Figure 10.

x	$P(x)$
-3	-25
-2	0
-1	9
0	8
1	3
2	0
3	5

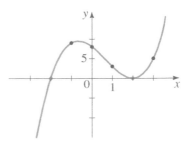

FIGURE 10 $P(x) = x^3 - 2x^2 - 4x + 8$

NOW TRY EXERCISE **33**

▼ Shape of the Graph Near a Zero

Although $x = 2$ is a zero of the polynomial in Example 7, the graph does not cross the x-axis at the x-intercept 2. This is because the factor $(x - 2)^2$ corresponding to that zero is raised to an even power, so it doesn't change sign as we test points on either side of 2. In the same way the graph does not cross the x-axis at $x = 0$ in Example 6.

In general, if c is a zero of P, and the corresponding factor $x - c$ occurs exactly m times in the factorization of P, then we say that c is a **zero of multiplicity m**. By considering test points on either side of the x-intercept c, we conclude that the graph crosses the x-axis at c if the multiplicity m is odd and does not cross the x-axis if m is even. Moreover, it can be shown by using calculus that near $x = c$ the graph has the same general shape as the graph of $y = A(x - c)^m$.

SHAPE OF THE GRAPH NEAR A ZERO OF MULTIPLICITY m

If c is a zero of P of multiplicity m, then the shape of the graph of P near c is as follows.

Multiplicity of c	Shape of the graph of P near the x-intercept c
m odd, $m > 1$	[graph] OR [graph]
m even, $m > 1$	[graph] OR [graph]

EXAMPLE 8 | Graphing a Polynomial Function Using Its Zeros

Graph the polynomial $P(x) = x^4(x - 2)^3(x + 1)^2$.

SOLUTION   The zeros of P are $-1, 0,$ and 2 with multiplicities 2, 4, and 3, respectively.

0 is a zero of multiplicity 4

2 is a zero of multiplicity 3

-1 is a zero of multiplicity 2

$$P(x) = x^4(x - 2)^3(x + 1)^2$$

The zero 2 has *odd* multiplicity, so the graph crosses the x-axis at the x-intercept 2. But the zeros 0 and -1 have *even* multiplicity, so the graph does not cross the x-axis at the x-intercepts 0 and -1.

Since P is a polynomial of degree 9 and has positive leading coefficient, it has the following end behavior:

$$y \to \infty \quad \text{as} \quad x \to \infty \quad \text{and} \quad y \to -\infty \quad \text{as} \quad x \to -\infty$$

With this information and a table of values we sketch the graph in Figure 11.

x	$P(x)$
-1.3	-9.2
-1	0
-0.5	-3.9
0	0
1	-4
2	0
2.3	8.2

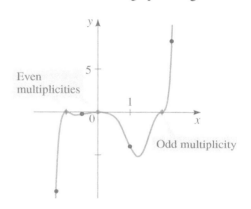

FIGURE 11 $P(x) = x^4(x - 2)^3(x + 1)^2$

■ . NOW TRY EXERCISE **25**

▼ Local Maxima and Minima of Polynomials

Recall from Section 2.3 that if the point $(a, f(a))$ is the highest point on the graph of f within some viewing rectangle, then $f(a)$ is a local maximum value of f, and if $(b, f(b))$ is the lowest point on the graph of f within a viewing rectangle, then $f(b)$ is a local minimum value (see Figure 12). We say that such a point $(a, f(a))$ is a **local maximum point** on the graph and that $(b, f(b))$ is a **local minimum point**. The local maximum and minimum points on the graph of a function are called its **local extrema**.

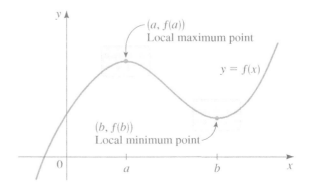

FIGURE 12

For a polynomial function the number of local extrema must be less than the degree, as the following principle indicates. (A proof of this principle requires calculus.)

LOCAL EXTREMA OF POLYNOMIALS

If $P(x) = a_n x^n + a_{n-1} x^{n-1} + \cdots + a_1 x + a_0$ is a polynomial of degree n, then the graph of P has at most $n - 1$ local extrema.

A polynomial of degree n may in fact have less than $n - 1$ local extrema. For example, $P(x) = x^5$ (graphed in Figure 2) has *no* local extrema, even though it is of degree 5. The preceding principle tells us only that a polynomial of degree n can have no more than $n - 1$ local extrema.

EXAMPLE 9 | The Number of Local Extrema

Determine how many local extrema each polynomial has.

(a) $P_1(x) = x^4 + x^3 - 16x^2 - 4x + 48$

(b) $P_2(x) = x^5 + 3x^4 - 5x^3 - 15x^2 + 4x - 15$

(c) $P_3(x) = 7x^4 + 3x^2 - 10x$

SOLUTION   The graphs are shown in Figure 13.

(a) P_1 has two local minimum points and one local maximum point, for a total of three local extrema.

(b) P_2 has two local minimum points and two local maximum points, for a total of four local extrema.

(c) P_3 has just one local extremum, a local minimum.

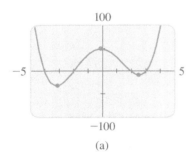

(a)

$P_1(x) = x^4 + x^3 - 16x^2 - 4x + 48$

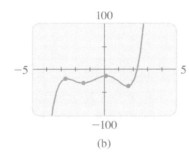

(b)

$P_2(x) = x^5 + 3x^4 - 5x^3 - 15x^2 + 4x - 15$

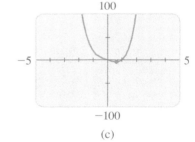

(c)

$P_3(x) = 7x^4 + 3x^2 - 10x$

FIGURE 13

NOW TRY EXERCISES **61** AND **63**

With a graphing calculator we can quickly draw the graphs of many functions at once, on the same viewing screen. This allows us to see how changing a value in the definition of the functions affects the shape of its graph. In the next example we apply this principle to a family of third-degree polynomials.

EXAMPLE 10 | A Family of Polynomials

Sketch the family of polynomials $P(x) = x^3 - cx^2$ for $c = 0, 1, 2,$ and 3. How does changing the value of c affect the graph?

SOLUTION The polynomials

$$P_0(x) = x^3 \qquad\qquad P_1(x) = x^3 - x^2$$
$$P_2(x) = x^3 - 2x^2 \qquad P_3(x) = x^3 - 3x^2$$

are graphed in Figure 14. We see that increasing the value of c causes the graph to develop an increasingly deep "valley" to the right of the y-axis, creating a local maximum at the origin and a local minimum at a point in Quadrant IV. This local minimum moves lower and farther to the right as c increases. To see why this happens, factor $P(x) = x^2(x - c)$. The polynomial P has zeros at 0 and c, and the larger c gets, the farther to the right the minimum between 0 and c will be.

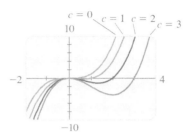

FIGURE 14 A family of polynomials
$P(x) = x^3 - cx^2$

NOW TRY EXERCISE **71**

3.2 EXERCISES

CONCEPTS

1. Only one of the following graphs could be the graph of a polynomial function. Which one? Why are the others not graphs of polynomials?

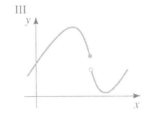

2. Every polynomial has one of the following behaviors:
  (i) $y \to \infty$ as $x \to \infty$ and $y \to \infty$ as $x \to -\infty$
  (ii) $y \to \infty$ as $x \to \infty$ and $y \to -\infty$ as $x \to -\infty$
  (iii) $y \to -\infty$ as $x \to \infty$ and $y \to \infty$ as $x \to -\infty$
  (iv) $y \to -\infty$ as $x \to \infty$ and $y \to -\infty$ as $x \to -\infty$

For each polynomial, choose the appropriate description of its end behavior from the list above.

(a) $y = x^3 - 8x^2 + 2x - 15$: end behavior _____.

(b) $y = -2x^4 + 12x + 100$: end behavior _____.

3. If c is a zero of the polynomial P, which of the following statements must be true?
  (a) $P(c) = 0$.   **(b)** $P(0) = c$.
  (c) $x - c$ is a factor of $P(x)$.
  (d) c is the y-intercept of the graph of P.

4. Which of the following statements couldn't possibly be true about the polynomial function P?
  (a) P has degree 3, two local maxima, and two local minima.
  (b) P has degree 3 and no local maxima or minima.
  (c) P has degree 4, one local maximum, and no local minima.

SKILLS

5–8 ■ Sketch the graph of each function by transforming the graph of an appropriate function of the form $y = x^n$ from Figure 2. Indicate all x- and y-intercepts on each graph.

5. **(a)** $P(x) = x^2 - 4$ **(b)** $Q(x) = (x - 4)^2$
  (c) $R(x) = 2x^2 - 2$ **(d)** $S(x) = 2(x - 2)^2$

6. **(a)** $P(x) = x^4 - 16$ **(b)** $Q(x) = (x + 2)^4$
  (c) $R(x) = (x + 2)^4 - 16$ **(d)** $S(x) = -2(x + 2)^4$

7. **(a)** $P(x) = x^3 - 8$ **(b)** $Q(x) = -x^3 + 27$
  (c) $R(x) = -(x + 2)^3$ **(d)** $S(x) = \frac{1}{2}(x - 1)^3 + 4$

8. **(a)** $P(x) = (x + 3)^5$ **(b)** $Q(x) = 2(x + 3)^5 - 64$
  (c) $R(x) = -\frac{1}{2}(x - 2)^5$ **(d)** $S(x) = -\frac{1}{2}(x - 2)^5 + 16$

9–14 ■ Match the polynomial function with one of the graphs I–VI on the next page. Give reasons for your choice.

9. $P(x) = x(x^2 - 4)$ **10.** $Q(x) = -x^2(x^2 - 4)$

11. $R(x) = -x^5 + 5x^3 - 4x$ **12.** $S(x) = \frac{1}{2}x^6 - 2x^4$

13. $T(x) = x^4 + 2x^3$ **14.** $U(x) = -x^3 + 2x^2$

I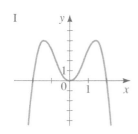

II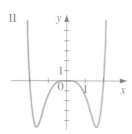

III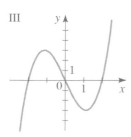

IV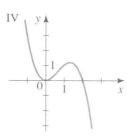

V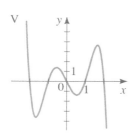

VI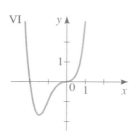

15–26 ■ Sketch the graph of the polynomial function. Make sure your graph shows all intercepts and exhibits the proper end behavior.

15. $P(x) = (x - 1)(x + 2)$

16. $P(x) = (x - 1)(x + 1)(x - 2)$

17. $P(x) = x(x - 3)(x + 2)$

18. $P(x) = (2x - 1)(x + 1)(x + 3)$

19. $P(x) = (x - 3)(x + 2)(3x - 2)$

20. $P(x) = \frac{1}{5}x(x - 5)^2$

21. $P(x) = (x - 1)^2(x - 3)$ **22.** $P(x) = \frac{1}{4}(x + 1)^3(x - 3)$

23. $P(x) = \frac{1}{12}(x + 2)^2(x - 3)^2$ **24.** $P(x) = (x - 1)^2(x + 2)^3$

25. $P(x) = x^3(x + 2)(x - 3)^2$ **26.** $P(x) = (x - 3)^2(x + 1)^2$

27–40 ■ Factor the polynomial and use the factored form to find the zeros. Then sketch the graph.

27. $P(x) = x^3 - x^2 - 6x$ **28.** $P(x) = x^3 + 2x^2 - 8x$

29. $P(x) = -x^3 + x^2 + 12x$ **30.** $P(x) = -2x^3 - x^2 + x$

31. $P(x) = x^4 - 3x^3 + 2x^2$ **32.** $P(x) = x^5 - 9x^3$

33. $P(x) = x^3 + x^2 - x - 1$ **34.** $P(x) = x^3 + 3x^2 - 4x - 12$

35. $P(x) = 2x^3 - x^2 - 18x + 9$

36. $P(x) = \frac{1}{8}(2x^4 + 3x^3 - 16x - 24)^2$

37. $P(x) = x^4 - 2x^3 - 8x + 16$

38. $P(x) = x^4 - 2x^3 + 8x - 16$

39. $P(x) = x^4 - 3x^2 - 4$ **40.** $P(x) = x^6 - 2x^3 + 1$

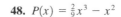 **41–46** ■ Determine the end behavior of P. Compare the graphs of P and Q in large and small viewing rectangles, as in Example 3(b).

41. $P(x) = 3x^3 - x^2 + 5x + 1$; $Q(x) = 3x^3$

42. $P(x) = -\frac{1}{8}x^3 + \frac{1}{4}x^2 + 12x$; $Q(x) = -\frac{1}{8}x^3$

43. $P(x) = x^4 - 7x^2 + 5x + 5$; $Q(x) = x^4$

44. $P(x) = -x^5 + 2x^2 + x$; $Q(x) = -x^5$

45. $P(x) = x^{11} - 9x^9$; $Q(x) = x^{11}$

46. $P(x) = 2x^2 - x^{12}$; $Q(x) = -x^{12}$

47–50 ■ The graph of a polynomial function is given. From the graph, find (**a**) the x- and y-intercepts, and (**b**) the coordinates of all local extrema.

47. $P(x) = -x^2 + 4x$ **48.** $P(x) = \frac{2}{9}x^3 - x^2$

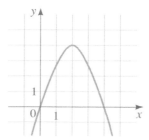   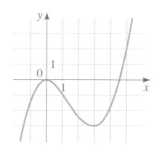

49. $P(x) = -\frac{1}{2}x^3 + \frac{3}{2}x - 1$ **50.** $P(x) = \frac{1}{9}x^4 - \frac{4}{9}x^3$

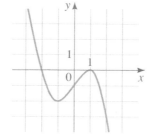   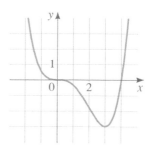

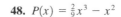 **51–58** ■ Graph the polynomial in the given viewing rectangle. Find the coordinates of all local extrema. State each answer rounded to two decimal places.

51. $y = -x^2 + 8x$, $[-4, 12]$ by $[-50, 30]$

52. $y = x^3 - 3x^2$, $[-2, 5]$ by $[-10, 10]$

53. $y = x^3 - 12x + 9$, $[-5, 5]$ by $[-30, 30]$

54. $y = 2x^3 - 3x^2 - 12x - 32$, $[-5, 5]$ by $[-60, 30]$

55. $y = x^4 + 4x^3$, $[-5, 5]$ by $[-30, 30]$

56. $y = x^4 - 18x^2 + 32$, $[-5, 5]$ by $[-100, 100]$

57. $y = 3x^5 - 5x^3 + 3$, $[-3, 3]$ by $[-5, 10]$

58. $y = x^5 - 5x^2 + 6$, $[-3, 3]$ by $[-5, 10]$

59–68 ■ Graph the polynomial and determine how many local maxima and minima it has.

59. $y = -2x^2 + 3x + 5$ **60.** $y = x^3 + 12x$

61. $y = x^3 - x^2 - x$ **62.** $y = 6x^3 + 3x + 1$

63. $y = x^4 - 5x^2 + 4$

64. $y = 1.2x^5 + 3.75x^4 - 7x^3 - 15x^2 + 18x$

65. $y = (x - 2)^5 + 32$ **66.** $y = (x^2 - 2)^3$

67. $y = x^8 - 3x^4 + x$ **68.** $y = \frac{1}{3}x^7 - 17x^2 + 7$

69–74 ■ Graph the family of polynomials in the same viewing rectangle, using the given values of c. Explain how changing the value of c affects the graph.

69. $P(x) = cx^3$; $c = 1, 2, 5, \frac{1}{2}$

70. $P(x) = (x - c)^4$; $c = -1, 0, 1, 2$

71. $P(x) = x^4 + c$; $c = -1, 0, 1, 2$

72. $P(x) = x^3 + cx$; $c = 2, 0, -2, -4$

73. $P(x) = x^4 - cx$; $c = 0, 1, 8, 27$

74. $P(x) = x^c$; $c = 1, 3, 5, 7$

75. (a) On the same coordinate axes, sketch graphs (as accurately as possible) of the functions

$$y = x^3 - 2x^2 - x + 2 \quad \text{and} \quad y = -x^2 + 5x + 2$$

(b) On the basis of your sketch in part (a), at how many points do the two graphs appear to intersect?

(c) Find the coordinates of all intersection points.

76. Portions of the graphs of $y = x^2$, $y = x^3$, $y = x^4$, $y = x^5$, and $y = x^6$ are plotted in the figures. Determine which function belongs to each graph.

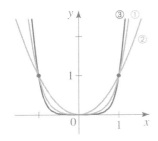 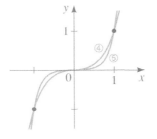

77. Recall that a function f is *odd* if $f(-x) = -f(x)$ or *even* if $f(-x) = f(x)$ for all real x.

(a) Show that a polynomial $P(x)$ that contains only odd powers of x is an odd function.

(b) Show that a polynomial $P(x)$ that contains only even powers of x is an even function.

(c) Show that if a polynomial $P(x)$ contains both odd and even powers of x, then it is neither an odd nor an even function.

(d) Express the function

$$P(x) = x^5 + 6x^3 - x^2 - 2x + 5$$

as the sum of an odd function and an even function.

78. (a) Graph the function $P(x) = (x - 1)(x - 3)(x - 4)$ and find all local extrema, correct to the nearest tenth.

(b) Graph the function

$$Q(x) = (x - 1)(x - 3)(x - 4) + 5$$

and use your answers to part (a) to find all local extrema, correct to the nearest tenth.

79. (a) Graph the function $P(x) = (x - 2)(x - 4)(x - 5)$ and determine how many local extrema it has.

(b) If $a < b < c$, explain why the function

$$P(x) = (x - a)(x - b)(x - c)$$

must have two local extrema.

80. (a) How many x-intercepts and how many local extrema does the polynomial $P(x) = x^3 - 4x$ have?

(b) How many x-intercepts and how many local extrema does the polynomial $Q(x) = x^3 + 4x$ have?

(c) If $a > 0$, how many x-intercepts and how many local extrema does each of the polynomials $P(x) = x^3 - ax$ and $Q(x) = x^3 + ax$ have? Explain your answer.

APPLICATIONS

81. Market Research A market analyst working for a small-appliance manufacturer finds that if the firm produces and sells x blenders annually, the total profit (in dollars) is

$$P(x) = 8x + 0.3x^2 - 0.0013x^3 - 372$$

Graph the function P in an appropriate viewing rectangle and use the graph to answer the following questions.

(a) When just a few blenders are manufactured, the firm loses money (profit is negative). (For example, $P(10) = -263.3$, so the firm loses \$263.30 if it produces and sells only 10 blenders.) How many blenders must the firm produce to break even?

(b) Does profit increase indefinitely as more blenders are produced and sold? If not, what is the largest possible profit the firm could have?

82. Population Change The rabbit population on a small island is observed to be given by the function

$$P(t) = 120t - 0.4t^4 + 1000$$

where t is the time (in months) since observations of the island began.

(a) When is the maximum population attained, and what is that maximum population?

(b) When does the rabbit population disappear from the island?

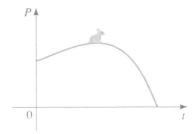

83. Volume of a Box An open box is to be constructed from a piece of cardboard 20 cm by 40 cm by cutting squares of side length x from each corner and folding up the sides, as shown in the figure.

(a) Express the volume V of the box as a function of x.

(b) What is the domain of V? (Use the fact that length and volume must be positive.)

 (c) Draw a graph of the function V, and use it to estimate the maximum volume for such a box.

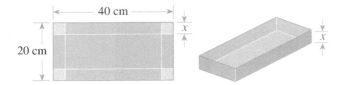

84. Volume of a Box A cardboard box has a square base, with each edge of the base having length x inches, as shown in the figure. The total length of all 12 edges of the box is 144 in.

(a) Show that the volume of the box is given by the function $V(x) = 2x^2(18 - x)$.

(b) What is the domain of V? (Use the fact that length and volume must be positive.)

 (c) Draw a graph of the function V and use it to estimate the maximum volume for such a box.

DISCOVERY ▪ DISCUSSION ▪ WRITING

85. Graphs of Large Powers Graph the functions $y = x^2$, $y = x^3$, $y = x^4$, and $y = x^5$, for $-1 \le x \le 1$, on the same coordinate axes. What do you think the graph of $y = x^{100}$ would look like on this same interval? What about $y = x^{101}$? Make a table of values to confirm your answers.

86. Maximum Number of Local Extrema What is the smallest possible degree that the polynomial whose graph is shown can have? Explain.

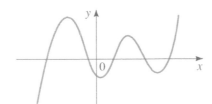

87. Possible Number of Local Extrema Is it possible for a third-degree polynomial to have exactly one local extremum? Can a fourth-degree polynomial have exactly two local extrema? How many local extrema can polynomials of third, fourth, fifth, and sixth degree have? (Think about the end behavior of such polynomials.) Now give an example of a polynomial that has six local extrema.

88. Impossible Situation? Is it possible for a polynomial to have two local maxima and no local minimum? Explain.

3.3 DIVIDING POLYNOMIALS

Long Division of Polynomials ▶ Synthetic Division ▶ The Remainder and Factor Theorems

So far in this chapter we have been studying polynomial functions *graphically*. In this section we begin to study polynomials *algebraically*. Most of our work will be concerned with factoring polynomials, and to factor, we need to know how to divide polynomials.

▼ Long Division of Polynomials

Dividing polynomials is much like the familiar process of dividing numbers. When we divide 38 by 7, the quotient is 5 and the remainder is 3. We write

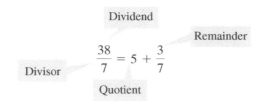

$$\frac{38}{7} = 5 + \frac{3}{7}$$

To divide polynomials, we use long division, as follows.

> **DIVISION ALGORITHM**
>
> If $P(x)$ and $D(x)$ are polynomials, with $D(x) \neq 0$, then there exist unique polynomials $Q(x)$ and $R(x)$, where $R(x)$ is either 0 or of degree less than the degree of $D(x)$, such that
>
> $$\underset{\text{Dividend}}{P(x)} = \underset{\text{Divisor}}{D(x)} \cdot \underset{\text{Quotient}}{Q(x)} + \underset{\text{Remainder}}{R(x)}$$
>
> The polynomials $P(x)$ and $D(x)$ are called the **dividend** and **divisor**, respectively, $Q(x)$ is the **quotient**, and $R(x)$ is the **remainder**.

To write the division algorithm another way, divide through by $D(x)$:

$$\frac{P(x)}{D(x)} = Q(x) + \frac{R(x)}{D(x)}$$

EXAMPLE 1 | Long Division of Polynomials

Divide $6x^2 - 26x + 12$ by $x - 4$.

SOLUTION The *dividend* is $6x^2 - 26x + 12$ and the *divisor* is $x - 4$. We begin by arranging them as follows:

$$x - 4 \overline{)6x^2 - 26x + 12}$$

Next we divide the leading term in the dividend by the leading term in the divisor to get the first term of the quotient: $6x^2/x = 6x$. Then we multiply the divisor by $6x$ and subtract the result from the dividend.

$$
\begin{array}{r}
6x \\
x - 4 \overline{)6x^2 - 26x + 12} \\
\underline{6x^2 - 24x} \\
-2x + 12
\end{array}
$$

Divide leading terms: $\dfrac{6x^2}{x} = 6x$

Multiply: $6x(x - 4) = 6x^2 - 24x$

Subtract and "bring down" 12

We repeat the process using the last line $-2x + 12$ as the dividend.

$$
\begin{array}{r}
6x - 2 \\
x - 4 \overline{)6x^2 - 26x + 12} \\
\underline{6x^2 - 24x} \\
-2x + 12 \\
\underline{-2x + 8} \\
4
\end{array}
$$

Divide leading terms: $\dfrac{-2x}{x} = -2$

Multiply: $-2(x - 4) = -2x + 8$

Subtract

The division process ends when the last line is of lesser degree than the divisor. The last line then contains the *remainder*, and the top line contains the *quotient*. The result of the division can be interpreted in either of two ways.

$$\underset{\text{Divisor}}{\underset{\big\uparrow}{}}\frac{\overset{\text{Dividend}}{\overbrace{6x^2 - 26x + 12}}}{x - 4} = \overset{\text{Quotient}}{6x - 2} + \underset{\text{Remainder}}{\frac{4}{x - 4}}$$

or

$$\underset{\text{Dividend}}{6x^2 - 26x + 12} = \underset{\text{Divisor}}{(x - 4)}\underset{\text{Quotient}}{(6x - 2)} + \underset{\text{Remainder}}{4}$$

■ NOW TRY EXERCISE 3

EXAMPLE 2 | Long Division of Polynomials

Let $P(x) = 8x^4 + 6x^2 - 3x + 1$ and $D(x) = 2x^2 - x + 2$. Find polynomials $Q(x)$ and $R(x)$ such that $P(x) = D(x) \cdot Q(x) + R(x)$.

SOLUTION We use long division after first inserting the term $0x^3$ into the dividend to ensure that the columns line up correctly.

$$
\begin{array}{r}
4x^2 + 2x \\
2x^2 - x + 2 \overline{)8x^4 + 0x^3 + 6x^2 - 3x + 1} \\
\underline{8x^4 - 4x^3 + 8x^2} \\
4x^3 - 2x^2 - 3x \\
\underline{4x^3 - 2x^2 + 4x} \\
-7x + 1
\end{array}
$$

Multiply divisor by $4x^2$
Subtract
Multiply divisor by $2x$
Subtract

The process is complete at this point because $-7x + 1$ is of lesser degree than the divisor $2x^2 - x + 2$. From the above long division we see that $Q(x) = 4x^2 + 2x$ and $R(x) = -7x + 1$, so

$$8x^4 + 6x^2 - 3x + 1 = (2x^2 - x + 2)(4x^2 + 2x) + (-7x + 1)$$

NOW TRY EXERCISE 19

▼ Synthetic Division

Synthetic division is a quick method of dividing polynomials; it can be used when the divisor is of the form $x - c$. In synthetic division we write only the essential parts of the long division. Compare the following long and synthetic divisions, in which we divide $2x^3 - 7x^2 + 5$ by $x - 3$. (We'll explain how to perform the synthetic division in Example 3.)

Long Division

$$
\begin{array}{r}
2x^2 - x - 3 \\
x - 3 \overline{)2x^3 - 7x^2 + 0x + 5} \\
\underline{2x^3 - 6x^2} \\
-x^2 + 0x \\
\underline{-x^2 + 3x} \\
-3x + 5 \\
\underline{-3x + 9} \\
-4
\end{array}
$$

Quotient

Remainder

Synthetic Division

$$
\begin{array}{r|rrrr}
3 & 2 & -7 & 0 & 5 \\
& & 6 & -3 & -9 \\
\hline
& 2 & -1 & -3 & -4
\end{array}
$$

Quotient   Remainder

Note that in synthetic division we abbreviate $2x^3 - 7x^2 + 5$ by writing only the coefficients: 2 −7 0 5, and instead of $x - 3$, we simply write 3. (Writing 3 instead of −3 allows us to add instead of subtract, but this changes the sign of all the numbers that appear in the gold boxes.)

The next example shows how synthetic division is performed.

EXAMPLE 3 | Synthetic Division

Use synthetic division to divide $2x^3 - 7x^2 + 5$ by $x - 3$.

SOLUTION We begin by writing the appropriate coefficients to represent the divisor and the dividend.

Divisor $x - 3$

$$
\begin{array}{r|rrrr}
3 & 2 & -7 & 0 & 5
\end{array}
$$

Dividend
$2x^3 - 7x^2 + 0x + 5$

We bring down the 2, multiply $3 \cdot 2 = 6$, and write the result in the middle row. Then we add.

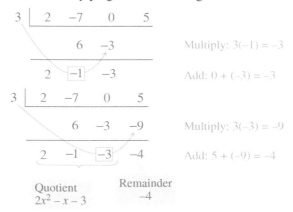

$$\begin{array}{r|rrrr} 3 & 2 & -7 & 0 & 5 \\ & & 6 & & \\ \hline & 2 & -1 & & \end{array}$$

Multiply: $3 \cdot 2 = 6$

Add: $-7 + 6 = -1$

We repeat this process of multiplying and then adding until the table is complete.

$$\begin{array}{r|rrrr} 3 & 2 & -7 & 0 & 5 \\ & & 6 & -3 & \\ \hline & 2 & -1 & -3 & \end{array}$$

Multiply: $3(-1) = -3$

Add: $0 + (-3) = -3$

$$\begin{array}{r|rrrr} 3 & 2 & -7 & 0 & 5 \\ & & 6 & -3 & -9 \\ \hline & 2 & -1 & -3 & -4 \end{array}$$

Multiply: $3(-3) = -9$

Add: $5 + (-9) = -4$

Quotient   Remainder
$2x^2 - x - 3$ -4

From the last line of the synthetic division we see that the quotient is $2x^2 - x - 3$ and the remainder is -4. Thus

$$2x^3 - 7x^2 + 5 = (x - 3)(2x^2 - x - 3) - 4$$

✹ . NOW TRY EXERCISE **31**

▼ The Remainder and Factor Theorems

The next theorem shows how synthetic division can be used to evaluate polynomials easily.

REMAINDER THEOREM

If the polynomial $P(x)$ is divided by $x - c$, then the remainder is the value $P(c)$.

PROOF If the divisor in the Division Algorithm is of the form $x - c$ for some real number c, then the remainder must be a constant (since the degree of the remainder is less than the degree of the divisor). If we call this constant r, then

$$P(x) = (x - c) \cdot Q(x) + r$$

Replacing x by c in this equation, we get $P(c) = (c - c) \cdot Q(x) + r = 0 + r = r$, that is, $P(c)$ is the remainder r. ∎

EXAMPLE 4 | Using the Remainder Theorem to Find the Value of a Polynomial

Let $P(x) = 3x^5 + 5x^4 - 4x^3 + 7x + 3$.

(a) Find the quotient and remainder when $P(x)$ is divided by $x + 2$.

(b) Use the Remainder Theorem to find $P(-2)$.

SOLUTION

(a) Since $x + 2 = x - (-2)$, the synthetic division for this problem takes the following form.

$$
\begin{array}{r|rrrrrr}
-2 & 3 & 5 & -4 & 0 & 7 & 3 \\
   &   & -6 & 2 & 4 & -8 & 2 \\
\hline
   & 3 & -1 & -2 & 4 & -1 & 5
\end{array}
$$

Remainder is 5, so $P(-2) = 5$

The quotient is $3x^4 - x^3 - 2x^2 + 4x - 1$, and the remainder is 5.

(b) By the Remainder Theorem, $P(-2)$ is the remainder when $P(x)$ is divided by $x - (-2) = x + 2$. From part (a) the remainder is 5, so $P(-2) = 5$.

✎. NOW TRY EXERCISE **39**   ◾

The next theorem says that *zeros* of polynomials correspond to *factors*; we used this fact in Section 3.2 to graph polynomials.

FACTOR THEOREM

c is a zero of P if and only if $x - c$ is a factor of $P(x)$.

PROOF   If $P(x)$ factors as $P(x) = (x - c) \cdot Q(x)$, then

$$P(c) = (c - c) \cdot Q(c) = 0 \cdot Q(c) = 0$$

Conversely, if $P(c) = 0$, then by the Remainder Theorem

$$P(x) = (x - c) \cdot Q(x) + 0 = (x - c) \cdot Q(x)$$

so $x - c$ is a factor of $P(x)$.   ◾

EXAMPLE 5 | Factoring a Polynomial Using the Factor Theorem

Let $P(x) = x^3 - 7x + 6$. Show that $P(1) = 0$, and use this fact to factor $P(x)$ completely.

$$
\begin{array}{r|rrrr}
1 & 1 & 0 & -7 & 6 \\
  &   & 1 & 1 & -6 \\
\hline
  & 1 & 1 & -6 & 0
\end{array}
$$

$$
\begin{array}{r}
x^2 + x - 6 \\
x - 1 \overline{)\, x^3 + 0x^2 - 7x + 6} \\
\underline{x^3 - x^2} \\
x^2 - 7x \\
\underline{x^2 - x} \\
-6x + 6 \\
\underline{-6x + 6} \\
0
\end{array}
$$

SOLUTION   Substituting, we see that $P(1) = 1^3 - 7 \cdot 1 + 6 = 0$. By the Factor Theorem this means that $x - 1$ is a factor of $P(x)$. Using synthetic or long division (shown in the margin), we see that

$$
\begin{aligned}
P(x) &= x^3 - 7x + 6 && \text{Given polynomial} \\
&= (x - 1)(x^2 + x - 6) && \text{See margin} \\
&= (x - 1)(x - 2)(x + 3) && \text{Factor quadratic } x^2 + x - 6
\end{aligned}
$$

✎. NOW TRY EXERCISES **53** AND **57**   ◾

EXAMPLE 6 | Finding a Polynomial with Specified Zeros

Find a polynomial of degree 4 that has zeros $-3, 0, 1,$ and 5.

SOLUTION   By the Factor Theorem $x - (-3)$, $x - 0$, $x - 1$, and $x - 5$ must all be factors of the desired polynomial.

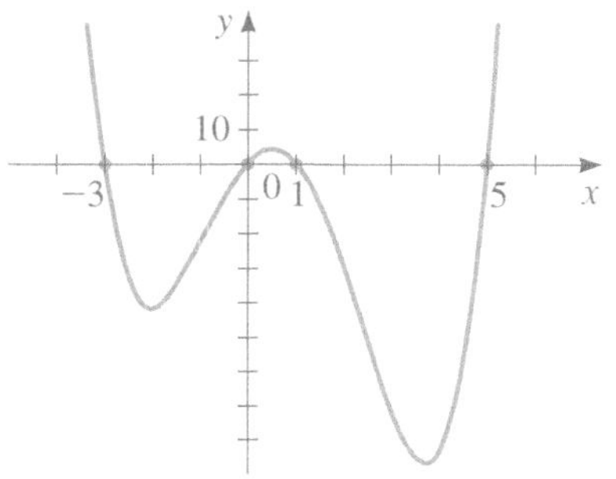

Let

$$P(x) = (x + 3)(x - 0)(x - 1)(x - 5)$$
$$= x^4 - 3x^3 - 13x^2 + 15x$$

Since $P(x)$ is of degree 4, it is a solution of the problem. Any other solution of the problem must be a constant multiple of $P(x)$, since only multiplication by a constant does not change the degree.

✎ NOW TRY EXERCISE **59**

FIGURE 1
$P(x) = (x + 3)x(x - 1)(x - 5)$ has zeros $-3, 0, 1$, and 5.

The polynomial P of Example 6 is graphed in Figure 1. Note that the zeros of P correspond to the x-intercepts of the graph.

3.3 EXERCISES

CONCEPTS

1. If we divide the polynomial P by the factor $x - c$ and we obtain the equation $P(x) = (x - c)Q(x) + R(x)$, then we say that $x - c$ is the divisor, $Q(x)$ is the _____, and $R(x)$ is the

_____.

2. (a) If we divide the polynomial $P(x)$ by the factor $x - c$ and we obtain a remainder of 0, then we know that c is a

_____ of P.

(b) If we divide the polynomial $P(x)$ by the factor $x - c$ and we obtain a remainder of k, then we know that

$P(c) =$ _____.

SKILLS

3–8 ■ Two polynomials P and D are given. Use either synthetic or long division to divide $P(x)$ by $D(x)$, and express P in the form $P(x) = D(x) \cdot Q(x) + R(x)$.

3. $P(x) = 3x^2 + 5x - 4, \quad D(x) = x + 3$

4. $P(x) = x^3 + 4x^2 - 6x + 1, \quad D(x) = x - 1$

5. $P(x) = 2x^3 - 3x^2 - 2x, \quad D(x) = 2x - 3$

6. $P(x) = 4x^3 + 7x + 9, \quad D(x) = 2x + 1$

7. $P(x) = x^4 - x^3 + 4x + 2, \quad D(x) = x^2 + 3$

8. $P(x) = 2x^5 + 4x^4 - 4x^3 - x - 3, \quad D(x) = x^2 - 2$

9–14 ■ Two polynomials P and D are given. Use either synthetic or long division to divide $P(x)$ by $D(x)$, and express the quotient $P(x)/D(x)$ in the form

$$\frac{P(x)}{D(x)} = Q(x) + \frac{R(x)}{D(x)}$$

9. $P(x) = x^2 + 4x - 8, \quad D(x) = x + 3$

10. $P(x) = x^3 + 6x + 5, \quad D(x) = x - 4$

11. $P(x) = 4x^2 - 3x - 7, \quad D(x) = 2x - 1$

12. $P(x) = 6x^3 + x^2 - 12x + 5, \quad D(x) = 3x - 4$

13. $P(x) = 2x^4 - x^3 + 9x^2, \quad D(x) = x^2 + 4$

14. $P(x) = x^5 + x^4 - 2x^3 + x + 1, \quad D(x) = x^2 + x - 1$

15–24 ■ Find the quotient and remainder using long division.

15. $\dfrac{x^2 - 6x - 8}{x - 4}$

16. $\dfrac{x^3 - x^2 - 2x + 6}{x - 2}$

17. $\dfrac{4x^3 + 2x^2 - 2x - 3}{2x + 1}$

18. $\dfrac{x^3 + 3x^2 + 4x + 3}{3x + 6}$

19. $\dfrac{x^3 + 6x + 3}{x^2 - 2x + 2}$

20. $\dfrac{3x^4 - 5x^3 - 20x - 5}{x^2 + x + 3}$

21. $\dfrac{6x^3 + 2x^2 + 22x}{2x^2 + 5}$

22. $\dfrac{9x^2 - x + 5}{3x^2 - 7x}$

23. $\dfrac{x^6 + x^4 + x^2 + 1}{x^2 + 1}$

24. $\dfrac{2x^5 - 7x^4 - 13}{4x^2 - 6x + 8}$

25–38 ■ Find the quotient and remainder using synthetic division.

25. $\dfrac{x^2 - 5x + 4}{x - 3}$

26. $\dfrac{x^2 - 5x + 4}{x - 1}$

27. $\dfrac{3x^2 + 5x}{x - 6}$

28. $\dfrac{4x^2 - 3}{x + 5}$

29. $\dfrac{x^3 + 2x^2 + 2x + 1}{x + 2}$

30. $\dfrac{3x^3 - 12x^2 - 9x + 1}{x - 5}$

31. $\dfrac{x^3 - 8x + 2}{x + 3}$

32. $\dfrac{x^4 - x^3 + x^2 - x + 2}{x - 2}$

33. $\dfrac{x^5 + 3x^3 - 6}{x - 1}$

34. $\dfrac{x^3 - 9x^2 + 27x - 27}{x - 3}$

35. $\dfrac{2x^3 + 3x^2 - 2x + 1}{x - \frac{1}{2}}$

36. $\dfrac{6x^4 + 10x^3 + 5x^2 + x + 1}{x + \frac{2}{3}}$

37. $\dfrac{x^3 - 27}{x - 3}$ **38.** $\dfrac{x^4 - 16}{x + 2}$

39–51 ■ Use synthetic division and the Remainder Theorem to evaluate $P(c)$.

39. $P(x) = 4x^2 + 12x + 5, \quad c = -1$

40. $P(x) = 2x^2 + 9x + 1, \quad c = \frac{1}{2}$

41. $P(x) = x^3 + 3x^2 - 7x + 6, \quad c = 2$

42. $P(x) = x^3 - x^2 + x + 5, \quad c = -1$

43. $P(x) = x^3 + 2x^2 - 7, \quad c = -2$

44. $P(x) = 2x^3 - 21x^2 + 9x - 200, \quad c = 11$

45. $P(x) = 5x^4 + 30x^3 - 40x^2 + 36x + 14, \quad c = -7$

46. $P(x) = 6x^5 + 10x^3 + x + 1, \quad c = -2$

47. $P(x) = x^7 - 3x^2 - 1, \quad c = 3$

48. $P(x) = -2x^6 + 7x^5 + 40x^4 - 7x^2 + 10x + 112, \quad c = -3$

49. $P(x) = 3x^3 + 4x^2 - 2x + 1, \quad c = \frac{2}{3}$

50. $P(x) = x^3 - x + 1, \quad c = \frac{1}{4}$

51. $P(x) = x^3 + 2x^2 - 3x - 8, \quad c = 0.1$

52. Let

$$P(x) = 6x^7 - 40x^6 + 16x^5 - 200x^4$$
$$- 60x^3 - 69x^2 + 13x - 139$$

Calculate $P(7)$ by **(a)** using synthetic division and **(b)** substituting $x = 7$ into the polynomial and evaluating directly.

53–56 ■ Use the Factor Theorem to show that $x - c$ is a factor of $P(x)$ for the given value(s) of c.

53. $P(x) = x^3 - 3x^2 + 3x - 1, \quad c = 1$

54. $P(x) = x^3 + 2x^2 - 3x - 10, \quad c = 2$

55. $P(x) = 2x^3 + 7x^2 + 6x - 5, \quad c = \frac{1}{2}$

56. $P(x) = x^4 + 3x^3 - 16x^2 - 27x + 63, \quad c = 3, -3$

57–58 ■ Show that the given value(s) of c are zeros of $P(x)$, and find all other zeros of $P(x)$.

57. $P(x) = x^3 - x^2 - 11x + 15, \quad c = 3$

58. $P(x) = 3x^4 - x^3 - 21x^2 - 11x + 6, \quad c = \frac{1}{3}, -2$

59–62 ■ Find a polynomial of the specified degree that has the given zeros.

59. Degree 3; zeros $-1, 1, 3$

60. Degree 4; zeros $-2, 0, 2, 4$

61. Degree 4; zeros $-1, 1, 3, 5$

62. Degree 5; zeros $-2, -1, 0, 1, 2$

63. Find a polynomial of degree 3 that has zeros 1, -2, and 3 and in which the coefficient of x^2 is 3.

64. Find a polynomial of degree 4 that has integer coefficients and zeros 1, -1, 2, and $\frac{1}{2}$.

65–68 ■ Find the polynomial of the specified degree whose graph is shown.

65. Degree 3

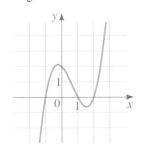

66. Degree 3

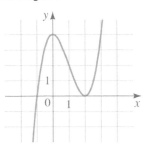

67. Degree 4

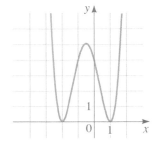

68. Degree 4

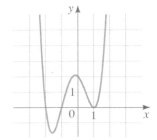

DISCOVERY ■ DISCUSSION ■ WRITING

69. Impossible Division? Suppose you were asked to solve the following two problems on a test:

A. Find the remainder when $6x^{1000} - 17x^{562} + 12x + 26$ is divided by $x + 1$.

B. Is $x - 1$ a factor of $x^{567} - 3x^{400} + x^9 + 2$?

Obviously, it's impossible to solve these problems by dividing, because the polynomials are of such large degree. Use one or more of the theorems in this section to solve these problems *without* actually dividing.

70. Nested Form of a Polynomial Expand Q to prove that the polynomials P and Q are the same.

$$P(x) = 3x^4 - 5x^3 + x^2 - 3x + 5$$
$$Q(x) = (((3x - 5)x + 1)x - 3)x + 5$$

Try to evaluate $P(2)$ and $Q(2)$ in your head, using the forms given. Which is easier? Now write the polynomial $R(x) = x^5 - 2x^4 + 3x^3 - 2x^2 + 3x + 4$ in "nested" form, like the polynomial Q. Use the nested form to find $R(3)$ in your head.

Do you see how calculating with the nested form follows the same arithmetic steps as calculating the value of a polynomial using synthetic division?

3.4 REAL ZEROS OF POLYNOMIALS

Rational Zeros of Polynomials ▶ Descartes' Rule of Signs and Upper and Lower Bounds for Roots ▶ Using Algebra and Graphing Devices to Solve Polynomial Equations

The Factor Theorem tells us that finding the zeros of a polynomial is really the same thing as factoring it into linear factors. In this section we study some algebraic methods that help us to find the real zeros of a polynomial and thereby factor the polynomial. We begin with the *rational* zeros of a polynomial.

▼ Rational Zeros of Polynomials

To help us understand the next theorem, let's consider the polynomial

$$P(x) = (x - 2)(x - 3)(x + 4) \qquad \text{Factored form}$$
$$= x^3 - x^2 - 14x + 24 \qquad \text{Expanded form}$$

From the factored form we see that the zeros of P are 2, 3, and -4. When the polynomial is expanded, the constant 24 is obtained by multiplying $(-2) \times (-3) \times 4$. This means that the zeros of the polynomial are all factors of the constant term. The following generalizes this observation.

RATIONAL ZEROS THEOREM

If the polynomial $P(x) = a_n x^n + a_{n-1}x^{n-1} + \cdots + a_1 x + a_0$ has integer coefficients, then every rational zero of P is of the form

$$\frac{p}{q}$$

where p is a factor of the constant coefficient a_0
and q is a factor of the leading coefficient a_n.

PROOF   If p/q is a rational zero, in lowest terms, of the polynomial P, then we have

$$a_n\left(\frac{p}{q}\right)^n + a_{n-1}\left(\frac{p}{q}\right)^{n-1} + \cdots + a_1\left(\frac{p}{q}\right) + a_0 = 0$$

$$a_n p^n + a_{n-1}p^{n-1}q + \cdots + a_1 pq^{n-1} + a_0 q^n = 0 \qquad \text{Multiply by } q^n$$

$$p(a_n p^{n-1} + a_{n-1}p^{n-2}q + \cdots + a_1 q^{n-1}) = -a_0 q^n \qquad \begin{array}{l}\text{Subtract } a_0 q^n \\ \text{and factor LHS}\end{array}$$

Now p is a factor of the left side, so it must be a factor of the right side as well. Since p/q is in lowest terms, p and q have no factor in common, so p must be a factor of a_0. A similar proof shows that q is a factor of a_n. ∎

We see from the Rational Zeros Theorem that if the leading coefficient is 1 or -1, then the rational zeros must be factors of the constant term.

EXAMPLE 1 | Using the Rational Zeros Theorem

Find the rational zeros of $P(x) = x^3 - 3x + 2$.

EVARISTE GALOIS (1811–1832) is one of the very few mathematicians to have an entire theory named in his honor. Not yet 21 when he died, he completely settled the central problem in the theory of equations by describing a criterion that reveals whether a polynomial equation can be solved by algebraic operations. Galois was one of the greatest mathematicians in the world at that time, although no one knew it but him. He repeatedly sent his work to the eminent mathematicians Cauchy and Poisson, who either lost his letters or did not understand his ideas. Galois wrote in a terse style and included few details, which probably played a role in his failure to pass the entrance exams at the Ecole Polytechnique in Paris. A political radical, Galois spent several months in prison for his revolutionary activities. His brief life came to a tragic end when he was killed in a duel over a love affair. The night before his duel, fearing that he would die, Galois wrote down the essence of his ideas and entrusted them to his friend Auguste Chevalier. He concluded by writing "there will, I hope, be people who will find it to their advantage to decipher all this mess." The mathematician Camille Jordan did just that, 14 years later.

SOLUTION   Since the leading coefficient is 1, any rational zero must be a divisor of the constant term 2. So the possible rational zeros are ± 1 and ± 2. We test each of these possibilities.

$$P(1) = (1)^3 - 3(1) + 2 = 0$$

$$P(-1) = (-1)^3 - 3(-1) + 2 = 4$$

$$P(2) = (2)^3 - 3(2) + 2 = 4$$

$$P(-2) = (-2)^3 - 3(-2) + 2 = 0$$

The rational zeros of P are 1 and -2.

✎. NOW TRY EXERCISE **15**

The following box explains how we use the Rational Zeros Theorem with synthetic division to factor a polynomial.

FINDING THE RATIONAL ZEROS OF A POLYNOMIAL

1. **List Possible Zeros.**   List all possible rational zeros, using the Rational Zeros Theorem.

2. **Divide.**   Use synthetic division to evaluate the polynomial at each of the candidates for the rational zeros that you found in Step 1. When the remainder is 0, note the quotient you have obtained.

3. **Repeat.**   Repeat Steps 1 and 2 for the quotient. Stop when you reach a quotient that is quadratic or factors easily, and use the quadratic formula or factor to find the remaining zeros.

EXAMPLE 2 | Finding Rational Zeros

Factor the polynomial $P(x) = 2x^3 + x^2 - 13x + 6$, and find all its zeros.

SOLUTION   By the Rational Zeros Theorem the rational zeros of P are of the form

$$\text{possible rational zero of } P = \frac{\text{factor of constant term}}{\text{factor of leading coefficient}}$$

The constant term is 6 and the leading coefficient is 2, so

$$\text{possible rational zero of } P = \frac{\text{factor of 6}}{\text{factor of 2}}$$

The factors of 6 are ± 1, ± 2, ± 3, ± 6, and the factors of 2 are ± 1, ± 2. Thus, the possible rational zeros of P are

$$\pm \frac{1}{1}, \quad \pm \frac{2}{1}, \quad \pm \frac{3}{1}, \quad \pm \frac{6}{1}, \quad \pm \frac{1}{2}, \quad \pm \frac{2}{2}, \quad \pm \frac{3}{2}, \quad \pm \frac{6}{2}$$

Simplifying the fractions and eliminating duplicates, we get the following list of possible rational zeros:

$$\pm 1, \quad \pm 2, \quad \pm 3, \quad \pm 6, \quad \pm \frac{1}{2}, \quad \pm \frac{3}{2}$$

To check which of these *possible* zeros actually *are* zeros, we need to evaluate P at each of these numbers. An efficient way to do this is to use synthetic division.

Test whether 1 is a zero

$$
\begin{array}{r|rrrr}
1 & 2 & 1 & -13 & 6 \\
  &   & 2 & 3 & -10 \\
\hline
  & 2 & 3 & -10 & -4
\end{array}
$$

Remainder is *not* 0, so 1 is *not* a zero

Test whether 2 is a zero

$$
\begin{array}{r|rrrr}
2 & 2 & 1 & -13 & 6 \\
  &   & 4 & 10 & -6 \\
\hline
  & 2 & 5 & -3 & 0
\end{array}
$$

Remainder *is* 0, so 2 *is* a zero

From the last synthetic division we see that 2 is a zero of P and that P factors as

$$
\begin{aligned}
P(x) &= 2x^3 + x^2 - 13x + 6 && \text{Given polynomial} \\
&= (x - 2)(2x^2 + 5x - 3) && \text{From synthetic division} \\
&= (x - 2)(2x - 1)(x + 3) && \text{Factor } 2x^2 + 5x - 3
\end{aligned}
$$

From the factored form we see that the zeros of P are 2, $\frac{1}{2}$, and –3.

▲ . NOW TRY EXERCISE **27**

EXAMPLE 3 | Using the Rational Zeros Theorem and the Quadratic Formula

Let $P(x) = x^4 - 5x^3 - 5x^2 + 23x + 10$.

(a) Find the zeros of P. **(b)** Sketch the graph of P.

SOLUTION

$$
\begin{array}{r|rrrrr}
1 & 1 & -5 & -5 & 23 & 10 \\
  &   & 1 & -4 & -9 & 14 \\
\hline
  & 1 & -4 & -9 & 14 & 24
\end{array}
$$

$$
\begin{array}{r|rrrrr}
2 & 1 & -5 & -5 & 23 & 10 \\
  &   & 2 & -6 & -22 & 2 \\
\hline
  & 1 & -3 & -11 & 1 & 12
\end{array}
$$

$$
\begin{array}{r|rrrrr}
5 & 1 & -5 & -5 & 23 & 10 \\
  &   & 5 & 0 & -25 & -10 \\
\hline
  & 1 & 0 & -5 & -2 & 0
\end{array}
$$

$$
\begin{array}{r|rrrr}
-2 & 1 & 0 & -5 & -2 \\
   &   & -2 & 4 & 2 \\
\hline
   & 1 & -2 & -1 & 0
\end{array}
$$

(a) The leading coefficient of P is 1, so all the rational zeros are integers: They are divisors of the constant term 10. Thus, the possible candidates are

$$\pm 1, \quad \pm 2, \quad \pm 5, \quad \pm 10$$

Using synthetic division (see the margin), we find that 1 and 2 are not zeros but that 5 is a zero and that P factors as

$$x^4 - 5x^3 - 5x^2 + 23x + 10 = (x - 5)(x^3 - 5x - 2)$$

We now try to factor the quotient $x^3 - 5x - 2$. Its possible zeros are the divisors of -2, namely,

$$\pm 1, \quad \pm 2$$

Since we already know that 1 and 2 are not zeros of the original polynomial P, we don't need to try them again. Checking the remaining candidates, -1 and -2, we see that -2 is a zero (see the margin), and P factors as

$$
\begin{aligned}
x^4 - 5x^3 - 5x^2 + 23x + 10 &= (x - 5)(x^3 - 5x - 2) \\
&= (x - 5)(x + 2)(x^2 - 2x - 1)
\end{aligned}
$$

Now we use the quadratic formula to obtain the two remaining zeros of P:

$$x = \frac{2 \pm \sqrt{(-2)^2 - 4(1)(-1)}}{2} = 1 \pm \sqrt{2}$$

The zeros of P are 5, -2, $1 + \sqrt{2}$, and $1 - \sqrt{2}$.

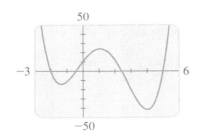

FIGURE 1

$P(x) = x^4 - 5x^3 - 5x^2 + 23x + 10$

(b) Now that we know the zeros of P, we can use the methods of Section 3.2 to sketch the graph. If we want to use a graphing calculator instead, knowing the zeros allows us to choose an appropriate viewing rectangle—one that is wide enough to contain all the x-intercepts of P. Numerical approximations to the zeros of P are

$$5, \quad -2, \quad 2.4, \quad \text{and} \quad -0.4$$

So in this case we choose the rectangle $[-3, 6]$ by $[-50, 50]$ and draw the graph shown in Figure 1.

✏. NOW TRY EXERCISES **47** AND **57**

▼ Descartes' Rule of Signs and Upper and Lower Bounds for Roots

In some cases, the following rule—discovered by the French philosopher and mathematician René Descartes around 1637 (see page 181)—is helpful in eliminating candidates from lengthy lists of possible rational roots. To describe this rule, we need the concept of *variation in sign*. If $P(x)$ is a polynomial with real coefficients, written with descending powers of x (and omitting powers with coefficient 0), then a **variation in sign** occurs whenever adjacent coefficients have opposite signs. For example,

$$P(x) = 5x^7 - 3x^5 - x^4 + 2x^2 + x - 3$$

has three variations in sign.

Polynomial	Variations in sign
$x^2 + 4x + 1$	0
$2x^3 + x - 6$	1
$x^4 - 3x^2 - x + 4$	2

DESCARTES' RULE OF SIGNS

Let P be a polynomial with real coefficients.

1. The number of positive real zeros of $P(x)$ either is equal to the number of variations in sign in $P(x)$ or is less than that by an even whole number.

2. The number of negative real zeros of $P(x)$ either is equal to the number of variations in sign in $P(-x)$ or is less than that by an even whole number.

EXAMPLE 4 | Using Descartes' Rule

Use Descartes' Rule of Signs to determine the possible number of positive and negative real zeros of the polynomial

$$P(x) = 3x^6 + 4x^5 + 3x^3 - x - 3$$

SOLUTION The polynomial has one variation in sign, so it has one positive zero. Now

$$P(-x) = 3(-x)^6 + 4(-x)^5 + 3(-x)^3 - (-x) - 3$$
$$= 3x^6 - 4x^5 - 3x^3 + x - 3$$

So $P(-x)$ has three variations in sign. Thus, $P(x)$ has either three or one negative zero(s), making a total of either two or four real zeros.

✏. NOW TRY EXERCISE **67**

We say that a is a **lower bound** and b is an **upper bound** for the zeros of a polynomial if every real zero c of the polynomial satisfies $a \le c \le b$. The next theorem helps us to find such bounds for the zeros of a polynomial.

> ### THE UPPER AND LOWER BOUNDS THEOREM
>
> Let P be a polynomial with real coefficients.
>
> **1.** If we divide $P(x)$ by $x - b$ (with $b > 0$) using synthetic division and if the row that contains the quotient and remainder has no negative entry, then b is an upper bound for the real zeros of P.
>
> **2.** If we divide $P(x)$ by $x - a$ (with $a < 0$) using synthetic division and if the row that contains the quotient and remainder has entries that are alternately nonpositive and nonnegative, then a is a lower bound for the real zeros of P.

A proof of this theorem is suggested in Exercise 97. The phrase "alternately nonpositive and nonnegative" simply means that the signs of the numbers alternate, with 0 considered to be positive or negative as required.

EXAMPLE 5 | Upper and Lower Bounds for Zeros of a Polynomial

Show that all the real zeros of the polynomial $P(x) = x^4 - 3x^2 + 2x - 5$ lie between -3 and 2.

SOLUTION   We divide $P(x)$ by $x - 2$ and $x + 3$ using synthetic division.

2	1	0	-3	2	-5
		2	4	2	8
	1	2	1	4	3

All entries positive

-3	1	0	-3	2	-5
		-3	9	-18	48
	1	-3	6	-16	43

Entries alternate in sign

By the Upper and Lower Bounds Theorem, -3 is a lower bound and 2 is an upper bound for the zeros. Since neither -3 nor 2 is a zero (the remainders are not 0 in the division table), all the real zeros lie between these numbers.

✎ . NOW TRY EXERCISE **71**

EXAMPLE 6 | Factoring a Fifth-Degree Polynomial

Factor completely the polynomial

$$P(x) = 2x^5 + 5x^4 - 8x^3 - 14x^2 + 6x + 9$$

SOLUTION   The possible rational zeros of P are $\pm\frac{1}{2}$, ± 1, $\pm\frac{3}{2}$, ± 3, $\pm\frac{9}{2}$, and ± 9. We check the positive candidates first, beginning with the smallest.

$\frac{1}{2}$	2	5	-8	-14	6	9
		1	3	$-\frac{5}{2}$	$-\frac{33}{4}$	$-\frac{9}{8}$
	2	6	-5	$-\frac{33}{2}$	$-\frac{9}{4}$	$\frac{63}{8}$

$\frac{1}{2}$ is not a zero

1	2	5	-8	-14	6	9
		2	7	-1	-15	-9
	2	7	-1	-15	-9	0

$P(1) = 0$

So 1 is a zero, and $P(x) = (x - 1)(2x^4 + 7x^3 - x^2 - 15x - 9)$. We continue by factoring the quotient. We still have the same list of possible zeros except that $\frac{1}{2}$ has been eliminated.

1	2	7	-1	-15	-9
		2	9	8	-7
	2	9	8	-7	-16

1 is not a zero

$\frac{3}{2}$	2	7	-1	-15	-9
		3	15	21	9
	2	10	14	6	0

$P\left(\frac{3}{2}\right) = 0$, all entries nonnegative

We see that $\frac{3}{2}$ is both a zero and an upper bound for the zeros of $P(x)$, so we do not need to check any further for positive zeros, because all the remaining candidates are greater than $\frac{3}{2}$.

$$P(x) = (x - 1)(x - \tfrac{3}{2})(2x^3 + 10x^2 + 14x + 6) \qquad \text{From synthetic division}$$

$$= (x - 1)(2x - 3)(x^3 + 5x^2 + 7x + 3) \qquad \begin{array}{l}\text{Factor 2 from last factor,}\\ \text{multiply into second factor}\end{array}$$

By Descartes' Rule of Signs, $x^3 + 5x^2 + 7x + 3$ has no positive zero, so its only possible rational zeros are -1 and -3.

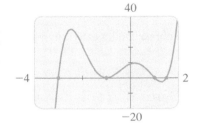

FIGURE 2

$P(x) = 2x^5 + 5x^4 - 8x^3 - 14x^2 + 6x + 9$

$\qquad = (x - 1)(2x - 3)(x + 1)^2(x + 3)$

$$\begin{array}{r|rrrr} -1 & 1 & 5 & 7 & 3 \\ & & -1 & -4 & -3 \\ \hline & 1 & 4 & 3 & 0 \end{array} \qquad P(-1) = 0$$

Therefore,

$$P(x) = (x - 1)(2x - 3)(x + 1)(x^2 + 4x + 3) \qquad \text{From synthetic division}$$

$$= (x - 1)(2x - 3)(x + 1)^2(x + 3) \qquad \text{Factor quadratic}$$

This means that the zeros of P are $1, \frac{3}{2}, -1,$ and -3. The graph of the polynomial is shown in Figure 2.

✎ NOW TRY EXERCISE **79**

▼ Using Algebra and Graphing Devices to Solve Polynomial Equations

In Section 1.9 we used graphing devices to solve equations graphically. We can now use the algebraic techniques that we've learned to select an appropriate viewing rectangle when solving a polynomial equation graphically.

EXAMPLE 7 | Solving a Fourth-Degree Equation Graphically

Find all real solutions of the following equation, rounded to the nearest tenth.

$$3x^4 + 4x^3 - 7x^2 - 2x - 3 = 0$$

SOLUTION To solve the equation graphically, we graph

$$P(x) = 3x^4 + 4x^3 - 7x^2 - 2x - 3$$

We use the Upper and Lower Bounds Theorem to see where the solutions can be found.

First we use the Upper and Lower Bounds Theorem to find two numbers between which all the solutions must lie. This allows us to choose a viewing rectangle that is certain to contain all the x-intercepts of P. We use synthetic division and proceed by trial and error.

To find an upper bound, we try the whole numbers, $1, 2, 3, \ldots,$ as potential candidates. We see that 2 is an upper bound for the solutions.

$$\begin{array}{r|rrrrr} 2 & 3 & 4 & -7 & -2 & -3 \\ & & 6 & 20 & 26 & 48 \\ \hline & 3 & 10 & 13 & 24 & 45 \end{array} \qquad \begin{array}{l}\text{All}\\ \text{positive}\end{array}$$

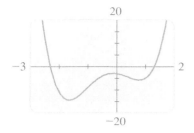

FIGURE 3

$y = 3x^4 + 4x^3 - 7x^2 - 2x - 3$

Now we look for a lower bound, trying the numbers -1, -2, and -3 as potential candidates. We see that -3 is a lower bound for the solutions.

$$
\begin{array}{r|rrrrr}
-3 & 3 & 4 & -7 & -2 & -3 \\
   &   & -9 & 15 & -24 & 78 \\
\hline
   & 3 & -5 & 8 & -26 & 75 \\
\end{array}
$$

Entries alternate in sign

Thus, all the solutions lie between -3 and 2. So the viewing rectangle $[-3, 2]$ by $[-20, 20]$ contains all the x-intercepts of P. The graph in Figure 3 has two x-intercepts, one between -3 and -2 and the other between 1 and 2. Zooming in, we find that the solutions of the equation, to the nearest tenth, are -2.3 and 1.3.

◆ . NOW TRY EXERCISE **93**

EXAMPLE 8 | Determining the Size of a Fuel Tank

A fuel tank consists of a cylindrical center section that is 4 ft long and two hemispherical end sections, as shown in Figure 4. If the tank has a volume of 100 ft^3, what is the radius r shown in the figure, rounded to the nearest hundredth of a foot?

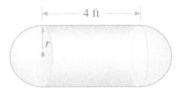

FIGURE 4

SOLUTION Using the volume formula listed on the inside back cover of this book, we see that the volume of the cylindrical section of the tank is

$$\pi \cdot r^2 \cdot 4$$

The two hemispherical parts together form a complete sphere whose volume is

$$\tfrac{4}{3}\pi r^3$$

Because the total volume of the tank is 100 ft^3, we get the following equation:

$$\tfrac{4}{3}\pi r^3 + 4\pi r^2 = 100$$

Volume of a cylinder: $V = \pi r^2 h$

Volume of a sphere: $V = \tfrac{4}{3}\pi r^3$

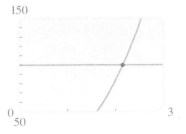

FIGURE 5

$y = \tfrac{4}{3}\pi x^3 + 4\pi x^2$ and $y = 100$

A negative solution for r would be meaningless in this physical situation, and by substitution we can verify that $r = 3$ leads to a tank that is over 226 ft^3 in volume, much larger than the required 100 ft^3. Thus, we know the correct radius lies somewhere between 0 and 3 ft, so we use a viewing rectangle of $[0, 3]$ by $[50, 150]$ to graph the function $y = \tfrac{4}{3}\pi x^3 + 4\pi x^2$, as shown in Figure 5. Since we want the value of this function to be 100, we also graph the horizontal line $y = 100$ in the same viewing rectangle. The correct radius will be the x-coordinate of the point of intersection of the curve and the line. Using the cursor and zooming in, we see that at the point of intersection $x \approx 2.15$, rounded to two decimal places. Thus the tank has a radius of about 2.15 ft.

◆ . NOW TRY EXERCISE **99**

Note that we also could have solved the equation in Example 8 by first writing it as

$$\tfrac{4}{3}\pi r^3 + 4\pi r^2 - 100 = 0$$

and then finding the x-intercept of the function $y = \tfrac{4}{3}\pi x^3 + 4\pi x^2 - 100$.

3.4 EXERCISES

CONCEPTS

1. If the polynomial function

$$P(x) = a_n x^n + a_{n-1}x^{n-1} + \cdots + a_1 x + a_0$$

has integer coefficients, then the only numbers that could possibly be rational zeros of P are all of the form $\dfrac{p}{q}$, where p is a factor of _____ and q is a factor of _____. The possible rational zeros of $P(x) = 6x^3 + 5x^2 - 19x - 10$ are

_____.

2. Using Descartes' Rule of Signs, we can tell that the polynomial $P(x) = x^5 - 3x^4 + 2x^3 - x^2 + 8x - 8$ has _____, _____, or _____ positive real zeros and _____ negative real zeros.

3. *True or false?* If c is a real zero of the polynomial P, then all the other zeros of P are zeros of $P(x)/(x - c)$.

4. *True or false?* If a is an upper bound for the real zeros of the polynomial P, then $-a$ is necessarily a lower bound for the real zeros of P.

SKILLS

5–10 ■ List all possible rational zeros given by the Rational Zeros Theorem (but don't check to see which actually are zeros).

5. $P(x) = x^3 - 4x^2 + 3$

6. $Q(x) = x^4 - 3x^3 - 6x + 8$

7. $R(x) = 2x^5 + 3x^3 + 4x^2 - 8$

8. $S(x) = 6x^4 - x^2 + 2x + 12$

9. $T(x) = 4x^4 - 2x^2 - 7$

10. $U(x) = 12x^5 + 6x^3 - 2x - 8$

11–14 ■ A polynomial function P and its graph are given. **(a)** List all possible rational zeros of P given by the Rational Zeros Theorem. **(b)** From the graph, determine which of the possible rational zeros actually turn out to be zeros.

11. $P(x) = 5x^3 - x^2 - 5x + 1$

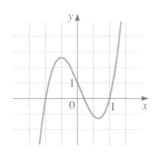

12. $P(x) = 3x^3 + 4x^2 - x - 2$

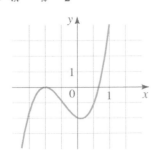

13. $P(x) = 2x^4 - 9x^3 + 9x^2 + x - 3$

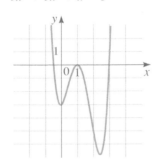

14. $P(x) = 4x^4 - x^3 - 4x + 1$

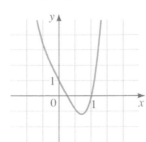

15–46 ■ Find all rational zeros of the polynomial, and write the polynomial in factored form.

15. $P(x) = x^3 + 3x^2 - 4$

16. $P(x) = x^3 - 7x^2 + 14x - 8$

17. $P(x) = x^3 - 3x - 2$

18. $P(x) = x^3 + 4x^2 - 3x - 18$

19. $P(x) = x^3 - 6x^2 + 12x - 8$

20. $P(x) = x^3 - x^2 - 8x + 12$

21. $P(x) = x^3 - 4x^2 + x + 6$

22. $P(x) = x^3 - 4x^2 - 7x + 10$

23. $P(x) = x^3 + 3x^2 - x - 3$

24. $P(x) = x^3 - 4x^2 - 11x + 30$

25. $P(x) = x^4 - 5x^2 + 4$

26. $P(x) = x^4 - 2x^3 - 3x^2 + 8x - 4$

27. $P(x) = x^4 + 6x^3 + 7x^2 - 6x - 8$

28. $P(x) = x^4 - x^3 - 23x^2 - 3x + 90$

29. $P(x) = 4x^4 - 25x^2 + 36$

30. $P(x) = 2x^4 - x^3 - 19x^2 + 9x + 9$

31. $P(x) = 3x^4 - 10x^3 - 9x^2 + 40x - 12$

32. $P(x) = 2x^3 + 7x^2 + 4x - 4$

33. $P(x) = 4x^3 + 4x^2 - x - 1$

34. $P(x) = 2x^3 - 3x^2 - 2x + 3$

35. $P(x) = 4x^3 - 7x + 3$

36. $P(x) = 8x^3 + 10x^2 - x - 3$

37. $P(x) = 4x^3 + 8x^2 - 11x - 15$

38. $P(x) = 6x^3 + 11x^2 - 3x - 2$

39. $P(x) = 20x^3 - 8x^2 - 5x + 2$

40. $P(x) = 12x^3 - 20x^2 + x + 3$

41. $P(x) = 2x^4 - 7x^3 + 3x^2 + 8x - 4$

42. $P(x) = 6x^4 - 7x^3 - 12x^2 + 3x + 2$

43. $P(x) = x^5 + 3x^4 - 9x^3 - 31x^2 + 36$

44. $P(x) = x^5 - 4x^4 - 3x^3 + 22x^2 - 4x - 24$

45. $P(x) = 3x^5 - 14x^4 - 14x^3 + 36x^2 + 43x + 10$

46. $P(x) = 2x^6 - 3x^5 - 13x^4 + 29x^3 - 27x^2 + 32x - 12$

47–56 ■ Find all the real zeros of the polynomial. Use the quadratic formula if necessary, as in Example 3(a).

47. $P(x) = x^3 + 4x^2 + 3x - 2$

48. $P(x) = x^3 - 5x^2 + 2x + 12$

49. $P(x) = x^4 - 6x^3 + 4x^2 + 15x + 4$

50. $P(x) = x^4 + 2x^3 - 2x^2 - 3x + 2$

51. $P(x) = x^4 - 7x^3 + 14x^2 - 3x - 9$

52. $P(x) = x^5 - 4x^4 - x^3 + 10x^2 + 2x - 4$

53. $P(x) = 4x^3 - 6x^2 + 1$

54. $P(x) = 3x^3 - 5x^2 - 8x - 2$

55. $P(x) = 2x^4 + 15x^3 + 17x^2 + 3x - 1$

56. $P(x) = 4x^5 - 18x^4 - 6x^3 + 91x^2 - 60x + 9$

57–64 ■ A polynomial P is given. (a) Find all the real zeros of P. (b) Sketch the graph of P.

57. $P(x) = x^3 - 3x^2 - 4x + 12$

58. $P(x) = -x^3 - 2x^2 + 5x + 6$

59. $P(x) = 2x^3 - 7x^2 + 4x + 4$

60. $P(x) = 3x^3 + 17x^2 + 21x - 9$

61. $P(x) = x^4 - 5x^3 + 6x^2 + 4x - 8$

62. $P(x) = -x^4 + 10x^2 + 8x - 8$

63. $P(x) = x^5 - x^4 - 5x^3 + x^2 + 8x + 4$

64. $P(x) = x^5 - x^4 - 6x^3 + 14x^2 - 11x + 3$

65–70 ■ Use Descartes' Rule of Signs to determine how many positive and how many negative real zeros the polynomial can have. Then determine the possible total number of real zeros.

65. $P(x) = x^3 - x^2 - x - 3$

66. $P(x) = 2x^3 - x^2 + 4x - 7$

67. $P(x) = 2x^6 + 5x^4 - x^3 - 5x - 1$

68. $P(x) = x^4 + x^3 + x^2 + x + 12$

69. $P(x) = x^5 + 4x^3 - x^2 + 6x$

70. $P(x) = x^8 - x^5 + x^4 - x^3 + x^2 - x + 1$

71–74 ■ Show that the given values for a and b are lower and upper bounds for the real zeros of the polynomial.

71. $P(x) = 2x^3 + 5x^2 + x - 2$; $a = -3, b = 1$

72. $P(x) = x^4 - 2x^3 - 9x^2 + 2x + 8$; $a = -3, b = 5$

73. $P(x) = 8x^3 + 10x^2 - 39x + 9$; $a = -3, b = 2$

74. $P(x) = 3x^4 - 17x^3 + 24x^2 - 9x + 1$; $a = 0, b = 6$

75–78 ■ Find integers that are upper and lower bounds for the real zeros of the polynomial.

75. $P(x) = x^3 - 3x^2 + 4$

76. $P(x) = 2x^3 - 3x^2 - 8x + 12$

77. $P(x) = x^4 - 2x^3 + x^2 - 9x + 2$

78. $P(x) = x^5 - x^4 + 1$

79–84 ■ Find all rational zeros of the polynomial, and then find the irrational zeros, if any. Whenever appropriate, use the Rational Zeros Theorem, the Upper and Lower Bounds Theorem, Descartes' Rule of Signs, the quadratic formula, or other factoring techniques.

79. $P(x) = 2x^4 + 3x^3 - 4x^2 - 3x + 2$

80. $P(x) = 2x^4 + 15x^3 + 31x^2 + 20x + 4$

81. $P(x) = 4x^4 - 21x^2 + 5$

82. $P(x) = 6x^4 - 7x^3 - 8x^2 + 5x$

83. $P(x) = x^5 - 7x^4 + 9x^3 + 23x^2 - 50x + 24$

84. $P(x) = 8x^5 - 14x^4 - 22x^3 + 57x^2 - 35x + 6$

85–88 ■ Show that the polynomial does not have any rational zeros.

85. $P(x) = x^3 - x - 2$

86. $P(x) = 2x^4 - x^3 + x + 2$

87. $P(x) = 3x^3 - x^2 - 6x + 12$

88. $P(x) = x^{50} - 5x^{25} + x^2 - 1$

89–92 ■ The real solutions of the given equation are rational. List all possible rational roots using the Rational Zeros Theorem, and then graph the polynomial in the given viewing rectangle to determine which values are actually solutions. (All solutions can be seen in the given viewing rectangle.)

89. $x^3 - 3x^2 - 4x + 12 = 0$; $[-4, 4]$ by $[-15, 15]$

90. $x^4 - 5x^2 + 4 = 0$; $[-4, 4]$ by $[-30, 30]$

91. $2x^4 - 5x^3 - 14x^2 + 5x + 12 = 0$; $[-2, 5]$ by $[-40, 40]$

92. $3x^3 + 8x^2 + 5x + 2 = 0$; $[-3, 3]$ by $[-10, 10]$

93–96 ■ Use a graphing device to find all real solutions of the equation, rounded to two decimal places.

93. $x^4 - x - 4 = 0$

94. $2x^3 - 8x^2 + 9x - 9 = 0$

95. $4.00x^4 + 4.00x^3 - 10.96x^2 - 5.88x + 9.09 = 0$

96. $x^5 + 2.00x^4 + 0.96x^3 + 5.00x^2 + 10.00x + 4.80 = 0$

97. Let $P(x)$ be a polynomial with real coefficients and let $b > 0$. Use the Division Algorithm to write

$$P(x) = (x - b) \cdot Q(x) + r$$

Suppose that $r \geq 0$ and that all the coefficients in $Q(x)$ are nonnegative. Let $z > b$.
(a) Show that $P(z) > 0$.
(b) Prove the first part of the Upper and Lower Bounds Theorem.
(c) Use the first part of the Upper and Lower Bounds Theorem to prove the second part. [*Hint:* Show that if $P(x)$ satisfies the second part of the theorem, then $P(-x)$ satisfies the first part.]

98. Show that the equation

$$x^5 - x^4 - x^3 - 5x^2 - 12x - 6 = 0$$

has exactly one rational root, and then prove that it must have either two or four irrational roots.

APPLICATIONS

99. Volume of a Silo A grain silo consists of a cylindrical main section and a hemispherical roof. If the total volume of the silo (including the part inside the roof section) is 15,000 ft³ and the cylindrical part is 30 ft tall, what is the radius of the silo, rounded to the nearest tenth of a foot?

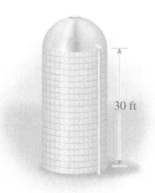

30 ft

100. Dimensions of a Lot A rectangular parcel of land has an area of 5000 ft². A diagonal between opposite corners is

measured to be 10 ft longer than one side of the parcel. What are the dimensions of the land, rounded to the nearest foot?

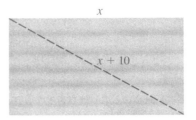

x

$x + 10$

101. Depth of Snowfall Snow began falling at noon on Sunday. The amount of snow on the ground at a certain location at time t was given by the function

$$h(t) = 11.60t - 12.41t^2 + 6.20t^3$$
$$- 1.58t^4 + 0.20t^5 - 0.01t^6$$

where t is measured in days from the start of the snowfall and $h(t)$ is the depth of snow in inches. Draw a graph of this function, and use your graph to answer the following questions.
(a) What happened shortly after noon on Tuesday?
(b) Was there ever more than 5 in. of snow on the ground? If so, on what day(s)?
(c) On what day and at what time (to the nearest hour) did the snow disappear completely?

102. Volume of a Box An open box with a volume of 1500 cm³ is to be constructed by taking a piece of cardboard 20 cm by 40 cm, cutting squares of side length x cm from each corner, and folding up the sides. Show that this can be done in two different ways, and find the exact dimensions of the box in each case.

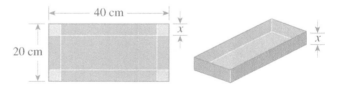

40 cm

20 cm

x

x

103. Volume of a Rocket A rocket consists of a right circular cylinder of height 20 m surmounted by a cone whose height and diameter are equal and whose radius is the same as that of the cylindrical section. What should this radius be (rounded to two decimal places) if the total volume is to be $500\pi/3$ m³?

20 m

104. Volume of a Box   A rectangular box with a volume of $2\sqrt{2}$ ft^3 has a square base as shown below. The diagonal of the box (between a pair of opposite corners) is 1 ft longer than each side of the base.

(a) If the base has sides of length x feet, show that

$$x^6 - 2x^5 - x^4 + 8 = 0$$

 (b) Show that two different boxes satisfy the given conditions. Find the dimensions in each case, rounded to the nearest hundredth of a foot.

105. Girth of a Box   A box with a square base has length plus girth of 108 in. (Girth is the distance "around" the box.) What is the length of the box if its volume is 2200 in^3?

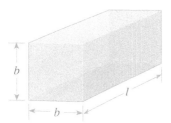

DISCOVERY ▪ DISCUSSION ▪ WRITING

106. How Many Real Zeros Can a Polynomial Have?
Give examples of polynomials that have the following properties, or explain why it is impossible to find such a polynomial.

(a) A polynomial of degree 3 that has no real zeros

(b) A polynomial of degree 4 that has no real zeros

(c) A polynomial of degree 3 that has three real zeros, only one of which is rational

(d) A polynomial of degree 4 that has four real zeros, none of which is rational

What must be true about the degree of a polynomial with integer coefficients if it has no real zeros?

107. The Depressed Cubic   The most general cubic (third-degree) equation with rational coefficients can be written as

$$x^3 + ax^2 + bx + c = 0$$

(a) Show that if we replace x by $X - a/3$ and simplify, we end up with an equation that doesn't have an X^2 term, that is, an equation of the form

$$X^3 + pX + q = 0$$

This is called a *depressed cubic*, because we have "depressed" the quadratic term.

(b) Use the procedure described in part (a) to depress the equation $x^3 + 6x^2 + 9x + 4 = 0$.

108. The Cubic Formula   The quadratic formula can be used to solve any quadratic (or second-degree) equation. You might have wondered whether similar formulas exist for cubic (third-degree), quartic (fourth-degree), and higher-degree equations. For the depressed cubic $x^3 + px + q = 0$, Cardano (page 274) found the following formula for one solution:

$$x = \sqrt[3]{-\frac{q}{2} + \sqrt{\frac{q^2}{4} + \frac{p^3}{27}}} + \sqrt[3]{-\frac{q}{2} - \sqrt{\frac{q^2}{4} + \frac{p^3}{27}}}$$

A formula for quartic equations was discovered by the Italian mathematician Ferrari in 1540. In 1824 the Norwegian mathematician Niels Henrik Abel proved that it is impossible to write a quintic formula, that is, a formula for fifth-degree equations. Finally, Galois (page 254) gave a criterion for determining which equations can be solved by a formula involving radicals.

Use the cubic formula to find a solution for the following equations. Then solve the equations using the methods you learned in this section. Which method is easier?

(a) $x^3 - 3x + 2 = 0$

(b) $x^3 - 27x - 54 = 0$

(c) $x^3 + 3x + 4 = 0$

DISCOVERY PROJECT   *Zeroing in on a Zero*

In this project we explore a numerical method for approximating the zeros of a polynomial function. You can find the project at the book companion website:
www.stewartmath.com

3.5 COMPLEX NUMBERS

Arithmetic Operations on Complex Numbers ▶ Square Roots of Negative Numbers ▶ Complex Solutions of Quadratic Equations

In Section 1.5 we saw that if the discriminant of a quadratic equation is negative, the equation has no real solution. For example, the equation

$$x^2 + 4 = 0$$

has no real solution. If we try to solve this equation, we get $x^2 = -4$, so

$$x = \pm\sqrt{-4}$$

But this is impossible, since the square of any real number is positive. [For example, $(-2)^2 = 4$, a positive number.] Thus, negative numbers don't have real square roots.

See the note on Cardano (page 274) for an example of how complex numbers are used to find real solutions of polynomial equations.

To make it possible to solve *all* quadratic equations, mathematicians invented an expanded number system, called the *complex number system*. First they defined the new number

$$i = \sqrt{-1}$$

This means that $i^2 = -1$. A complex number is then a number of the form $a + bi$, where a and b are real numbers.

DEFINITION OF COMPLEX NUMBERS

A **complex number** is an expression of the form

$$a + bi$$

where a and b are real numbers and $i^2 = -1$. The **real part** of this complex number is a and the **imaginary part** is b. Two complex numbers are **equal** if and only if their real parts are equal and their imaginary parts are equal.

Note that both the real and imaginary parts of a complex number are real numbers.

EXAMPLE 1 | Complex Numbers

The following are examples of complex numbers.

$3 + 4i$	Real part 3, imaginary part 4
$\frac{1}{2} - \frac{2}{3}i$	Real part $\frac{1}{2}$, imaginary part $-\frac{2}{3}$
$6i$	Real part 0, imaginary part 6
-7	Real part -7, imaginary part 0

✎ NOW TRY EXERCISES **5** AND **9**

A number such as $6i$, which has real part 0, is called a **pure imaginary number**. A real number such as -7 can be thought of as a complex number with imaginary part 0.

In the complex number system every quadratic equation has solutions. The numbers $2i$ and $-2i$ are solutions of $x^2 = -4$ because

$$(2i)^2 = 2^2i^2 = 4(-1) = -4 \qquad \text{and} \qquad (-2i)^2 = (-2)^2i^2 = 4(-1) = -4$$

Although we use the term *imaginary* in this context, imaginary numbers should not be thought of as any less "real" (in the ordinary rather than the mathematical sense of that word) than negative numbers or irrational numbers. All numbers (except possibly the positive integers) are creations of the human mind—the numbers -1 and $\sqrt{2}$ as well as the number i. We study complex numbers because they complete, in a useful and elegant fashion, our study of the solutions of equations. In fact, imaginary numbers are useful not only in algebra and mathematics, but in the other sciences as well. To give just one example, in electrical theory the *reactance* of a circuit is a quantity whose measure is an imaginary number.

▼ Arithmetic Operations on Complex Numbers

Complex numbers are added, subtracted, multiplied, and divided just as we would any number of the form $a + b\sqrt{c}$. The only difference that we need to keep in mind is that $i^2 = -1$. Thus, the following calculations are valid.

$$(a + bi)(c + di) = ac + (ad + bc)i + bdi^2 \qquad \text{Multiply and collect like terms}$$

$$= ac + (ad + bc)i + bd(-1) \qquad i^2 = -1$$

$$= (ac - bd) + (ad + bc)i \qquad \text{Combine real and imaginary parts}$$

We therefore define the sum, difference, and product of complex numbers as follows.

ADDING, SUBTRACTING, AND MULTIPLYING COMPLEX NUMBERS

Definition	Description
Addition	
$(a + bi) + (c + di) = (a + c) + (b + d)i$	To add complex numbers, add the real parts and the imaginary parts.
Subtraction	
$(a + bi) - (c + di) = (a - c) + (b - d)i$	To subtract complex numbers, subtract the real parts and the imaginary parts.
Multiplication	
$(a + bi) \cdot (c + di) = (ac - bd) + (ad + bc)i$	Multiply complex numbers like binomials, using $i^2 = -1$.

EXAMPLE 2 | **Adding, Subtracting, and Multiplying Complex Numbers**

Express the following in the form $a + bi$.

(a) $(3 + 5i) + (4 - 2i)$ **(b)** $(3 + 5i) - (4 - 2i)$

(c) $(3 + 5i)(4 - 2i)$ **(d)** i^{23}

SOLUTION

(a) According to the definition, we add the real parts and we add the imaginary parts.

$$(3 + 5i) + (4 - 2i) = (3 + 4) + (5 - 2)i = 7 + 3i$$

(b) $(3 + 5i) - (4 - 2i) = (3 - 4) + [5 - (-2)]i = -1 + 7i$

(c) $(3 + 5i)(4 - 2i) = [3 \cdot 4 - 5(-2)] + [3(-2) + 5 \cdot 4]i = 22 + 14i$

(d) $i^{23} = i^{22+1} = (i^2)^{11}i = (-1)^{11}i = (-1)i = -i$

✎. NOW TRY EXERCISES **15, 19, 25,** AND **33**

Graphing calculators can perform arithmetic operations on complex numbers.

```
(3+5i)+(4-2i)
              7+3i
(3+5i)*(4-2i)
             22+14i
```

Complex Conjugates

Number	Conjugate
$3 + 2i$	$3 - 2i$
$1 - i$	$1 + i$
$4i$	$-4i$
5	5

Division of complex numbers is much like rationalizing the denominator of a radical expression, which we considered in Section 1.4. For the complex number $z = a + bi$ we define its **complex conjugate** to be $\bar{z} = a - bi$. Note that

$$z \cdot \bar{z} = (a + bi)(a - bi) = a^2 + b^2$$

LEONHARD EULER (1707–1783) was born in Basel, Switzerland, the son of a pastor. When Euler was 13, his father sent him to the University at Basel to study theology, but Euler soon decided to devote himself to the sciences. Besides theology he studied mathematics, medicine, astronomy, physics, and Asian languages. It is said that Euler could calculate as effortlessly as "men breathe or as eagles fly." One hundred years before Euler, Fermat (see page 99) had conjectured that $2^{2^n} + 1$ is a prime number for all n. The first five of these numbers are 5, 17, 257, 65537, and 4,294,967,297. It is easy to show that the first four are prime. The fifth was also thought to be prime until Euler, with his phenomenal calculating ability, showed that it is the product $641 \times 6,700,417$ and so is not prime. Euler published more than any other mathematician in history. His collected works comprise 75 large volumes. Although he was blind for the last 17 years of his life, he continued to work and publish. In his writings he popularized the use of the symbols π, e, and i, which you will find in this textbook. One of Euler's most lasting contributions is his development of complex numbers.

So the product of a complex number and its conjugate is always a nonnegative real number. We use this property to divide complex numbers.

DIVIDING COMPLEX NUMBERS

To simplify the quotient $\dfrac{a + bi}{c + di}$, multiply the numerator and the denominator by the complex conjugate of the denominator:

$$\frac{a + bi}{c + di} = \left(\frac{a + bi}{c + di}\right)\left(\frac{c - di}{c - di}\right) = \frac{(ac + bd) + (bc - ad)i}{c^2 + d^2}$$

Rather than memorizing this entire formula, it is easier to just remember the first step and then multiply out the numerator and the denominator as usual.

EXAMPLE 3 | Dividing Complex Numbers

Express the following in the form $a + bi$.

(a) $\dfrac{3 + 5i}{1 - 2i}$ **(b)** $\dfrac{7 + 3i}{4i}$

SOLUTION We multiply both the numerator and denominator by the complex conjugate of the denominator to make the new denominator a real number.

(a) The complex conjugate of $1 - 2i$ is $\overline{1 - 2i} = 1 + 2i$.

$$\frac{3 + 5i}{1 - 2i} = \left(\frac{3 + 5i}{1 - 2i}\right)\left(\frac{1 + 2i}{1 + 2i}\right) = \frac{-7 + 11i}{5} = -\frac{7}{5} + \frac{11}{5}i$$

(b) The complex conjugate of $4i$ is $-4i$. Therefore,

$$\frac{7 + 3i}{4i} = \left(\frac{7 + 3i}{4i}\right)\left(\frac{-4i}{-4i}\right) = \frac{12 - 28i}{16} = \frac{3}{4} - \frac{7}{4}i$$

✎ NOW TRY EXERCISES **37** AND **43**

▼ Square Roots of Negative Numbers

Just as every positive real number r has two square roots ($\sqrt{r}$ and $-\sqrt{r}$), every negative number has two square roots as well. If $-r$ is a negative number, then its square roots are $\pm i\sqrt{r}$, because $(i\sqrt{r})^2 = i^2 r = -r$ and $(-i\sqrt{r})^2 = (-1)^2 i^2 r = -r$.

SQUARE ROOTS OF NEGATIVE NUMBERS

If $-r$ is negative, then the **principal square root** of $-r$ is

$$\sqrt{-r} = i\sqrt{r}$$

The two square roots of $-r$ are $i\sqrt{r}$ and $-i\sqrt{r}$.

We usually write $i\sqrt{b}$ instead of $\sqrt{b}\,i$ to avoid confusion with $\sqrt{bi}$.

EXAMPLE 4 | Square Roots of Negative Numbers

(a) $\sqrt{-1} = i\sqrt{1} = i$ **(b)** $\sqrt{-16} = i\sqrt{16} = 4i$ **(c)** $\sqrt{-3} = i\sqrt{3}$

✎ NOW TRY EXERCISES **47** AND **49**

Special care must be taken in performing calculations that involve square roots of negative numbers. Although $\sqrt{a} \cdot \sqrt{b} = \sqrt{ab}$ when a and b are positive, this is *not* true when both are negative. For example,

$$\sqrt{-2} \cdot \sqrt{-3} = i\sqrt{2} \cdot i\sqrt{3} = i^2\sqrt{6} = -\sqrt{6}$$

but

$$\sqrt{(-2)(-3)} = \sqrt{6}$$

so

$$\sqrt{-2} \cdot \sqrt{-3} \ne \sqrt{(-2)(-3)}$$

 When multiplying radicals of negative numbers, express them first in the form $i\sqrt{r}$ (where $r > 0$) to avoid possible errors of this type.

EXAMPLE 5 | Using Square Roots of Negative Numbers

Evaluate $(\sqrt{12} - \sqrt{-3})(3 + \sqrt{-4})$ and express in the form $a + bi$.

SOLUTION

$$
\begin{aligned}
(\sqrt{12} - \sqrt{-3})(3 + \sqrt{-4}) &= (\sqrt{12} - i\sqrt{3})(3 + i\sqrt{4}) \\
&= (2\sqrt{3} - i\sqrt{3})(3 + 2i) \\
&= (6\sqrt{3} + 2\sqrt{3}) + i(2 \cdot 2\sqrt{3} - 3\sqrt{3}) \\
&= 8\sqrt{3} + i\sqrt{3}
\end{aligned}
$$

. NOW TRY EXERCISE **51**

▼ Complex Solutions of Quadratic Equations

We have already seen that if $a \ne 0$, then the solutions of the quadratic equation $ax^2 + bx + c = 0$ are

$$x = \frac{-b \pm \sqrt{b^2 - 4ac}}{2a}$$

If $b^2 - 4ac < 0$, then the equation has no real solution. But in the complex number system, this equation will always have solutions, because negative numbers have square roots in this expanded setting.

EXAMPLE 6 | Quadratic Equations with Complex Solutions

Solve each equation.

(a) $x^2 + 9 = 0$ **(b)** $x^2 + 4x + 5 = 0$

SOLUTION

(a) The equation $x^2 + 9 = 0$ means $x^2 = -9$, so

$$x = \pm\sqrt{-9} = \pm i\sqrt{9} = \pm 3i$$

The solutions are therefore $3i$ and $-3i$.

(b) By the Quadratic Formula we have

$$
\begin{aligned}
x &= \frac{-4 \pm \sqrt{4^2 - 4 \cdot 5}}{2} \\
&= \frac{-4 \pm \sqrt{-4}}{2} \\
&= \frac{-4 \pm 2i}{2} = \frac{2(-2 \pm i)}{2} = -2 \pm i
\end{aligned}
$$

So the solutions are $-2 + i$ and $-2 - i$.

. NOW TRY EXERCISES **57** AND **59**

We see from Example 6 that if a quadratic equation with real coefficients has complex solutions, then these solutions are complex conjugates of each other. So if $a + bi$ is a solution, then $a - bi$ is also a solution.

EXAMPLE 7 | Complex Conjugates as Solutions of a Quadratic

Show that the solutions of the equation

$$4x^2 - 24x + 37 = 0$$

are complex conjugates of each other.

SOLUTION We use the Quadratic Formula to get

$$x = \frac{24 \pm \sqrt{(24)^2 - 4(4)(37)}}{2(4)}$$

$$= \frac{24 \pm \sqrt{-16}}{8} = \frac{24 \pm 4i}{8} = 3 \pm \frac{1}{2}i$$

So the solutions are $3 + \frac{1}{2}i$ and $3 - \frac{1}{2}i$, and these are complex conjugates.

✎. NOW TRY EXERCISE **65** ■

3.5 EXERCISES

CONCEPTS

1. The imaginary number i has the property that $i^2 =$ _____.

2. For the complex number $3 + 4i$ the real part is _____ and the imaginary part is _____.

3. (a) The complex conjugate of $3 + 4i$ is $\overline{3 + 4i} =$ _____.

   (b) $(3 + 4i)(\overline{3 + 4i}) =$ _____.

4. If $3 + 4i$ is a solution of a quadratic equation with real coefficients, then _____ is also a solution of the equation.

SKILLS

5–14 ■ Find the real and imaginary parts of the complex number.

5. $5 - 7i$

6. $-6 + 4i$

7. $\dfrac{-2 - 5i}{3}$

8. $\dfrac{4 + 7i}{2}$

9. 3

10. $-\frac{1}{2}$

11. $-\frac{2}{3}i$

12. $i\sqrt{3}$

13. $\sqrt{3} + \sqrt{-4}$

14. $2 - \sqrt{-5}$

15–46 ■ Evaluate the expression and write the result in the form $a + bi$.

15. $(2 - 5i) + (3 + 4i)$

16. $(2 + 5i) + (4 - 6i)$

17. $(-6 + 6i) + (9 - i)$

18. $(3 - 2i) + \left(-5 - \frac{1}{3}i\right)$

19. $\left(7 - \frac{1}{2}i\right) - \left(5 + \frac{3}{2}i\right)$

20. $(-4 + i) - (2 - 5i)$

21. $(-12 + 8i) - (7 + 4i)$

22. $6i - (4 - i)$

23. $4(-1 + 2i)$

24. $2i\left(\frac{1}{2} - i\right)$

25. $(7 - i)(4 + 2i)$

26. $(5 - 3i)(1 + i)$

27. $(3 - 4i)(5 - 12i)$

28. $\left(\frac{2}{3} + 12i\right)\left(\frac{1}{6} + 24i\right)$

29. $(6 + 5i)(2 - 3i)$

30. $(-2 + i)(3 - 7i)$

31. i^3

32. $(2i)^4$

33. i^{100}

34. i^{1002}

35. $\dfrac{1}{i}$

36. $\dfrac{1}{1 + i}$

37. $\dfrac{2 - 3i}{1 - 2i}$

38. $\dfrac{5 - i}{3 + 4i}$

39. $\dfrac{26 + 39i}{2 - 3i}$

40. $\dfrac{25}{4 - 3i}$

41. $\dfrac{10i}{1 - 2i}$

42. $(2 - 3i)^{-1}$

43. $\dfrac{4 + 6i}{3i}$

44. $\dfrac{-3 + 5i}{15i}$

45. $\dfrac{1}{1 + i} - \dfrac{1}{1 - i}$

46. $\dfrac{(1 + 2i)(3 - i)}{2 + i}$

47–56 ■ Evaluate the radical expression and express the result in the form $a + bi$.

47. $\sqrt{-25}$

48. $\sqrt{\dfrac{-9}{4}}$

49. $\sqrt{-3}\sqrt{-12}$

50. $\sqrt{\frac{1}{3}}\sqrt{-27}$

51. $(3 - \sqrt{-5})(1 + \sqrt{-1})$

52. $(\sqrt{3} - \sqrt{-4})(\sqrt{6} - \sqrt{-8})$

53. $\dfrac{2 + \sqrt{-8}}{1 + \sqrt{-2}}$

54. $\dfrac{1 - \sqrt{-1}}{1 + \sqrt{-1}}$

55. $\dfrac{\sqrt{-36}}{\sqrt{-2}\,\sqrt{-9}}$

56. $\dfrac{\sqrt{-7}\,\sqrt{-49}}{\sqrt{28}}$

57–72 ■ Find all solutions of the equation and express them in the form $a + bi$.

57. $x^2 + 49 = 0$

58. $9x^2 + 4 = 0$

59. $x^2 - 4x + 5 = 0$

60. $x^2 + 2x + 2 = 0$

61. $x^2 + 2x + 5 = 0$

62. $x^2 - 6x + 10 = 0$

63. $x^2 + x + 1 = 0$

64. $x^2 - 3x + 3 = 0$

65. $2x^2 - 2x + 1 = 0$

66. $2x^2 + 3 = 2x$

67. $t + 3 + \dfrac{3}{t} = 0$

68. $z + 4 + \dfrac{12}{z} = 0$

69. $6x^2 + 12x + 7 = 0$

70. $4x^2 - 16x + 19 = 0$

71. $\frac{1}{2}x^2 - x + 5 = 0$

72. $x^2 + \frac{1}{2}x + 1 = 0$

73–80 ■ Recall that the symbol $\bar{z}$ represents the complex conjugate of z. If $z = a + bi$ and $w = c + di$, prove each statement.

73. $\bar{z} + \bar{w} = \overline{z + w}$

74. $\overline{zw} = \bar{z} \cdot \bar{w}$

75. $(\bar{z})^2 = \overline{z^2}$

76. $\bar{\bar{z}} = z$

77. $z + \bar{z}$ is a real number.

78. $z - \bar{z}$ is a pure imaginary number.

79. $z \cdot \bar{z}$ is a real number.

80. $z = \bar{z}$ if and only if z is real.

DISCOVERY ■ DISCUSSION ■ WRITING

81. Complex Conjugate Roots Suppose that the equation $ax^2 + bx + c = 0$ has real coefficients and complex roots. Why must the roots be complex conjugates of each other? (Think about how you would find the roots using the Quadratic Formula.)

82. Powers of i Calculate the first 12 powers of i, that is, $i, i^2, i^3, \ldots, i^{12}$. Do you notice a pattern? Explain how you would calculate any whole number power of i, using the pattern that you have discovered. Use this procedure to calculate i^{4446}.

3.6 COMPLEX ZEROS AND THE FUNDAMENTAL THEOREM OF ALGEBRA

The Fundamental Theorem of Algebra and Complete Factorization ▶ Zeros and Their Multiplicities ▶ Complex Zeros Come in Conjugate Pairs ▶ Linear and Quadratic Factors

We have already seen that an nth-degree polynomial can have at most n real zeros. In the complex number system an nth-degree polynomial has exactly n zeros and so can be factored into exactly n linear factors. This fact is a consequence of the Fundamental Theorem of Algebra, which was proved by the German mathematician C. F. Gauss in 1799 (see page 272).

▼ The Fundamental Theorem of Algebra and Complete Factorization

The following theorem is the basis for much of our work in factoring polynomials and solving polynomial equations.

FUNDAMENTAL THEOREM OF ALGEBRA

Every polynomial

$$P(x) = a_n x^n + a_{n-1} x^{n-1} + \cdots + a_1 x + a_0 \qquad (n \geq 1, a_n \neq 0)$$

with complex coefficients has at least one complex zero.

Because any real number is also a complex number, the theorem applies to polynomials with real coefficients as well.

The Fundamental Theorem of Algebra and the Factor Theorem together show that a polynomial can be factored completely into linear factors, as we now prove.

COMPLETE FACTORIZATION THEOREM

If $P(x)$ is a polynomial of degree $n \geq 1$, then there exist complex numbers $a, c_1, c_2, \ldots, c_n$ (with $a \neq 0$) such that

$$P(x) = a(x - c_1)(x - c_2) \cdots (x - c_n)$$

PROOF   By the Fundamental Theorem of Algebra, P has at least one zero. Let's call it c_1. By the Factor Theorem (see page 250), $P(x)$ can be factored as

$$P(x) = (x - c_1) \cdot Q_1(x)$$

where $Q_1(x)$ is of degree $n - 1$. Applying the Fundamental Theorem to the quotient $Q_1(x)$ gives us the factorization

$$P(x) = (x - c_1) \cdot (x - c_2) \cdot Q_2(x)$$

where $Q_2(x)$ is of degree $n - 2$ and c_2 is a zero of $Q_1(x)$. Continuing this process for n steps, we get a final quotient $Q_n(x)$ of degree 0, a nonzero constant that we will call a. This means that P has been factored as

$$P(x) = a(x - c_1)(x - c_2) \cdots (x - c_n)$$
■

To actually find the complex zeros of an nth-degree polynomial, we usually first factor as much as possible, then use the quadratic formula on parts that we can't factor further.

EXAMPLE 1 | Factoring a Polynomial Completely

Let $P(x) = x^3 - 3x^2 + x - 3$.

(a) Find all the zeros of P.

(b) Find the complete factorization of P.

SOLUTION

(a) We first factor P as follows.

$$
\begin{aligned}
P(x) &= x^3 - 3x^2 + x - 3 && \text{Given} \\
&= x^2(x - 3) + (x - 3) && \text{Group terms} \\
&= (x - 3)(x^2 + 1) && \text{Factor } x - 3
\end{aligned}
$$

We find the zeros of P by setting each factor equal to 0:

$$P(x) = (x - 3)(x^2 + 1)$$

This factor is 0 when $x = 3$ This factor is 0 when $x = i$ or $-i$

Setting $x - 3 = 0$, we see that $x = 3$ is a zero. Setting $x^2 + 1 = 0$, we get $x^2 = -1$, so $x = \pm i$. So the zeros of P are 3, i, and $-i$.

(b) Since the zeros are 3, i, and $-i$, by the Complete Factorization Theorem P factors as

$$
\begin{aligned}
P(x) &= (x - 3)(x - i)[x - (-i)] \\
&= (x - 3)(x - i)(x + i)
\end{aligned}
$$

■ NOW TRY EXERCISE 5

EXAMPLE 2 | Factoring a Polynomial Completely

Let $P(x) = x^3 - 2x + 4$.

(a) Find all the zeros of P.

(b) Find the complete factorization of P.

SOLUTION

$$
\begin{array}{r|rrrr}
-2 & 1 & -0 & -2 & -4 \\
   &   & -2 & 4 & -4 \\
\hline
   & 1 & -2 & -2 & 0
\end{array}
$$

(a) The possible rational zeros are the factors of 4, which are ±1, ±2, ±4. Using synthetic division (see the margin), we find that -2 is a zero, and the polynomial factors as

$$P(x) = (x + 2)(x^2 - 2x + 2)$$

This factor is 0 when $x = -2$ Use the Quadratic Formula to find when this factor is 0

To find the zeros, we set each factor equal to 0. Of course, $x + 2 = 0$ means that $x = -2$. We use the quadratic formula to find when the other factor is 0.

$$x^2 - 2x + 2 = 0 \quad \text{Set factor equal to 0}$$

$$x = \frac{2 \pm \sqrt{4 - 8}}{2} \quad \text{Quadratic Formula}$$

$$x = \frac{2 \pm 2i}{2} \quad \text{Take square root}$$

$$x = 1 \pm i \quad \text{Simplify}$$

So the zeros of P are -2, $1 + i$, and $1 - i$.

(b) Since the zeros are -2, $1 + i$, and $1 - i$, by the Complete Factorization Theorem, P factors as

$$P(x) = [x - (-2)][x - (1 + i)][x - (1 - i)]$$
$$= (x + 2)(x - 1 - i)(x - 1 + i)$$

. NOW TRY EXERCISE 19

▼ Zeros and Their Multiplicities

In the Complete Factorization Theorem the numbers $c_1, c_2, \ldots, c_n$ are the zeros of P. These zeros need not all be different. If the factor $x - c$ appears k times in the complete factorization of $P(x)$, then we say that c is a zero of **multiplicity k** (see page 240). For example, the polynomial

$$P(x) = (x - 1)^3(x + 2)^2(x + 3)^5$$

has the following zeros:

$$1 \text{ (multiplicity 3)}, \qquad -2 \text{ (multiplicity 2)}, \qquad -3 \text{ (multiplicity 5)}$$

The polynomial P has the same number of zeros as its degree: It has degree 10 and has 10 zeros, provided that we count multiplicities. This is true for all polynomials, as we prove in the following theorem.

ZEROS THEOREM

Every polynomial of degree $n \geq 1$ has exactly n zeros, provided that a zero of multiplicity k is counted k times.

CARL FRIEDRICH GAUSS
(1777–1855) is considered the greatest mathematician of modern times. His contemporaries called him the "Prince of Mathematics." He was born into a poor family; his father made a living as a mason. As a very small child, Gauss found a calculation error in his father's accounts, the first of many incidents that gave evidence of his mathematical precocity. (See also page 796.) At 19, Gauss demonstrated that the regular 17-sided polygon can be constructed with straight-edge and compass alone. This was remarkable because, since the time of Euclid, it had been thought that the only regular polygons constructible in this way were the triangle and pentagon. Because of this discovery Gauss decided to pursue a career in mathematics instead of languages, his other passion. In his doctoral dissertation, written at the age of 22, Gauss proved the Fundamental Theorem of Algebra: A polynomial of degree n with complex coefficients has n roots. His other accomplishments range over every branch of mathematics, as well as physics and astronomy.

PROOF Let P be a polynomial of degree n. By the Complete Factorization Theorem

$$P(x) = a(x - c_1)(x - c_2) \cdots (x - c_n)$$

Now suppose that c is a zero of P other than $c_1, c_2, \ldots, c_n$. Then

$$P(c) = a(c - c_1)(c - c_2) \cdots (c - c_n) = 0$$

Thus, by the Zero-Product Property, one of the factors $c - c_i$ must be 0, so $c = c_i$ for some i. It follows that P has exactly the n zeros $c_1, c_2, \ldots, c_n$.

EXAMPLE 3 | Factoring a Polynomial with Complex Zeros

Find the complete factorization and all five zeros of the polynomial

$$P(x) = 3x^5 + 24x^3 + 48x$$

SOLUTION Since $3x$ is a common factor, we have

$$P(x) = 3x(x^4 + 8x^2 + 16)$$
$$= 3x(x^2 + 4)^2$$

This factor is 0 when $x = 0$	This factor is 0 when $x = 2i$ or $x = -2i$

To factor $x^2 + 4$, note that $2i$ and $-2i$ are zeros of this polynomial. Thus, $x^2 + 4 = (x - 2i)(x + 2i)$, so

$$P(x) = 3x[(x - 2i)(x + 2i)]^2$$
$$= 3x(x - 2i)^2(x + 2i)^2$$

0 is a zero of multiplicity 1	$2i$ is a zero of multiplicity 2	$-2i$ is a zero of multiplicity 2

The zeros of P are 0, $2i$, and $-2i$. Since the factors $x - 2i$ and $x + 2i$ each occur twice in the complete factorization of P, the zeros $2i$ and $-2i$ are of multiplicity 2 (or *double* zeros). Thus, we have found all five zeros.

◆. NOW TRY EXERCISE 29

The following table gives further examples of polynomials with their complete factorizations and zeros.

Degree	Polynomial	Zero(s)	Number of zeros
1	$P(x) = x - 4$	4	1
2	$P(x) = x^2 - 10x + 25$ $= (x - 5)(x - 5)$	5 (multiplicity 2)	2
3	$P(x) = x^3 + x$ $= x(x - i)(x + i)$	$0, i, -i$	3
4	$P(x) = x^4 + 18x^2 + 81$ $= (x - 3i)^2(x + 3i)^2$	$3i$ (multiplicity 2), $-3i$ (multiplicity 2)	4
5	$P(x) = x^5 - 2x^4 + x^3$ $= x^3(x - 1)^2$	0 (multiplicity 3), 1 (multiplicity 2)	5

EXAMPLE 4 | Finding Polynomials with Specified Zeros

(a) Find a polynomial $P(x)$ of degree 4, with zeros i, $-i$, 2, and -2, and with $P(3) = 25$.

(b) Find a polynomial $Q(x)$ of degree 4, with zeros -2 and 0, where -2 is a zero of multiplicity 3.

SOLUTION

(a) The required polynomial has the form

$$P(x) = a(x - i)(x - (-i))(x - 2)(x - (-2))$$

$$= a(x^2 + 1)(x^2 - 4) \qquad \text{Difference of squares}$$

$$= a(x^4 - 3x^2 - 4) \qquad \text{Multiply}$$

We know that $P(3) = a(3^4 - 3 \cdot 3^2 - 4) = 50a = 25$, so $a = \frac{1}{2}$. Thus,

$$P(x) = \tfrac{1}{2}x^4 - \tfrac{3}{2}x^2 - 2$$

(b) We require

$$Q(x) = a[x - (-2)]^3(x - 0)$$

$$= a(x + 2)^3 x$$

$$= a(x^3 + 6x^2 + 12x + 8)x \qquad \text{Special Product Formula 4 (Section 1.3)}$$

$$= a(x^4 + 6x^3 + 12x^2 + 8x)$$

Since we are given no information about Q other than its zeros and their multiplicity, we can choose any number for a. If we use $a = 1$, we get

$$Q(x) = x^4 + 6x^3 + 12x^2 + 8x$$

✎ NOW TRY EXERCISE **35**

EXAMPLE 5 | Finding All the Zeros of a Polynomial

Find all four zeros of $P(x) = 3x^4 - 2x^3 - x^2 - 12x - 4$.

SOLUTION Using the Rational Zeros Theorem from Section 3.4, we obtain the following list of possible rational zeros: ± 1, ± 2, ± 4, $\pm\frac{1}{3}$, $\pm\frac{2}{3}$, $\pm\frac{4}{3}$. Checking these using synthetic division, we find that 2 and $-\frac{1}{3}$ are zeros, and we get the following factorization:

$$P(x) = 3x^4 - 2x^3 - x^2 - 12x - 4$$

$$= (x - 2)(3x^3 + 4x^2 + 7x + 2) \qquad \text{Factor } x - 2$$

$$= (x - 2)(x + \tfrac{1}{3})(3x^2 + 3x + 6) \qquad \text{Factor } x + \tfrac{1}{3}$$

$$= 3(x - 2)(x + \tfrac{1}{3})(x^2 + x + 2) \qquad \text{Factor 3}$$

The zeros of the quadratic factor are

$$x = \frac{-1 \pm \sqrt{1 - 8}}{2} = -\frac{1}{2} \pm i\frac{\sqrt{7}}{2} \qquad \text{Quadratic Formula}$$

so the zeros of $P(x)$ are

$$2, \quad -\frac{1}{3}, \quad -\frac{1}{2} + i\frac{\sqrt{7}}{2}, \quad \text{and} \quad -\frac{1}{2} - i\frac{\sqrt{7}}{2}$$

✎ NOW TRY EXERCISE **45**

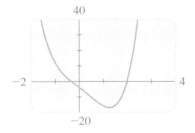

FIGURE 1

$P(x) = 3x^4 - 2x^3 - x^2 - 12x - 4$

Figure 1 shows the graph of the polynomial P in Example 5. The x-intercepts correspond to the real zeros of P. The imaginary zeros cannot be determined from the graph.

GEROLAMO CARDANO
(1501–1576) is certainly one of the most colorful figures in the history of mathematics. He was the best-known physician in Europe in his day, yet throughout his life he was plagued by numerous maladies, including ruptures, hemorrhoids, and an irrational fear of encountering rabid dogs. He was a doting father, but his beloved sons broke his heart—his favorite was eventually beheaded for murdering his own wife. Cardano was also a compulsive gambler; indeed, this vice might have driven him to write the *Book on Games of Chance,* the first study of probability from a mathematical point of view.

In Cardano's major mathematical work, the *Ars Magna,* he detailed the solution of the general third- and fourth-degree polynomial equations. At the time of its publication, mathematicians were uncomfortable even with negative numbers, but Cardano's formulas paved the way for the acceptance not just of negative numbers, but also of imaginary numbers, because they occurred naturally in solving polynomial equations. For example, for the cubic equation

$$x^3 - 15x - 4 = 0$$

one of his formulas gives the solution

$$x = \sqrt[3]{2 + \sqrt{-121}} + \sqrt[3]{2 - \sqrt{-121}}$$

(See page 263, Exercise 108). This value for *x* actually turns out to be the *integer* 4, yet to find it, Cardano had to use the imaginary number $\sqrt{-121} = 11i$.

▼ Complex Zeros Come in Conjugate Pairs

As you might have noticed from the examples so far, the complex zeros of polynomials with real coefficients come in pairs. Whenever $a + bi$ is a zero, its complex conjugate $a - bi$ is also a zero.

> **CONJUGATE ZEROS THEOREM**
>
> If the polynomial P has real coefficients and if the complex number z is a zero of P, then its complex conjugate $\bar{z}$ is also a zero of P.

PROOF Let

$$P(x) = a_n x^n + a_{n-1} x^{n-1} + \cdots + a_1 x + a_0$$

where each coefficient is real. Suppose that $P(z) = 0$. We must prove that $P(\bar{z}) = 0$. We use the facts that the complex conjugate of a sum of two complex numbers is the sum of the conjugates and that the conjugate of a product is the product of the conjugates.

$$
\begin{aligned}
P(\bar{z}) &= a_n(\bar{z})^n + a_{n-1}(\bar{z})^{n-1} + \cdots + a_1 \bar{z} + a_0 \\
&= \overline{a_n}\,\overline{z^n} + \overline{a_{n-1}}\,\overline{z^{n-1}} + \cdots + \overline{a_1}\,\overline{z} + \overline{a_0} \qquad \text{Because the coefficients are real} \\
&= \overline{a_n z^n} + \overline{a_{n-1} z^{n-1}} + \cdots + \overline{a_1 z} + \overline{a_0} \\
&= \overline{a_n z^n + a_{n-1} z^{n-1} + \cdots + a_1 z + a_0} \\
&= \overline{P(z)} = \overline{0} = 0
\end{aligned}
$$

This shows that $\bar{z}$ is also a zero of $P(x)$, which proves the theorem. ∎

EXAMPLE 6 | A Polynomial with a Specified Complex Zero

Find a polynomial $P(x)$ of degree 3 that has integer coefficients and zeros $\frac{1}{2}$ and $3 - i$.

SOLUTION Since $3 - i$ is a zero, then so is $3 + i$ by the Conjugate Zeros Theorem. This means that $P(x)$ must have the following form.

$$
\begin{aligned}
P(x) &= a\left(x - \tfrac{1}{2}\right)[x - (3 - i)][x - (3 + i)] \\
&= a\left(x - \tfrac{1}{2}\right)[(x - 3) + i][(x - 3) - i] \qquad \text{Regroup} \\
&= a\left(x - \tfrac{1}{2}\right)[(x - 3)^2 - i^2] \qquad \text{Difference of Squares Formula} \\
&= a\left(x - \tfrac{1}{2}\right)(x^2 - 6x + 10) \qquad \text{Expand} \\
&= a\left(x^3 - \tfrac{13}{2}x^2 + 13x - 5\right) \qquad \text{Expand}
\end{aligned}
$$

To make all coefficients integers, we set $a = 2$ and get

$$P(x) = 2x^3 - 13x^2 + 26x - 10$$

Any other polynomial that satisfies the given requirements must be an integer multiple of this one.

✎ NOW TRY EXERCISE **39**

▼ Linear and Quadratic Factors

We have seen that a polynomial factors completely into linear factors if we use complex numbers. If we don't use complex numbers, then a polynomial with real coefficients can always be factored into linear and quadratic factors. We use this property in Section 10.7 when we study partial fractions. A quadratic polynomial with no real zeros is called **irreducible** over the real numbers. Such a polynomial cannot be factored without using complex numbers.

> **LINEAR AND QUADRATIC FACTORS THEOREM**
>
> Every polynomial with real coefficients can be factored into a product of linear and irreducible quadratic factors with real coefficients.

PROOF We first observe that if $c = a + bi$ is a complex number, then

$$(x - c)(x - \bar{c}) = [x - (a + bi)][x - (a - bi)]$$

$$= [(x - a) - bi][(x - a) + bi]$$

$$= (x - a)^2 - (bi)^2$$

$$= x^2 - 2ax + (a^2 + b^2)$$

The last expression is a quadratic with *real* coefficients.

Now, if P is a polynomial with real coefficients, then by the Complete Factorization Theorem

$$P(x) = a(x - c_1)(x - c_2) \cdots (x - c_n)$$

Since the complex roots occur in conjugate pairs, we can multiply the factors corresponding to each such pair to get a quadratic factor with real coefficients. This results in P being factored into linear and irreducible quadratic factors. ∎

EXAMPLE 7 | **Factoring a Polynomial into Linear and Quadratic Factors**

Let $P(x) = x^4 + 2x^2 - 8$.

(a) Factor P into linear and irreducible quadratic factors with real coefficients.

(b) Factor P completely into linear factors with complex coefficients.

SOLUTION

(a)
$$P(x) = x^4 + 2x^2 - 8$$
$$= (x^2 - 2)(x^2 + 4)$$
$$= (x - \sqrt{2})(x + \sqrt{2})(x^2 + 4)$$

The factor $x^2 + 4$ is irreducible, since it has no real zeros.

(b) To get the complete factorization, we factor the remaining quadratic factor.

$$P(x) = (x - \sqrt{2})(x + \sqrt{2})(x^2 + 4)$$
$$= (x - \sqrt{2})(x + \sqrt{2})(x - 2i)(x + 2i)$$

. NOW TRY EXERCISE 65

3.6 EXERCISES

CONCEPTS

1. The polynomial $P(x) = 3(x - 5)^3(x - 3)(x + 2)$ has degree

_____. It has zeros 5, 3, and _____. The zero 5 has

multiplicity _____, and the zero 3 has multiplicity

_____.

2. (a) If a is a zero of the polynomial P, then _____ must be
a factor of $P(x)$.

(b) If a is a zero of multiplicity m of the polynomial P, then

_____ must be a factor of $P(x)$ when we factor P
completely.

3. A polynomial of degree $n \geq 1$ has exactly _____ zeros if
a zero of multiplicity m is counted m times.

4. If the polynomial function P has real coefficients and if $a + bi$

is a zero of P, then _____ is also a zero of P.

SKILLS

5–16 ■ A polynomial P is given. **(a)** Find all zeros of P, real and
complex. **(b)** Factor P completely.

5. $P(x) = x^4 + 4x^2$ **6.** $P(x) = x^5 + 9x^3$

7. $P(x) = x^3 - 2x^2 + 2x$ **8.** $P(x) = x^3 + x^2 + x$

9. $P(x) = x^4 + 2x^2 + 1$ **10.** $P(x) = x^4 - x^2 - 2$

11. $P(x) = x^4 - 16$ **12.** $P(x) = x^4 + 6x^2 + 9$

13. $P(x) = x^3 + 8$ **14.** $P(x) = x^3 - 8$

15. $P(x) = x^6 - 1$ **16.** $P(x) = x^6 - 7x^3 - 8$

17–34 ■ Factor the polynomial completely, and find all its zeros.
State the multiplicity of each zero.

17. $P(x) = x^2 + 25$ **18.** $P(x) = 4x^2 + 9$

19. $Q(x) = x^2 + 2x + 2$ **20.** $Q(x) = x^2 - 8x + 17$

21. $P(x) = x^3 + 4x$ **22.** $P(x) = x^3 - x^2 + x$

23. $Q(x) = x^4 - 1$ **24.** $Q(x) = x^4 - 625$

25. $P(x) = 16x^4 - 81$ **26.** $P(x) = x^3 - 64$

27. $P(x) = x^3 + x^2 + 9x + 9$ **28.** $P(x) = x^6 - 729$

29. $Q(x) = x^4 + 2x^2 + 1$ **30.** $Q(x) = x^4 + 10x^2 + 25$

31. $P(x) = x^4 + 3x^2 - 4$ **32.** $P(x) = x^5 + 7x^3$

33. $P(x) = x^5 + 6x^3 + 9x$ **34.** $P(x) = x^6 + 16x^3 + 64$

35–44 ■ Find a polynomial with integer coefficients that satisfies
the given conditions.

35. P has degree 2 and zeros $1 + i$ and $1 - i$.

36. P has degree 2 and zeros $1 + i\sqrt{2}$ and $1 - i\sqrt{2}$.

37. Q has degree 3 and zeros 3, $2i$, and $-2i$.

38. Q has degree 3 and zeros 0 and i.

39. P has degree 3 and zeros 2 and i.

40. Q has degree 3 and zeros -3 and $1 + i$.

41. R has degree 4 and zeros $1 - 2i$ and 1, with 1 a zero of multiplicity 2.

42. S has degree 4 and zeros $2i$ and $3i$.

43. T has degree 4, zeros i and $1 + i$, and constant term 12.

44. U has degree 5, zeros $\frac{1}{2}$, -1, and $-i$, and leading coefficient 4;
the zero -1 has multiplicity 2.

45–62 ■ Find all zeros of the polynomial.

45. $P(x) = x^3 + 2x^2 + 4x + 8$

46. $P(x) = x^3 - 7x^2 + 17x - 15$

47. $P(x) = x^3 - 2x^2 + 2x - 1$

48. $P(x) = x^3 + 7x^2 + 18x + 18$

49. $P(x) = x^3 - 3x^2 + 3x - 2$

50. $P(x) = x^3 - x - 6$

51. $P(x) = 2x^3 + 7x^2 + 12x + 9$

52. $P(x) = 2x^3 - 8x^2 + 9x - 9$

53. $P(x) = x^4 + x^3 + 7x^2 + 9x - 18$

54. $P(x) = x^4 - 2x^3 - 2x^2 - 2x - 3$

55. $P(x) = x^5 - x^4 + 7x^3 - 7x^2 + 12x - 12$

56. $P(x) = x^5 + x^3 + 8x^2 + 8$ [*Hint:* Factor by grouping.]

57. $P(x) = x^4 - 6x^3 + 13x^2 - 24x + 36$

58. $P(x) = x^4 - x^2 + 2x + 2$

59. $P(x) = 4x^4 + 4x^3 + 5x^2 + 4x + 1$

60. $P(x) = 4x^4 + 2x^3 - 2x^2 - 3x - 1$

61. $P(x) = x^5 - 3x^4 + 12x^3 - 28x^2 + 27x - 9$

62. $P(x) = x^5 - 2x^4 + 2x^3 - 4x^2 + x - 2$

63–68 ■ A polynomial P is given. **(a)** Factor P into linear and irreducible quadratic factors with real coefficients. **(b)** Factor P
completely into linear factors with complex coefficients.

63. $P(x) = x^3 - 5x^2 + 4x - 20$

64. $P(x) = x^3 - 2x - 4$

65. $P(x) = x^4 + 8x^2 - 9$ **66.** $P(x) = x^4 + 8x^2 + 16$

67. $P(x) = x^6 - 64$ **68.** $P(x) = x^5 - 16x$

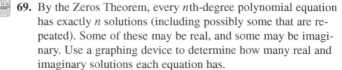

69. By the Zeros Theorem, every nth-degree polynomial equation
has exactly n solutions (including possibly some that are repeated). Some of these may be real, and some may be imaginary. Use a graphing device to determine how many real and
imaginary solutions each equation has.

(a) $x^4 - 2x^3 - 11x^2 + 12x = 0$

(b) $x^4 - 2x^3 - 11x^2 + 12x - 5 = 0$

(c) $x^4 - 2x^3 - 11x^2 + 12x + 40 = 0$

70–72 ■ So far, we have worked only with polynomials that have
real coefficients. These exercises involve polynomials with real and
imaginary coefficients.

70. Find all solutions of the equation.

(a) $2x + 4i = 1$ **(b)** $x^2 - ix = 0$

(c) $x^2 + 2ix - 1 = 0$ **(d)** $ix^2 - 2x + i = 0$

71. (a) Show that $2i$ and $1 - i$ are both solutions of the equation

$$x^2 - (1 + i)x + (2 + 2i) = 0$$

but that their complex conjugates $-2i$ and $1 + i$ are not.
(b) Explain why the result of part (a) does not violate the Conjugate Zeros Theorem.

72. (a) Find the polynomial with *real* coefficients of the smallest possible degree for which i and $1 + i$ are zeros and in which the coefficient of the highest power is 1.
(b) Find the polynomial with *complex* coefficients of the smallest possible degree for which i and $1 + i$ are zeros and in which the coefficient of the highest power is 1.

DISCOVERY ▪ DISCUSSION ▪ WRITING

73. Polynomials of Odd Degree   The Conjugate Zeros Theorem says that the complex zeros of a polynomial with real coefficients occur in complex conjugate pairs. Explain how this fact proves that a polynomial with real coefficients and odd degree has at least one real zero.

74. Roots of Unity   There are two square roots of 1, namely, 1 and -1. These are the solutions of $x^2 = 1$. The fourth roots of 1 are the solutions of the equation $x^4 = 1$ or $x^4 - 1 = 0$. How many fourth roots of 1 are there? Find them. The cube roots of 1 are the solutions of the equation $x^3 = 1$ or $x^3 - 1 = 0$. How many cube roots of 1 are there? Find them. How would you find the sixth roots of 1? How many are there? Make a conjecture about the number of nth roots of 1.

3.7 RATIONAL FUNCTIONS

| Rational Functions and Asymptotes ▶ Transformations of $y = 1/x$ ▶ Asymptotes of Rational Functions ▶ Graphing Rational Functions ▶ Slant Asymptotes and End Behavior ▶ Applications

A rational function is a function of the form

$$r(x) = \frac{P(x)}{Q(x)}$$

where P and Q are polynomials. We assume that $P(x)$ and $Q(x)$ have no factor in common. Even though rational functions are constructed from polynomials, their graphs look quite different from the graphs of polynomial functions.

▼ Rational Functions and Asymptotes

Domains of rational expressions are discussed in Section 1.4.

The *domain* of a rational function consists of all real numbers x except those for which the denominator is zero. When graphing a rational function, we must pay special attention to the behavior of the graph near those x-values. We begin by graphing a very simple rational function.

EXAMPLE 1 | A Simple Rational Function

Graph the rational function $f(x) = \dfrac{1}{x}$, and state the domain and range.

SOLUTION   The function f is not defined for $x = 0$. The following tables show that when x is close to zero, the value of $|f(x)|$ is large, and the closer x gets to zero, the larger $|f(x)|$ gets.

For positive real numbers,

$$\frac{1}{\text{BIG NUMBER}} = \text{small number}$$

$$\frac{1}{\text{small number}} = \text{BIG NUMBER}$$

x	$f(x)$
-0.1	-10
-0.01	-100
-0.00001	$-100{,}000$

x	$f(x)$
0.1	10
0.01	100
0.00001	$100{,}000$

Approaching 0^- Approaching $-\infty$ Approaching 0^+ Approaching ∞

We describe this behavior in words and in symbols as follows. The first table shows that as x approaches 0 from the left, the values of $y = f(x)$ decrease without bound. In symbols,

$$f(x) \to -\infty \quad \text{as} \quad x \to 0^-$$
"y approaches negative infinity as x approaches 0 from the left"

The second table shows that as x approaches 0 from the right, the values of $f(x)$ increase without bound. In symbols,

$$f(x) \to \infty \quad \text{as} \quad x \to 0^+$$
"y approaches infinity as x approaches 0 from the right"

The next two tables show how $f(x)$ changes as $|x|$ becomes large.

x	$f(x)$
-10	-0.1
-100	-0.01
$-100,000$	-0.00001

x	$f(x)$
10	0.1
100	0.01
$100,000$	0.00001

Approaching $-\infty$ Approaching 0 Approaching ∞ Approaching 0

These tables show that as $|x|$ becomes large, the value of $f(x)$ gets closer and closer to zero. We describe this situation in symbols by writing

$$f(x) \to 0 \quad \text{as} \quad x \to -\infty \qquad \text{and} \qquad f(x) \to 0 \quad \text{as} \quad x \to \infty$$

Using the information in these tables and plotting a few additional points, we obtain the graph shown in Figure 1.

x	$f(x) = \frac{1}{x}$
-2	$-\frac{1}{2}$
-1	-1
$-\frac{1}{2}$	-2
$\frac{1}{2}$	2
1	1
2	$\frac{1}{2}$

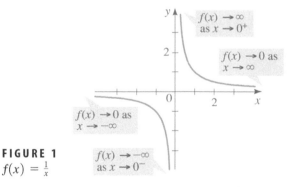

FIGURE 1
$f(x) = \frac{1}{x}$

The function f is defined for all values of x other than 0, so the domain is $\{x \mid x \neq 0\}$. From the graph we see that the range is $\{y \mid y \neq 0\}$.

✎. NOW TRY EXERCISE **7**

In Example 1 we used the following arrow notation.

Symbol	Meaning
$x \to a^-$	x approaches a from the left
$x \to a^+$	x approaches a from the right
$x \to -\infty$	x goes to negative infinity; that is, x decreases without bound
$x \to \infty$	x goes to infinity; that is, x increases without bound

The line $x = 0$ is called a *vertical asymptote* of the graph in Figure 1, and the line $y = 0$ is a *horizontal asymptote*. Informally speaking, an asymptote of a function is a line to which the graph of the function gets closer and closer as one travels along that line.

DEFINITION OF VERTICAL AND HORIZONTAL ASYMPTOTES

1. The line $x = a$ is a **vertical asymptote** of the function $y = f(x)$ if y approaches $\pm\infty$ as x approaches a from the right or left.

$y \to \infty$ as $x \to a^+$ $y \to \infty$ as $x \to a^-$ $y \to -\infty$ as $x \to a^+$ $y \to -\infty$ as $x \to a^-$

2. The line $y = b$ is a **horizontal asymptote** of the function $y = f(x)$ if y approaches b as x approaches $\pm\infty$.

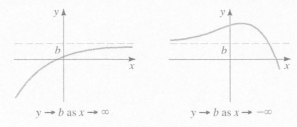

$y \to b$ as $x \to \infty$ $y \to b$ as $x \to -\infty$

A rational function has vertical asymptotes where the function is undefined, that is, where the denominator is zero.

▼ Transformations of $y = 1/x$

A rational function of the form

$$r(x) = \frac{ax + b}{cx + d}$$

can be graphed by shifting, stretching, and/or reflecting the graph of $f(x) = \frac{1}{x}$ shown in Figure 1, using the transformations studied in Section 2.5. (Such functions are called *linear fractional transformations*.)

EXAMPLE 2 | Using Transformations to Graph Rational Functions

Graph each rational function, and state the domain and range.

(a) $r(x) = \dfrac{2}{x - 3}$ **(b)** $s(x) = \dfrac{3x + 5}{x + 2}$

SOLUTION

(a) Let $f(x) = \frac{1}{x}$. Then we can express r in terms of f as follows:

$$r(x) = \frac{2}{x - 3}$$

$$= 2\left(\frac{1}{x - 3}\right) \qquad \text{Factor 2}$$

$$= 2(f(x - 3)) \qquad \text{Since } f(x) = \frac{1}{x}$$

From this form we see that the graph of r is obtained from the graph of f by shifting 3 units to the right and stretching vertically by a factor of 2. Thus, r has vertical asymptote $x = 3$ and horizontal asymptote $y = 0$. The graph of r is shown in Figure 2.

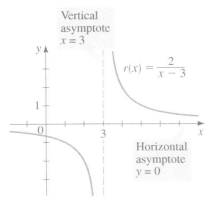

Vertical asymptote
$x = 3$

$r(x) = \dfrac{2}{x - 3}$

Horizontal asymptote
$y = 0$

FIGURE 2

$$\begin{array}{r} 3 \\ x+2\overline{\smash{\big)}\,3x+5} \\ \underline{3x+6} \\ -1 \end{array}$$

The function r is defined for all x other than 3, so the domain is $\{x \mid x \neq 3\}$. From the graph we see that the range is $\{y \mid y \neq 0\}$.

(b) Using long division (see the margin), we get $s(x) = 3 - \frac{1}{x+2}$. Thus, we can express s in terms of f as follows:

$$s(x) = 3 - \frac{1}{x+2}$$

$$= -\frac{1}{x+2} + 3 \qquad \text{Rearrange terms}$$

$$= -f(x+2) + 3 \qquad \text{Since } f(x) = \frac{1}{x}$$

From this form we see that the graph of s is obtained from the graph of f by shifting 2 units to the left, reflecting in the x-axis, and shifting upward 3 units. Thus, s has vertical asymptote $x = -2$ and horizontal asymptote $y = 3$. The graph of s is shown in Figure 3.

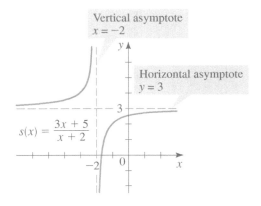

FIGURE 3

The function s is defined for all x other than -2, so the domain is $\{x \mid x \neq -2\}$. From the graph we see that the range is $\{y \mid y \neq 3\}$.

✎ NOW TRY EXERCISES **35** AND **37**

▼ Asymptotes of Rational Functions

The methods of Example 2 work only for simple rational functions. To graph more complicated ones, we need to take a closer look at the behavior of a rational function near its vertical and horizontal asymptotes.

EXAMPLE 3 | Asymptotes of a Rational Function

Graph $r(x) = \dfrac{2x^2 - 4x + 5}{x^2 - 2x + 1}$, and state the domain and range.

SOLUTION

Vertical asymptote: We first factor the denominator

$$r(x) = \frac{2x^2 - 4x + 5}{(x - 1)^2}$$

The line $x = 1$ is a vertical asymptote because the denominator of r is zero when $x = 1$.

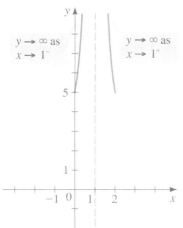

FIGURE 4

To see what the graph of r looks like near the vertical asymptote, we make tables of values for x-values to the left and to the right of 1. From the tables shown below we see that

$$y \to \infty \quad \text{as} \quad x \to 1^- \quad \text{and} \quad y \to \infty \quad \text{as} \quad x \to 1^+$$

$x \to 1^-$	
x	y
0	5
0.5	14
0.9	302
0.99	30,002

$x \to 1^+$	
x	y
2	5
1.5	14
1.1	302
1.01	30,002

Approaching 1^- Approaching ∞ Approaching 1^+ Approaching ∞

Thus, near the vertical asymptote $x = 1$, the graph of r has the shape shown in Figure 4.

Horizontal asymptote: The horizontal asymptote is the value that y approaches as $x \to \pm\infty$. To help us find this value, we divide both numerator and denominator by x^2, the highest power of x that appears in the expression:

$$y = \frac{2x^2 - 4x + 5}{x^2 - 2x + 1} \cdot \frac{\dfrac{1}{x^2}}{\dfrac{1}{x^2}} = \frac{2 - \dfrac{4}{x} + \dfrac{5}{x^2}}{1 - \dfrac{2}{x} + \dfrac{1}{x^2}}$$

The fractional expressions $\frac{4}{x}$, $\frac{5}{x^2}$, $\frac{2}{x}$, and $\frac{1}{x^2}$ all approach 0 as $x \to \pm\infty$ (see Exercise 83, page 12). So as $x \to \pm\infty$, we have

These terms approach 0

$$y = \frac{2 - \dfrac{4}{x} + \dfrac{5}{x^2}}{1 - \dfrac{2}{x} + \dfrac{1}{x^2}} \quad \longrightarrow \quad \frac{2 - 0 + 0}{1 - 0 + 0} = 2$$

These terms approach 0

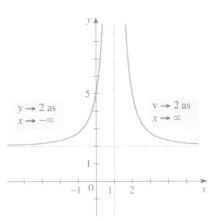

FIGURE 5

$$r(x) = \frac{2x^2 - 4x + 5}{x^2 - 2x + 1}$$

Thus, the horizontal asymptote is the line $y = 2$.

Since the graph must approach the horizontal asymptote, we can complete it as in Figure 5.

Domain and range: The function r is defined for all values of x other than 1, so the domain is $\{x \mid x \neq 1\}$. From the graph we see that the range is $\{y \mid y > 2\}$.

✎ NOW TRY EXERCISE **45**

From Example 3 we see that the horizontal asymptote is determined by the leading coefficients of the numerator and denominator, since after dividing through by x^2 (the highest power of x), all other terms approach zero. In general, if $r(x) = P(x)/Q(x)$ and the degrees of P and Q are the same (both n, say), then dividing both numerator and denominator by x^n shows that the horizontal asymptote is

$$y = \frac{\text{leading coefficient of } P}{\text{leading coefficient of } Q}$$

The following box summarizes the procedure for finding asymptotes.

FINDING ASYMPTOTES OF RATIONAL FUNCTIONS

Let r be the rational function

$$r(x) = \frac{a_n x^n + a_{n-1} x^{n-1} + \cdots + a_1 x + a_0}{b_m x^m + b_{m-1} x^{m-1} + \cdots + b_1 x + b_0}$$

1. The vertical asymptotes of r are the lines $x = a$, where a is a zero of the denominator.

2. **(a)** If $n < m$, then r has horizontal asymptote $y = 0$.

   (b) If $n = m$, then r has horizontal asymptote $y = \dfrac{a_n}{b_m}$.

   (c) If $n > m$, then r has no horizontal asymptote.

EXAMPLE 4 | Asymptotes of a Rational Function

Find the vertical and horizontal asymptotes of $r(x) = \dfrac{3x^2 - 2x - 1}{2x^2 + 3x - 2}$.

SOLUTION

Vertical asymptotes: We first factor

$$r(x) = \frac{3x^2 - 2x - 1}{(2x - 1)(x + 2)}$$

> This factor is 0 when $x = \frac{1}{2}$ This factor is 0 when $x = -2$

The vertical asymptotes are the lines $x = \frac{1}{2}$ and $x = -2$.

Horizontal asymptote: The degrees of the numerator and denominator are the same, and

$$\frac{\text{leading coefficient of numerator}}{\text{leading coefficient of denominator}} = \frac{3}{2}$$

Thus, the horizontal asymptote is the line $y = \frac{3}{2}$.

To confirm our results, we graph r using a graphing calculator (see Figure 6).

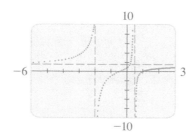

FIGURE 6

$r(x) = \dfrac{3x^2 - 2x - 1}{2x^2 + 3x - 2}$

Graph is drawn using dot mode to avoid extraneous lines.

✎ NOW TRY EXERCISES **23** AND **25**

▼ Graphing Rational Functions

We have seen that asymptotes are important when graphing rational functions. In general, we use the following guidelines to graph rational functions.

SKETCHING GRAPHS OF RATIONAL FUNCTIONS

1. **Factor.**   Factor the numerator and denominator.

2. **Intercepts.**   Find the x-intercepts by determining the zeros of the numerator and the y-intercept from the value of the function at $x = 0$.

3. **Vertical Asymptotes.**   Find the vertical asymptotes by determining the zeros of the denominator, and then see whether $y \to \infty$ or $y \to -\infty$ on each side of each vertical asymptote by using test values.

4. **Horizontal Asymptote.**   Find the horizontal asymptote (if any), using the procedure described in the box on page 282.

5. **Sketch the Graph.**   Graph the information provided by the first four steps. Then plot as many additional points as needed to fill in the rest of the graph of the function.

A fraction is 0 if and only if its numerator is 0.

EXAMPLE 5 | Graphing a Rational Function

Graph $r(x) = \dfrac{2x^2 + 7x - 4}{x^2 + x - 2}$, and state the domain and range.

SOLUTION   We factor the numerator and denominator, find the intercepts and asymptotes, and sketch the graph.

Factor: $y = \dfrac{(2x - 1)(x + 4)}{(x - 1)(x + 2)}$

x-Intercepts: The x-intercepts are the zeros of the numerator, $x = \frac{1}{2}$ and $x = -4$.

y-Intercept: To find the y-intercept, we substitute $x = 0$ into the original form of the function.

$$r(0) = \frac{2(0)^2 + 7(0) - 4}{(0)2 + (0) - 2} = \frac{-4}{-2} = 2$$

The y-intercept is 2.

Vertical asymptotes: The vertical asymptotes occur where the denominator is 0, that is, where the function is undefined. From the factored form we see that the vertical asymptotes are the lines $x = 1$ and $x = -2$.

When choosing test values, we must make sure that there is no x-intercept between the test point and the vertical asymptote.

Behavior near vertical asymptotes: We need to know whether $y \to \infty$ or $y \to -\infty$ on each side of each vertical asymptote. To determine the sign of y for x-values near the vertical asymptotes, we use test values. For instance, as $x \to 1^-$, we use a test value close to and to the left of 1 ($x = 0.9$, say) to check whether y is positive or negative to the left of $x = 1$.

$$y = \frac{(2(0.9) - 1)((0.9) + 4)}{((0.9) - 1)((0.9) + 2)} \qquad \text{whose sign is} \qquad \frac{(+)(+)}{(-)(+)} \quad \text{(negative)}$$

So $y \to -\infty$ as $x \to 1^-$. On the other hand, as $x \to 1^+$, we use a test value close to and to the right of 1 ($x = 1.1$, say), to get

$$y = \frac{(2(1.1) - 1)((1.1) + 4)}{((1.1) - 1)((1.1) + 2)} \qquad \text{whose sign is} \qquad \frac{(+)(+)}{(+)(+)} \quad \text{(positive)}$$

So $y \to \infty$ as $x \to 1^+$. The other entries in the following table are calculated similarly.

As $x \to$	-2^-	-2^+	1^-	1^+
the sign of $y = \dfrac{(2x - 1)(x + 4)}{(x - 1)(x + 2)}$ is	$\dfrac{(-)(+)}{(-)(-)}$	$\dfrac{(-)(+)}{(-)(+)}$	$\dfrac{(+)(+)}{(-)(+)}$	$\dfrac{(+)(+)}{(+)(+)}$
so $y \to$	$-\infty$	∞	$-\infty$	∞

Horizontal asymptote: The degrees of the numerator and denominator are the same, and

$$\frac{\text{leading coefficient of numerator}}{\text{leading coefficient of denominator}} = \frac{2}{1} = 2$$

Thus, the horizontal asymptote is the line $y = 2$.

Graph: We use the information we have found, together with some additional values, to sketch the graph in Figure 7.

x	y
-6	0.93
-3	-1.75
-1	4.50
1.5	6.29
2	4.50
3	3.50

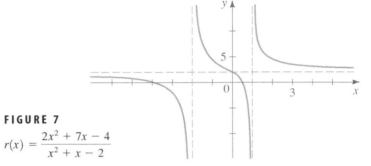

FIGURE 7

$$r(x) = \frac{2x^2 + 7x - 4}{x^2 + x - 2}$$

Domain and range: The domain is $\{x \mid x \neq 1, x \neq -2\}$. From the graph we see that the range is all real numbers.

✎. NOW TRY EXERCISE **53**

EXAMPLE 6 | Graphing a Rational Function

Graph $r(x) = \dfrac{5x + 21}{x^2 + 10x + 25}$, and state the domain and range.

SOLUTION

Factor: $y = \dfrac{5x + 21}{(x + 5)^2}$

x-Intercept: $-\dfrac{21}{5}$, from $5x + 21 = 0$

y-Intercept: $\dfrac{21}{25}$, because $r(0) = \dfrac{5 \cdot 0 + 21}{0^2 + 10 \cdot 0 + 25}$

$$= \frac{21}{25}$$

Vertical asymptote: $x = -5$, from the zeros of the denominator

Behavior near vertical asymptote:

As $x \to$	-5^-	-5^+
the sign of $y = \dfrac{5x + 21}{(x + 5)^2}$ is	$\dfrac{(-)}{(-)(-)}$	$\dfrac{(-)}{(+)(+)}$
so $y \to$	$-\infty$	$-\infty$

Horizontal asymptote: $y = 0$, because the degree of the numerator is less than the degree of the denominator

Graph: We use the information we have found, together with some additional values, to sketch the graph in Figure 8.

x	y
−15	−0.5
−10	−1.2
−3	1.5
−1	1.0
3	0.6
5	0.5
10	0.3

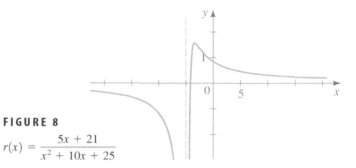

FIGURE 8

$$r(x) = \frac{5x + 21}{x^2 + 10x + 25}$$

Domain and range: The domain is $\{x \mid x \neq -5\}$. From the graph we see that the range is approximately the interval $(-\infty, 1.5]$.

✎ . NOW TRY EXERCISE **55**

From the graph in Figure 8 we see that, contrary to common misconception, a graph may cross a horizontal asymptote. The graph in Figure 8 crosses the x-axis (the horizontal asymptote) from below, reaches a maximum value near $x = -3$, and then approaches the x-axis from above as $x \to \infty$.

EXAMPLE 7 | Graphing a Rational Function

Graph the rational function $r(x) = \dfrac{x^2 - 3x - 4}{2x^2 + 4x}$.

SOLUTION

Factor: $y = \dfrac{(x + 1)(x - 4)}{2x(x + 2)}$

x-Intercepts: -1 and 4, from $x + 1 = 0$ and $x - 4 = 0$

y-Intercept: None, because $r(0)$ is undefined

Vertical asymptotes: $x = 0$ and $x = -2$, from the zeros of the denominator

Behavior near vertical asymptotes:

As $x \to$	-2^-	-2^+	0^-	0^+
the sign of $y = \dfrac{(x + 1)(x - 4)}{2x(x + 2)}$ is	$\dfrac{(-)(-)}{(-)(-)}$	$\dfrac{(-)(-)}{(-)(+)}$	$\dfrac{(+)(-)}{(-)(+)}$	$\dfrac{(+)(-)}{(+)(+)}$
so $y \to$	∞	$-\infty$	∞	$-\infty$

Horizontal asymptote: $y = \frac{1}{2}$, because the degree of the numerator and the degree of the denominator are the same and

$$\frac{\text{leading coefficient of numerator}}{\text{leading coefficient of denominator}} = \frac{1}{2}$$

Graph: We use the information we have found, together with some additional values, to sketch the graph in Figure 9.

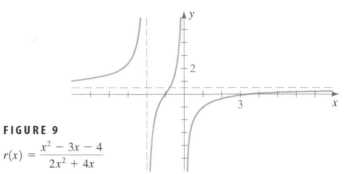

x	y
-3	2.33
-2.5	3.90
-0.5	1.50
1	-1.00
3	-0.13
5	0.09

FIGURE 9

$$r(x) = \frac{x^2 - 3x - 4}{2x^2 + 4x}$$

Domain and range: The domain is $\{x \mid x \neq 0, x \neq -2\}$. From the graph we see that the range is all real numbers.

NOW TRY EXERCISE **57**

▼ Slant Asymptotes and End Behavior

If $r(x) = P(x)/Q(x)$ is a rational function in which the degree of the numerator is one more than the degree of the denominator, we can use the Division Algorithm to express the function in the form

$$r(x) = ax + b + \frac{R(x)}{Q(x)}$$

where the degree of R is less than the degree of Q and $a \neq 0$. This means that as $x \to \pm\infty$, $R(x)/Q(x) \to 0$, so for large values of $|x|$ the graph of $y = r(x)$ approaches the graph of the line $y = ax + b$. In this situation we say that $y = ax + b$ is a **slant asymptote**, or an **oblique asymptote**.

EXAMPLE 8 | A Rational Function with a Slant Asymptote

Graph the rational function $r(x) = \dfrac{x^2 - 4x - 5}{x - 3}$.

SOLUTION

Factor: $y = \dfrac{(x + 1)(x - 5)}{x - 3}$

x-Intercepts: -1 and 5, from $x + 1 = 0$ and $x - 5 = 0$

y-Intercepts: $\dfrac{5}{3}$, because $r(0) = \dfrac{0^2 - 4 \cdot 0 - 5}{0 - 3} = \dfrac{5}{3}$

Horizontal asymptote: None, because the degree of the numerator is greater than the degree of the denominator

Vertical asymptote: $x = 3$, from the zero of the denominator

Behavior near vertical asymptote: $y \to \infty$ as $x \to 3^-$ and $y \to -\infty$ as $x \to 3^+$

$$x - 3 \overline{\smash{)}x^2 - 4x - 5}$$ with steps $x - 1$, $x^2 - 3x$, $-x - 5$, $-x + 3$, -8

Slant asymptote: Since the degree of the numerator is one more than the degree of the denominator, the function has a slant asymptote. Dividing (see the margin), we obtain

$$r(x) = x - 1 - \frac{8}{x - 3}$$

Thus, $y = x - 1$ is the slant asymptote.

Graph: We use the information we have found, together with some additional values, to sketch the graph in Figure 10.

x	y
-2	-1.4
1	4
2	9
4	-5
6	2.33

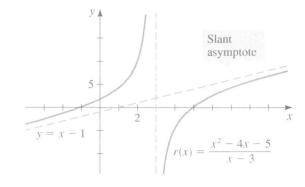

FIGURE 10

✎ NOW TRY EXERCISE **65**

So far, we have considered only horizontal and slant asymptotes as end behaviors for rational functions. In the next example we graph a function whose end behavior is like that of a parabola.

EXAMPLE 9 | End Behavior of a Rational Function

Graph the rational function

$$r(x) = \frac{x^3 - 2x^2 + 3}{x - 2}$$

and describe its end behavior.

SOLUTION

Factor: $\quad y = \dfrac{(x + 1)(x^2 - 3x + 3)}{x - 2}$

x-Intercepts: $\quad -1$, from $x + 1 = 0$ (The other factor in the numerator has no real zeros.)

y-Intercepts: $\quad -\dfrac{3}{2}$, because $r(0) = \dfrac{0^3 - 2 \cdot 0^2 + 3}{0 - 2} = -\dfrac{3}{2}$

Vertical asymptote: $\quad x = 2$, from the zero of the denominator

Behavior near vertical asymptote: $\quad y \to -\infty$ as $x \to 2^-$ and $y \to \infty$ as $x \to 2^+$

Horizontal asymptote: None, because the degree of the numerator is greater than the degree of the denominator

End behavior: Dividing (see the margin), we get

$$r(x) = x^2 + \frac{3}{x - 2}$$

$$x - 2 \overline{\smash{)}x^3 - 2x^2 + 0x + 3}$$ with steps x^2, $x^3 - 2x^2$, 3

This shows that the end behavior of r is like that of the parabola $y = x^2$ because $3/(x - 2)$ is small when $|x|$ is large. That is, $3/(x - 2) \to 0$ as $x \to \pm\infty$. This means that the graph of r will be close to the graph of $y = x^2$ for large $|x|$.

Graph: In Figure 11(a) we graph r in a small viewing rectangle; we can see the intercepts, the vertical asymptotes, and the local minimum. In Figure 11(b) we graph r in a larger viewing rectangle; here the graph looks almost like the graph of a parabola. In Figure 11(c) we graph both $y = r(x)$ and $y = x^2$; these graphs are very close to each other except near the vertical asymptote.

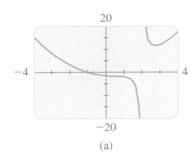

(a)

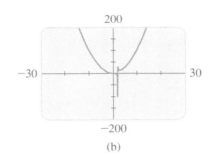

(b)

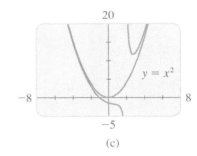

(c)

FIGURE 11

$$r(x) = \frac{x^3 - 2x^2 + 3}{x - 2}$$

◥ NOW TRY EXERCISE **73**

▼ Applications

Rational functions occur frequently in scientific applications of algebra. In the next example we analyze the graph of a function from the theory of electricity.

EXAMPLE 10 | Electrical Resistance

When two resistors with resistances R_1 and R_2 are connected in parallel, their combined resistance R is given by the formula

$$R = \frac{R_1 R_2}{R_1 + R_2}$$

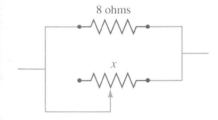

8 ohms

x

FIGURE 12

Suppose that a fixed 8-ohm resistor is connected in parallel with a variable resistor, as shown in Figure 12. If the resistance of the variable resistor is denoted by x, then the combined resistance R is a function of x. Graph R, and give a physical interpretation of the graph.

SOLUTION Substituting $R_1 = 8$ and $R_2 = x$ into the formula gives the function

$$R(x) = \frac{8x}{8 + x}$$

Since resistance cannot be negative, this function has physical meaning only when $x > 0$. The function is graphed in Figure 13(a) using the viewing rectangle $[0, 20]$ by $[0, 10]$. The function has no vertical asymptote when x is restricted to positive values. The combined resistance R increases as the variable resistance x increases. If we widen the viewing rectangle to $[0, 100]$ by $[0, 10]$, we obtain the graph in Figure 13(b). For large x the combined resistance R levels off, getting closer and closer to the horizontal asymptote $R = 8$. No matter how large the variable resistance x, the combined resistance is never greater than 8 ohms.

FIGURE 13

$$R(x) = \frac{8x}{8 + x}$$

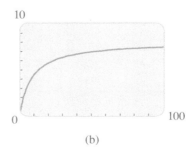

(a)

(b)

◥ NOW TRY EXERCISE **83**

3.7 EXERCISES

CONCEPTS

1. If the rational function $y = r(x)$ has the vertical asymptote

$x = 2$, then as $x \to 2^+$, either $y \to$ _____ or $y \to$ _____.

2. If the rational function $y = r(x)$ has the horizontal asymptote

$y = 2$, then $y \to$ _____ as $x \to \pm\infty$.

3–6 ■ The following questions are about the rational function

$$r(x) = \frac{(x + 1)(x - 2)}{(x + 2)(x - 3)}$$

3. The function r has x-intercepts _____ and _____.

4. The function r has y-intercept _____.

5. The function r has vertical asymptotes $x =$ _____ and

$x =$ _____.

6. The function r has horizontal asymptote $y =$ _____.

SKILLS

7–10 ■ A rational function is given. **(a)** Complete each table for the function. **(b)** Describe the behavior of the function near its vertical asymptote, based on Tables 1 and 2. **(c)** Determine the horizontal asymptote, based on Tables 3 and 4.

TABLE 1

x	$r(x)$
1.5	
1.9	
1.99	
1.999	

TABLE 2

x	$r(x)$
2.5	
2.1	
2.01	
2.001	

TABLE 3

x	$r(x)$
10	
50	
100	
1000	

TABLE 4

x	$r(x)$
-10	
-50	
-100	
-1000	

7. $r(x) = \dfrac{x}{x - 2}$

8. $r(x) = \dfrac{4x + 1}{x - 2}$

9. $r(x) = \dfrac{3x - 10}{(x - 2)^2}$

10. $r(x) = \dfrac{3x^2 + 1}{(x - 2)^2}$

11–16 ■ Find the x- and y-intercepts of the rational function.

11. $r(x) = \dfrac{x - 1}{x + 4}$

12. $s(x) = \dfrac{3x}{x - 5}$

13. $t(x) = \dfrac{x^2 - x - 2}{x - 6}$

14. $r(x) = \dfrac{2}{x^2 + 3x - 4}$

15. $r(x) = \dfrac{x^2 - 9}{x^2}$

16. $r(x) = \dfrac{x^3 + 8}{x^2 + 4}$

17–20 ■ From the graph, determine the x- and y-intercepts and the vertical and horizontal asymptotes.

17.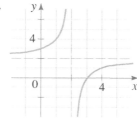

18.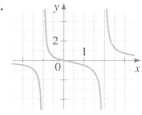

19.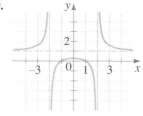

20.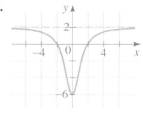

21–32 ■ Find all horizontal and vertical asymptotes (if any).

21. $r(x) = \dfrac{5}{x - 2}$

22. $r(x) = \dfrac{2x - 3}{x^2 - 1}$

23. $r(x) = \dfrac{6x}{x^2 + 2}$

24. $r(x) = \dfrac{2x - 4}{x^2 + x + 1}$

25. $s(x) = \dfrac{6x^2 + 1}{2x^2 + x - 1}$

26. $s(x) = \dfrac{8x^2 + 1}{4x^2 + 2x - 6}$

27. $s(x) = \dfrac{(5x - 1)(x + 1)}{(3x - 1)(x + 2)}$

28. $s(x) = \dfrac{(2x - 1)(x + 3)}{(3x - 1)(x - 4)}$

29. $r(x) = \dfrac{6x^3 - 2}{2x^3 + 5x^2 + 6x}$

30. $r(x) = \dfrac{5x^3}{x^3 + 2x^2 + 5x}$

31. $t(x) = \dfrac{x^2 + 2}{x - 1}$

32. $r(x) = \dfrac{x^3 + 3x^2}{x^2 - 4}$

33–40 ■ Use transformations of the graph of $y = \frac{1}{x}$ to graph the rational function, as in Example 2.

33. $r(x) = \dfrac{1}{x - 1}$

34. $r(x) = \dfrac{1}{x + 4}$

35. $s(x) = \dfrac{3}{x + 1}$

36. $s(x) = \dfrac{-2}{x - 2}$

37. $t(x) = \dfrac{2x - 3}{x - 2}$

38. $t(x) = \dfrac{3x - 3}{x + 2}$

39. $r(x) = \dfrac{x + 2}{x + 3}$

40. $r(x) = \dfrac{2x - 9}{x - 4}$

41–64 ■ Find the intercepts and asymptotes, and then sketch a graph of the rational function and state the domain and range. Use a graphing device to confirm your answer.

41. $r(x) = \dfrac{4x - 4}{x + 2}$

42. $r(x) = \dfrac{2x + 6}{-6x + 3}$

43. $s(x) = \dfrac{4 - 3x}{x + 7}$

44. $s(x) = \dfrac{1 - 2x}{2x + 3}$

45. $r(x) = \dfrac{18}{(x - 3)^2}$

46. $r(x) = \dfrac{x - 2}{(x + 1)^2}$

47. $s(x) = \dfrac{4x - 8}{(x - 4)(x + 1)}$

48. $s(x) = \dfrac{x + 2}{(x + 3)(x - 1)}$

49. $s(x) = \dfrac{6}{x^2 - 5x - 6}$

50. $s(x) = \dfrac{2x - 4}{x^2 + x - 2}$

51. $t(x) = \dfrac{3x + 6}{x^2 + 2x - 8}$

52. $t(x) = \dfrac{x - 2}{x^2 - 4x}$

53. $r(x) = \dfrac{(x - 1)(x + 2)}{(x + 1)(x - 3)}$

54. $r(x) = \dfrac{2x(x + 2)}{(x - 1)(x - 4)}$

55. $r(x) = \dfrac{x^2 - 2x + 1}{x^2 + 2x + 1}$

56. $r(x) = \dfrac{4x^2}{x^2 - 2x - 3}$

57. $r(x) = \dfrac{2x^2 + 10x - 12}{x^2 + x - 6}$

58. $r(x) = \dfrac{2x^2 + 2x - 4}{x^2 + x}$

59. $r(x) = \dfrac{x^2 - x - 6}{x^2 + 3x}$

60. $r(x) = \dfrac{x^2 + 3x}{x^2 - x - 6}$

61. $r(x) = \dfrac{3x^2 + 6}{x^2 - 2x - 3}$

62. $r(x) = \dfrac{5x^2 + 5}{x^2 + 4x + 4}$

63. $s(x) = \dfrac{x^2 - 2x + 1}{x^3 - 3x^2}$

64. $t(x) = \dfrac{x^3 - x^2}{x^3 - 3x - 2}$

65–72 ■ Find the slant asymptote, the vertical asymptotes, and sketch a graph of the function.

65. $r(x) = \dfrac{x^2}{x - 2}$

66. $r(x) = \dfrac{x^2 + 2x}{x - 1}$

67. $r(x) = \dfrac{x^2 - 2x - 8}{x}$

68. $r(x) = \dfrac{3x - x^2}{2x - 2}$

69. $r(x) = \dfrac{x^2 + 5x + 4}{x - 3}$

70. $r(x) = \dfrac{x^3 + 4}{2x^2 + x - 1}$

71. $r(x) = \dfrac{x^3 + x^2}{x^2 - 4}$

72. $r(x) = \dfrac{2x^3 + 2x}{x^2 - 1}$

 73–76 ■ Graph the rational function f, and determine all vertical asymptotes from your graph. Then graph f and g in a sufficiently large viewing rectangle to show that they have the same end behavior.

73. $f(x) = \dfrac{2x^2 + 6x + 6}{x + 3}$, $g(x) = 2x$

74. $f(x) = \dfrac{-x^3 + 6x^2 - 5}{x^2 - 2x}$, $g(x) = -x + 4$

75. $f(x) = \dfrac{x^3 - 2x^2 + 16}{x - 2}$, $g(x) = x^2$

76. $f(x) = \dfrac{-x^4 + 2x^3 - 2x}{(x - 1)^2}$, $g(x) = 1 - x^2$

 77–82 ■ Graph the rational function, and find all vertical asymptotes, x- and y-intercepts, and local extrema, correct to the nearest decimal. Then use long division to find a polynomial that has the same end behavior as the rational function, and graph both func-

tions in a sufficiently large viewing rectangle to verify that the end behaviors of the polynomial and the rational function are the same.

77. $y = \dfrac{2x^2 - 5x}{2x + 3}$

78. $y = \dfrac{x^4 - 3x^3 + x^2 - 3x + 3}{x^2 - 3x}$

79. $y = \dfrac{x^5}{x^3 - 1}$

80. $y = \dfrac{x^4}{x^2 - 2}$

81. $r(x) = \dfrac{x^4 - 3x^3 + 6}{x - 3}$

82. $r(x) = \dfrac{4 + x^2 - x^4}{x^2 - 1}$

APPLICATIONS

83. Population Growth   Suppose that the rabbit population on Mr. Jenkins' farm follows the formula

$$p(t) = \frac{3000t}{t + 1}$$

where $t \geq 0$ is the time (in months) since the beginning of the year.
(a) Draw a graph of the rabbit population.
(b) What eventually happens to the rabbit population?

84. Drug Concentration   After a certain drug is injected into a patient, the concentration c of the drug in the bloodstream is monitored. At time $t \geq 0$ (in minutes since the injection), the concentration (in mg/L) is given by

$$c(t) = \frac{30t}{t^2 + 2}$$

(a) Draw a graph of the drug concentration.
(b) What eventually happens to the concentration of drug in the bloodstream?

85. Drug Concentration   A drug is administered to a patient, and the concentration of the drug in the bloodstream is monitored. At time $t \geq 0$ (in hours since giving the drug), the concentration (in mg/L) is given by

$$c(t) = \frac{5t}{t^2 + 1}$$

Graph the function c with a graphing device.
(a) What is the highest concentration of drug that is reached in the patient's bloodstream?
(b) What happens to the drug concentration after a long period of time?
(c) How long does it take for the concentration to drop below 0.3 mg/L?

86. Flight of a Rocket   Suppose a rocket is fired upward from the surface of the earth with an initial velocity v (measured in meters per second). Then the maximum height h (in meters) reached by the rocket is given by the function

$$h(v) = \frac{Rv^2}{2gR - v^2}$$

where $R = 6.4 \times 10^6$ m is the radius of the earth and $g = 9.8$ m/s^2 is the acceleration due to gravity. Use a graphing device to draw a graph of the function h. (Note that h and v must both be positive, so the viewing rectangle need not contain negative values.) What does the vertical asymptote represent physically?

 87. The Doppler Effect   As a train moves toward an observer (see the figure), the pitch of its whistle sounds higher to the observer than it would if the train were at rest, because the crests of the sound waves are compressed closer together. This phenomenon is called the *Doppler effect*. The observed pitch P is a function of the speed v of the train and is given by

$$P(v) = P_0\left(\frac{s_0}{s_0 - v}\right)$$

where P_0 is the actual pitch of the whistle at the source and $s_0 = 332$ m/s is the speed of sound in air. Suppose that a train has a whistle pitched at $P_0 = 440$ Hz. Graph the function $y = P(v)$ using a graphing device. How can the vertical asymptote of this function be interpreted physically?

 88. Focusing Distance   For a camera with a lens of fixed focal length F to focus on an object located a distance x from the lens, the film must be placed a distance y behind the lens, where F, x, and y are related by

$$\frac{1}{x} + \frac{1}{y} = \frac{1}{F}$$

(See the figure.) Suppose the camera has a 55-mm lens ($F = 55$).
(a) Express y as a function of x and graph the function.
(b) What happens to the focusing distance y as the object moves far away from the lens?
(c) What happens to the focusing distance y as the object moves close to the lens?

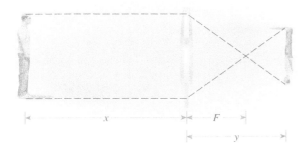

DISCOVERY ▪ DISCUSSION ▪ WRITING

 89. Constructing a Rational Function from Its Asymptotes   Give an example of a rational function that has vertical asymptote $x = 3$. Now give an example of one that has vertical asymptote $x = 3$ *and* horizontal asymptote $y = 2$. Now give an example of a rational function with vertical asymptotes $x = 1$ and $x = -1$, horizontal asymptote $y = 0$, and x-intercept 4.

90. A Rational Function with No Asymptote   Explain how you can tell (without graphing it) that the function

$$r(x) = \frac{x^6 + 10}{x^4 + 8x^2 + 15}$$

has no x-intercept and no horizontal, vertical, or slant asymptote. What is its end behavior?'

91. Graphs with Holes   In this chapter we adopted the convention that in rational functions, the numerator and denominator don't share a common factor. In this exercise we consider the graph of a rational function that does not satisfy this rule.
(a) Show that the graph of

$$r(x) = \frac{3x^2 - 3x - 6}{x - 2}$$

is the line $y = 3x + 3$ with the point $(2, 9)$ removed. [*Hint*: Factor. What is the domain of r?]
(b) Graph the rational functions:

$$s(x) = \frac{x^2 + x - 20}{x + 5}$$

$$t(x) = \frac{2x^2 - x - 1}{x - 1}$$

$$u(x) = \frac{x - 2}{x^2 - 2x}$$

92. Transformations of $y = 1/x^2$ In Example 2 we saw that some simple rational functions can be graphed by shifting, stretching, or reflecting the graph of $y = 1/x$. In this exercise we consider rational functions that can be graphed by transforming the graph of $y = 1/x^2$, shown on the following page.
(a) Graph the function

$$r(x) = \frac{1}{(x - 2)^2}$$

by transforming the graph of $y = 1/x^2$.
(b) Use long division and factoring to show that the function

$$s(x) = \frac{2x^2 + 4x + 5}{x^2 + 2x + 1}$$

can be written as

$$s(x) = 2 + \frac{3}{(x + 1)^2}$$

Then graph s by transforming the graph of $y = 1/x^2$.

(c) One of the following functions can be graphed by transforming the graph of $y = 1/x^2$; the other cannot. Use transformations to graph the one that can be, and explain why this method doesn't work for the other one.

$$p(x) = \frac{2 - 3x^2}{x^2 - 4x + 4} \qquad q(x) = \frac{12x - 3x^2}{x^2 - 4x + 4}$$

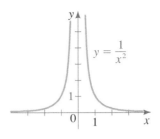

CHAPTER 3 | REVIEW

■ CONCEPT CHECK

1. (a) Write the defining equation for a polynomial P of degree n.

(b) What does it mean to say that c is a zero of P?

2. Sketch graphs showing the possible end behaviors of polynomials of odd degree and of even degree.

3. What steps would you follow to graph a polynomial by hand?

4. (a) What is meant by a local maximum point or local minimum point of a polynomial?

(b) How many local extrema can a polynomial of degree n have?

5. State the Division Algorithm and identify the dividend, divisor, quotient, and remainder.

6. How does synthetic division work?

7. (a) State the Remainder Theorem.

(b) State the Factor Theorem.

8. (a) State the Rational Zeros Theorem.

(b) What steps would you take to find the rational zeros of a polynomial?

9. State Descartes' Rule of Signs.

10. (a) What does it mean to say that a is a lower bound and b is an upper bound for the zeros of a polynomial?

(b) State the Upper and Lower Bounds Theorem.

11. (a) What is a complex number?

(b) What are the real and imaginary parts of a complex number?

(c) What is the complex conjugate of a complex number?

(d) How do you add, subtract, multiply, and divide complex numbers?

12. (a) State the Fundamental Theorem of Algebra.

(b) State the Complete Factorization Theorem.

(c) What does it mean to say that c is a zero of multiplicity k of a polynomial P?

(d) State the Zeros Theorem.

(e) State the Conjugate Zeros Theorem.

13. (a) What is a rational function?

(b) What does it mean to say that $x = a$ is a vertical asymptote of $y = f(x)$?

(c) How do you locate a vertical asymptote?

(d) What does it mean to say that $y = b$ is a horizontal asymptote of $y = f(x)$?

(e) How do you locate a horizontal asymptote?

(f) What steps do you follow to sketch the graph of a rational function by hand?

(g) Under what circumstances does a rational function have a slant asymptote? If one exists, how do you find it?

(h) How do you determine the end behavior of a rational function?

■ EXERCISES

1–4 ■ A quadratic function is given. **(a)** Express the function in standard form. **(b)** Graph the function.

1. $f(x) = x^2 + 4x + 1$

2. $f(x) = -2x^2 + 12x + 12$

3. $g(x) = 1 + 8x - x^2$

4. $g(x) = 6x - 3x^2$

5–6 ■ Find the maximum or minimum value of the quadratic function.

5. $f(x) = 2x^2 + 4x - 5$

6. $g(x) = 1 - x - x^2$

7. A stone is thrown upward from the top of a building. Its height (in feet) above the ground after t seconds is given by the function $h(t) = -16t^2 + 48t + 32$. What maximum height does the stone reach?

8. The profit P (in dollars) generated by selling x units of a certain commodity is given by the function

$$P(x) = -1500 + 12x - 0.004x^2$$

What is the maximum profit, and how many units must be sold to generate it?

9–14 ■ Graph the polynomial by transforming an appropriate graph of the form $y = x^n$. Show clearly all x- and y-intercepts.

9. $P(x) = -x^3 + 64$

10. $P(x) = 2x^3 - 16$

11. $P(x) = 2(x + 1)^4 - 32$

12. $P(x) = 81 - (x - 3)^4$

13. $P(x) = 32 + (x - 1)^5$

14. $P(x) = -3(x + 2)^5 + 96$

15–16 ■ A polynomial function P is given. **(a)** Determine the multiplicity of each zero of P. **(b)** Sketch a graph of P.

15. $P(x) = x^3(x - 2)^2$ **16.** $P(x) = x(x + 1)^3(x - 1)^2$

 17–20 ■ Use a graphing device to graph the polynomial. Find the x- and y-intercepts and the coordinates of all local extrema, correct to the nearest decimal. Describe the end behavior of the polynomial.

17. $P(x) = x^3 - 4x + 1$ **18.** $P(x) = -2x^3 + 6x^2 - 2$

19. $P(x) = 3x^4 - 4x^3 - 10x - 1$

20. $P(x) = x^5 + x^4 - 7x^3 - x^2 + 6x + 3$

21. The strength S of a wooden beam of width x and depth y is given by the formula $S = 13.8xy^2$. A beam is to be cut from a log of diameter 10 in., as shown in the figure.

   (a) Express the strength S of this beam as a function of x only.

   (b) What is the domain of the function S?

 (c) Draw a graph of S.

   (d) What width will make the beam the strongest?

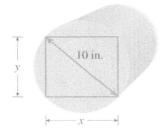

22. A small shelter for delicate plants is to be constructed of thin plastic material. It will have square ends and a rectangular top and back, with an open bottom and front, as shown in the figure. The total area of the four plastic sides is to be 1200 in².

   (a) Express the volume V of the shelter as a function of the depth x.

 (b) Draw a graph of V.

   (c) What dimensions will maximize the volume of the shelter?

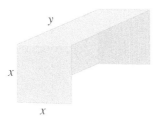

23–30 ■ Find the quotient and remainder.

23. $\dfrac{x^2 - 3x + 5}{x - 2}$ **24.** $\dfrac{x^2 + x - 12}{x - 3}$

25. $\dfrac{x^3 - x^2 + 11x + 2}{x - 4}$ **26.** $\dfrac{x^3 + 2x^2 - 10}{x + 3}$

27. $\dfrac{x^4 - 8x^2 + 2x + 7}{x + 5}$ **28.** $\dfrac{2x^4 + 3x^3 - 12}{x + 4}$

29. $\dfrac{2x^3 + x^2 - 8x + 15}{x^2 + 2x - 1}$ **30.** $\dfrac{x^4 - 2x^2 + 7x}{x^2 - x + 3}$

31–32 ■ Find the indicated value of the polynomial using the Remainder Theorem.

31. $P(x) = 2x^3 - 9x^2 - 7x + 13$;   find $P(5)$

32. $Q(x) = x^4 + 4x^3 + 7x^2 + 10x + 15$;   find $Q(-3)$

33. Show that $\frac{1}{2}$ is a zero of the polynomial
$$P(x) = 2x^4 + x^3 - 5x^2 + 10x - 4$$

34. Use the Factor Theorem to show that $x + 4$ is a factor of the polynomial
$$P(x) = x^5 + 4x^4 - 7x^3 - 23x^2 + 23x + 12$$

35. What is the remainder when the polynomial
$$P(x) = x^{500} + 6x^{201} - x^2 - 2x + 4$$
is divided by $x - 1$?

36. What is the remainder when $x^{101} - x^4 + 2$ is divided by $x + 1$?

37–38 ■ A polynomial P is given. **(a)** List all possible rational zeros (without testing to see whether they actually are zeros). **(b)** Determine the possible number of positive and negative real zeros using Descartes' Rule of Signs.

37. $P(x) = x^5 - 6x^3 - x^2 + 2x + 18$

38. $P(x) = 6x^4 + 3x^3 + x^2 + 3x + 4$

39–46 ■ A polynomial P is given. **(a)** Find all real zeros of P, and state their multiplicities. **(b)** Sketch the graph of P.

39. $P(x) = x^3 - 16x$

40. $P(x) = x^3 - 3x^2 - 4x$

41. $P(x) = x^4 + x^3 - 2x^2$

42. $P(x) = x^4 - 5x^2 + 4$

43. $P(x) = x^4 - 2x^3 - 7x^2 + 8x + 12$

44. $P(x) = x^4 - 2x^3 - 2x^2 + 8x - 8$

45. $P(x) = 2x^4 + x^3 + 2x^2 - 3x - 2$

46. $P(x) = 9x^5 - 21x^4 + 10x^3 + 6x^2 - 3x - 1$

47–56 ■ Evaluate the expression and write in the form $a + bi$.

47. $(2 - 3i) + (1 + 4i)$ **48.** $(3 - 6i) - (6 - 4i)$

49. $(2 + i)(3 - 2i)$ **50.** $4i(2 - \frac{1}{2}i)$

51. $\dfrac{4 + 2i}{2 - i}$ **52.** $\dfrac{8 + 3i}{4 + 3i}$

53. i^{25} **54.** $(1 + i)^3$

55. $(1 - \sqrt{-1})(1 + \sqrt{-1})$ **56.** $\sqrt{-10} \cdot \sqrt{-40}$

57. Find a polynomial of degree 3 with constant coefficient 12 and zeros $-\frac{1}{2}$, 2, and 3.

58. Find a polynomial of degree 4 that has integer coefficients and zeros $3i$ and 4, with 4 a double zero.

59. Does there exist a polynomial of degree 4 with integer coefficients that has zeros i, $2i$, $3i$, and $4i$? If so, find it. If not, explain why.

60. Prove that the equation $3x^4 + 5x^2 + 2 = 0$ has no real root.

61–70 ■ Find all rational, irrational, and complex zeros (and state their multiplicities). Use Descartes' Rule of Signs, the Upper and Lower Bounds Theorem, the Quadratic Formula, or other factoring techniques to help you whenever possible.

61. $P(x) = x^3 - 3x^2 - 13x + 15$

62. $P(x) = 2x^3 + 5x^2 - 6x - 9$

63. $P(x) = x^4 + 6x^3 + 17x^2 + 28x + 20$

64. $P(x) = x^4 + 7x^3 + 9x^2 - 17x - 20$

65. $P(x) = x^5 - 3x^4 - x^3 + 11x^2 - 12x + 4$

66. $P(x) = x^4 - 81$

67. $P(x) = x^6 - 64$

68. $P(x) = 18x^3 + 3x^2 - 4x - 1$

69. $P(x) = 6x^4 - 18x^3 + 6x^2 - 30x + 36$

70. $P(x) = x^4 + 15x^2 + 54$

71–74 ■ Use a graphing device to find all real solutions of the equation.

71. $2x^2 = 5x + 3$

72. $x^3 + x^2 - 14x - 24 = 0$

73. $x^4 - 3x^3 - 3x^2 - 9x - 2 = 0$

74. $x^5 = x + 3$

75–76 ■ A polynomial function P is given. Find all the real zeros of P, and factor P completely into linear and irreducible quadratic factors with real coefficients.

75. $P(x) = x^3 - 2x - 4$

76. $P(x) = x^4 + 3x^2 - 4$

77–82 ■ Graph the rational function. Show clearly all x- and y-intercepts and asymptotes.

77. $r(x) = \dfrac{3x - 12}{x + 1}$

78. $r(x) = \dfrac{1}{(x + 2)^2}$

79. $r(x) = \dfrac{x - 2}{x^2 - 2x - 8}$

80. $r(x) = \dfrac{2x^2 - 6x - 7}{x - 4}$

81. $r(x) = \dfrac{x^2 - 9}{2x^2 + 1}$

82. $r(x) = \dfrac{x^3 + 27}{x + 4}$

 83–86 ■ Use a graphing device to analyze the graph of the rational function. Find all x- and y-intercepts and all vertical, horizontal, and slant asymptotes. If the function has no horizontal or slant asymptote, find a polynomial that has the same end behavior as the rational function.

83. $r(x) = \dfrac{x - 3}{2x + 6}$

84. $r(x) = \dfrac{2x - 7}{x^2 + 9}$

85. $r(x) = \dfrac{x^3 + 8}{x^2 - x - 2}$

86. $r(x) = \dfrac{2x^3 - x^2}{x + 1}$

87. Find the coordinates of all points of intersection of the graphs of

$$y = x^4 + x^2 + 24x \quad \text{and} \quad y = 6x^3 + 20$$

1. Express the quadratic function $f(x) = x^2 - x - 6$ in standard form, and sketch its graph.

2. Find the maximum or minimum value of the quadratic function $g(x) = 2x^2 + 6x + 3$.

3. A cannonball fired out to sea from a shore battery follows a parabolic trajectory given by the graph of the equation
$$h(x) = 10x - 0.01x^2$$
where $h(x)$ is the height of the cannonball above the water when it has traveled a horizontal distance of x feet.

   (a) What is the maximum height that the cannonball reaches?

   (b) How far does the cannonball travel horizontally before splashing into the water?

4. Graph the polynomial $P(x) = -(x + 2)^3 + 27$, showing clearly all x- and y-intercepts.

5. (a) Use synthetic division to find the quotient and remainder when $x^4 - 4x^2 + 2x + 5$ is divided by $x - 2$.

   (b) Use long division to find the quotient and remainder when $2x^5 + 4x^4 - x^3 - x^2 + 7$ is divided by $2x^2 - 1$.

6. Let $P(x) = 2x^3 - 5x^2 - 4x + 3$.

   (a) List all possible rational zeros of P.

   (b) Find the complete factorization of P.

   (c) Find the zeros of P.

   (d) Sketch the graph of P.

7. Perform the indicated operation and write the result in the form $a + bi$.

   (a) $(3 - 2i) + (4 + 3i)$ (b) $(3 - 2i) - (4 + 3i)$

   (c) $(3 - 2i)(4 + 3i)$ (d) $\dfrac{3 - 2i}{4 + 3i}$

   (e) i^{48} (f) $(\sqrt{2} - \sqrt{-2})(\sqrt{8} + \sqrt{-2})$

8. Find all real and complex zeros of $P(x) = x^3 - x^2 - 4x - 6$.

9. Find the complete factorization of $P(x) = x^4 - 2x^3 + 5x^2 - 8x + 4$.

10. Find a fourth-degree polynomial with integer coefficients that has zeros $3i$ and -1, with -1 a zero of multiplicity 2.

11. Let $P(x) = 2x^4 - 7x^3 + x^2 - 18x + 3$.

    (a) Use Descartes' Rule of Signs to determine how many positive and how many negative real zeros P can have.

    (b) Show that 4 is an upper bound and -1 is a lower bound for the real zeros of P.

     (c) Draw a graph of P, and use it to estimate the real zeros of P, correct to two decimal places.

    (d) Find the coordinates of all local extrema of P, correct to two decimals.

12. Consider the following rational functions:

    $$r(x) = \frac{2x - 1}{x^2 - x - 2} \qquad s(x) = \frac{x^3 + 27}{x^2 + 4} \qquad t(x) = \frac{x^3 - 9x}{x + 2} \qquad u(x) = \frac{x^2 + x - 6}{x^2 - 25}$$

    (a) Which of these rational functions has a horizontal asymptote?

    (b) Which of these functions has a slant asymptote?

    (c) Which of these functions has no vertical asymptote?

    (d) Graph $y = u(x)$, showing clearly any asymptotes and x- and y-intercepts the function may have.

     (e) Use long division to find a polynomial P that has the same end behavior as t. Graph both P and t on the same screen to verify that they have the same end behavior.

We have learned how to fit a line to data (see *Focus on Modeling*, page 130). The line models the increasing or decreasing trend in the data. If the data exhibit more variability, such as an increase followed by a decrease, then to model the data, we need to use a curve rather than a line. Figure 1 shows a scatter plot with three possible models that appear to fit the data. Which model fits the data best?

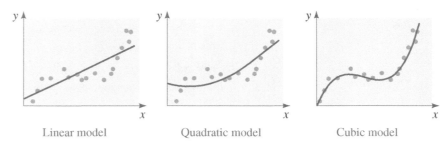

<table>
<tr><td>Linear model</td><td>Quadratic model</td><td>Cubic model</td></tr>
</table>

FIGURE 1

▼ Polynomial Functions as Models

Polynomial functions are ideal for modeling data for which the scatter plot has peaks or valleys (that is, local maxima or minima). For example, if the data have a single peak as in Figure 2(a), then it may be appropriate to use a quadratic polynomial to model the data. The more peaks or valleys the data exhibit, the higher the degree of the polynomial needed to model the data (see Figure 2).

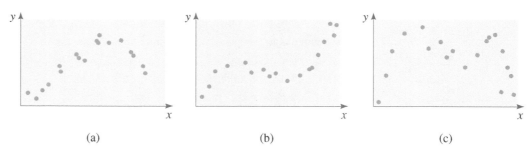

<table>
<tr><td>(a)</td><td>(b)</td><td>(c)</td></tr>
</table>

FIGURE 2

Graphing calculators are programmed to find the **polynomial of best fit** of a specified degree. As is the case for lines (see page 131), a polynomial of a given degree fits the data *best* if the sum of the squares of the distances between the graph of the polynomial and the data points is minimized.

EXAMPLE 1 | Rainfall and Crop Yield

Rain is essential for crops to grow, but too much rain can diminish crop yields. The data give rainfall and cotton yield per acre for several seasons in a certain county.

(a) Make a scatter plot of the data. What degree polynomial seems appropriate for modeling the data?

(b) Use a graphing calculator to find the polynomial of best fit. Graph the polynomial on the scatter plot.

(c) Use the model that you found to estimate the yield if there are 25 in. of rainfall.

Season	Rainfall (in.)	Yield (kg/acre)
1	23.3	5311
2	20.1	4382
3	18.1	3950
4	12.5	3137
5	30.9	5113
6	33.6	4814
7	35.8	3540
8	15.5	3850
9	27.6	5071
10	34.5	3881

SOLUTION

(a) The scatter plot is shown in Figure 3. The data appear to have a peak, so it is appropriate to model the data by a quadratic polynomial (degree 2).

FIGURE 3 Scatter plot of yield
vs. rainfall data

(b) Using a graphing calculator, we find that the quadratic polynomial of best fit is

$$y = -12.6x^2 + 651.5x - 3283.2$$

The calculator output and the scatter plot, together with the graph of the quadratic model, are shown in Figure 4.

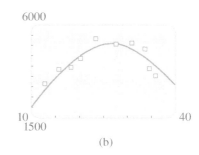

(a)   (b)

FIGURE 4

(c) Using the model with $x = 25$, we get

$$y = -12.6(25)^2 + 651.5(25) - 3283.2 \approx 5129.3$$

We estimate the yield to be about 5130 kg/acre.

Cod   Redfish   Hake

Otoliths for several fish species

EXAMPLE 2 | Length-at-Age Data for Fish

Otoliths ("earstones") are tiny structures that are found in the heads of fish. Microscopic growth rings on the otoliths, not unlike growth rings on a tree, record the age of a fish. The table gives the lengths of rock bass caught at different ages, as determined by the otoliths. Scientists have proposed a cubic polynomial to model this data.

(a) Use a graphing calculator to find the cubic polynomial of best fit for the data.

(b) Make a scatter plot of the data and graph the polynomial from part (a).

(c) A fisherman catches a rock bass 20 in. long. Use the model to estimate its age.

Age (yr)	Length (in.)	Age (yr)	Length (in.)
1	4.8	9	18.2
2	8.8	9	17.1
2	8.0	10	18.8
3	7.9	10	19.5
4	11.9	11	18.9
5	14.4	12	21.7
6	14.1	12	21.9
6	15.8	13	23.8
7	15.6	14	26.9
8	17.8	14	25.1

SOLUTION

(a) Using a graphing calculator (see Figure 5(a)), we find the cubic polynomial of best fit:

$$y = 0.0155x^3 - 0.372x^2 + 3.95x + 1.21$$

(b) The scatter plot of the data and the cubic polynomial are graphed in Figure 5(b).

(a)

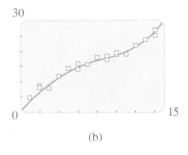

(b)

FIGURE 5

(c) Moving the cursor along the graph of the polynomial, we find that $y = 20$ when $x \approx 10.8$. Thus, the fish is about 11 years old.

PROBLEMS

1. Tire Inflation and Treadwear Car tires need to be inflated properly. Overinflation or underinflation can cause premature treadwear. The data and scatter plot on the next page show tire life for different inflation values for a certain type of tire.

(a) Find the quadratic polynomial that best fits the data.

(b) Draw a graph of the polynomial from part (a) together with a scatter plot of the data.

(c) Use your result from part (b) to estimate the pressure that gives the longest tire life.

Pressure (lb/in^2)	Tire life (mi)
26	50,000
28	66,000
31	78,000
35	81,000
38	74,000
42	70,000
45	59,000

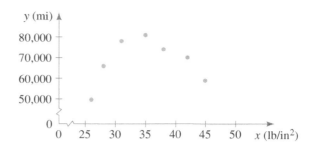

2. **Too Many Corn Plants per Acre?**   The more corn a farmer plants per acre, the greater is the yield the farmer can expect, but only up to a point. Too many plants per acre can cause overcrowding and decrease yields. The data give crop yields per acre for various densities of corn plantings, as found by researchers at a university test farm.

(a) Find the quadratic polynomial that best fits the data.

(b) Draw a graph of the polynomial from part (a) together with a scatter plot of the data.

(c) Use your result from part (b) to estimate the yield for 37,000 plants per acre.

Density (plants/acre)	Crop yield (bushels/acre)
15,000	43
20,000	98
25,000	118
30,000	140
35,000	142
40,000	122
45,000	93
50,000	67

3. **How Fast Can You List Your Favorite Things?**   If you are asked to make a list of objects in a certain category, how fast you can list them follows a predictable pattern. For example, if you try to name as many vegetables as you can, you'll probably think of several right away—for example, carrots, peas, beans, corn, and so on. Then after a pause you might think of ones you eat less frequently—perhaps zucchini, eggplant, and asparagus. Finally, a few more exotic vegetables might come to mind—artichokes, jicama, bok choy, and the like. A psychologist performs this experiment on a number of subjects. The table below gives the average number of vegetables that the subjects named by a given number of seconds.

(a) Find the cubic polynomial that best fits the data.

(b) Draw a graph of the polynomial from part (a) together with a scatter plot of the data.

(c) Use your result from part (b) to estimate the number of vegetables that subjects would be able to name in 40 seconds.

(d) According to the model, how long (to the nearest 0.1 second) would it take a person to name five vegetables?

Seconds	Number of vegetables
1	2
2	6
5	10
10	12
15	14
20	15
25	18
30	21

4. **Clothing Sales Are Seasonal** Clothing sales tend to vary by season, with more clothes sold in spring and fall. The table gives sales figures for each month at a certain clothing store.

   (a) Find the quartic (fourth-degree) polynomial that best fits the data.

   (b) Draw a graph of the polynomial from part (a) together with a scatter plot of the data.

   (c) Do you think that a quartic polynomial is a good model for these data? Explain.

Month	Sales ($)
January	8,000
February	18,000
March	22,000
April	31,000
May	29,000
June	21,000
July	22,000
August	26,000
September	38,000
October	40,000
November	27,000
December	15,000

5. **Height of a Baseball** A baseball is thrown upward, and its height measured at 0.5-second intervals using a strobe light. The resulting data are given in the table.

   (a) Draw a scatter plot of the data. What degree polynomial is appropriate for modeling the data?

   (b) Find a polynomial model that best fits the data, and graph it on the scatter plot.

   (c) Find the times when the ball is 20 ft above the ground.

   (d) What is the maximum height attained by the ball?

Time (s)	Height (ft)
0	4.2
0.5	26.1
1.0	40.1
1.5	46.0
2.0	43.9
2.5	33.7
3.0	15.8

6. **Torricelli's Law** Water in a tank will flow out of a small hole in the bottom faster when the tank is nearly full than when it is nearly empty. According to Torricelli's Law, the height $h(t)$ of water remaining at time t is a quadratic function of t.

   A certain tank is filled with water and allowed to drain. The height of the water is measured at different times as shown in the table.

   (a) Find the quadratic polynomial that best fits the data.

   (b) Draw a graph of the polynomial from part (a) together with a scatter plot of the data.

   (c) Use your graph from part (b) to estimate how long it takes for the tank to drain completely.

Time (min)	Height (ft)
0	5.0
4	3.1
8	1.9
12	0.8
16	0.2

SCE/Sandia National Laboratory

CONIC SECTIONS

Conic sections are the curves we get when we make a straight cut in a cone, as shown in the figure. For example, if a cone is cut horizontally, the cross section is a circle. So a circle is a conic section. Other ways of cutting a cone produce parabolas, ellipses, and hyperbolas.

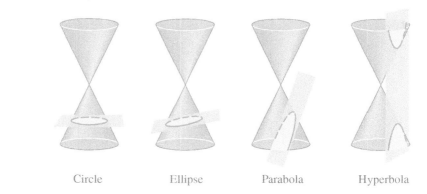

Circle   Ellipse   Parabola   Hyperbola

Our goal in this chapter is to find equations whose graphs are the conic sections. We already know from Section 1.8 that the graph of the equation $x^2 + y^2 = r^2$ is a circle. We will find equations for each of the other conic sections by analyzing their *geometric* properties.

The conic sections have interesting properties that make them useful for many real-world applications. For instance, a reflecting surface with parabolic cross-sections concentrates light at a single point. This property of a parabola is used in the construction of solar power plants, like the one in California pictured above.

11.1 PARABOLAS

Geometric Definition of a Parabola ▶ Equations and Graphs of Parabolas ▶ Applications

▼ Geometric Definition of a Parabola

We saw in Section 3.1 that the graph of the equation

$$y = ax^2 + bx + c$$

is a U-shaped curve called a *parabola* that opens either upward or downward, depending on whether the sign of a is positive or negative.

In this section we study parabolas from a geometric rather than an algebraic point of view. We begin with the geometric definition of a parabola and show how this leads to the algebraic formula that we are already familiar with.

> **GEOMETRIC DEFINITION OF A PARABOLA**
>
> A **parabola** is the set of points in the plane that are equidistant from a fixed point F (called the **focus**) and a fixed line l (called the **directrix**).

This definition is illustrated in Figure 1. The **vertex** V of the parabola lies halfway between the focus and the directrix, and the **axis of symmetry** is the line that runs through the focus perpendicular to the directrix.

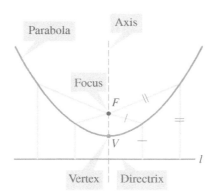

FIGURE 1

In this section we restrict our attention to parabolas that are situated with the vertex at the origin and that have a vertical or horizontal axis of symmetry. (Parabolas in more general positions will be considered in Sections 11.4 and 11.5.) If the focus of such a parabola is the point $F(0, p)$, then the axis of symmetry must be vertical, and the directrix has the equation $y = -p$. Figure 2 illustrates the case $p > 0$.

If $P(x, y)$ is any point on the parabola, then the distance from P to the focus F (using the Distance Formula) is

$$\sqrt{x^2 + (y - p)^2}$$

The distance from P to the directrix is

$$|y - (-p)| = |y + p|$$

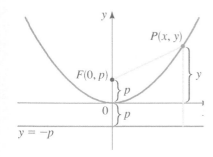

FIGURE 2

By the definition of a parabola these two distances must be equal:

$$\sqrt{x^2 + (y - p)^2} = |y + p|$$

$$x^2 + (y - p)^2 = |y + p|^2 = (y + p)^2 \qquad \text{Square both sides}$$

$$x^2 + y^2 - 2py + p^2 = y^2 + 2py + p^2 \qquad \text{Expand}$$

$$x^2 - 2py = 2py \qquad \text{Simplify}$$

$$x^2 = 4py$$

If $p > 0$, then the parabola opens upward; but if $p < 0$, it opens downward. When x is replaced by $-x$, the equation remains unchanged, so the graph is symmetric about the y-axis.

▼ Equations and Graphs of Parabolas

The following box summarizes what we have just proved about the equation and features of a parabola with a vertical axis.

PARABOLA WITH VERTICAL AXIS

The graph of the equation

$$x^2 = 4py$$

is a parabola with the following properties.

VERTEX	$V(0, 0)$
FOCUS	$F(0, p)$
DIRECTRIX	$y = -p$

The parabola opens upward if $p > 0$ or downward if $p < 0$.

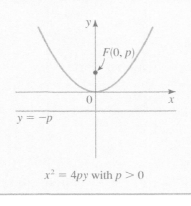 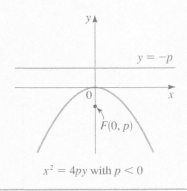

$x^2 = 4py$ with $p > 0$ $x^2 = 4py$ with $p < 0$

EXAMPLE 1 | Finding the Equation of a Parabola

Find an equation for the parabola with vertex $V(0, 0)$ and focus $F(0, 2)$, and sketch its graph.

SOLUTION Since the focus is $F(0, 2)$, we conclude that $p = 2$ (so the directrix is $y = -2$). Thus the equation of the parabola is

$$x^2 = 4(2)y \qquad x^2 = 4py \text{ with } p = 2$$

$$x^2 = 8y$$

Since $p = 2 > 0$, the parabola opens upward. See Figure 3.

❧ NOW TRY EXERCISES **29** AND **41**

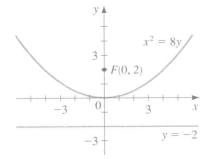

FIGURE 3

EXAMPLE 2 | Finding the Focus and Directrix of a Parabola
from Its Equation

Find the focus and directrix of the parabola $y = -x^2$, and sketch the graph.

SOLUTION   To find the focus and directrix, we put the given equation in the standard form $x^2 = -y$. Comparing this to the general equation $x^2 = 4py$, we see that $4p = -1$, so $p = -\frac{1}{4}$. Thus the focus is $F\left(0, -\frac{1}{4}\right)$, and the directrix is $y = \frac{1}{4}$. The graph of the parabola, together with the focus and the directrix, is shown in Figure 4(a). We can also draw the graph using a graphing calculator as shown in Figure 4(b).

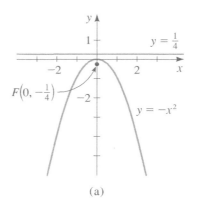

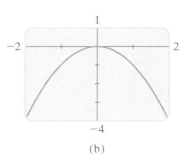

FIGURE 4

(a)   (b)

✎ NOW TRY EXERCISE **11**

Reflecting the graph in Figure 2 about the diagonal line $y = x$ has the effect of interchanging the roles of x and y. This results in a parabola with horizontal axis. By the same method as before, we can prove the following properties.

PARABOLA WITH HORIZONTAL AXIS

The graph of the equation

$$y^2 = 4px$$

is a parabola with the following properties.

VERTEX	$V(0, 0)$
FOCUS	$F(p, 0)$
DIRECTRIX	$x = -p$

The parabola opens to the right if $p > 0$ or to the left if $p < 0$.

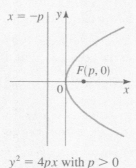

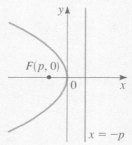

$y^2 = 4px$ with $p > 0$ $y^2 = 4px$ with $p < 0$

EXAMPLE 3 | A Parabola with Horizontal Axis

A parabola has the equation $6x + y^2 = 0$.

(a) Find the focus and directrix of the parabola, and sketch the graph.

(b) Use a graphing calculator to draw the graph.

SOLUTION

(a) To find the focus and directrix, we put the given equation in the standard form $y^2 = -6x$. Comparing this to the general equation $y^2 = 4px$, we see that $4p = -6$, so $p = -\frac{3}{2}$. Thus the focus is $F\left(-\frac{3}{2}, 0\right)$ and the directrix is $x = \frac{3}{2}$. Since $p < 0$, the parabola opens to the left. The graph of the parabola, together with the focus and the directrix, is shown in Figure 5(a) below.

(b) To draw the graph using a graphing calculator, we need to solve for y.

$$6x + y^2 = 0$$

$$y^2 = -6x \qquad \text{Subtract } 6x$$

$$y = \pm\sqrt{-6x} \qquad \text{Take square roots}$$

To obtain the graph of the parabola, we graph both functions

$$y = \sqrt{-6x} \qquad \text{and} \qquad y = -\sqrt{-6x}$$

as shown in Figure 5(b).

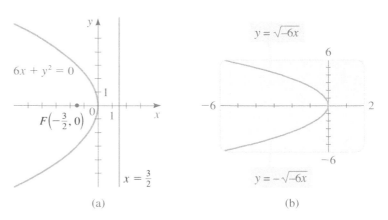

FIGURE 5

(a)   (b)

NOW TRY EXERCISE **13**

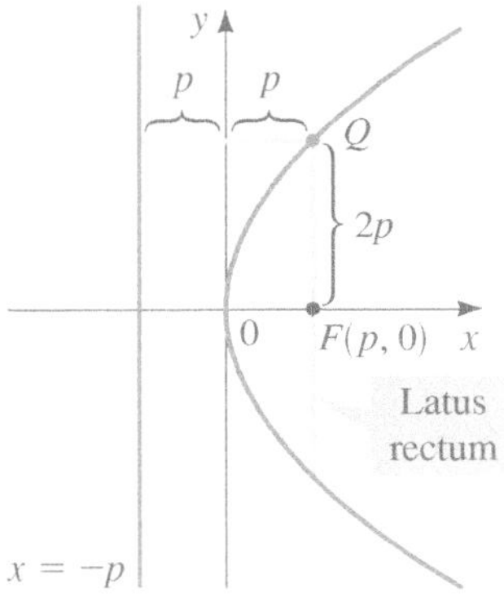

The equation $y^2 = 4px$, does not define y as a function of x (see page 158). So to use a graphing calculator to graph a parabola with a horizontal axis, we must first solve for y. This leads to two functions: $y = \sqrt{4px}$ and $y = -\sqrt{4px}$. We need to graph both functions to get the complete graph of the parabola. For example, in Figure 5(b) we had to graph both $y = \sqrt{-6x}$ and $y = -\sqrt{-6x}$ to graph the parabola $y^2 = -6x$.

We can use the coordinates of the focus to estimate the "width" of a parabola when sketching its graph. The line segment that runs through the focus perpendicular to the axis, with endpoints on the parabola, is called the **latus rectum**, and its length is the **focal diameter**. From Figure 6 we can see that the distance from an endpoint Q of the latus rectum to the directrix is $|2p|$. Thus the distance from Q to the focus must be $|2p|$ as well (by the definition of a parabola), so the focal diameter is $|4p|$. In the next example we use the focal diameter to determine the "width" of a parabola when graphing it.

FIGURE 6

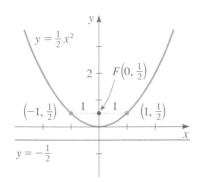

FIGURE 7

EXAMPLE 4 | The Focal Diameter of a Parabola

Find the focus, directrix, and focal diameter of the parabola $y = \frac{1}{2}x^2$, and sketch its graph.

SOLUTION   We first put the equation in the form $x^2 = 4py$.

$$y = \tfrac{1}{2}x^2$$

$$x^2 = 2y \qquad \text{Multiply by 2, switch sides}$$

From this equation we see that $4p = 2$, so the focal diameter is 2. Solving for p gives $p = \frac{1}{2}$, so the focus is $\left(0, \frac{1}{2}\right)$ and the directrix is $y = -\frac{1}{2}$. Since the focal diameter is 2, the latus rectum extends 1 unit to the left and 1 unit to the right of the focus. The graph is sketched in Figure 7.

✎. NOW TRY EXERCISE **15**

In the next example we graph a family of parabolas, to show how changing the distance between the focus and the vertex affects the "width" of a parabola.

EXAMPLE 5 | A Family of Parabolas

(a) Find equations for the parabolas with vertex at the origin and foci $F_1\left(0, \frac{1}{8}\right)$, $F_2\left(0, \frac{1}{2}\right)$, $F_3(0, 1)$, and $F_4(0, 4)$.

(b) Draw the graphs of the parabolas in part (a). What do you conclude?

SOLUTION

(a) Since the foci are on the positive y-axis, the parabolas open upward and have equations of the form $x^2 = 4py$. This leads to the following equations.

Focus	p	Equation $x^2 = 4py$	Form of the equation for graphing calculator
$F_1\left(0, \frac{1}{8}\right)$	$p = \frac{1}{8}$	$x^2 = \frac{1}{2}y$	$y = 2x^2$
$F_2\left(0, \frac{1}{2}\right)$	$p = \frac{1}{2}$	$x^2 = 2y$	$y = 0.5x^2$
$F_3(0, 1)$	$p = 1$	$x^2 = 4y$	$y = 0.25x^2$
$F_4(0, 4)$	$p = 4$	$x^2 = 16y$	$y = 0.0625x^2$

(b) The graphs are drawn in Figure 8. We see that the closer the focus is to the vertex, the narrower the parabola.

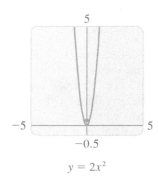

$y = 2x^2$

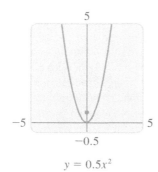

$y = 0.5x^2$

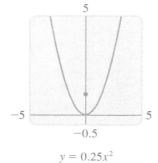

$y = 0.25x^2$

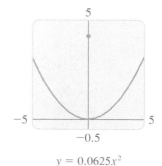

$y = 0.0625x^2$

FIGURE 8   A family of parabolas

✎. NOW TRY EXERCISE **51**

▼ Applications

Parabolas have an important property that makes them useful as reflectors for lamps and telescopes. Light from a source placed at the focus of a surface with parabolic cross section will be reflected in such a way that it travels parallel to the axis of the parabola (see Figure 9). Thus, a parabolic mirror reflects the light into a beam of parallel rays. Conversely, light approaching the reflector in rays parallel to its axis of symmetry is concentrated to the focus. This *reflection property*, which can be proved by using calculus, is used in the construction of reflecting telescopes.

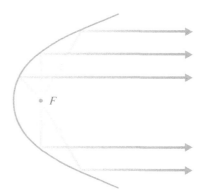

FIGURE 9 Parabolic reflector

EXAMPLE 6 | Finding the Focal Point of a Searchlight Reflector

A searchlight has a parabolic reflector that forms a "bowl," which is 12 in. wide from rim to rim and 8 in. deep, as shown in Figure 10. If the filament of the light bulb is located at the focus, how far from the vertex of the reflector is it?

FIGURE 10 A parabolic reflector

ARCHIMEDES (287–212 B.C.) was the greatest mathematician of the ancient world. He was born in Syracuse, a Greek colony on Sicily, a generation after Euclid (see page 497). One of his many discoveries is the Law of the Lever (see page 71). He famously said, "Give me a place to stand and a fulcrum for my lever, and I can lift the earth." Renowned as a mechanical genius for his many engineering inventions, he designed pulleys for lifting heavy ships and the spiral screw for transporting water to higher levels. He is said to have used parabolic mirrors to concentrate the rays of the sun to set fire to Roman ships attacking Syracuse.

King Hieron II of Syracuse once suspected a goldsmith of keeping part of the gold intended for the king's crown and replacing it with an equal amount of silver. The king asked Archimedes for advice. While in deep thought at a public bath, Archimedes discovered the solution to the king's problem when he noticed that his body's volume was the same as the volume of water it displaced from the tub. Using this insight he was able to measure the volume of each crown, and so determine which was the denser, all-gold crown. As the story is told, he ran home naked, shouting "Eureka, eureka!" ("I have found it, I have found it!") This incident attests to his enormous powers of concentration.

In spite of his engineering prowess, Archimedes was most proud of his mathematical discoveries. These include the formulas for the volume of a sphere, $\left(V = \frac{4}{3}\pi r^3\right)$ and the surface area of a sphere $\left(S = 4\pi r^2\right)$ and a careful analysis of the properties of parabolas and other conics.

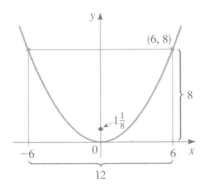

FIGURE 11

SOLUTION We introduce a coordinate system and place a parabolic cross section of the reflector so that its vertex is at the origin and its axis is vertical (see Figure 11). Then the equation of this parabola has the form $x^2 = 4py$. From Figure 11 we see that the point $(6, 8)$ lies on the parabola. We use this to find p.

$$6^2 = 4p(8) \qquad \text{The point } (6, 8) \text{ satisfies the equation } x^2 = 4py$$
$$36 = 32p$$
$$p = \tfrac{9}{8}$$

The focus is $F\left(0, \tfrac{9}{8}\right)$, so the distance between the vertex and the focus is $\tfrac{9}{8} = 1\tfrac{1}{8}$ in. Because the filament is positioned at the focus, it is located $1\tfrac{1}{8}$ in. from the vertex of the reflector.

▸ NOW TRY EXERCISE **53**

11.1 EXERCISES

CONCEPTS

1. A parabola is the set of all points in the plane that are equidistant from a fixed point called the _____ and a fixed line called the _____ of the parabola.

2. The graph of the equation $x^2 = 4py$ is a parabola with focus $F(\_\_, \_\_)$ and directrix $y =$ _____. So the graph of $x^2 = 12y$ is a parabola with focus $F(\_\_, \_\_)$ and directrix $y =$ _____.

3. The graph of the equation $y^2 = 4px$ is a parabola with focus $F(\_\_, \_\_)$ and directrix $x =$ _____. So the graph of $y^2 = 12x$ is a parabola with focus $F(\_\_, \_\_)$ and directrix $x =$ _____.

4. Label the focus, directrix, and vertex on the graphs given for the parabolas in Exercises 2 and 3.
  (a) $x^2 = 12y$ **(b)** $y^2 = 12x$

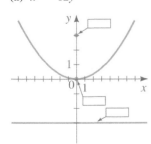

SKILLS

5–10 ■ Match the equation with the graphs labeled I–VI. Give reasons for your answers.

5. $y^2 = 2x$ **6.** $y^2 = -\tfrac{1}{4}x$

7. $x^2 = -6y$ **8.** $2x^2 = y$

9. $y^2 - 8x = 0$ **10.** $12y + x^2 = 0$

I
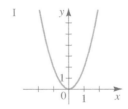

II
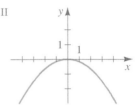

III
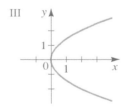

IV
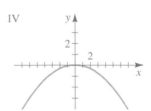

V
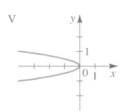

VI
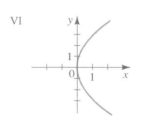

11–22 ■ Find the focus, directrix, and focal diameter of the parabola, and sketch its graph.

11. $x^2 = 9y$ **12.** $x^2 = y$

13. $y^2 = 4x$ **14.** $y^2 = 3x$

15. $y = 5x^2$ **16.** $y = -2x^2$

17. $x = -8y^2$ **18.** $x = \tfrac{1}{2}y^2$

19. $x^2 + 6y = 0$ **20.** $x - 7y^2 = 0$

21. $5x + 3y^2 = 0$ **22.** $8x^2 + 12y = 0$

23–28 ■ Use a graphing device to graph the parabola.

23. $x^2 = 16y$ **24.** $x^2 = -8y$

25. $y^2 = -\frac{1}{3}x$ **26.** $8y^2 = x$

27. $4x + y^2 = 0$ **28.** $x - 2y^2 = 0$

29–40 ■ Find an equation for the parabola that has its vertex at the origin and satisfies the given condition(s).

29. Focus: $F(0, 2)$ **30.** Focus: $F\left(0, -\frac{1}{2}\right)$

31. Focus: $F(-8, 0)$ **32.** Focus: $F(5, 0)$

33. Directrix: $x = 2$ **34.** Directrix: $y = 6$

35. Directrix: $y = -10$ **36.** Directrix: $x = -\frac{1}{8}$

37. Focus on the positive x-axis, 2 units away from the directrix

38. Directrix has y-intercept 6

39. Opens upward with focus 5 units from the vertex

40. Focal diameter 8 and focus on the negative y-axis

41–50 ■ Find an equation of the parabola whose graph is shown.

41.

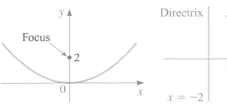

42.

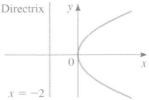

43.

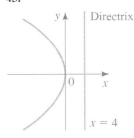

44.

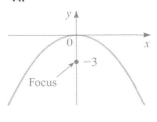

45.

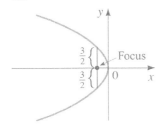

46.

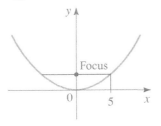

47.

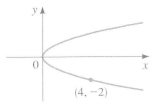

48.

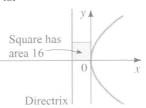

49.

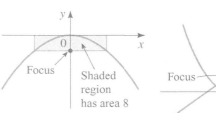

50.

51. (a) Find equations for the family of parabolas with vertex at the origin and with directrixes $y = \frac{1}{2}$, $y = 1$, $y = 4$, and $y = 8$.
  (b) Draw the graphs. What do you conclude?

52. (a) Find equations for the family of parabolas with vertex at the origin, focus on the positive y-axis, and with focal diameters 1, 2, 4, and 8.
  (b) Draw the graphs. What do you conclude?

APPLICATIONS

53. Parabolic Reflector A lamp with a parabolic reflector is shown in the figure. The bulb is placed at the focus, and the focal diameter is 12 cm.
  (a) Find an equation of the parabola.
  (b) Find the diameter $d(C, D)$ of the opening, 20 cm from the vertex.

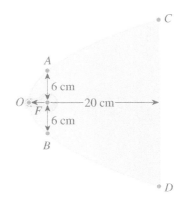

54. Satellite Dish A reflector for a satellite dish is parabolic in cross section, with the receiver at the focus F. The reflector is 1 ft deep and 20 ft wide from rim to rim (see the figure). How far is the receiver from the vertex of the parabolic reflector?

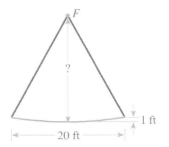

55. Suspension Bridge In a suspension bridge the shape of the suspension cables is parabolic. The bridge shown in the figure has towers that are 600 m apart, and the lowest point of the suspension cables is 150 m below the top of the towers. Find the equation of the parabolic part of the cables, placing the origin of the coordinate system at the vertex. [*Note*: This equation is used to find the length of cable needed in the construction of the bridge.]

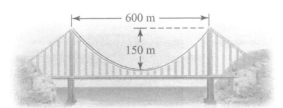

56. Reflecting Telescope The Hale telescope at the Mount Palomar Observatory has a 200-in. mirror, as shown in the figure. The mirror is constructed in a parabolic shape that collects light from the stars and focuses it at the **prime focus**, that is, the focus of the parabola. The mirror is 3.79 in. deep at its center. Find the **focal length** of this parabolic mirror, that is, the distance from the vertex to the focus.

DISCOVERY ▪ DISCUSSION ▪ WRITING

57. Parabolas in the Real World Several examples of the uses of parabolas are given in the text. Find other situations in real life in which parabolas occur. Consult a scientific encyclopedia in the reference section of your library, or search the Internet.

58. Light Cone from a Flashlight A flashlight is held to form a lighted area on the ground, as shown in the figure. Is it possible to angle the flashlight in such a way that the boundary of the lighted area is a parabola? Explain your answer.

> **DISCOVERY PROJECT** Rolling Down a Ramp
>
> In this project we investigate the process of modeling the motion of falling objects using a calculator-based motion detector. You can find the project at the book companion website: **www.stewartmath.com**

11.2 ELLIPSES

Geometric Definition of an Ellipse ▶ Equations and Graphs of Ellipses ▶ Eccentricity of an Ellipse

▼ Geometric Definition of an Ellipse

An ellipse is an oval curve that looks like an elongated circle. More precisely, we have the following definition.

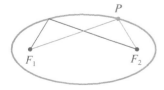

FIGURE 1

> **GEOMETRIC DEFINITION OF AN ELLIPSE**
>
> An **ellipse** is the set of all points in the plane the sum of whose distances from two fixed points F_1 and F_2 is a constant. (See Figure 1.) These two fixed points are the **foci** (plural of **focus**) of the ellipse.

The geometric definition suggests a simple method for drawing an ellipse. Place a sheet of paper on a drawing board, and insert thumbtacks at the two points that are to be the foci of the ellipse. Attach the ends of a string to the tacks, as shown in Figure 2(a). With the point of a pencil, hold the string taut. Then carefully move the pencil around the foci, keeping the string taut at all times. The pencil will trace out an ellipse, because the sum of the distances from the point of the pencil to the foci will always equal the length of the string, which is constant.

If the string is only slightly longer than the distance between the foci, then the ellipse that is traced out will be elongated in shape, as in Figure 2(a), but if the foci are close together relative to the length of the string, the ellipse will be almost circular, as shown in Figure 2(b).

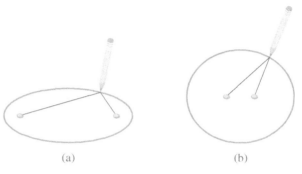

(a)   (b)

FIGURE 2

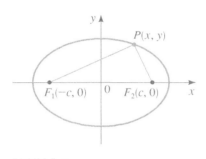

FIGURE 3

To obtain the simplest equation for an ellipse, we place the foci on the x-axis at $F_1(-c, 0)$ and $F_2(c, 0)$ so that the origin is halfway between them (see Figure 3).

For later convenience we let the sum of the distances from a point on the ellipse to the foci be $2a$. Then if $P(x, y)$ is any point on the ellipse, we have

$$d(P, F_1) + d(P, F_2) = 2a$$

So from the Distance Formula we have

$$\sqrt{(x + c)^2 + y^2} + \sqrt{(x - c)^2 + y^2} = 2a$$

or
$$\sqrt{(x - c)^2 + y^2} = 2a - \sqrt{(x + c)^2 + y^2}$$

Squaring each side and expanding, we get

$$x^2 - 2cx + c^2 + y^2 = 4a^2 - 4a\sqrt{(x + c)^2 + y^2} + (x^2 + 2cx + c^2 + y^2)$$

which simplifies to

$$4a\sqrt{(x + c)^2 + y^2} = 4a^2 + 4cx$$

Dividing each side by 4 and squaring again, we get

$$a^2[(x + c)^2 + y^2] = (a^2 + cx)^2$$

$$a^2x^2 + 2a^2cx + a^2c^2 + a^2y^2 = a^4 + 2a^2cx + c^2x^2$$

$$(a^2 - c^2)x^2 + a^2y^2 = a^2(a^2 - c^2)$$

Since the sum of the distances from P to the foci must be larger than the distance between the foci, we have that $2a > 2c$, or $a > c$. Thus $a^2 - c^2 > 0$, and we can divide each side of the preceding equation by $a^2(a^2 - c^2)$ to get

$$\frac{x^2}{a^2} + \frac{y^2}{a^2 - c^2} = 1$$

For convenience let $b^2 = a^2 - c^2$ (with $b > 0$). Since $b^2 < a^2$, it follows that $b < a$. The preceding equation then becomes

$$\frac{x^2}{a^2} + \frac{y^2}{b^2} = 1 \qquad \text{with } a > b$$

This is the equation of the ellipse. To graph it, we need to know the x- and y-intercepts. Setting $y = 0$, we get

$$\frac{x^2}{a^2} = 1$$

so $x^2 = a^2$, or $x = \pm a$. Thus, the ellipse crosses the x-axis at $(a, 0)$ and $(-a, 0)$, as in Figure 4. These points are called the **vertices** of the ellipse, and the segment that joins them is called the **major axis**. Its length is $2a$.

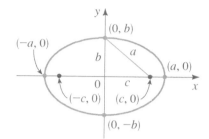

FIGURE 4
$\dfrac{x^2}{a^2} + \dfrac{y^2}{b^2} = 1$ with $a > b$

Similarly, if we set $x = 0$, we get $y = \pm b$, so the ellipse crosses the y-axis at $(0, b)$ and $(0, -b)$. The segment that joins these points is called the **minor axis**, and it has length $2b$. Note that $2a > 2b$, so the major axis is longer than the minor axis. The origin is the **center** of the ellipse.

If the foci of the ellipse are placed on the y-axis at $(0, \pm c)$ rather than on the x-axis, then the roles of x and y are reversed in the preceding discussion, and we get a vertical ellipse.

▼ Equations and Graphs of Ellipses

The following box summarizes what we have just proved about the equation and features of an ellipse centered at the origin.

ELLIPSE WITH CENTER AT THE ORIGIN

The graph of each of the following equations is an ellipse with center at the origin and having the given properties.

In the standard equation for an ellipse, a^2 is the *larger* denominator and b^2 is the *smaller*. To find c^2, we subtract: larger denominator minus smaller denominator.

EQUATION	$\dfrac{x^2}{a^2} + \dfrac{y^2}{b^2} = 1$	$\dfrac{x^2}{b^2} + \dfrac{y^2}{a^2} = 1$
	$a > b > 0$	$a > b > 0$
VERTICES	$(\pm a, 0)$	$(0, \pm a)$
MAJOR AXIS	Horizontal, length $2a$	Vertical, length $2a$
MINOR AXIS	Vertical, length $2b$	Horizontal, length $2b$
FOCI	$(\pm c, 0)$, $c^2 = a^2 - b^2$	$(0, \pm c)$, $c^2 = a^2 - b^2$
GRAPH		

EXAMPLE 1 | Sketching an Ellipse

An ellipse has the equation

$$\frac{x^2}{9} + \frac{y^2}{4} = 1$$

(a) Find the foci, the vertices, and the lengths of the major and minor axes, and sketch the graph.

(b) Draw the graph using a graphing calculator.

SOLUTION

(a) Since the denominator of x^2 is larger, the ellipse has a horizontal major axis. This gives $a^2 = 9$ and $b^2 = 4$, so $c^2 = a^2 - b^2 = 9 - 4 = 5$. Thus $a = 3$, $b = 2$, and $c = \sqrt{5}$.

FOCI	$(\pm\sqrt{5}, 0)$
VERTICES	$(\pm 3, 0)$
LENGTH OF MAJOR AXIS	6
LENGTH OF MINOR AXIS	4

The graph is shown in Figure 5(a).

(b) To draw the graph using a graphing calculator, we need to solve for y.

$$\frac{x^2}{9} + \frac{y^2}{4} = 1$$

$$\frac{y^2}{4} = 1 - \frac{x^2}{9} \qquad \text{Subtract } \frac{x^2}{9}$$

$$y^2 = 4\left(1 - \frac{x^2}{9}\right) \qquad \text{Multiply by 4}$$

$$y = \pm 2\sqrt{1 - \frac{x^2}{9}} \qquad \text{Take square roots}$$

To obtain the graph of the ellipse, we graph both functions

$$y = 2\sqrt{1 - x^2/9} \qquad \text{and} \qquad y = -2\sqrt{1 - x^2/9}$$

as shown in Figure 5(b).

The orbits of the planets are ellipses, with the sun at one focus.

Note that the equation of an ellipse does not define y as a function of x (see page 158). That's why we need to graph two functions to graph an ellipse.

FIGURE 5
$$\frac{x^2}{9} + \frac{y^2}{4} = 1$$

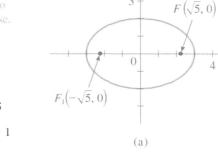

(a)

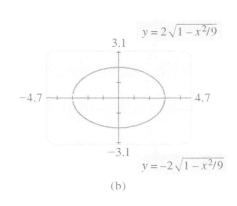

(b)

NOW TRY EXERCISE **9**

EXAMPLE 2 | Finding the Foci of an Ellipse

Find the foci of the ellipse $16x^2 + 9y^2 = 144$, and sketch its graph.

SOLUTION First we put the equation in standard form. Dividing by 144, we get

$$\frac{x^2}{9} + \frac{y^2}{16} = 1$$

Since $16 > 9$, this is an ellipse with its foci on the y-axis and with $a = 4$ and $b = 3$. We have

$$c^2 = a^2 - b^2 = 16 - 9 = 7$$
$$c = \sqrt{7}$$

Thus the foci are $(0, \pm\sqrt{7})$. The graph is shown in Figure 6(a).

We can also draw the graph using a graphing calculator as shown in Figure 6(b).

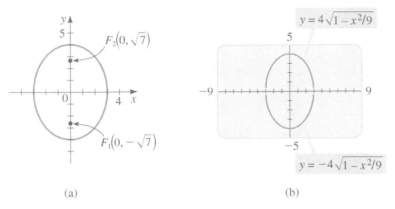

FIGURE 6
$16x^2 + 9y^2 = 144$

(a)

(b)

✎. NOW TRY EXERCISE **11**

EXAMPLE 3 | Finding the Equation of an Ellipse

The vertices of an ellipse are $(\pm4, 0)$, and the foci are $(\pm2, 0)$. Find its equation, and sketch the graph.

SOLUTION Since the vertices are $(\pm4, 0)$, we have $a = 4$ and the major axis is horizontal. The foci are $(\pm2, 0)$, so $c = 2$. To write the equation, we need to find b. Since $c^2 = a^2 - b^2$, we have

$$2^2 = 4^2 - b^2$$
$$b^2 = 16 - 4 = 12$$

Thus the equation of the ellipse is

$$\frac{x^2}{16} + \frac{y^2}{12} = 1$$

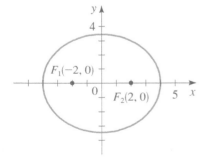

FIGURE 7
$$\frac{x^2}{16} + \frac{y^2}{12} = 1$$

The graph is shown in Figure 7.

✎. NOW TRY EXERCISES **25** AND **33**

▼ Eccentricity of an Ellipse

We saw earlier in this section (Figure 2) that if $2a$ is only slightly greater than $2c$, the ellipse is long and thin, whereas if $2a$ is much greater than $2c$, the ellipse is almost circular. We measure the deviation of an ellipse from being circular by the ratio of a and c.

DEFINITION OF ECCENTRICITY

For the ellipse $\dfrac{x^2}{a^2} + \dfrac{y^2}{b^2} = 1$ or $\dfrac{x^2}{b^2} + \dfrac{y^2}{a^2} = 1$ (with $a > b > 0$), the **eccentricity e** is the number

$$e = \frac{c}{a}$$

where $c = \sqrt{a^2 - b^2}$. The eccentricity of every ellipse satisfies $0 < e < 1$.

Thus if e is close to 1, then c is almost equal to a, and the ellipse is elongated in shape, but if e is close to 0, then the ellipse is close to a circle in shape. The eccentricity is a measure of how "stretched" the ellipse is.

In Figure 8 we show a number of ellipses to demonstrate the effect of varying the eccentricity e.

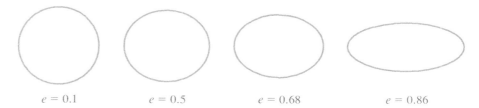

$e = 0.1$ $\qquad\qquad$ $e = 0.5$ $\qquad\qquad$ $e = 0.68$ $\qquad\qquad$ $e = 0.86$

FIGURE 8 Ellipses with various eccentricities

EXAMPLE 4 | Finding the Equation of an Ellipse from Its Eccentricity and Foci

Find the equation of the ellipse with foci $(0, \pm 8)$ and eccentricity $e = \frac{4}{5}$, and sketch its graph.

SOLUTION We are given $e = \frac{4}{5}$ and $c = 8$. Thus

$$\frac{4}{5} = \frac{8}{a} \qquad \text{Eccentricity } e = \frac{c}{a}$$

$$4a = 40 \qquad \text{Cross-multiply}$$

$$a = 10$$

To find b, we use the fact that $c^2 = a^2 - b^2$.

$$8^2 = 10^2 - b^2$$

$$b^2 = 10^2 - 8^2 = 36$$

$$b = 6$$

Thus the equation of the ellipse is

$$\frac{x^2}{36} + \frac{y^2}{100} = 1$$

Because the foci are on the y-axis, the ellipse is oriented vertically. To sketch the ellipse, we find the intercepts: The x-intercepts are ± 6, and the y-intercepts are ± 10. The graph is sketched in Figure 9.

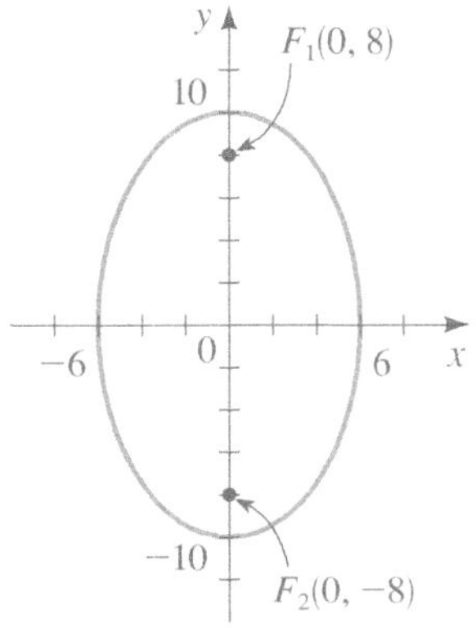

✎. NOW TRY EXERCISE **43**

FIGURE 9

$$\frac{x^2}{36} + \frac{y^2}{100} = 1$$

Gravitational attraction causes the planets to move in elliptical orbits around the sun with the sun at one focus. This remarkable property was first observed by Johannes Kepler and was later deduced by Isaac Newton from his inverse square Law of Gravity, using calculus. The orbits of the planets have different eccentricities, but most are nearly circular (see the margin).

Ellipses, like parabolas, have an interesting *reflection property* that leads to a number of practical applications. If a light source is placed at one focus of a reflecting surface with elliptical cross sections, then all the light will be reflected off the surface to the other focus, as shown in Figure 10. This principle, which works for sound waves as well as for light, is used in *lithotripsy*, a treatment for kidney stones. The patient is placed in a tub of water with elliptical cross sections in such a way that the kidney stone is accurately located at one focus. High-intensity sound waves generated at the other focus are reflected to the stone and destroy it with minimal damage to surrounding tissue. The patient is spared the trauma of surgery and recovers within days instead of weeks.

The reflection property of ellipses is also used in the construction of *whispering galleries*. Sound coming from one focus bounces off the walls and ceiling of an elliptical room and passes through the other focus. In these rooms even quiet whispers spoken at one focus can be heard clearly at the other. Famous whispering galleries include the National Statuary Hall of the U.S. Capitol in Washington, D.C. (see page 776), and the Mormon Tabernacle in Salt Lake City, Utah.

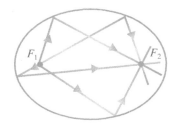

FIGURE 10

11.2 EXERCISES

CONCEPTS

1. An ellipse is the set of all points in the plane for which the _____ of the distances from two fixed points F_1 and F_2 is constant. The points F_1 and F_2 are called the _____ of the ellipse.

2. The graph of the equation $\dfrac{x^2}{a^2} + \dfrac{y^2}{b^2} = 1$ with $a > b > 0$ is an ellipse with vertices (__, __) and (__, __) and foci ($\pm c, 0$), where $c = $ _____. So the graph of $\dfrac{x^2}{5^2} + \dfrac{y^2}{4^2} = 1$ is an ellipse with vertices (__, __) and (__, __) and foci (__, __) and (__, __).

3. The graph of the equation $\dfrac{x^2}{b^2} + \dfrac{y^2}{a^2} = 1$ with $a > b > 0$ is an ellipse with vertices (__, __) and (__, __) and foci $(0, \pm c)$, where $c = $ _____. So the graph of $\dfrac{x^2}{4^2} + \dfrac{y^2}{5^2} = 1$

is an ellipse with vertices (__, __) and (__, __) and foci (__, __) and (__, __).

4. Label the vertices and foci on the graphs given for the ellipses in Exercises 2 and 3.

(a) $\dfrac{x^2}{5^2} + \dfrac{y^2}{4^2} = 1$ (b) $\dfrac{x^2}{4^2} + \dfrac{y^2}{5^2} = 1$

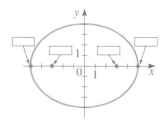

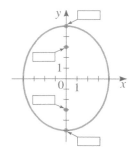

SKILLS

5–8 ■ Match the equation with the graphs labeled I–IV. Give reasons for your answers.

5. $\dfrac{x^2}{16} + \dfrac{y^2}{4} = 1$

6. $x^2 + \dfrac{y^2}{9} = 1$

7. $4x^2 + y^2 = 4$

8. $16x^2 + 25y^2 = 400$

I
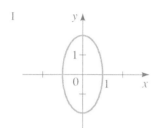

II
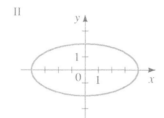

III
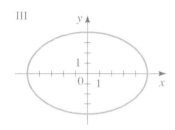

IV
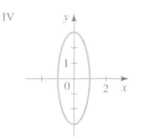

9–22 ■ Find the vertices, foci, and eccentricity of the ellipse. Determine the lengths of the major and minor axes, and sketch the graph.

9. $\dfrac{x^2}{25} + \dfrac{y^2}{9} = 1$

10. $\dfrac{x^2}{16} + \dfrac{y^2}{25} = 1$

11. $9x^2 + 4y^2 = 36$

12. $4x^2 + 25y^2 = 100$

13. $x^2 + 4y^2 = 16$

14. $4x^2 + y^2 = 16$

15. $2x^2 + y^2 = 3$

16. $5x^2 + 6y^2 = 30$

17. $x^2 + 4y^2 = 1$

18. $9x^2 + 4y^2 = 1$

19. $\frac{1}{2}x^2 + \frac{1}{8}y^2 = \frac{1}{4}$

20. $x^2 = 4 - 2y^2$

21. $y^2 = 1 - 2x^2$

22. $20x^2 + 4y^2 = 5$

23–28 ■ Find an equation for the ellipse whose graph is shown.

23.
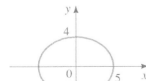

24.
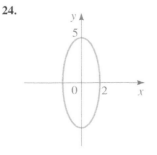

25.
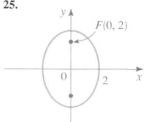

26.
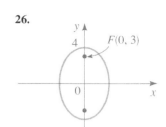

27.
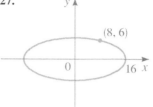

28.
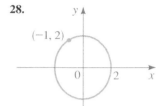

29–32 ■ Use a graphing device to graph the ellipse.

29. $\dfrac{x^2}{25} + \dfrac{y^2}{20} = 1$

30. $x^2 + \dfrac{y^2}{12} = 1$

31. $6x^2 + y^2 = 36$

32. $x^2 + 2y^2 = 8$

33–44 ■ Find an equation for the ellipse that satisfies the given conditions.

33. Foci: $(\pm 4, 0)$, vertices: $(\pm 5, 0)$

34. Foci: $(0, \pm 3)$, vertices: $(0, \pm 5)$

35. Length of major axis: 4, length of minor axis: 2, foci on y-axis

36. Length of major axis: 6, length of minor axis: 4, foci on x-axis

37. Foci: $(0, \pm 2)$, length of minor axis: 6

38. Foci: $(\pm 5, 0)$, length of major axis: 12

39. Endpoints of major axis: $(\pm 10, 0)$, distance between foci: 6

40. Endpoints of minor axis: $(0, \pm 3)$, distance between foci: 8

41. Length of major axis: 10, foci on x-axis, ellipse passes through the point $(\sqrt{5}, 2)$

42. Eccentricity: $\frac{1}{9}$, foci: $(0, \pm 2)$

43. Eccentricity: 0.8, foci: $(\pm 1.5, 0)$

44. Eccentricity: $\sqrt{3}/2$, foci on y-axis, length of major axis: 4

45–47 ■ Find the intersection points of the pair of ellipses. Sketch the graphs of each pair of equations on the same coordinate axes, and label the points of intersection.

45. $\begin{cases} 4x^2 + y^2 = 4 \\ 4x^2 + 9y^2 = 36 \end{cases}$

46. $\begin{cases} \dfrac{x^2}{16} + \dfrac{y^2}{9} = 1 \\ \dfrac{x^2}{9} + \dfrac{y^2}{16} = 1 \end{cases}$

47. $\begin{cases} 100x^2 + 25y^2 = 100 \\ x^2 + \dfrac{y^2}{9} = 1 \end{cases}$

48. The **ancillary circle** of an ellipse is the circle with radius equal to half the length of the minor axis and center the same as the ellipse (see the figure). The ancillary circle is thus the largest circle that can fit within an ellipse.

(a) Find an equation for the ancillary circle of the ellipse $x^2 + 4y^2 = 16$.

(b) For the ellipse and ancillary circle of part (a), show that if (s, t) is a point on the ancillary circle, then $(2s, t)$ is a point on the ellipse.

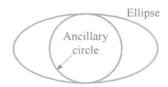

49. (a) Use a graphing device to sketch the top half (the portion in the first and second quadrants) of the family of ellipses $x^2 + ky^2 = 100$ for $k = 4, 10, 25$, and 50.

(b) What do the members of this family of ellipses have in common? How do they differ?

50. If $k > 0$, the following equation represents an ellipse:

$$\frac{x^2}{k} + \frac{y^2}{4 + k} = 1$$

Show that all the ellipses represented by this equation have the same foci, no matter what the value of k.

APPLICATIONS

51. Perihelion and Aphelion The planets move around the sun in elliptical orbits with the sun at one focus. The point in the orbit at which the planet is closest to the sun is called **perihelion**, and the point at which it is farthest is called **aphelion**. These points are the vertices of the orbit. The earth's distance from the sun is 147,000,000 km at perihelion and 153,000,000 km at aphelion. Find an equation for the earth's orbit. (Place the origin at the center of the orbit with the sun on the x-axis.)

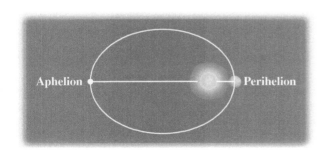

52. The Orbit of Pluto With an eccentricity of 0.25, Pluto's orbit is the most eccentric in the solar system. The length of the minor axis of its orbit is approximately 10,000,000,000 km. Find the distance between Pluto and the sun at perihelion and at aphelion. (See Exercise 51.)

53. Lunar Orbit For an object in an elliptical orbit around the moon, the points in the orbit that are closest to and farthest from the center of the moon are called **perilune** and **apolune**, respectively. These are the vertices of the orbit. The center of the moon is at one focus of the orbit. The *Apollo 11* spacecraft was placed in a lunar orbit with perilune at 68 mi and apolune at 195 mi above the surface of the moon. Assuming that the moon is a sphere of radius 1075 mi, find an equation for the orbit of *Apollo 11*. (Place the coordinate axes so that the origin is at the center of the orbit and the foci are located on the x-axis.)

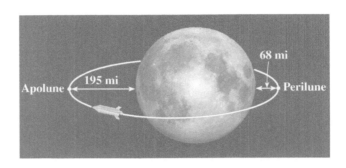

54. Plywood Ellipse A carpenter wishes to construct an elliptical table top from a sheet of plywood, 4 ft by 8 ft. He will trace out the ellipse using the "thumbtack and string" method illustrated in Figures 2 and 3. What length of string should he use, and how far apart should the tacks be located, if the ellipse is to be the largest possible that can be cut out of the plywood sheet?

55. Sunburst Window A "sunburst" window above a doorway is constructed in the shape of the top half of an ellipse, as shown in the figure. The window is 20 in. tall at its highest point and 80 in. wide at the bottom. Find the height of the window 25 in. from the center of the base.

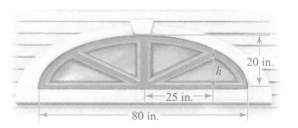

DISCOVERY ■ DISCUSSION ■ WRITING

56. Drawing an Ellipse on a Blackboard Try drawing an ellipse as accurately as possible on a blackboard. How would a piece of string and two friends help this process?

57. Light Cone from a Flashlight A flashlight shines on a wall, as shown in the figure. What is the shape of the boundary of the lighted area? Explain your answer.

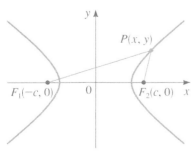

58. How Wide Is an Ellipse at Its Foci? A *latus rectum* for an ellipse is a line segment perpendicular to the major axis at a focus, with endpoints on the ellipse, as shown in the figure at the top of the next column. Show that the length of a latus rectum is $2b^2/a$ for the ellipse

$$\frac{x^2}{a^2} + \frac{y^2}{b^2} = 1 \quad \text{with } a > b$$

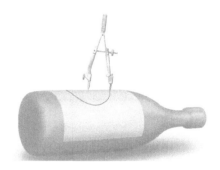

59. Is It an Ellipse? A piece of paper is wrapped around a cylindrical bottle, and then a compass is used to draw a circle on the paper, as shown in the figure. When the paper is laid flat, is the shape drawn on the paper an ellipse? (You don't need to prove your answer, but you might want to do the experiment and see what you get.)

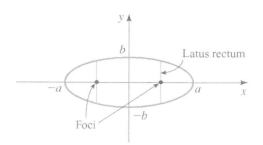

11.3 HYPERBOLAS

| Geometric Definition of a Hyperbola ▶ Equations and Graphs of Hyperbolas

▼ Geometric Definition of a Hyperbola

Although ellipses and hyperbolas have completely different shapes, their definitions and equations are similar. Instead of using the *sum* of distances from two fixed foci, as in the case of an ellipse, we use the *difference* to define a hyperbola.

> **GEOMETRIC DEFINITION OF A HYPERBOLA**
>
> A **hyperbola** is the set of all points in the plane, the difference of whose distances from two fixed points F_1 and F_2 is a constant. (See Figure 1.) These two fixed points are the **foci** of the hyperbola.

FIGURE 1 P is on the hyperbola if $|d(P, F_1) - d(P, F_2)| = 2a$.

As in the case of the ellipse, we get the simplest equation for the hyperbola by placing the foci on the x-axis at $(\pm c, 0)$, as shown in Figure 1. By definition, if $P(x, y)$ lies on the hyperbola, then either $d(P, F_1) - d(P, F_2)$ or $d(P, F_2) - d(P, F_1)$ must equal some positive constant, which we call $2a$. Thus we have

$$d(P, F_1) - d(P, F_2) = \pm 2a$$

or

$$\sqrt{(x + c)^2 + y^2} - \sqrt{(x - c)^2 + y^2} = \pm 2a$$

Proceeding as we did in the case of the ellipse (Section 11.2), we simplify this to

$$(c^2 - a^2)x^2 - a^2y^2 = a^2(c^2 - a^2)$$

From triangle PF_1F_2 in Figure 1 we see that $|\,d(P, F_1) - d(P, F_2)\,| < 2c$. It follows that $2a < 2c$, or $a < c$. Thus $c^2 - a^2 > 0$, so we can set $b^2 = c^2 - a^2$. We then simplify the last displayed equation to get

$$\frac{x^2}{a^2} - \frac{y^2}{b^2} = 1$$

This is the *equation of the hyperbola*. If we replace x by $-x$ or y by $-y$ in this equation, it remains unchanged, so the hyperbola is symmetric about both the x- and y-axes and about the origin. The x-intercepts are $\pm a$, and the points $(a, 0)$ and $(-a, 0)$ are the **vertices** of the hyperbola. There is no y-intercept, because setting $x = 0$ in the equation of the hyperbola leads to $-y^2 = b^2$, which has no real solution. Furthermore, the equation of the hyperbola implies that

$$\frac{x^2}{a^2} = \frac{y^2}{b^2} + 1 \geq 1$$

so $x^2/a^2 \geq 1$; thus $x^2 \geq a^2$, and hence $x \geq a$ or $x \leq -a$. This means that the hyperbola consists of two parts, called its **branches**. The segment joining the two vertices on the separate branches is the **transverse axis** of the hyperbola, and the origin is called its **center**.

If we place the foci of the hyperbola on the y-axis rather than on the x-axis, this has the effect of reversing the roles of x and y in the derivation of the equation of the hyperbola. This leads to a hyperbola with a vertical transverse axis.

▼ Equations and Graphs of Hyperbolas

The main properties of hyperbolas are listed in the following box.

HYPERBOLA WITH CENTER AT THE ORIGIN

The graph of each of the following equations is a hyperbola with center at the origin and having the given properties.

EQUATION	$\dfrac{x^2}{a^2} - \dfrac{y^2}{b^2} = 1 \quad (a > 0, b > 0)$	$\dfrac{y^2}{a^2} - \dfrac{x^2}{b^2} = 1 \quad (a > 0, b > 0)$
VERTICES	$(\pm a, 0)$	$(0, \pm a)$
TRANSVERSE AXIS	Horizontal, length $2a$	Vertical, length $2a$
ASYMPTOTES	$y = \pm \dfrac{b}{a}x$	$y = \pm \dfrac{a}{b}x$
FOCI	$(\pm c, 0), \quad c^2 = a^2 + b^2$	$(0, \pm c), \quad c^2 = a^2 + b^2$
GRAPH	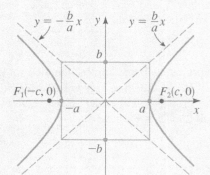	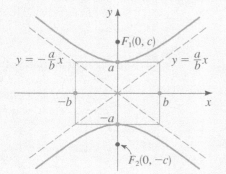

The *asymptotes* mentioned in this box are lines that the hyperbola approaches for large values of x and y. To find the asymptotes in the first case in the box, we solve the equation for y to get

$$y = \pm\frac{b}{a}\sqrt{x^2 - a^2}$$

$$= \pm\frac{b}{a}x\sqrt{1 - \frac{a^2}{x^2}}$$

As x gets large, a^2/x^2 gets closer to zero. In other words, as $x \to \infty$, we have $a^2/x^2 \to 0$. So for large x the value of y can be approximated as $y = \pm(b/a)x$. This shows that these lines are asymptotes of the hyperbola.

Asymptotes are an essential aid for graphing a hyperbola; they help us to determine its shape. A convenient way to find the asymptotes, for a hyperbola with horizontal transverse axis, is to first plot the points $(a, 0)$, $(-a, 0)$, $(0, b)$, and $(0, -b)$. Then sketch horizontal and vertical segments through these points to construct a rectangle, as shown in Figure 2(a). We call this rectangle the **central box** of the hyperbola. The slopes of the diagonals of the central box are $\pm b/a$, so by extending them, we obtain the asymptotes $y = \pm(b/a)x$, as sketched in Figure 2(b). Finally, we plot the vertices and use the asymptotes as a guide in sketching the hyperbola shown in Figure 2(c). (A similar procedure applies to graphing a hyperbola that has a vertical transverse axis.)

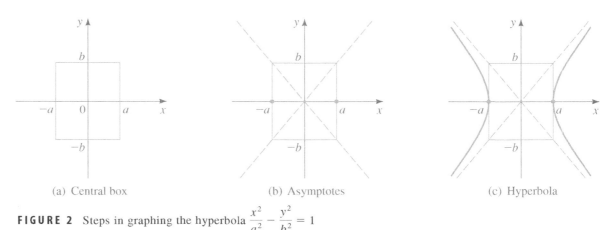

(a) Central box   (b) Asymptotes   (c) Hyperbola

FIGURE 2 Steps in graphing the hyperbola $\dfrac{x^2}{a^2} - \dfrac{y^2}{b^2} = 1$

HOW TO SKETCH A HYPERBOLA

1. **Sketch the Central Box.** This is the rectangle centered at the origin, with sides parallel to the axes, that crosses one axis at $\pm a$, the other at $\pm b$.

2. **Sketch the Asymptotes.** These are the lines obtained by extending the diagonals of the central box.

3. **Plot the Vertices.** These are the two x-intercepts or the two y-intercepts.

4. **Sketch the Hyperbola.** Start at a vertex, and sketch a branch of the hyperbola, approaching the asymptotes. Sketch the other branch in the same way.

EXAMPLE 1 | A Hyperbola with Horizontal Transverse Axis

A hyperbola has the equation

$$9x^2 - 16y^2 = 144$$

(a) Find the vertices, foci, and asymptotes, and sketch the graph.

(b) Draw the graph using a graphing calculator.

SOLUTION

(a) First we divide both sides of the equation by 144 to put it into standard form:

$$\frac{x^2}{16} - \frac{y^2}{9} = 1$$

Because the x^2-term is positive, the hyperbola has a horizontal transverse axis; its vertices and foci are on the x-axis. Since $a^2 = 16$ and $b^2 = 9$, we get $a = 4$, $b = 3$, and $c = \sqrt{16 + 9} = 5$. Thus we have

VERTICES	$(\pm 4, 0)$
FOCI	$(\pm 5, 0)$
ASYMPTOTES	$y = \pm \frac{3}{4} x$

After sketching the central box and asymptotes, we complete the sketch of the hyperbola as in Figure 3(a).

(b) To draw the graph using a graphing calculator, we need to solve for y.

$$9x^2 - 16y^2 = 144$$

$$-16y^2 = -9x^2 + 144 \qquad \text{Subtract } 9x^2$$

$$y^2 = 9\left(\frac{x^2}{16} - 1\right) \qquad \text{Divide by } -16 \text{ and factor } 9$$

$$y = \pm 3\sqrt{\frac{x^2}{16} - 1} \qquad \text{Take square roots}$$

To obtain the graph of the hyperbola, we graph the functions

$$y = 3\sqrt{(x^2/16) - 1} \qquad \text{and} \qquad y = -3\sqrt{(x^2/16) - 1}$$

as shown in Figure 3(b).

Note that the equation of a hyperbola does not define y as a function of x (see page 158). That's why we need to graph two functions to graph a hyperbola.

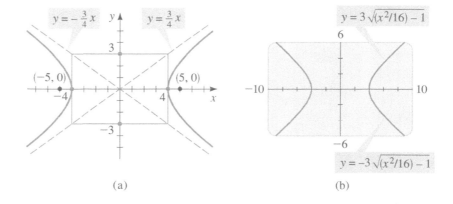

FIGURE 3
$9x^2 - 16y^2 = 144$

(a)　　　　(b)

NOW TRY EXERCISE **9**

EXAMPLE 2 | A Hyperbola with Vertical Transverse Axis

Find the vertices, foci, and asymptotes of the hyperbola, and sketch its graph.

$$x^2 - 9y^2 + 9 = 0$$

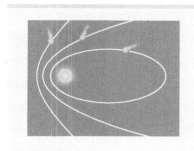

Paths of Comets

The path of a comet is an ellipse, a parabola, or a hyperbola with the sun at a focus. This fact can be proved by using calculus and Newton's laws of motion.* If the path is a parabola or a hyperbola, the comet will never return. If the path is an ellipse, it can be determined precisely when and where the comet can be seen again. Halley's comet has an elliptical path and returns every 75 years; it was last seen in 1987. The brightest comet of the 20th century was comet Hale-Bopp, seen in 1997. Its orbit is a very eccentric ellipse; it is expected to return to the inner solar system around the year 4377.

———
*James Stewart, *Calculus,* 7th ed. (Belmont, CA: Brooks/Cole, 2012), pages 868 and 872.

FIGURE 4
$x^2 - 9y^2 + 9 = 0$

SOLUTION We begin by writing the equation in the standard form for a hyperbola.

$$x^2 - 9y^2 = -9$$

$$y^2 - \frac{x^2}{9} = 1 \qquad \text{Divide by } -9$$

Because the y^2-term is positive, the hyperbola has a vertical transverse axis; its foci and vertices are on the y-axis. Since $a^2 = 1$ and $b^2 = 9$, we get $a = 1$, $b = 3$, and $c = \sqrt{1+9} = \sqrt{10}$. Thus we have

VERTICES	$(0, \pm 1)$
FOCI	$(0, \pm\sqrt{10})$
ASYMPTOTES	$y = \pm\frac{1}{3}x$

We sketch the central box and asymptotes, then complete the graph, as shown in Figure 4(a). We can also draw the graph using a graphing calculator, as shown in Figure 4(b).

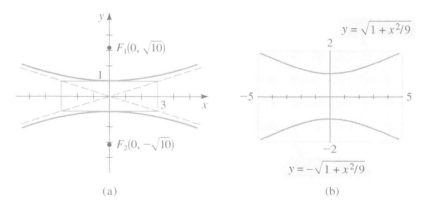

(a)   (b)

NOW TRY EXERCISE **17**

EXAMPLE 3 | Finding the Equation of a Hyperbola from Its Vertices and Foci

Find the equation of the hyperbola with vertices $(\pm 3, 0)$ and foci $(\pm 4, 0)$. Sketch the graph.

SOLUTION Since the vertices are on the x-axis, the hyperbola has a horizontal transverse axis. Its equation is of the form

$$\frac{x^2}{3^2} - \frac{y^2}{b^2} = 1$$

We have $a = 3$ and $c = 4$. To find b, we use the relation $a^2 + b^2 = c^2$:

$$3^2 + b^2 = 4^2$$

$$b^2 = 4^2 - 3^2 = 7$$

$$b = \sqrt{7}$$

Thus the equation of the hyperbola is

$$\frac{x^2}{9} - \frac{y^2}{7} = 1$$

The graph is shown in Figure 5.

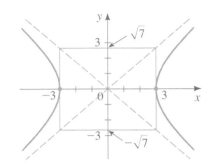

FIGURE 5

$$\frac{x^2}{9} - \frac{y^2}{7} = 1$$

✎ NOW TRY EXERCISES **21** AND **31**

EXAMPLE 4 | Finding the Equation of a Hyperbola from Its Vertices and Asymptotes

Find the equation and the foci of the hyperbola with vertices $(0, \pm 2)$ and asymptotes $y = \pm 2x$. Sketch the graph.

SOLUTION Since the vertices are on the y-axis, the hyperbola has a vertical transverse axis with $a = 2$. From the asymptote equation we see that $a/b = 2$. Since $a = 2$, we get $2/b = 2$, so $b = 1$. Thus the equation of the hyperbola is

$$\frac{y^2}{4} - x^2 = 1$$

To find the foci, we calculate $c^2 = a^2 + b^2 = 2^2 + 1^2 = 5$, so $c = \sqrt{5}$. Thus the foci are $(0, \pm\sqrt{5})$. The graph is shown in Figure 6.

✎ NOW TRY EXERCISES **25** AND **35**

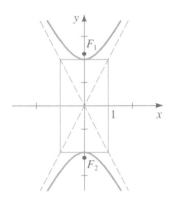

FIGURE 6

$$\frac{y^2}{4} - x^2 = 1$$

Like parabolas and ellipses, hyperbolas have an interesting *reflection property*. Light aimed at one focus of a hyperbolic mirror is reflected toward the other focus, as shown in Figure 7. This property is used in the construction of Cassegrain-type telescopes. A hyperbolic mirror is placed in the telescope tube so that light reflected from the primary parabolic reflector is aimed at one focus of the hyperbolic mirror. The light is then refocused at a more accessible point below the primary reflector (Figure 8).

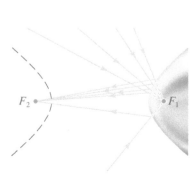

FIGURE 7 Reflection property of hyperbolas

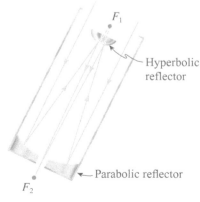

FIGURE 8 Cassegrain-type telescope

The LORAN (LOng RAnge Navigation) system was used until the early 1990s; it has now been superseded by the GPS system (see page 700). In the LORAN system, hyperbolas are used onboard a ship to determine its location. In Figure 9, radio stations at A and B transmit signals simultaneously for reception by the ship at P. The onboard computer converts the time difference in reception of these signals into a distance difference $d(P, A) - d(P, B)$. From the definition of a hyperbola this locates the ship on one branch of a hyperbola with foci at A and B (sketched in black in the figure). The same procedure is carried out with two other radio stations at C and D, and this locates the ship on a second hyperbola (shown in red in the figure). (In practice, only three stations are needed because one station can be used as a focus for both hyperbolas.) The coordinates of the intersection point of these two hyperbolas, which can be calculated precisely by the computer, give the location of P.

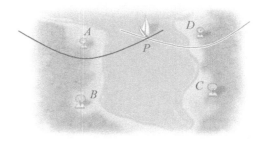

FIGURE 9 LORAN system for finding the location of a ship

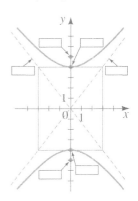

11.3 EXERCISES

CONCEPTS

1. A hyperbola is the set of all points in the plane for which the _____ of the distances from two fixed points F_1 and F_2 is constant. The points F_1 and F_2 are called the _____ of the hyperbola.

2. The graph of the equation $\dfrac{x^2}{a^2} - \dfrac{y^2}{b^2} = 1$ with $a > 0, b > 0$

   is a hyperbola with vertices (___, ___) and (___, ___) and foci $(\pm c, 0)$, where $c =$ _____. So the graph of

   $\dfrac{x^2}{4^2} - \dfrac{y^2}{3^2} = 1$ is a hyperbola with vertices (___, ___) and

   (___, ___) and foci (___, ___) and (___, ___).

3. The graph of the equation $\dfrac{y^2}{a^2} - \dfrac{x^2}{b^2} = 1$ with $a > 0, b > 0$

   is a hyperbola with vertices (___, ___) and (___, ___) and foci $(0, \pm c)$, where $c =$ _____. So the graph of

$\dfrac{y^2}{4^2} - \dfrac{x^2}{3^2} = 1$ is a hyperbola with vertices (___, ___) and

(___, ___) and foci (___, ___) and (___, ___).

4. Label the vertices, foci, and asymptotes on the graphs given for the hyperbolas in Exercises 2 and 3.

   (a) $\dfrac{x^2}{4^2} - \dfrac{y^2}{3^2} = 1$ (b) $\dfrac{y^2}{4^2} - \dfrac{x^2}{3^2} = 1$

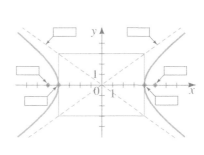

SKILLS

5–8 ■ Match the equation with the graphs labeled I–IV. Give reasons for your answers.

5. $\dfrac{x^2}{4} - y^2 = 1$

6. $y^2 - \dfrac{x^2}{9} = 1$

7. $16y^2 - x^2 = 144$

8. $9x^2 - 25y^2 = 225$

I
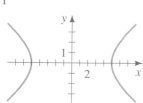

II
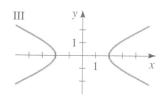

III
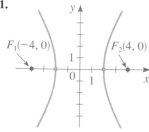

IV
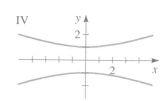

9–20 ■ Find the vertices, foci, and asymptotes of the hyperbola, and sketch its graph.

9. $\dfrac{x^2}{4} - \dfrac{y^2}{16} = 1$

10. $\dfrac{y^2}{9} - \dfrac{x^2}{16} = 1$

11. $y^2 - \dfrac{x^2}{25} = 1$

12. $\dfrac{x^2}{2} - y^2 = 1$

13. $x^2 - y^2 = 1$

14. $9x^2 - 4y^2 = 36$

15. $25y^2 - 9x^2 = 225$

16. $x^2 - y^2 + 4 = 0$

17. $x^2 - 4y^2 - 8 = 0$

18. $x^2 - 2y^2 = 3$

19. $4y^2 - x^2 = 1$

20. $9x^2 - 16y^2 = 1$

21–26 ■ Find the equation for the hyperbola whose graph is shown.

21.
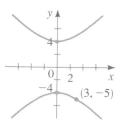

22.
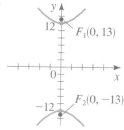

23.
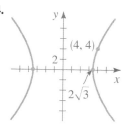

24.

25.
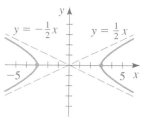

26.
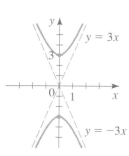

27–30 ■ Use a graphing device to graph the hyperbola.

27. $x^2 - 2y^2 = 8$

28. $3y^2 - 4x^2 = 24$

29. $\dfrac{y^2}{2} - \dfrac{x^2}{6} = 1$

30. $\dfrac{x^2}{100} - \dfrac{y^2}{64} = 1$

31–42 ■ Find an equation for the hyperbola that satisfies the given conditions.

31. Foci: $(\pm 5, 0)$, vertices: $(\pm 3, 0)$

32. Foci: $(0, \pm 10)$, vertices: $(0, \pm 8)$

33. Foci: $(0, \pm 2)$, vertices: $(0, \pm 1)$

34. Foci: $(\pm 6, 0)$, vertices: $(\pm 2, 0)$

35. Vertices: $(\pm 1, 0)$, asymptotes: $y = \pm 5x$

36. Vertices: $(0, \pm 6)$, asymptotes: $y = \pm \frac{1}{3}x$

37. Foci: $(0, \pm 8)$, asymptotes: $y = \pm \frac{1}{2}x$

38. Vertices: $(0, \pm 6)$, hyperbola passes through $(-5, 9)$

39. Asymptotes: $y = \pm x$, hyperbola passes through $(5, 3)$

40. Foci: $(\pm 3, 0)$, hyperbola passes through $(4, 1)$

41. Foci: $(\pm 5, 0)$, length of transverse axis: 6

42. Foci: $(0, \pm 1)$, length of transverse axis: 1

43. (a) Show that the asymptotes of the hyperbola $x^2 - y^2 = 5$ are perpendicular to each other.
(b) Find an equation for the hyperbola with foci $(\pm c, 0)$ and with asymptotes perpendicular to each other.

44. The hyperbolas

$$\frac{x^2}{a^2} - \frac{y^2}{b^2} = 1 \qquad \text{and} \qquad \frac{x^2}{a^2} - \frac{y^2}{b^2} = -1$$

are said to be **conjugate** to each other.
(a) Show that the hyperbolas

$$x^2 - 4y^2 + 16 = 0 \qquad \text{and} \qquad 4y^2 - x^2 + 16 = 0$$

are conjugate to each other, and sketch their graphs on the same coordinate axes.
(b) What do the hyperbolas of part (a) have in common?
(c) Show that any pair of conjugate hyperbolas have the relationship you discovered in part (b).

45. In the derivation of the equation of the hyperbola at the beginning of this section, we said that the equation

$$\sqrt{(x + c)^2 + y^2} - \sqrt{(x - c)^2 + y^2} = \pm 2a$$

simplifies to

$$(c^2 - a^2)x^2 - a^2 y^2 = a^2(c^2 - a^2)$$

Supply the steps needed to show this.

46. (a) For the hyperbola

$$\frac{x^2}{9} - \frac{y^2}{16} = 1$$

determine the values of a, b, and c, and find the coordinates of the foci F_1 and F_2.

(b) Show that the point $P(5, \frac{16}{3})$ lies on this hyperbola.

(c) Find $d(P, F_1)$ and $d(P, F_2)$.

(d) Verify that the difference between $d(P, F_1)$ and $d(P, F_2)$ is $2a$.

47. Hyperbolas are called **confocal** if they have the same foci.

(a) Show that the hyperbolas

$$\frac{y^2}{k} - \frac{x^2}{16 - k} = 1 \quad \text{with } 0 < k < 16$$

are confocal.

 (b) Use a graphing device to draw the top branches of the family of hyperbolas in part (a) for $k = 1, 4, 8,$ and 12. How does the shape of the graph change as k increases?

APPLICATIONS

48. Navigation In the figure, the LORAN stations at A and B are 500 mi apart, and the ship at P receives station A's signal 2640 microseconds (μs) before it receives the signal from station B.

(a) Assuming that radio signals travel at 980 ft/μs, find $d(P, A) - d(P, B)$.

(b) Find an equation for the branch of the hyperbola indicated in red in the figure. (Use miles as the unit of distance.)

(c) If A is due north of B and if P is due east of A, how far is P from A?

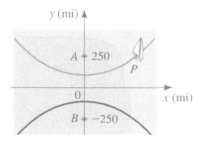

49. Comet Trajectories Some comets, such as Halley's comet, are a permanent part of the solar system, traveling in elliptical orbits around the sun. Other comets pass through the solar system only once, following a hyperbolic path with the sun at a focus. The figure at the top of the next column shows the path of such a comet. Find an equation for the path, assuming that the closest the comet comes to the sun is 2×10^9 mi and that the path the comet was taking before it neared the solar system is at a right angle to the path it continues on after leaving the solar system.

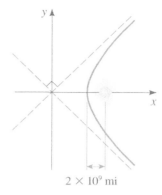

2×10^9 mi

50. Ripples in Pool Two stones are dropped simultaneously into a calm pool of water. The crests of the resulting waves form equally spaced concentric circles, as shown in the figures. The waves interact with each other to create certain interference patterns.

(a) Explain why the red dots lie on an ellipse.

(b) Explain why the blue dots lie on a hyperbola.

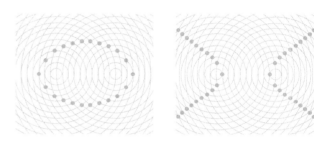

DISCOVERY ■ DISCUSSION ▶ WRITING

51. Hyperbolas in the Real World Several examples of the uses of hyperbolas are given in the text. Find other situations in real life in which hyperbolas occur. Consult a scientific encyclopedia in the reference section of your library, or search the Internet.

52. Light from a Lamp The light from a lamp forms a lighted area on a wall, as shown in the figure. Why is the boundary of this lighted area a hyperbola? How can one hold a flashlight so that its beam forms a hyperbola on the ground?

11.4 SHIFTED CONICS

Shifting Graphs of Equations ▶ Shifted Ellipses ▶ Shifted Parabolas ▶
Shifted Hyperbolas ▶ The General Equation of a Shifted Conic

In the preceding sections we studied parabolas with vertices at the origin and ellipses and hyperbolas with centers at the origin. We restricted ourselves to these cases because these equations have the simplest form. In this section we consider conics whose vertices and centers are not necessarily at the origin, and we determine how this affects their equations.

▼ Shifting Graphs of Equations

In Section 2.5 we studied transformations of functions that have the effect of shifting their graphs. In general, for any equation in x and y, if we replace x by $x - h$ or by $x + h$, the graph of the new equation is simply the old graph shifted horizontally; if y is replaced by $y - k$ or by $y + k$, the graph is shifted vertically. The following box gives the details.

SHIFTING GRAPHS OF EQUATIONS

If h and k are positive real numbers, then replacing x by $x - h$ or by $x + h$ and replacing y by $y - k$ or by $y + k$ has the following effect(s) on the graph of any equation in x and y.

Replacement	How the graph is shifted
1. x replaced by $x - h$	Right h units
2. x replaced by $x + h$	Left h units
3. y replaced by $y - k$	Upward k units
4. y replaced by $y + k$	Downward k units

▼ Shifted Ellipses

Let's apply horizontal and vertical shifting to the ellipse with equation

$$\frac{x^2}{a^2} + \frac{y^2}{b^2} = 1$$

whose graph is shown in Figure 1. If we shift it so that its center is at the point (h, k) instead of at the origin, then its equation becomes

$$\frac{(x - h)^2}{a^2} + \frac{(y - k)^2}{b^2} = 1$$

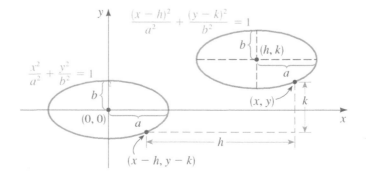

FIGURE 1 Shifted ellipse

EXAMPLE 1 | Sketching the Graph of a Shifted Ellipse

Sketch a graph of the ellipse

$$\frac{(x+1)^2}{4} + \frac{(y-2)^2}{9} = 1$$

and determine the coordinates of the foci.

SOLUTION   The ellipse

$$\frac{(x+1)^2}{4} + \frac{(y-2)^2}{9} = 1 \qquad \text{Shifted ellipse}$$

is shifted so that its center is at $(-1, 2)$. It is obtained from the ellipse

$$\frac{x^2}{4} + \frac{y^2}{9} = 1 \qquad \text{Ellipse with center at origin}$$

by shifting it left 1 unit and upward 2 units. The endpoints of the minor and major axes of the ellipse with center at the origin are $(2, 0)$, $(-2, 0)$, $(0, 3)$, $(0, -3)$. We apply the required shifts to these points to obtain the corresponding points on the shifted ellipse:

$$(2, 0) \;\rightarrow\; (2-1, 0+2) = (1, 2)$$
$$(-2, 0) \;\rightarrow\; (-2-1, 0+2) = (-3, 2)$$
$$(0, 3) \;\rightarrow\; (0-1, 3+2) = (-1, 5)$$
$$(0, -3) \;\rightarrow\; (0-1, -3+2) = (-1, -1)$$

This helps us sketch the graph in Figure 2.

To find the foci of the shifted ellipse, we first find the foci of the ellipse with center at the origin. Since $a^2 = 9$ and $b^2 = 4$, we have $c^2 = 9 - 4 = 5$, so $c = \sqrt{5}$. So the foci are $(0, \pm\sqrt{5})$. Shifting left 1 unit and upward 2 units, we get

$$\left(0, \sqrt{5}\right) \;\rightarrow\; \left(0-1, \sqrt{5}+2\right) = \left(-1, 2+\sqrt{5}\right)$$
$$\left(0, -\sqrt{5}\right) \;\rightarrow\; \left(0-1, -\sqrt{5}+2\right) = \left(-1, 2-\sqrt{5}\right)$$

Thus the foci of the shifted ellipse are

$$\left(-1, 2+\sqrt{5}\right) \qquad \text{and} \qquad \left(-1, 2-\sqrt{5}\right)$$

■ NOW TRY EXERCISE **7**

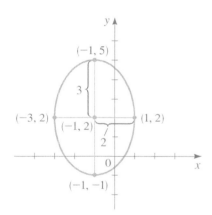

FIGURE 2
$$\frac{(x+1)^2}{4} + \frac{(y-2)^2}{9} = 1$$

▼ Shifted Parabolas

Applying shifts to parabolas leads to the equations and graphs shown in Figure 3.

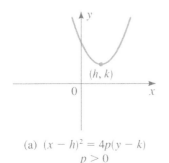

(a) $(x-h)^2 = 4p(y-k)$
$p > 0$

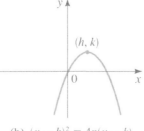

(b) $(x-h)^2 = 4p(y-k)$
$p < 0$

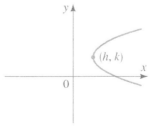

(c) $(y-k)^2 = 4p(x-h)$
$p > 0$

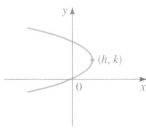

(d) $(y-k)^2 = 4p(x-h)$
$p < 0$

FIGURE 3   Shifted parabolas

EXAMPLE 2 | Graphing a Shifted Parabola

Determine the vertex, focus, and directrix, and sketch a graph of the parabola.

$$x^2 - 4x = 8y - 28$$

SOLUTION We complete the square in x to put this equation into one of the forms in Figure 3.

$$x^2 - 4x + 4 = 8y - 28 + 4 \qquad \text{Add 4 to complete the square}$$

$$(x - 2)^2 = 8y - 24$$

$$(x - 2)^2 = 8(y - 3) \qquad \text{Shifted parabola}$$

This parabola opens upward with vertex at $(2, 3)$. It is obtained from the parabola

$$x^2 = 8y \qquad \text{Parabola with vertex at origin}$$

by shifting right 2 units and upward 3 units. Since $4p = 8$, we have $p = 2$, so the focus is 2 units above the vertex and the directrix is 2 units below the vertex. Thus the focus is $(2, 5)$, and the directrix is $y = 1$. The graph is shown in Figure 4.

✎ NOW TRY EXERCISES **9** AND **23**

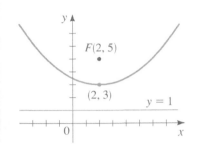

FIGURE 4
$x^2 - 4x = 8y - 28$

▼ Shifted Hyperbolas

Applying shifts to hyperbolas leads to the equations and graphs shown in Figure 5.

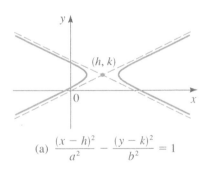

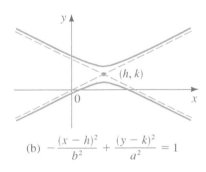

(a) $\dfrac{(x - h)^2}{a^2} - \dfrac{(y - k)^2}{b^2} = 1$

(b) $-\dfrac{(x - h)^2}{b^2} + \dfrac{(y - k)^2}{a^2} = 1$

FIGURE 5 Shifted hyperbolas

EXAMPLE 3 | Graphing a Shifted Hyperbola

A shifted conic has the equation

$$9x^2 - 72x - 16y^2 - 32y = 16$$

(a) Complete the square in x and y to show that the equation represents a hyperbola.

(b) Find the center, vertices, foci, and asymptotes of the hyperbola, and sketch its graph.

(c) Draw the graph using a graphing calculator.

SOLUTION

(a) We complete the squares in both x and y:

$$9(x^2 - 8x \qquad) - 16(y^2 + 2y \qquad) = 16 \qquad \text{Group terms and factor}$$

$$9(x^2 - 8x + 16) - 16(y^2 + 2y + 1) = 16 + 9 \cdot 16 - 16 \cdot 1 \qquad \text{Complete the squares}$$

$$9(x - 4)^2 - 16(y + 1)^2 = 144 \qquad \text{Divide this by 144}$$

$$\frac{(x - 4)^2}{16} - \frac{(y + 1)^2}{9} = 1 \qquad \text{Shifted hyperbola}$$

Comparing this to Figure 5(a), we see that this is the equation of a shifted hyperbola.

(b) The shifted hyperbola has center $(4, -1)$ and a horizontal transverse axis.

$$\textbf{CENTER} \quad (4, -1)$$

Its graph will have the same shape as the unshifted hyperbola

$$\frac{x^2}{16} - \frac{y^2}{9} = 1 \qquad \text{Hyperbola with center at origin}$$

Since $a^2 = 16$ and $b^2 = 9$, we have $a = 4$, $b = 3$, and $c = \sqrt{a^2 + b^2} = \sqrt{16 + 9} = 5$. Thus the foci lie 5 units to the left and to the right of the center, and the vertices lie 4 units to either side of the center.

$$\textbf{FOCI} \qquad (-1, -1) \quad \text{and} \quad (9, -1)$$

$$\textbf{VERTICES} \quad (0, -1) \quad \text{and} \quad (8, -1)$$

The asymptotes of the unshifted hyperbola are $y = \pm\frac{3}{4}x$, so the asymptotes of the shifted hyperbola are found as follows.

$$\textbf{ASYMPTOTES} \quad y + 1 = \pm\tfrac{3}{4}(x - 4)$$

$$y + 1 = \pm\tfrac{3}{4}x \mp 3$$

$$y = \tfrac{3}{4}x - 4 \qquad \text{and} \qquad y = -\tfrac{3}{4}x + 2$$

To help us sketch the hyperbola, we draw the central box; it extends 4 units left and right from the center and 3 units upward and downward from the center. We then draw the asymptotes and complete the graph of the shifted hyperbola as shown in Figure 6(a).

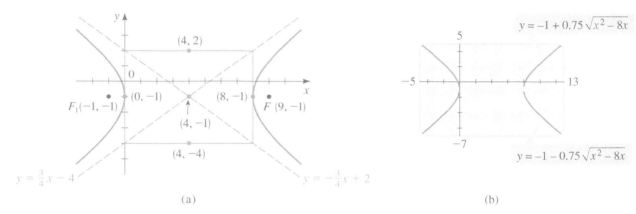

(a)   (b)

FIGURE 6 $9x^2 - 72x - 16y^2 - 32y = 16$

(c) To draw the graph using a graphing calculator, we need to solve for y. The given equation is a quadratic equation in y, so we use the Quadratic Formula to solve for y. Writing the equation in the form

$$16y^2 + 32y - 9x^2 + 72x + 16 = 0$$

Note that the equation of a hyperbola does not define y as a function of x (see page 158). That's why we need to graph two functions to graph a hyperbola.

we get

$$y = \frac{-32 \pm \sqrt{32^2 - 4(16)(-9x^2 + 72x + 16)}}{2(16)} \qquad \text{Quadratic Formula}$$

$$= \frac{-32 \pm \sqrt{576x^2 - 4608x}}{32} \qquad \text{Expand}$$

$$= \frac{-32 \pm 24\sqrt{x^2 - 8x}}{32} \qquad \text{Factor 576 from under the radical}$$

$$= -1 \pm \tfrac{3}{4}\sqrt{x^2 - 8x} \qquad \text{Simplify}$$

JOHANNES KEPLER (1571–1630)
was the first to give a correct description of the motion of the planets. The
cosmology of his time postulated complicated systems of circles moving on
circles to describe these motions.
Kepler sought a simpler and more har-
monious description. As the official astronomer at the imperial court in
Prague, he studied the astronomical
observations of the Danish astronomer
Tycho Brahe, whose data were the
most accurate available at the time. After numerous attempts to find a theory,
Kepler made the momentous discovery
that the orbits of the planets are elliptical. His three great laws of planetary
motion are

1. The orbit of each planet is an ellipse
   with the sun at one focus.
2. The line segment that joins the sun
   to a planet sweeps out equal areas
   in equal time (see the figure).
3. The square of the period of revolution of a planet is proportional to
   the cube of the length of the major
   axis of its orbit.

His formulation of these laws is perhaps the most impressive deduction
from empirical data in the history of
science.

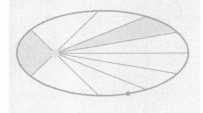

To obtain the graph of the hyperbola, we graph the functions

$$y = -1 + 0.75 \sqrt{x^2 - 8x}$$

and

$$y = -1 - 0.75 \sqrt{x^2 - 8x}$$

as shown in Figure 6(b).

✎ NOW TRY EXERCISES **13** AND **25** ■

▼ The General Equation of a Shifted Conic

If we expand and simplify the equations of any of the shifted conics illustrated in Figures
1, 3, and 5, then we will always obtain an equation of the form

$$Ax^2 + Cy^2 + Dx + Ey + F = 0$$

where A and C are not both 0. Conversely, if we begin with an equation of this form,
then we can complete the square in x and y to see which type of conic section the equation represents. In some cases the graph of the equation turns out to be just a pair of
lines or a single point, or there might be no graph at all. These cases are called **degenerate conics**. If the equation is not degenerate, then we can tell whether it represents a parabola, an ellipse, or a hyperbola simply by examining the signs of A and C,
as described in the box below.

GENERAL EQUATION OF A SHIFTED CONIC

The graph of the equation

$$Ax^2 + Cy^2 + Dx + Ey + F = 0$$

where A and C are not both 0, is a conic or a degenerate conic. In the nondegenerate cases the graph is

1. a parabola if A or C is 0,
2. an ellipse if A and C have the same sign (or a circle if $A = C$),
3. a hyperbola if A and C have opposite signs.

EXAMPLE 4 | An Equation That Leads to a Degenerate Conic

Sketch the graph of the equation

$$9x^2 - y^2 + 18x + 6y = 0$$

SOLUTION Because the coefficients of x^2 and y^2 are of opposite sign, this equation
looks as if it should represent a hyperbola (like the equation of Example 3). To see
whether this is in fact the case, we complete the squares:

$$9(x^2 + 2x \quad) - (y^2 - 6y \quad) = 0 \qquad \text{Group terms and factor 9}$$

$$9(x^2 + 2x + 1) - (y^2 - 6y + 9) = 0 + 9 \cdot 1 - 9 \qquad \text{Complete the squares}$$

$$9(x + 1)^2 - (y - 3)^2 = 0 \qquad \text{Factor}$$

$$(x + 1)^2 - \frac{(y - 3)^2}{9} = 0 \qquad \text{Divide by 9}$$

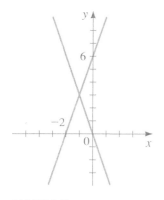

FIGURE 7

$9x^2 - y^2 + 18x + 6y = 0$

For this to fit the form of the equation of a hyperbola, we would need a nonzero constant to the right of the equal sign. In fact, further analysis shows that this is the equation of a pair of intersecting lines:

$$(y - 3)^2 = 9(x + 1)^2$$

$$y - 3 = \pm 3(x + 1) \qquad \text{Take square roots}$$

$$y = 3(x + 1) + 3 \qquad \text{or} \qquad y = -3(x + 1) + 3$$

$$y = 3x + 6 \qquad\qquad\qquad y = -3x$$

These lines are graphed in Figure 7.

◆◦ NOW TRY EXERCISE **31**

Because the equation in Example 4 looked at first glance like the equation of a hyperbola but, in fact, turned out to represent simply a pair of lines, we refer to its graph as a **degenerate hyperbola**. Degenerate ellipses and parabolas can also arise when we complete the square(s) in an equation that seems to represent a conic. For example, the equation

$$4x^2 + y^2 - 8x + 2y + 6 = 0$$

looks as if it should represent an ellipse, because the coefficients of x^2 and y^2 have the same sign. But completing the squares leads to

$$(x - 1)^2 + \frac{(y + 1)^2}{4} = -\frac{1}{4}$$

which has no solution at all (since the sum of two squares cannot be negative). This equation is therefore degenerate.

11.4 EXERCISES

CONCEPTS

1. Suppose we want to graph an equation in x and y.

   (a) If we replace x by $x - 3$, the graph of the equation is shifted to the _____ by 3 units. If we replace x by $x + 3$, the graph of the equation is shifted to the _____ by 3 units.

   (b) If we replace y by $y - 1$, the graph of the equation is shifted _____ by 1 unit. If we replace y by $y + 1$, the graph of the equation is shifted _____ by 1 unit.

2. The graphs of $x^2 = 12y$ and $(x - 3)^2 = 12(y - 1)$ are given. Label the focus, directrix, and vertex on each parabola.

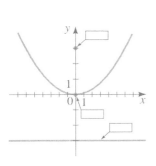

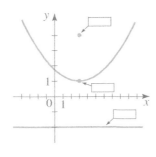

3. The graphs of $\dfrac{x^2}{5^2} + \dfrac{y^2}{4^2} = 1$ and $\dfrac{(x - 3)^2}{5^2} + \dfrac{(y - 1)^2}{4^2} = 1$

   are given. Label the vertices and foci on each ellipse.

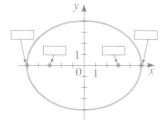

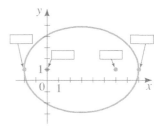

4. The graphs of $\dfrac{x^2}{4^2} - \dfrac{y^2}{3^2} = 1$ and $\dfrac{(x-3)^2}{4^2} - \dfrac{(y-1)^2}{3^2} = 1$

are given. Label the vertices, foci, and asymptotes on each hyperbola.

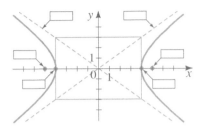

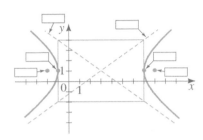

SKILLS

5–8 ■ Find the center, foci, and vertices of the ellipse, and determine the lengths of the major and minor axes. Then sketch the graph.

5. $\dfrac{(x-2)^2}{9} + \dfrac{(y-1)^2}{4} = 1$ **6.** $\dfrac{(x-3)^2}{16} + (y+3)^2 = 1$

 7. $\dfrac{x^2}{9} + \dfrac{(y+5)^2}{25} = 1$ **8.** $\dfrac{(x+2)^2}{4} + y^2 = 1$

9–12 ■ Find the vertex, focus, and directrix of the parabola. Then sketch the graph.

9. $(x-3)^2 = 8(y+1)$ **10.** $(y+5)^2 = -6x + 12$

11. $-4\left(x+\tfrac{1}{2}\right)^2 = y$ **12.** $y^2 = 16x - 8$

13–16 ■ Find the center, foci, vertices, and asymptotes of the hyperbola. Then sketch the graph.

 13. $\dfrac{(x+1)^2}{9} - \dfrac{(y-3)^2}{16} = 1$ **14.** $(x-8)^2 - (y+6)^2 = 1$

15. $y^2 - \dfrac{(x+1)^2}{4} = 1$ **16.** $\dfrac{(y-1)^2}{25} - (x+3)^2 = 1$

17–22 ■ Find an equation for the conic whose graph is shown.

17.

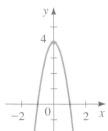

18.

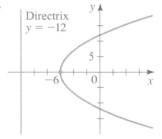

19.

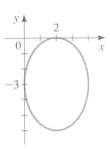

20.

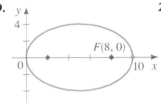

21.

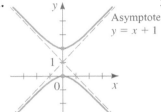

22.

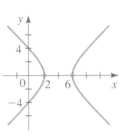

23–34 ■ Complete the square to determine whether the equation represents an ellipse, a parabola, a hyperbola, or a degenerate conic. If the graph is an ellipse, find the center, foci, vertices, and lengths of the major and minor axes. If it is a parabola, find the vertex, focus, and directrix. If it is a hyperbola, find the center, foci, vertices, and asymptotes. Then sketch the graph of the equation. If the equation has no graph, explain why.

23. $y^2 = 4(x + 2y)$

24. $9x^2 - 36x + 4y^2 = 0$

25. $x^2 - 4y^2 - 2x + 16y = 20$

26. $x^2 + 6x + 12y + 9 = 0$

27. $4x^2 + 25y^2 - 24x + 250y + 561 = 0$

28. $2x^2 + y^2 = 2y + 1$

29. $16x^2 - 9y^2 - 96x + 288 = 0$

30. $4x^2 - 4x - 8y + 9 = 0$

31. $x^2 + 16 = 4(y^2 + 2x)$

32. $x^2 - y^2 = 10(x - y) + 1$

33. $3x^2 + 4y^2 - 6x - 24y + 39 = 0$

34. $x^2 + 4y^2 + 20x - 40y + 300 = 0$

35–38 ■ Use a graphing device to graph the conic.

35. $2x^2 - 4x + y + 5 = 0$

36. $4x^2 + 9y^2 - 36y = 0$

37. $9x^2 + 36 = y^2 + 36x + 6y$

38. $x^2 - 4y^2 + 4x + 8y = 0$

39. Determine what the value of F must be if the graph of the equation

$$4x^2 + y^2 + 4(x - 2y) + F = 0$$

is **(a)** an ellipse, **(b)** a single point, or **(c)** the empty set.

40. Find an equation for the ellipse that shares a vertex and a focus with the parabola $x^2 + y = 100$ and has its other focus at the origin.

41. This exercise deals with **confocal parabolas**, that is, families of parabolas that have the same focus.

(a) Draw graphs of the family of parabolas

$$x^2 = 4p(y + p)$$

for $p = -2, -\frac{3}{2}, -1, -\frac{1}{2}, \frac{1}{2}, 1, \frac{3}{2}, 2$.

(b) Show that each parabola in this family has its focus at the origin.

(c) Describe the effect on the graph of moving the vertex closer to the origin.

APPLICATIONS

42. Path of a Cannonball   A cannon fires a cannonball as shown in the figure. The path of the cannonball is a parabola with vertex at the highest point of the path. If the cannonball lands 1600 ft from the cannon and the highest point it reaches is 3200 ft above the ground, find an equation for the path of the cannonball. Place the origin at the location of the cannon.

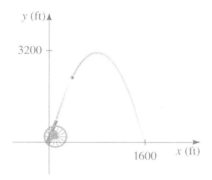

43. Orbit of a Satellite   A satellite is in an elliptical orbit around the earth with the center of the earth at one focus, as shown in the figure at the top of the right-hand column. The height of the satellite above the earth varies between 140 mi and 440 mi. Assume that the earth is a sphere with radius 3960 mi. Find an equation for the path of the satellite with the origin at the center of the earth.

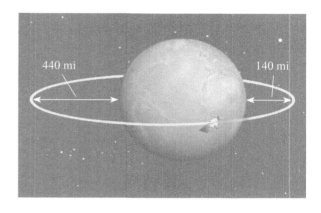

DISCOVERY ▪ DISCUSSION ▪ WRITING

44. A Family of Confocal Conics   Conics that share a focus are called **confocal**. Consider the family of conics that have a focus at $(0, 1)$ and a vertex at the origin, as shown in the figure.

(a) Find equations of two different ellipses that have these properties.

(b) Find equations of two different hyperbolas that have these properties.

(c) Explain why only one parabola satisfies these properties. Find its equation.

(d) Sketch the conics you found in parts (a), (b), and (c) on the same coordinate axes (for the hyperbolas, sketch the top branches only).

(e) How are the ellipses and hyperbolas related to the parabola?

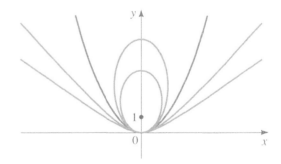

11.5 ROTATION OF AXES

| Rotation of Axes ▶ General Equation of a Conic ▶ The Discriminant

In Section 11.4 we studied conics with equations of the form

$$Ax^2 + Cy^2 + Dx + Ey + F = 0$$

We saw that the graph is always an ellipse, parabola, or hyperbola with horizontal or vertical axes (except in the degenerate cases). In this section we study the most general second-degree equation

$$Ax^2 + Bxy + Cy^2 + Dx + Ey + F = 0$$

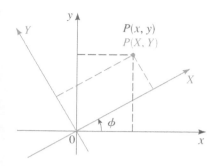

FIGURE 1

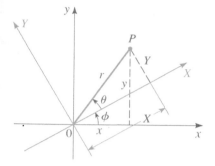

FIGURE 2

We will see that the graph of an equation of this form is also a conic. In fact, by rotating the coordinate axes through an appropriate angle, we can eliminate the term Bxy and then use our knowledge of conic sections to analyze the graph.

▼ Rotation of Axes

In Figure 1 the x- and y-axes have been rotated through an acute angle ϕ about the origin to produce a new pair of axes, which we call the X- and Y-axes. A point P that has coordinates (x, y) in the old system has coordinates (X, Y) in the new system. If we let r denote the distance of P from the origin and let θ be the angle that the segment OP makes with the new X-axis, then we can see from Figure 2 (by considering the two right triangles in the figure) that

$$X = r \cos \theta \qquad\qquad Y = r \sin \theta$$
$$x = r \cos(\theta + \phi) \qquad y = r \sin(\theta + \phi)$$

Using the Addition Formula for Cosine, we see that

$$x = r \cos(\theta + \phi)$$
$$= r(\cos \theta \cos \phi - \sin \theta \sin \phi)$$
$$= (r \cos \theta) \cos \phi - (r \sin \theta) \sin \phi$$
$$= X \cos \phi - Y \sin \phi$$

Similarly, we can apply the Addition Formula for Sine to the expression for y to obtain $y = X \sin \phi + Y \cos \phi$. By treating these equations for x and y as a system of linear equations in the variables X and Y (see Exercise 35), we obtain expressions for X and Y in terms of x and y, as detailed in the following box.

ROTATION OF AXES FORMULAS

Suppose the x- and y-axes in a coordinate plane are rotated through the acute angle ϕ to produce the X- and Y-axes, as shown in Figure 1. Then the coordinates (x, y) and (X, Y) of a point in the xy- and the XY-planes are related as follows:

$$x = X \cos \phi - Y \sin \phi \qquad\qquad X = x \cos \phi + y \sin \phi$$
$$y = X \sin \phi + Y \cos \phi \qquad\qquad Y = -x \sin \phi + y \cos \phi$$

EXAMPLE 1 | Rotation of Axes

If the coordinate axes are rotated through $30°$, find the XY-coordinates of the point with xy-coordinates $(2, -4)$.

SOLUTION Using the Rotation of Axes Formulas with $x = 2$, $y = -4$, and $\phi = 30°$, we get

$$X = 2 \cos 30° + (-4) \sin 30° = 2\left(\frac{\sqrt{3}}{2}\right) - 4\left(\frac{1}{2}\right) = \sqrt{3} - 2$$

$$Y = -2 \sin 30° + (-4) \cos 30° = -2\left(\frac{1}{2}\right) - 4\left(\frac{\sqrt{3}}{2}\right) = -1 - 2\sqrt{3}$$

The XY-coordinates are $(-2 + \sqrt{3}, -1 - 2\sqrt{3})$.

✎ NOW TRY EXERCISE **3**

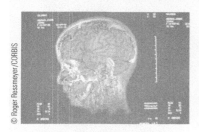

© Roger Ressmeyer/CORBIS

Looking Inside Your Head
How would you like to look inside your head? The idea isn't particularly appealing to most of us, but doctors often need to do just that. If they can look without invasive surgery, all the better. An X-ray doesn't really give a look inside, it simply gives a "graph" of the density of tissue the X-rays must pass through. So an X-ray is a "flattened" view in one direction. Suppose you get an X-ray view from many different directions. Can these "graphs" be used to reconstruct the three-dimensional inside view? This is a purely mathematical problem and was solved by mathematicians a long time ago. However, reconstructing the inside view requires thousands of tedious computations. Today, mathematics and high-speed computers make it possible to "look inside" by a process called computer-aided tomography (or CAT scan). Mathematicians continue to search for better ways of using mathematics to reconstruct images. One of the latest techniques, called magnetic resonance imaging (MRI), combines molecular biology and mathematics for a clear "look inside."

EXAMPLE 2 | Rotating a Hyperbola

Rotate the coordinate axes through $45°$ to show that the graph of the equation $xy = 2$ is a hyperbola.

SOLUTION   We use the Rotation of Axes Formulas with $\phi = 45°$ to obtain

$$x = X \cos 45° - Y \sin 45° = \frac{X}{\sqrt{2}} - \frac{Y}{\sqrt{2}}$$

$$y = X \sin 45° + Y \cos 45° = \frac{X}{\sqrt{2}} + \frac{Y}{\sqrt{2}}$$

Substituting these expressions into the original equation gives

$$\left(\frac{X}{\sqrt{2}} - \frac{Y}{\sqrt{2}} \right)\left(\frac{X}{\sqrt{2}} + \frac{Y}{\sqrt{2}} \right) = 2$$

$$\frac{X^2}{2} - \frac{Y^2}{2} = 2$$

$$\frac{X^2}{4} - \frac{Y^2}{4} = 1$$

We recognize this as a hyperbola with vertices $(\pm 2, 0)$ in the XY-coordinate system. Its asymptotes are $Y = \pm X$, which correspond to the coordinate axes in the xy-system (see Figure 3).

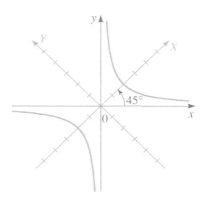

FIGURE 3
$xy = 2$

✎ . NOW TRY EXERCISE **11**

▼ General Equation of a Conic

The method of Example 2 can be used to transform any equation of the form

$$Ax^2 + Bxy + Cy^2 + Dx + Ey + F = 0$$

into an equation in X and Y that doesn't contain an XY-term by choosing an appropriate angle of rotation. To find the angle that works, we rotate the axes through an angle ϕ and substitute for x and y using the Rotation of Axes Formulas:

$$A(X \cos \phi - Y \sin \phi)^2 + B(X \cos \phi - Y \sin \phi)(X \sin \phi + Y \cos \phi)$$
$$+ C(X \sin \phi + Y \cos \phi)^2 + D(X \cos \phi - Y \sin \phi)$$
$$+ E(X \sin \phi + Y \cos \phi) + F = 0$$

If we expand this and collect like terms, we obtain an equation of the form

$$A'X^2 + B'XY + C'Y^2 + D'X + E'Y + F' = 0$$

where

$$A' = A \cos^2\phi + B \sin \phi \cos \phi + C \sin^2\phi$$

$$B' = 2(C - A) \sin \phi \cos \phi + B(\cos^2\phi - \sin^2\phi)$$

$$C' = A \sin^2\phi - B \sin \phi \cos \phi + C \cos^2\phi$$

$$D' = D \cos \phi + E \sin \phi$$

$$E' = -D \sin \phi + E \cos \phi$$

$$F' = F$$

To eliminate the XY-term, we would like to choose ϕ so that $B' = 0$, that is,

Double-Angle Formulas

$\sin 2\phi = 2 \sin \phi \cos \phi$

$\cos 2\phi = \cos^2\phi - \sin^2\phi$

$$2(C - A) \sin \phi \cos \phi + B(\cos^2\phi - \sin^2\phi) = 0 \qquad \text{Double-Angle}$$
$$(C - A) \sin 2\phi + B \cos 2\phi = 0 \qquad \text{Formulas for Sine}$$
$$\qquad\qquad\qquad\qquad\qquad \text{and Cosine}$$

$$B \cos 2\phi = (A - C) \sin 2\phi$$

$$\cot 2\phi = \frac{A - C}{B} \qquad \text{Divide by } B \sin 2\phi$$

The preceding calculation proves the following theorem.

SIMPLIFYING THE GENERAL CONIC EQUATION

To eliminate the xy-term in the general conic equation

$$Ax^2 + Bxy + Cy^2 + Dx + Ey + F = 0$$

rotate the axes through the acute angle ϕ that satisfies

$$\cot 2\phi = \frac{A - C}{B}$$

EXAMPLE 3 | Eliminating the xy-Term

Use a rotation of axes to eliminate the xy-term in the equation

$$6\sqrt{3}x^2 + 6xy + 4\sqrt{3}y^2 = 21\sqrt{3}$$

Identify and sketch the curve.

SOLUTION   To eliminate the xy-term, we rotate the axes through an angle ϕ that satisfies

$$\cot 2\phi = \frac{A - C}{B} = \frac{6\sqrt{3} - 4\sqrt{3}}{6} = \frac{\sqrt{3}}{3}$$

Thus $2\phi = 60°$ and hence $\phi = 30°$. With this value of ϕ, we get

$$x = X\left(\frac{\sqrt{3}}{2}\right) - Y\left(\frac{1}{2}\right) \qquad \text{Rotation of Axes Formulas}$$

$$y = X\left(\frac{1}{2}\right) + Y\left(\frac{\sqrt{3}}{2}\right) \qquad \cos\phi = \frac{\sqrt{3}}{2}, \sin\phi = \frac{1}{2}$$

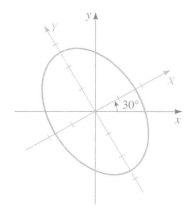

FIGURE 4

$6\sqrt{3}x^2 + 6xy + 4\sqrt{3}y^2 = 21\sqrt{3}$

Substituting these values for x and y into the given equation leads to

$$6\sqrt{3}\left(\frac{X\sqrt{3}}{2} - \frac{Y}{2}\right)^2 + 6\left(\frac{X\sqrt{3}}{2} - \frac{Y}{2}\right)\left(\frac{X}{2} + \frac{Y\sqrt{3}}{2}\right) + 4\sqrt{3}\left(\frac{X}{2} + \frac{Y\sqrt{3}}{2}\right)^2 = 21\sqrt{3}$$

Expanding and collecting like terms, we get

$$7\sqrt{3}X^2 + 3\sqrt{3}Y^2 = 21\sqrt{3}$$

$$\frac{X^2}{3} + \frac{Y^2}{7} = 1 \qquad \text{Divide by } 21\sqrt{3}$$

This is the equation of an ellipse in the XY-coordinate system. The foci lie on the Y-axis. Because $a^2 = 7$ and $b^2 = 3$, the length of the major axis is $2\sqrt{7}$, and the length of the minor axis is $2\sqrt{3}$. The ellipse is sketched in Figure 4.

✎ **NOW TRY EXERCISE 17**

In the preceding example we were able to determine ϕ without difficulty, since we remembered that $\cot 60° = \sqrt{3}/3$. In general, finding ϕ is not quite so easy. The next example illustrates how the following Half-Angle Formulas, which are valid for $0 < \phi < \pi/2$, are useful in determining ϕ (see Section 7.3).

$$\cos\phi = \sqrt{\frac{1 + \cos 2\phi}{2}} \qquad \sin\phi = \sqrt{\frac{1 - \cos 2\phi}{2}}$$

EXAMPLE 4 | Graphing a Rotated Conic

A conic has the equation

$$64x^2 + 96xy + 36y^2 - 15x + 20y - 25 = 0$$

(a) Use a rotation of axes to eliminate the xy-term.

(b) Identify and sketch the graph.

(c) Draw the graph using a graphing calculator.

SOLUTION

(a) To eliminate the xy-term, we rotate the axes through an angle ϕ that satisfies

$$\cot 2\phi = \frac{A - C}{B} = \frac{64 - 36}{96} = \frac{7}{24}$$

FIGURE 5

In Figure 5 we sketch a triangle with $\cot 2\phi = \frac{7}{24}$. We see that

$$\cos 2\phi = \frac{7}{25}$$

so, using the Half-Angle Formulas, we get

$$\cos\phi = \sqrt{\frac{1 + \frac{7}{25}}{2}} = \sqrt{\frac{16}{25}} = \frac{4}{5}$$

$$\sin\phi = \sqrt{\frac{1 - \frac{7}{25}}{2}} = \sqrt{\frac{9}{25}} = \frac{3}{5}$$

The Rotation of Axes Formulas then give

$$x = \tfrac{4}{5}X - \tfrac{3}{5}Y \qquad \text{and} \qquad y = \tfrac{3}{5}X + \tfrac{4}{5}Y$$

Substituting into the given equation, we have

$$64\left(\tfrac{4}{5}X - \tfrac{3}{5}Y\right)^2 + 96\left(\tfrac{4}{5}X - \tfrac{3}{5}Y\right)\left(\tfrac{3}{5}X + \tfrac{4}{5}Y\right)$$
$$+ 36\left(\tfrac{3}{5}X + \tfrac{4}{5}Y\right)^2 - 15\left(\tfrac{4}{5}X - \tfrac{3}{5}Y\right) + 20\left(\tfrac{3}{5}X + \tfrac{4}{5}Y\right) - 25 = 0$$

Expanding and collecting like terms, we get

$$100X^2 + 25Y - 25 = 0$$

$$-4X^2 = Y - 1 \qquad \text{Simplify}$$

$$X^2 = -\tfrac{1}{4}(Y - 1) \qquad \text{Divide by 4}$$

(b) We recognize this as the equation of a parabola that opens along the negative Y-axis and has vertex $(0, 1)$ in XY-coordinates. Since $4p = -\tfrac{1}{4}$, we have $p = -\tfrac{1}{16}$, so the focus is $\left(0, \tfrac{15}{16}\right)$ and the directrix is $Y = \tfrac{17}{16}$. Using

$$\phi = \cos^{-1} \tfrac{4}{5} \approx 37°$$

we sketch the graph in Figure 6(a).

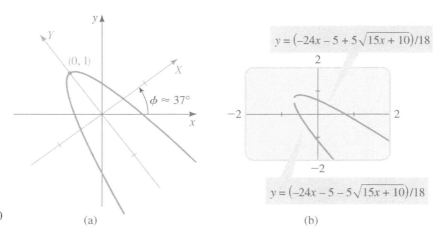

FIGURE 6

$64x^2 + 96xy + 36y^2 - 15x + 20y - 25 = 0$

(a)   (b)

(c) To draw the graph using a graphing calculator, we need to solve for y. The given equation is a quadratic equation in y, so we can use the Quadratic Formula to solve for y. Writing the equation in the form

$$36y^2 + (96x + 20)y + (64x^2 - 15x - 25) = 0$$

we get

$$y = \frac{-(96x + 20) \pm \sqrt{(96x + 20)^2 - 4(36)(64x^2 - 15x - 25)}}{2(36)} \qquad \begin{array}{l}\text{Quadratic}\\\text{Formula}\end{array}$$

$$= \frac{-(96x + 20) \pm \sqrt{6000x + 4000}}{72} \qquad \text{Expand}$$

$$= \frac{-96x - 20 \pm 20\sqrt{15x + 10}}{72} \qquad \text{Simplify}$$

$$= \frac{-24x - 5 \pm 5\sqrt{15x + 10}}{18} \qquad \text{Simplify}$$

To obtain the graph of the parabola, we graph the functions

$$y = \left(-24x - 5 + 5\sqrt{15x + 10}\right)/18 \qquad \text{and} \qquad y = \left(-24x - 5 - 5\sqrt{15x + 10}\right)/18$$

as shown in Figure 6(b).

✎ **NOW TRY EXERCISE 23**

▼ The Discriminant

In Examples 3 and 4 we were able to identify the type of conic by rotating the axes. The next theorem gives rules for identifying the type of conic directly from the equation, without rotating axes.

IDENTIFYING CONICS BY THE DISCRIMINANT

The graph of the equation

$$Ax^2 + Bxy + Cy^2 + Dx + Ey + F = 0$$

is either a conic or a degenerate conic. In the nondegenerate cases, the graph is

1. a parabola if $B^2 - 4AC = 0$

2. an ellipse if $B^2 - 4AC < 0$

3. a hyperbola if $B^2 - 4AC > 0$

The quantity $B^2 - 4AC$ is called the **discriminant** of the equation.

PROOF   If we rotate the axes through an angle ϕ, we get an equation of the form

$$A'X^2 + B'XY + C'Y^2 + D'X + E'Y + F' = 0$$

where $A', B', C', \ldots$ are given by the formulas on page 760. A straightforward calculation shows that

$$(B')^2 - 4A'C' = B^2 - 4AC$$

Thus the expression $B^2 - 4AC$ remains unchanged for any rotation. In particular, if we choose a rotation that eliminates the xy-term ($B' = 0$), we get

$$A'X^2 + C'Y^2 + D'X + E'Y + F' = 0$$

In this case, $B^2 - 4AC = -4A'C'$. So $B^2 - 4AC = 0$ if either A' or C' is zero; $B^2 - 4AC < 0$ if A' and C' have the same sign; and $B^2 - 4AC > 0$ if A' and C' have opposite signs. According to the box on page 754, these cases correspond to the graph of the last displayed equation being a parabola, an ellipse, or a hyperbola, respectively. ∎

In the proof we indicated that the discriminant is unchanged by any rotation; for this reason, the discriminant is said to be **invariant** under rotation.

EXAMPLE 5 | Identifying a Conic by the Discriminant

A conic has the equation

$$3x^2 + 5xy - 2y^2 + x - y + 4 = 0$$

(a) Use the discriminant to identify the conic.

(b) Confirm your answer to part (a) by graphing the conic with a graphing calculator.

SOLUTION

(a) Since $A = 3$, $B = 5$, and $C = -2$, the discriminant is

$$B^2 - 4AC = 5^2 - 4(3)(-2) = 49 > 0$$

So the conic is a hyperbola.

(b) Using the Quadratic Formula, we solve for y to get

$$y = \frac{5x - 1 \pm \sqrt{49x^2 - 2x + 33}}{4}$$

We graph these functions in Figure 7. The graph confirms that this is a hyperbola.

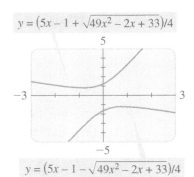

$y = (5x - 1 + \sqrt{49x^2 - 2x + 33})/4$

$y = (5x - 1 - \sqrt{49x^2 - 2x + 33})/4$

FIGURE 7

✎. NOW TRY EXERCISE **29**

11.5 EXERCISES

CONCEPTS

1. Suppose the x- and y-axes are rotated through an acute angle ϕ to produce the new X- and Y-axes. A point P in the plane can be described by its xy-coordinates (x, y) or its XY-coordinates (X, Y). These coordinates are related by the following formulas.

$x = $ _____ $X = $ _____

$y = $ _____ $Y = $ _____

2. Consider the equation

$$Ax^2 + Bxy + Cy^2 + Dx + Ey + F = 0$$

(a) In general, the graph of this equation is a _____.

(b) To eliminate the xy-term from this equation, we rotate the axes through an angle ϕ that satisfies

$\cot 2\phi = $ _____.

(c) The discriminant of this equation is _____.

If the discriminant is 0, the graph is a _____;

if it is negative, the graph is _____; and

if it is positive, the graph is _____.

SKILLS

3–8 ■ Determine the XY-coordinates of the given point if the coordinate axes are rotated through the indicated angle.

3. $(1, 1)$, $\phi = 45°$

4. $(-2, 1)$, $\phi = 30°$

5. $(3, -\sqrt{3})$, $\phi = 60°$

6. $(2, 0)$, $\phi = 15°$

7. $(0, 2)$, $\phi = 55°$

8. $(\sqrt{2}, 4\sqrt{2})$, $\phi = 45°$

9–14 ■ Determine the equation of the given conic in XY-coordinates when the coordinate axes are rotated through the indicated angle.

9. $x^2 - 3y^2 = 4$, $\phi = 60°$

10. $y = (x - 1)^2$, $\phi = 45°$

11. $x^2 - y^2 = 2y$, $\phi = \cos^{-1} \frac{3}{5}$

12. $x^2 + 2y^2 = 16$, $\phi = \sin^{-1} \frac{3}{5}$

13. $x^2 + 2\sqrt{3}xy - y^2 = 4$, $\phi = 30°$

14. $xy = x + y$, $\phi = \pi/4$

15–28 ■ **(a)** Use the discriminant to determine whether the graph of the equation is a parabola, an ellipse, or a hyperbola. **(b)** Use a rotation of axes to eliminate the xy-term. **(c)** Sketch the graph.

15. $xy = 8$

16. $xy + 4 = 0$

17. $x^2 + 2\sqrt{3}xy - y^2 + 2 = 0$

18. $13x^2 + 6\sqrt{3}xy + 7y^2 = 16$

19. $11x^2 - 24xy + 4y^2 + 20 = 0$

20. $21x^2 + 10\sqrt{3}xy + 31y^2 = 144$

21. $\sqrt{3}x^2 + 3xy = 3$

22. $153x^2 + 192xy + 97y^2 = 225$

23. $x^2 + 2xy + y^2 + x - y = 0$

24. $25x^2 - 120xy + 144y^2 - 156x - 65y = 0$

25. $2\sqrt{3}x^2 - 6xy + \sqrt{3}x + 3y = 0$

26. $9x^2 - 24xy + 16y^2 = 100(x - y - 1)$

27. $52x^2 + 72xy + 73y^2 = 40x - 30y + 75$

28. $(7x + 24y)^2 = 600x - 175y + 25$

 29–32 ■ **(a)** Use the discriminant to identify the conic.
(b) Confirm your answer by graphing the conic using a graphing device.

29. $2x^2 - 4xy + 2y^2 - 5x - 5 = 0$

30. $x^2 - 2xy + 3y^2 = 8$

31. $6x^2 + 10xy + 3y^2 - 6y = 36$

32. $9x^2 - 6xy + y^2 + 6x - 2y = 0$

33. (a) Use rotation of axes to show that the following equation represents a hyperbola.

$$7x^2 + 48xy - 7y^2 - 200x - 150y + 600 = 0$$

(b) Find the *XY*- and *xy*-coordinates of the center, vertices, and foci.
(c) Find the equations of the asymptotes in *XY*- and *xy*-coordinates.

34. (a) Use rotation of axes to show that the following equation represents a parabola.

$$2\sqrt{2}(x + y)^2 = 7x + 9y$$

(b) Find the *XY*- and *xy*-coordinates of the vertex and focus.
(c) Find the equation of the directrix in *XY*- and *xy*-coordinates.

35. Solve the equations

$$x = X \cos \phi - Y \sin \phi$$
$$y = X \sin \phi + Y \cos \phi$$

for *X* and *Y* in terms of *x* and *y*. [*Hint:* To begin, multiply the first equation by $\cos \phi$ and the second by $\sin \phi$, and then add the two equations to solve for *X*.]

36. Show that the graph of the equation

$$\sqrt{x} + \sqrt{y} = 1$$

is part of a parabola by rotating the axes through an angle of 45°. [*Hint:* First convert the equation to one that does not involve radicals.]

DISCOVERY ■ DISCUSSION ■ WRITING

37. Matrix Form of Rotation of Axes Formulas

Let *Z*, *Z′*, and *R* be the matrices

$$Z = \begin{bmatrix} x \\ y \end{bmatrix} \qquad Z' = \begin{bmatrix} X \\ Y \end{bmatrix}$$

$$R = \begin{bmatrix} \cos \phi & -\sin \phi \\ \sin \phi & \cos \phi \end{bmatrix}$$

Show that the Rotation of Axes Formulas can be written as

$$Z = RZ' \qquad \text{and} \qquad Z' = R^{-1}Z$$

38. Algebraic Invariants A quantity is invariant under rotation if it does not change when the axes are rotated. It was stated in the text that for the general equation of a conic the quantity $B^2 - 4AC$ is invariant under rotation.

(a) Use the formulas for *A′*, *B′*, and *C′* on page 760 to prove that the quantity $B^2 - 4AC$ is invariant under rotation; that is, show that

$$B^2 - 4AC = B'^2 - 4A'C'$$

(b) Prove that $A + C$ is invariant under rotation.
(c) Is the quantity *F* invariant under rotation?

39. Geometric Invariants Do you expect that the distance between two points is invariant under rotation? Prove your answer by comparing the distance $d(P, Q)$ and $d(P', Q')$ where P' and Q' are the images of *P* and *Q* under a rotation of axes.

DISCOVERY PROJECT **Computer Graphics II**

In this project we investigate how matrices are used to rotate images on a computer screen. You can find the project at the book companion website: **www.stewartmath.com**

11.6 POLAR EQUATIONS OF CONICS

| A Unified Geometric Description of Conics ▶ Polar Equations of Conics

▼ A Unified Geometric Description of Conics

Earlier in this chapter, we defined a parabola in terms of a focus and directrix, but we defined the ellipse and hyperbola in terms of two foci. In this section we give a more unified treatment of all three types of conics in terms of a focus and directrix. If we place the focus at the origin, then a conic section has a simple polar equation. Moreover, in polar form, rotation of conics becomes a simple matter. Polar equations of ellipses are crucial in the derivation of Kepler's Laws (see page 754).

EQUIVALENT DESCRIPTION OF CONICS

Let F be a fixed point (the **focus**), ℓ a fixed line (the **directrix**), and let e be a fixed positive number (the **eccentricity**). The set of all points P such that the ratio of the distance from P to F to the distance from P to ℓ is the constant e is a conic. That is, the set of all points P such that

$$\frac{d(P, F)}{d(P, \ell)} = e$$

is a conic. The conic is a parabola if $e = 1$, an ellipse if $e < 1$, or a hyperbola if $e > 1$.

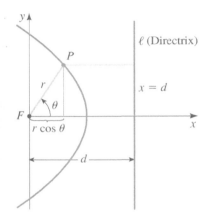

FIGURE 1

PROOF If $e = 1$, then $d(P, F) = d(P, \ell)$, and so the given condition becomes the definition of a parabola as given in Section 11.1.

Now, suppose $e \neq 1$. Let's place the focus F at the origin and the directrix parallel to the y-axis and d units to the right. In this case the directrix has equation $x = d$ and is perpendicular to the polar axis. If the point P has polar coordinates (r, θ), we see from Figure 1 that $d(P, F) = r$ and $d(P, \ell) = d - r \cos \theta$. Thus the condition $d(P, F)/d(P, \ell) = e$, or $d(P, F) = e \cdot d(P, \ell)$, becomes

$$r = e(d - r \cos \theta)$$

If we square both sides of this polar equation and convert to rectangular coordinates, we get

$$x^2 + y^2 = e^2(d - x)^2$$

$$(1 - e^2)x^2 + 2de^2x + y^2 = e^2d^2 \qquad \text{Expand and simplify}$$

$$\left(x + \frac{e^2d}{1 - e^2}\right)^2 + \frac{y^2}{1 - e^2} = \frac{e^2d^2}{(1 - e^2)^2} \qquad \begin{array}{l}\text{Divide by } 1 - e^2 \text{ and complete} \\ \text{the square}\end{array}$$

If $e < 1$, then dividing both sides of this equation by $e^2d^2/(1 - e^2)^2$ gives an equation of the form

$$\frac{(x - h)^2}{a^2} + \frac{y^2}{b^2} = 1$$

where

$$h = \frac{-e^2d}{1 - e^2} \qquad a^2 = \frac{e^2d^2}{(1 - e^2)^2} \qquad b^2 = \frac{e^2d^2}{1 - e^2}$$

This is the equation of an ellipse with center $(h, 0)$. In Section 11.2 we found that the foci of an ellipse are a distance c from the center, where $c^2 = a^2 - b^2$. In our case

$$c^2 = a^2 - b^2 = \frac{e^4d^2}{(1 - e^2)^2}$$

Thus $c = e^2d/(1 - e^2) = -h$, which confirms that the focus defined in the theorem (namely the origin) is the same as the focus defined in Section 11.2. It also follows that

$$e = \frac{c}{a}$$

If $e > 1$, a similar proof shows that the conic is a hyperbola with $e = c/a$, where $c^2 = a^2 + b^2$.

▼ Polar Equations of Conics

In the proof we saw that the polar equation of the conic in Figure 1 is $r = e(d - r \cos \theta)$. Solving for r, we get

$$r = \frac{ed}{1 + e \cos \theta}$$

If the directrix is chosen to be to the *left* of the focus ($x = -d$), then we get the equation $r = ed/(1 - e \cos \theta)$. If the directrix is *parallel* to the polar axis ($y = d$ or $y = -d$), then we get $\sin \theta$ instead of $\cos \theta$ in the equation. These observations are summarized in the following box and in Figure 2.

POLAR EQUATIONS OF CONICS

A polar equation of the form

$$r = \frac{ed}{1 \pm e \cos \theta} \qquad \text{or} \qquad r = \frac{ed}{1 \pm e \sin \theta}$$

represents a conic with one focus at the origin and with eccentricity e. The conic is

1. a parabola if $e = 1$

2. an ellipse if $0 < e < 1$

3. a hyperbola if $e > 1$

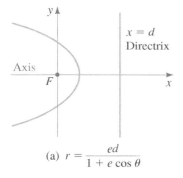

(a) $r = \dfrac{ed}{1 + e \cos \theta}$

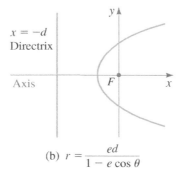

(b) $r = \dfrac{ed}{1 - e \cos \theta}$

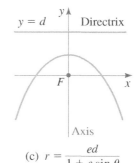

(c) $r = \dfrac{ed}{1 + e \sin \theta}$

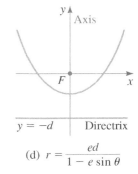

(d) $r = \dfrac{ed}{1 - e \sin \theta}$

FIGURE 2 The form of the polar equation of a conic indicates the location of the directrix.

To graph the polar equation of a conic, we first determine the location of the directrix from the form of the equation. The four cases that arise are shown in Figure 2. (The figure shows only the parts of the graphs that are close to the focus at the origin. The shape of the rest of the graph depends on whether the equation represents a parabola, an ellipse, or a hyperbola.) The axis of a conic is perpendicular to the directrix—specifically we have the following:

1. For a parabola the axis of symmetry is perpendicular to the directrix.

2. For an ellipse the major axis is perpendicular to the directrix.

3. For a hyperbola the transverse axis is perpendicular to the directrix.

EXAMPLE 1 | Finding a Polar Equation for a Conic

Find a polar equation for the parabola that has its focus at the origin and whose directrix is the line $y = -6$.

SOLUTION Using $e = 1$ and $d = 6$ and using part (d) of Figure 2, we see that the polar equation of the parabola is

$$r = \frac{6}{1 - \sin \theta}$$

✎. NOW TRY EXERCISE **3**

To graph a polar conic, it is helpful to plot the points for which $\theta = 0$, $\pi/2$, π, and $3\pi/2$. Using these points and a knowledge of the type of conic (which we obtain from the eccentricity), we can easily get a rough idea of the shape and location of the graph.

EXAMPLE 2 | Identifying and Sketching a Conic

A conic is given by the polar equation

$$r = \frac{10}{3 - 2 \cos \theta}$$

(a) Show that the conic is an ellipse, and sketch the graph.

(b) Find the center of the ellipse and the lengths of the major and minor axes.

SOLUTION

(a) Dividing the numerator and denominator by 3, we have

$$r = \frac{\frac{10}{3}}{1 - \frac{2}{3} \cos \theta}$$

Since $e = \frac{2}{3} < 1$, the equation represents an ellipse. For a rough graph we plot the points for which $\theta = 0$, $\pi/2$, π, $3\pi/2$ (see Figure 3).

θ	r
0	10
$\frac{\pi}{2}$	$\frac{10}{3}$
π	2
$\frac{3\pi}{2}$	$\frac{10}{3}$

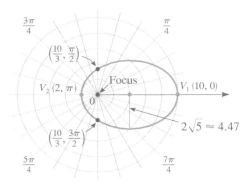

FIGURE 3 $r = \dfrac{10}{3 - 2 \cos \theta}$

(b) Comparing the equation to those in Figure 2, we see that the major axis is horizontal. Thus the endpoints of the major axis are $V_1(10, 0)$ and $V_2(2, \pi)$. So the center of the ellipse is at $C(4, 0)$, the midpoint of V_1V_2.

The distance between the vertices V_1 and V_2 is 12; thus the length of the major axis is $2a = 12$, so $a = 6$. To determine the length of the minor axis, we need to find b. From page 766 we have $c = ae = 6\left(\frac{2}{3}\right) = 4$, so

$$b^2 = a^2 - c^2 = 6^2 - 4^2 = 20$$

Thus $b = \sqrt{20} = 2\sqrt{5} \approx 4.47$, and the length of the minor axis is $2b = 4\sqrt{5} \approx 8.94$.

✎. NOW TRY EXERCISES **17** AND **21**

EXAMPLE 3 | Identifying and Sketching a Conic

A conic is given by the polar equation

$$r = \frac{12}{2 + 4\sin\theta}$$

(a) Show that the conic is a hyperbola and sketch the graph.

(b) Find the center of the hyperbola and sketch the asymptotes.

SOLUTION

(a) Dividing the numerator and denominator by 2, we have

$$r = \frac{6}{1 + 2\sin\theta}$$

Since $e = 2 > 1$, the equation represents a hyperbola. For a rough graph we plot the points for which $\theta = 0, \pi/2, \pi, 3\pi/2$ (see Figure 4).

(b) Comparing the equation to those in Figure 2, we see that the transverse axis is vertical. Thus the endpoints of the transverse axis (the vertices of the hyperbola) are $V_1(2, \pi/2)$ and $V_2(-6, 3\pi/2) = V_2(6, \pi/2)$. So the center of the hyperbola is $C(4, \pi/2)$, the midpoint of V_1V_2.

To sketch the asymptotes, we need to find a and b. The distance between V_1 and V_2 is 4; thus the length of the transverse axis is $2a = 4$, so $a = 2$. To find b, we first find c. From page 766 we have $c = ae = 2 \cdot 2 = 4$, so

$$b^2 = c^2 - a^2 = 4^2 - 2^2 = 12$$

Thus $b = \sqrt{12} = 2\sqrt{3} \approx 3.46$. Knowing a and b allows us to sketch the central box, from which we obtain the asymptotes shown in Figure 4.

θ	r
0	6
$\frac{\pi}{2}$	2
π	6
$\frac{3\pi}{2}$	-6

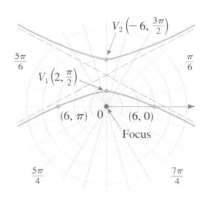

FIGURE 4 $r = \dfrac{12}{2 + 4\sin\theta}$

. NOW TRY EXERCISE 25

When we rotate conic sections, it is much more convenient to use polar equations than Cartesian equations. We use the fact that the graph of $r = f(\theta - \alpha)$ is the graph of $r = f(\theta)$ rotated counterclockwise about the origin through an angle α (see Exercise 61 in Section 8.2).

EXAMPLE 4 | Rotating an Ellipse

Suppose the ellipse of Example 2 is rotated through an angle $\pi/4$ about the origin. Find a polar equation for the resulting ellipse, and draw its graph.

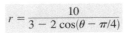

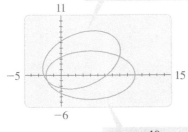

$$r = \frac{10}{3 - 2\cos\theta}$$

FIGURE 5

SOLUTION We get the equation of the rotated ellipse by replacing θ with $\theta - \pi/4$ in the equation given in Example 2. So the new equation is

$$r = \frac{10}{3 - 2\cos(\theta - \pi/4)}$$

We use this equation to graph the rotated ellipse in Figure 5. Notice that the ellipse has been rotated about the focus at the origin.

◥. NOW TRY EXERCISE **37**

In Figure 6 we use a computer to sketch a number of conics to demonstrate the effect of varying the eccentricity e. Notice that when e is close to 0, the ellipse is nearly circular, and it becomes more elongated as e increases. When $e = 1$, of course, the conic is a parabola. As e increases beyond 1, the conic is an ever steeper hyperbola.

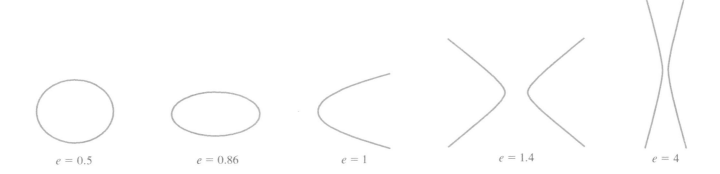

$e = 0.5$ $e = 0.86$ $e = 1$ $e = 1.4$ $e = 4$

FIGURE 6

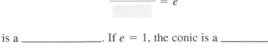

CONCEPTS

1. All conics can be described geometrically using a fixed point F called the _____ and a fixed line ℓ called the

_____. For a fixed positive number e the set of all points P satisfying

$$\underline{\hspace{2cm}} = e$$

is a _____. If $e = 1$, the conic is a _____;

if $e < 1$, the conic is a _____; and if $e > 1$, the

conic is a _____. The number e is called the

_____ of the conic.

2. The polar equation of a conic with eccentricity e has one of the following forms:

$$r = \underline{\hspace{2cm}} \quad \text{or} \quad r = \underline{\hspace{2cm}}$$

SKILLS

3–10 ■ Write a polar equation of a conic that has its focus at the origin and satisfies the given conditions.

3. Ellipse, eccentricity $\frac{2}{3}$, directrix $x = 3$

4. Hyperbola, eccentricity $\frac{4}{3}$, directrix $x = -3$

5. Parabola, directrix $y = 2$

6. Ellipse, eccentricity $\frac{1}{2}$, directrix $y = -4$

7. Hyperbola, eccentricity 4, directrix $r = 5 \sec\theta$

8. Ellipse, eccentricity 0.6, directrix $r = 2 \csc\theta$

9. Parabola, vertex at $(5, \pi/2)$

10. Ellipse, eccentricity 0.4, vertex at $(2, 0)$

11–16 ■ Match the polar equations with the graphs labeled I–VI. Give reasons for your answer.

11. $r = \dfrac{6}{1 + \cos\theta}$ **12.** $r = \dfrac{2}{2 - \cos\theta}$

13. $r = \dfrac{3}{1 - 2\sin\theta}$ **14.** $r = \dfrac{5}{3 - 3\sin\theta}$

15. $r = \dfrac{12}{3 + 2\sin\theta}$ **16.** $r = \dfrac{12}{2 + 3\cos\theta}$

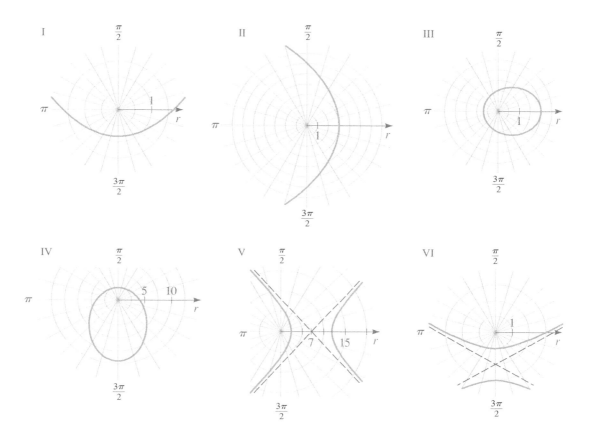

17–20 ■ A polar equation of a conic is given. (**a**) Show that the conic is a parabola and sketch its graph. (**b**) Find the vertex and directrix and indicate them on the graph.

17. $r = \dfrac{4}{1 - \sin\theta}$ **18.** $r = \dfrac{3}{2 + 2\sin\theta}$

19. $r = \dfrac{5}{3 + 3\cos\theta}$ **20.** $r = \dfrac{2}{5 - 5\cos\theta}$

21–24 ■ A polar equation of a conic is given. (**a**) Show that the conic is an ellipse, and sketch its graph. (**b**) Find the vertices and directrix, and indicate them on the graph. (**c**) Find the center of the ellipse and the lengths of the major and minor axes.

21. $r = \dfrac{4}{2 - \cos\theta}$ **22.** $r = \dfrac{6}{3 - 2\sin\theta}$

23. $r = \dfrac{12}{4 + 3\sin\theta}$ **24.** $r = \dfrac{18}{4 + 3\cos\theta}$

25–28 ■ A polar equation of a conic is given. (**a**) Show that the conic is a hyperbola, and sketch its graph. (**b**) Find the vertices and directrix, and indicate them on the graph. (**c**) Find the center of the hyperbola, and sketch the asymptotes.

25. $r = \dfrac{8}{1 + 2\cos\theta}$ **26.** $r = \dfrac{10}{1 - 4\sin\theta}$

27. $r = \dfrac{20}{2 - 3\sin\theta}$ **28.** $r = \dfrac{6}{2 + 7\cos\theta}$

29–36 ■ (**a**) Find the eccentricity and identify the conic. (**b**) Sketch the conic and label the vertices.

29. $r = \dfrac{4}{1 + 3\cos\theta}$ **30.** $r = \dfrac{8}{3 + 3\cos\theta}$

31. $r = \dfrac{2}{1 - \cos\theta}$ **32.** $r = \dfrac{10}{3 - 2\sin\theta}$

33. $r = \dfrac{6}{2 + \sin\theta}$ **34.** $r = \dfrac{5}{2 - 3\sin\theta}$

35. $r = \dfrac{7}{2 - 5\sin\theta}$ **36.** $r = \dfrac{8}{3 + \cos\theta}$

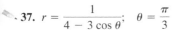

37–40 ■ A polar equation of a conic is given. **(a)** Find the eccentricity and the directrix of the conic. **(b)** If this conic is rotated about the origin through the given angle θ, write the resulting equation. **(c)** Draw graphs of the original conic and the rotated conic on the same screen.

37. $r = \dfrac{1}{4 - 3 \cos \theta}; \quad \theta = \dfrac{\pi}{3}$

38. $r = \dfrac{2}{5 - 3 \sin \theta}; \quad \theta = \dfrac{2\pi}{3}$

39. $r = \dfrac{2}{1 + \sin \theta}; \quad \theta = -\dfrac{\pi}{4}$

40. $r = \dfrac{9}{2 + 2 \cos \theta}; \quad \theta = -\dfrac{5\pi}{6}$

41. Graph the conics $r = e/(1 - e \cos \theta)$ with $e = 0.4, 0.6, 0.8$, and 1.0 on a common screen. How does the value of e affect the shape of the curve?

42. (a) Graph the conics

$$r = \frac{ed}{(1 + e \sin \theta)}$$

for $e = 1$ and various values of d. How does the value of d affect the shape of the conic?

(b) Graph these conics for $d = 1$ and various values of e. How does the value of e affect the shape of the conic?

APPLICATIONS

43. Orbit of the Earth The polar equation of an ellipse can be expressed in terms of its eccentricity e and the length a of its major axis.

(a) Show that the polar equation of an ellipse with directrix $x = -d$ can be written in the form

$$r = \frac{a(1 - e^2)}{1 - e \cos \theta}$$

[*Hint:* Use the relation $a^2 = e^2 d^2/(1 - e^2)^2$ given in the proof on page 766.]

(b) Find an approximate polar equation for the elliptical orbit of the earth around the sun (at one focus) given that the eccentricity is about 0.017 and the length of the major axis is about 2.99×10^8 km.

44. Perihelion and Aphelion The planets move around the sun in elliptical orbits with the sun at one focus. The positions of a planet that are closest to, and farthest from, the sun are called its **perihelion** and **aphelion**, respectively.

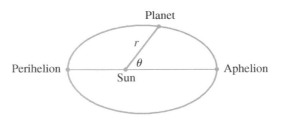

(a) Use Exercise 43(a) to show that the perihelion distance from a planet to the sun is $a(1 - e)$ and the aphelion distance is $a(1 + e)$.

(b) Use the data of Exercise 43(b) to find the distances from the earth to the sun at perihelion and at aphelion.

45. Orbit of Pluto The distance from Pluto to the sun is 4.43×10^9 km at perihelion and 7.37×10^9 km at aphelion. Use Exercise 44 to find the eccentricity of Pluto's orbit.

DISCOVERY ■ DISCUSSION ■ WRITING

46. Distance to a Focus When we found polar equations for the conics, we placed one focus at the pole. It's easy to find the distance from that focus to any point on the conic. Explain how the polar equation gives us this distance.

47. Polar Equations of Orbits When a satellite orbits the earth, its path is an ellipse with one focus at the center of the earth. Why do scientists use polar (rather than rectangular) coordinates to track the position of satellites? [*Hint:* Your answer to Exercise 46 is relevant here.]

CHAPTER 11 | REVIEW

■ CONCEPT CHECK

1. (a) Give the geometric definition of a parabola. What are the focus and directrix of the parabola?

(b) Sketch the parabola $x^2 = 4py$ for the case $p > 0$. Identify on your diagram the vertex, focus, and directrix. What happens if $p < 0$?

(c) Sketch the parabola $y^2 = 4px$, together with its vertex, focus, and directrix, for the case $p > 0$. What happens if $p < 0$?

2. (a) Give the geometric definition of an ellipse. What are the foci of the ellipse?

(b) For the ellipse with equation

$$\frac{x^2}{a^2} + \frac{y^2}{b^2} = 1$$

where $a > b > 0$, what are the coordinates of the vertices and the foci? What are the major and minor axes? Illustrate with a graph.

(c) Give an expression for the eccentricity of the ellipse in part (b).

(d) State the equation of an ellipse with foci on the y-axis.

3. (a) Give the geometric definition of a hyperbola. What are the foci of the hyperbola?

(b) For the hyperbola with equation

$$\frac{x^2}{a^2} - \frac{y^2}{b^2} = 1$$

what are the coordinates of the vertices and foci? What are the equations of the asymptotes? What is the transverse axis? Illustrate with a graph.

(c) State the equation of a hyperbola with foci on the y-axis.

(d) What steps would you take to sketch a hyperbola with a given equation?

4. Suppose h and k are positive numbers. What is the effect on the graph of an equation in x and y if

(a) x is replaced by $x - h$? By $x + h$?

(b) y is replaced by $y - k$? By $y + k$?

5. How can you tell whether the following nondegenerate conic is a parabola, an ellipse, or a hyperbola?

$$Ax^2 + Cy^2 + Dx + Ey + F = 0$$

6. Suppose the x- and y-axes are rotated through an acute angle ϕ to produce the X- and Y-axes. Write equations that relate the coordinates (x, y) and (X, Y) of a point in the xy-plane and XY-plane, respectively.

7. (a) How do you eliminate the xy-term in this equation?

$$Ax^2 + Bxy + Cy^2 + Dx + Ey + F = 0$$

(b) What is the discriminant of the conic in part (a)? How can you use the discriminant to determine whether the conic is a parabola, an ellipse, or a hyperbola?

8. (a) Write polar equations that represent a conic with eccentricity e.

(b) For what values of e is the conic an ellipse? A hyperbola? A parabola?

■ EXERCISES

1–8 ■ Find the vertex, focus, and directrix of the parabola, and sketch the graph.

1. $y^2 = 4x$

2. $x = \frac{1}{12}y^2$

3. $x^2 + 8y = 0$

4. $2x - y^2 = 0$

5. $x - y^2 + 4y - 2 = 0$

6. $2x^2 + 6x + 5y + 10 = 0$

7. $\frac{1}{2}x^2 + 2x = 2y + 4$

8. $x^2 = 3(x + y)$

9–16 ■ Find the center, vertices, foci, and the lengths of the major and minor axes of the ellipse, and sketch the graph.

9. $\frac{x^2}{9} + \frac{y^2}{25} = 1$

10. $\frac{x^2}{49} + \frac{y^2}{9} = 1$

11. $x^2 + 4y^2 = 16$

12. $9x^2 + 4y^2 = 1$

13. $\frac{(x-3)^2}{9} + \frac{y^2}{16} = 1$

14. $\frac{(x-2)^2}{25} + \frac{(y+3)^2}{16} = 1$

15. $4x^2 + 9y^2 = 36y$

16. $2x^2 + y^2 = 2 + 4(x - y)$

17–24 ■ Find the center, vertices, foci, and asymptotes of the hyperbola, and sketch the graph.

17. $-\frac{x^2}{9} + \frac{y^2}{16} = 1$

18. $\frac{x^2}{49} - \frac{y^2}{32} = 1$

19. $x^2 - 2y^2 = 16$

20. $x^2 - 4y^2 + 16 = 0$

21. $\frac{(x+4)^2}{16} - \frac{y^2}{16} = 1$

22. $\frac{(x-2)^2}{8} - \frac{(y+2)^2}{8} = 1$

23. $9y^2 + 18y = x^2 + 6x + 18$

24. $y^2 = x^2 + 6y$

25–30 ■ Find an equation for the conic whose graph is shown.

25.

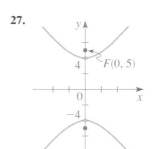

26.

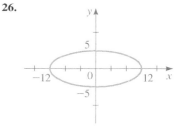

27.

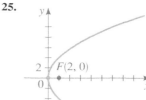

28.

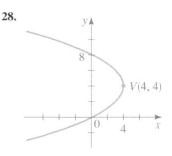

29.

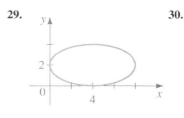

30.

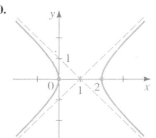

31–42 ■ Determine the type of curve represented by the equation. Find the foci and vertices (if any), and sketch the graph.

31. $\dfrac{x^2}{12} + y = 1$

32. $\dfrac{x^2}{12} + \dfrac{y^2}{144} = \dfrac{y}{12}$

33. $x^2 - y^2 + 144 = 0$

34. $x^2 + 6x = 9y^2$

35. $4x^2 + y^2 = 8(x + y)$

36. $3x^2 - 6(x + y) = 10$

37. $x = y^2 - 16y$

38. $2x^2 + 4 = 4x + y^2$

39. $2x^2 - 12x + y^2 + 6y + 26 = 0$

40. $36x^2 - 4y^2 - 36x - 8y = 31$

41. $9x^2 + 8y^2 - 15x + 8y + 27 = 0$

42. $x^2 + 4y^2 = 4x + 8$

43–50 ■ Find an equation for the conic section with the given properties.

43. The parabola with focus $F(0, 1)$ and directrix $y = -1$

44. The ellipse with center $C(0, 4)$, foci $F_1(0, 0)$ and $F_2(0, 8)$, and major axis of length 10

45. The hyperbola with vertices $V(0, \pm2)$ and asymptotes $y = \pm\frac{1}{2}x$

46. The hyperbola with center $C(2, 4)$, foci $F_1(2, 1)$ and $F_2(2, 7)$, and vertices $V_1(2, 6)$ and $V_2(2, 2)$

47. The ellipse with foci $F_1(1, 1)$ and $F_2(1, 3)$, and with one vertex on the x-axis

48. The parabola with vertex $V(5, 5)$ and directrix the y-axis

49. The ellipse with vertices $V_1(7, 12)$ and $V_2(7, -8)$, and passing through the point $P(1, 8)$

50. The parabola with vertex $V(-1, 0)$ and horizontal axis of symmetry, and crossing the y-axis at $y = 2$

51. The path of the earth around the sun is an ellipse with the sun at one focus. The ellipse has major axis 186,000,000 mi and eccentricity 0.017. Find the distance between the earth and the sun when the earth is **(a)** closest to the sun and **(b)** farthest from the sun.

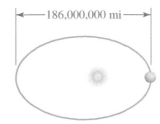

52. A ship is located 40 mi from a straight shoreline. LORAN stations A and B are located on the shoreline, 300 mi apart. From the LORAN signals, the captain determines that his ship is

80 mi closer to A than to B. Find the location of the ship. (Place A and B on the y-axis with the x-axis halfway between them. Find the x- and y-coordinates of the ship.)

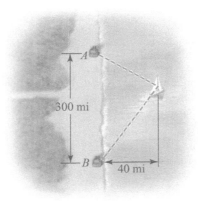

53. (a) Draw graphs of the following family of ellipses for $k = 1, 2, 4,$ and 8.

$$\frac{x^2}{16 + k^2} + \frac{y^2}{k^2} = 1$$

(b) Prove that all the ellipses in part (a) have the same foci.

 54. (a) Draw graphs of the following family of parabolas for $k = \frac{1}{2}, 1, 2,$ and 4.

$$y = kx^2$$

(b) Find the foci of the parabolas in part (a).

(c) How does the location of the focus change as k increases?

55–58 ■ An equation of a conic is given. **(a)** Use the discriminant to determine whether the graph of the equation is a parabola, an ellipse, or a hyperbola. **(b)** Use a rotation of axes to eliminate the xy-term. **(c)** Sketch the graph.

55. $x^2 + 4xy + y^2 = 1$

56. $5x^2 - 6xy + 5y^2 - 8x + 8y - 8 = 0$

57. $7x^2 - 6\sqrt{3}xy + 13y^2 - 4\sqrt{3}x - 4y = 0$

58. $9x^2 + 24xy + 16y^2 = 25$

 59–62 ■ Use a graphing device to graph the conic. Identify the type of conic from the graph.

59. $5x^2 + 3y^2 = 60$ **60.** $9x^2 - 12y^2 + 36 = 0$

61. $6x + y^2 - 12y = 30$ **62.** $52x^2 - 72xy + 73y^2 = 100$

63–66 ■ A polar equation of a conic is given. **(a)** Find the eccentricity and identify the conic. **(b)** Sketch the conic and label the vertices.

63. $r = \dfrac{1}{1 - \cos\theta}$ **64.** $r = \dfrac{2}{3 + 2\sin\theta}$

65. $r = \dfrac{4}{1 + 2\sin\theta}$ **66.** $r = \dfrac{12}{1 - 4\cos\theta}$

1. Find the focus and directrix of the parabola $x^2 = -12y$, and sketch its graph.

2. Find the vertices, foci, and the lengths of the major and minor axes for the ellipse $\dfrac{x^2}{16} + \dfrac{y^2}{4} = 1$. Then sketch its graph.

3. Find the vertices, foci, and asymptotes of the hyperbola $\dfrac{y^2}{9} - \dfrac{x^2}{16} = 1$. Then sketch its graph.

4–6 ■ Find an equation for the conic whose graph is shown.

4.
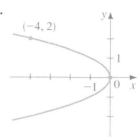

5.
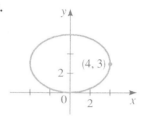

6.
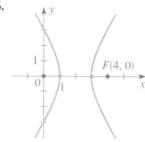

7–9 ■ Sketch the graph of the equation.

7. $16x^2 + 36y^2 - 96x + 36y + 9 = 0$

8. $9x^2 - 8y^2 + 36x + 64y = 164$

9. $2x + y^2 + 8y + 8 = 0$

10. Find an equation for the hyperbola with foci $(0, \pm 5)$ and with asymptotes $y = \pm\frac{3}{4}x$.

11. Find an equation for the parabola with focus $(2, 4)$ and directrix the x-axis.

12. A parabolic reflector for a car headlight forms a bowl shape that is 6 in. wide at its opening and 3 in. deep, as shown in the figure at the left. How far from the vertex should the filament of the bulb be placed if it is to be located at the focus?

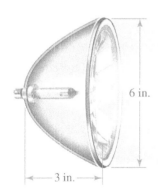

6 in.

3 in.

13. (a) Use the discriminant to determine whether the graph of this equation is a parabola, an ellipse, or a hyperbola:
$$5x^2 + 4xy + 2y^2 = 18$$

   (b) Use rotation of axes to eliminate the xy-term in the equation.

   (c) Sketch the graph of the equation.

   (d) Find the coordinates of the vertices of this conic (in the xy-coordinate system).

14. (a) Find the polar equation of the conic that has a focus at the origin, eccentricity $e = \frac{1}{2}$, and directrix $x = 2$. Sketch the graph.

   (b) What type of conic is represented by the following equation? Sketch its graph.
$$r = \dfrac{3}{2 - \sin\theta}$$

Many buildings employ conic sections in their design. Architects have various reasons for using these curves, ranging from structural stability to simple beauty. But how can a huge parabola, ellipse, or hyperbola be accurately constructed in concrete and steel? In this *Focus on Modeling,* we will see how the geometric properties of the conics can be used to construct these shapes.

▼ Conics in Buildings

In ancient times architecture was part of mathematics, so architects had to be mathematicians. Many of the structures they built—pyramids, temples, amphitheaters, and irrigation projects—still stand. In modern times architects employ even more sophisticated mathematical principles. The photographs below show some structures that employ conic sections in their design.

Roman Amphitheater in
Alexandria, Egypt (circle)
© Nick Wheeler/CORBIS

Ceiling of Statuary Hall in the
U.S. Capitol (ellipse)
Architect of the Capitol

Roof of the Skydome in
Toronto, Canada (parabola)
Walter Schmid/© Stone/Getty Images

Roof of Washington Dulles Airport
(hyperbola and parabola)
© Richard T. Nowitz/CORBIS

McDonnell Planetarium,
St. Louis, MO (hyperbola)
VisionsofAmerica/Joe Sohm

Attic in La Pedrera,
Barcelona, Spain (parabola)
© O. Alamany & E. Vincens/CORBIS

Architects have different reasons for using conics in their designs. For example, the Spanish architect Antoni Gaudí used parabolas in the attic of La Pedrera (see photo above). He reasoned that since a rope suspended between two points with an equally distributed load (as in a suspension bridge) has the shape of a parabola, an inverted parabola would provide the best support for a flat roof.

▼ Constructing Conics

The equations of the conics are helpful in manufacturing small objects, because a computer-controlled cutting tool can accurately trace a curve given by an equation. But in a building project, how can we construct a portion of a parabola, ellipse, or hyperbola that spans the ceiling or walls of a building? The geometric properties of the conics provide practical ways of constructing them. For example, if you were building a circular tower, you would choose a center point, then make sure that the walls of the tower were a fixed

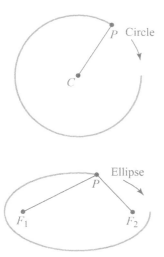

FIGURE 1 Constructing a circle
and an ellipse

distance from that point. Elliptical walls can be constructed using a string anchored at two points, as shown in Figure 1.

To construct a parabola, we can use the apparatus shown in Figure 2. A piece of string of length a is anchored at F and A. The T-square, also of length a, slides along the straight bar L. A pencil at P holds the string taut against the T-square. As the T-square slides to the right the pencil traces out a curve.

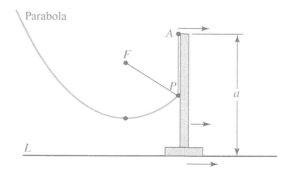

FIGURE 2 Constructing a parabola

From the figure we see that

$$d(F, P) + d(P, A) = a \qquad \text{The string is of length } a$$

$$d(L, P) + d(P, A) = a \qquad \text{The T-square is of length } a$$

It follows that $d(F, P) + d(P, A) = d(L, P) + d(P, A)$. Subtracting $d(P, A)$ from each side, we get

$$d(F, P) = d(L, P)$$

The last equation says that the distance from F to P is equal to the distance from P to the line L. Thus, the curve is a parabola with focus F and directrix L.

In building projects it is easier to construct a straight line than a curve. So in some buildings, such as in the Kobe Tower (see Problem 4), a curved surface is produced by using many straight lines. We can also produce a curve using straight lines, such as the parabola shown in Figure 3.

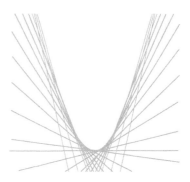

FIGURE 3 Tangent lines to a parabola

Each line is **tangent** to the parabola; that is, the line meets the parabola at exactly one point and does not cross the parabola. The line tangent to the parabola $y = x^2$ at the point (a, a^2) is

$$y = 2ax - a^2$$

You are asked to show this in Problem 6. The parabola is called the **envelope** of all such lines.

PROBLEMS

1. **Conics in Architecture** The photographs on page 776 show six examples of buildings that contain conic sections. Search the Internet to find other examples of structures that employ parabolas, ellipses, or hyperbolas in their design. Find at least one example for each type of conic.

2. **Constructing a Hyperbola** In this problem we construct a hyperbola. The wooden bar in the figure can pivot at F_1. A string that is shorter than the bar is anchored at F_2 and at A, the other end of the bar. A pencil at P holds the string taut against the bar as it moves counterclockwise around F_1.

   (a) Show that the curve traced out by the pencil is one branch of a hyperbola with foci at F_1 and F_2.

   (b) How should the apparatus be reconfigured to draw the other branch of the hyperbola?

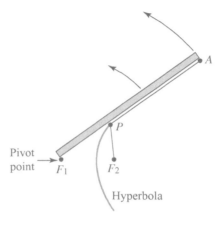

3. **A Parabola in a Rectangle** The following method can be used to construct a parabola that fits in a given rectangle. The parabola will be approximated by many short line segments.

   First, draw a rectangle. Divide the rectangle in half by a vertical line segment, and label the top endpoint V. Next, divide the length and width of each half rectangle into an equal number of parts to form grid lines, as shown in the figure below. Draw lines from V to the endpoints of horizontal grid line 1, and mark the points where these lines cross the vertical grid lines labeled 1. Next, draw lines from V to the endpoints of horizontal grid line 2, and mark the points where these lines cross the vertical grid lines labeled 2. Continue in this way until you have used all the horizontal grid lines. Now use line segments to connect the points you have marked to obtain an approximation to the desired parabola. Apply this procedure to draw a parabola that fits into a 6 ft by 10 ft rectangle on a lawn.

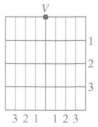
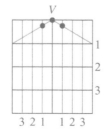
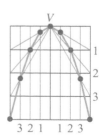

4. **Hyperbolas from Straight Lines** In this problem we construct hyperbolic shapes using straight lines. Punch equally spaced holes into the edges of two large plastic lids. Connect corresponding holes with strings of equal lengths as shown in the figure on the next page. Holding the strings taut, twist one lid against the other. An imaginary surface passing through the strings has hyperbolic cross sections. (An architectural example of this is the

Kobe Tower in Japan, shown in the photograph.) What happens to the vertices of the hyperbolic cross sections as the lids are twisted more?

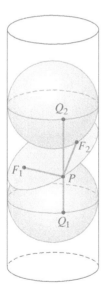

$y = x^2$

Tangent line

5. Tangent Lines to a Parabola   In this problem we show that the line tangent to the parabola $y = x^2$ at the point (a, a^2) has the equation $y = 2ax - a^2$.

(a) Let m be the slope of the tangent line at (a, a^2). Show that the equation of the tangent line is $y - a^2 = m(x - a)$.

(b) Use the fact that the tangent line intersects the parabola at only one point to show that (a, a^2) is the only solution of the system.

$$\begin{cases} y - a^2 = m(x - a) \\ y = x^2 \end{cases}$$

(c) Eliminate y from the system in part (b) to get a quadratic equation in x. Show that the discriminant of this quadratic is $(m - 2a)^2$. Since the system in part (b) has exactly one solution, the discriminant must equal 0. Find m.

(d) Substitute the value for m you found in part (c) into the equation in part (a), and simplify to get the equation of the tangent line.

6. A Cut Cylinder   In this problem we prove that when a cylinder is cut by a plane, an ellipse is formed. An architectural example of this is the Tycho Brahe Planetarium in Copenhagen (see the photograph). In the figure, a cylinder is cut by a plane, resulting in the red curve. Two spheres with the same radius as the cylinder slide inside the cylinder so that they just touch the plane at F_1 and F_2. Choose an arbitrary point P on the curve, and let Q_1 and Q_2 be the two points on the cylinder where a vertical line through P touches the "equator" of each sphere.

(a) Show that $PF_1 = PQ_1$ and $PF_2 = PQ_2$.   [*Hint:* Use the fact that all tangents to a sphere from a given point outside the sphere are of the same length.]

(b) Explain why $PQ_1 + PQ_2$ is the same for all points P on the curve.

(c) Show that $PF_1 + PF_2$ is the same for all points P on the curve.

(d) Conclude that the curve is an ellipse with foci F_1 and F_2.

1. Consider the following system of equations.

$$\begin{cases} x^2 + y^2 = 4y \\ x^2 - 2y = 0 \end{cases}$$

   (a) Is the system linear or nonlinear? Explain.
   (b) Find all solutions of the system.
   (c) The graph of each equation is a conic section. Name the type of conic section in each case.
   (d) Graph both equations on the same set of axes.
   (e) On your graph, shade the region that corresponds to the solution of the system of inequalities.

$$\begin{cases} x^2 + y^2 \le 4y \\ x^2 - 2y \le 0 \end{cases}$$

2. Find the complete solution of each linear system, or show that no solution exists.

   (a) $\begin{cases} x + y - z = 2 \\ 2x + 3y - z = 5 \\ 3x + 5y + 2z = 11 \end{cases}$

   (b) $\begin{cases} y - z = 2 \\ x + 2y - 3z = 3 \\ 3x + 5y - 8z = 7 \end{cases}$

3. Xavier, Yolanda, and Zacharay go fishing. Yolanda catches as many fish as Xavier and Zachary put together. Zachary catches 2 more fish than Xavier. The total catch for all three people is 20 fish. How many did each person catch?

4. Let $A = \begin{bmatrix} 1 & 5 \\ 2 & 0 \end{bmatrix}$, $B = \begin{bmatrix} -2 & 1 & 0 \\ -\frac{1}{2} & 0 & 1 \end{bmatrix}$, $C = \begin{bmatrix} 1 & 0 & 1 \\ 0 & 2 & 1 \\ -1 & 0 & 0 \end{bmatrix}$, and $D = \begin{bmatrix} 1 & 4 & 3 \\ 1 & 6 & 5 \\ 0 & 1 & 1 \end{bmatrix}$.

   (a) Calculate each of the following, or explain why the calculation can't be done.

   $$A + B, \quad C - D, \quad AB, \quad CB, \quad BD, \quad \det(B), \quad \det(C), \quad \det(D)$$

   (b) Based on the values you calculated for $\det(C)$ and $\det(D)$, which matrix, C or D, has an inverse? Find the inverse of the invertible one.

5. Consider the following system of equations.

$$\begin{cases} 5x - 3y = 5 \\ 6x - 4y = 0 \end{cases}$$

   (a) Write a matrix equation of the form $AX = B$ that is equivalent to this system.
   (b) Find A^{-1}, the inverse of the coefficient matrix.
   (c) Solve the matrix equation by multiplying each side by A^{-1}.
   (d) Now solve the system using the Cramer's Rule. Did you get the same solution as in part (b)?

6. Find the partial fraction decomposition of the rational function $r(x) = \dfrac{4x + 8}{x^4 + 4x^2}$.

7. Find an equation for the parabola with vertex at the origin and focus $F(0, 3)$.

8. Sketch the graph of each conic section, and find the coordinates of its foci. What type of conic section does each equation represent?

   (a) $9x^2 + 4y^2 = 24y$

   (b) $r = \dfrac{6}{1 - 2\cos\theta}$

9. Find an equation for the conic whose graph is shown.

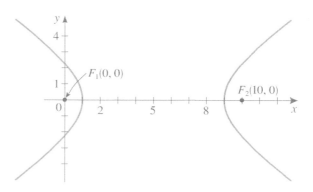

10. Use rotation of axes to graph the equation $7x^2 - 6\sqrt{3}xy + 13y^2 = 16$.

Most of the applied examples and exercises in this book involve approximate values. For example, one exercise states that the moon has a radius of 1074 miles. This does not mean that the moon's radius is exactly 1074 miles but simply that this is the radius rounded to the nearest mile.

One simple method for specifying the accuracy of a number is to state how many **significant digits** it has. The significant digits in a number are the ones from the first nonzero digit to the last nonzero digit (reading from left to right). Thus, 1074 has four significant digits, 1070 has three, 1100 has two, and 1000 has one significant digit. This rule may sometimes lead to ambiguities. For example, if a distance is 200 km to the nearest kilometer, then the number 200 really has three significant digits, not just one. This ambiguity is avoided if we use scientific notation—that is, if we express the number as a multiple of a power of 10:

$$2.00 \times 10^2$$

When working with approximate values, students often make the mistake of giving a final answer with *more* significant digits than the original data. This is incorrect because you cannot "create" precision by using a calculator. The final result can be no more accurate than the measurements given in the problem. For example, suppose we are told that the two shorter sides of a right triangle are measured to be 1.25 and 2.33 inches long. By the Pythagorean Theorem, we find, using a calculator, that the hypotenuse has length

$$\sqrt{1.25^2 + 2.33^2} \approx 2.644125564 \text{ in.}$$

But since the given lengths were expressed to three significant digits, the answer cannot be any more accurate. We can therefore say only that the hypotenuse is 2.64 in. long, rounding to the nearest hundredth.

In general, the final answer should be expressed with the same accuracy as the *least*-accurate measurement given in the statement of the problem. The following rules make this principle more precise.

RULES FOR WORKING WITH APPROXIMATE DATA

1. When multiplying or dividing, round off the final result so that it has as many *significant digits* as the given value with the fewest number of significant digits.

2. When adding or subtracting, round off the final result so that it has its last significant digit in the *decimal place* in which the least-accurate given value has its last significant digit.

3. When taking powers or roots, round off the final result so that it has the same number of *significant digits* as the given value.

As an example, suppose that a rectangular table top is measured to be 122.64 in. by 37.3 in. We express its area and perimeter as follows:

Area = length × width = 122.64 × 37.3 ≈ 4570 in²   Three significant digits

Perimeter = 2(length + width) = 2(122.64 + 37.3) ≈ 319.9 in.   Tenths digit

Note that in the formula for the perimeter, the value 2 is an exact value, not an approximate measurement. It therefore does not affect the accuracy of the final result. In general, if a problem involves only exact values, we may express the final answer with as many significant digits as we wish.

Note also that to make the final result as accurate as possible, *you should wait until the last step to round off your answer*. If necessary, use the memory feature of your calculator to retain the results of intermediate calculations.

ANSWERS to Selected Exercises and Chapter Tests

PROLOGUE ▪ PAGE P4

1. It can't go fast enough. **2.** 40% discount **3.** 427, $3n + 1$
4. 57 min **5.** No, not necessarily **6.** The same amount **7.** 2π
8. The North Pole is one such point; there are infinitely many others near the South Pole.

CHAPTER 1

SECTION 1.1 ▪ PAGE 10

1. Answers may vary. Examples: **(a)** 2 **(b)** -3 **(c)** $\frac{3}{2}$ **(d)** $\sqrt{2}$
2. (a) ba; Commutative **(b)** $(a + b) + c$; Associative
(c) $ab + ac$; Distributive **3.** $\{x \mid 2 < x < 7\}$; $(2, 7)$
4. absolute value; positive **5. (a)** 50 **(b)** $0, -10, 50$
(c) $0, -10, 50, \frac{22}{7}, 0.538, 1.2\overline{3}, -\frac{1}{3}$ **(d)** $\sqrt{7}, \sqrt[3]{2}$
7. Commutative Property for addition
9. Associative Property for addition **11.** Distributive Property
13. Commutative Property for multiplication
15. $3 + x$ **17.** $4A + 4B$ **19.** $3x + 3y$ **21.** $8m$
23. $-5x + 10y$ **25. (a)** $\frac{17}{30}$ **(b)** $\frac{9}{20}$ **27. (a)** 3 **(b)** $\frac{25}{72}$
29. (a) $\frac{8}{3}$ **(b)** 6 **31. (a)** $<$ **(b)** $>$ **(c)** $=$ **33. (a)** False
(b) True **35. (a)** False **(b)** True **37. (a)** $x > 0$ **(b)** $t < 4$
(c) $a \geq \pi$ **(d)** $-5 < x < \frac{1}{3}$ **(e)** $|p - 3| \leq 5$
39. (a) $\{1, 2, 3, 4, 5, 6, 7, 8\}$ **(b)** $\{2, 4, 6\}$
41. (a) $\{1, 2, 3, 4, 5, 6, 7, 8, 9, 10\}$ **(b)** $\{7\}$
43. (a) $\{x \mid x \leq 5\}$ **(b)** $\{x \mid -1 < x < 4\}$
45. $-3 < x < 0$ **47.** $2 \leq x < 8$

49. $x \geq 2$ **51.** $(-\infty, 1]$

53. $(-2, 1]$

55. $(-1, \infty)$

57. (a) $[-3, 5]$ **(b)** $(-3, 5]$

59. **61.**

63.

65. (a) 100 **(b)** 73 **67. (a)** 2 **(b)** -1 **69. (a)** 12 **(b)** 5
71. 5 **73. (a)** 15 **(b)** 24 **(c)** $\frac{67}{40}$ **75. (a)** $\frac{7}{9}$ **(b)** $\frac{13}{45}$ **(c)** $\frac{19}{33}$
77. Distributive Property **79. (a)** Yes, no **(b)** 6 ft

SECTION 1.2 ▪ PAGE 21

1. (a) 5^6 **(b)** base, exponent **2. (a)** add, 3^9 **(b)** subtract, 3^3
3. (a) $5^{1/3}$ **(b)** $\sqrt{5}$ **(c)** No **4.** $(4^{1/2})^3 = 8, (4^3)^{1/2} = 8$
5. $\frac{1}{\sqrt{3}} = \frac{1}{\sqrt{3}} \cdot \frac{\sqrt{3}}{\sqrt{3}} = \frac{\sqrt{3}}{3}$ **6.** $\frac{2}{3}$ **7.** $5^{-1/2}$ **9.** $\sqrt[3]{4^2}$ **11.** $5^{3/5}$
13. $\sqrt[5]{a^2}$ **15. (a)** -9 **(b)** 9 **(c)** $\frac{1}{9}$ **17. (a)** $\frac{1}{2}$ **(b)** $\frac{1}{8}$
(c) 16 **19. (a)** 4 **(b)** 2 **(c)** $\frac{1}{2}$ **21. (a)** $\frac{2}{3}$ **(b)** 4 **(c)** $\frac{1}{2}$
23. (a) $\frac{3}{2}$ **(b)** 4 **(c)** -4 **25.** 5 **27.** 14 **29.** $7\sqrt{2}$
31. $3\sqrt[5]{3}$ **33.** $(x^2 + 4)\sqrt{x}$ **35. (a)** x^{10} **(b)** $12y^7$ **(c)** $\frac{1}{x^4}$
37. (a) y^3 **(b)** $\frac{1}{x^4}$ **(c)** a^6 **39. (a)** a^{18} **(b)** $\frac{a^6}{64}$ **(c)** $\frac{1}{24z^4}$
41. (a) $8x^7y^5$ **(b)** $4a^5z^5$ **43. (a)** $405x^{10}y^{23}$ **(b)** $500a^{12}b^{19}$
45. (a) $\frac{3y^2}{z}$ **(b)** $\frac{y^2z^9}{x^2}$ **47. (a)** $\frac{a^{19}b}{c^9}$ **(b)** $\frac{v^{10}}{u^{11}}$
49. (a) $\frac{4a^8}{b^9}$ **(b)** $\frac{125}{x^6y^3}$ **51. (a)** $\frac{b^3}{3a}$ **(b)** $\frac{s^3}{q^7r^4}$ **53.** $|x|$
55. $2x^2$ **57.** $2ab\sqrt[6]{b}$ **59.** $2|x|$ **61. (a)** x^2 **(b)** y^2
63. (a) $w^{5/3}$ **(b)** $4s^{9/2}$ **65. (a)** $4a^4b$ **(b)** $8a^9b^{12}$
67. (a) $4st^4$ **(b)** 4 **69. (a)** $\frac{1}{x}$ **(b)** $\frac{8y^8}{x^2}$ **71. (a)** $y^{3/2}$
(b) $10x^{7/12}$ **73. (a)** $2st^{11/6}$ **(b)** x **75. (a)** $y^{1/2}$ **(b)** $\frac{4u}{v^2}$
77. (a) 6.93×10^7 **(b)** 7.2×10^{12} **(c)** 2.8536×10^{-5}
(d) 1.213×10^{-4} **79. (a)** 319,000 **(b)** 272,100,000
(c) 0.00000002670 **(d)** 0.000000009999 **81. (a)** 5.9×10^{12} mi
(b) 4×10^{-13} cm **(c)** 3.3×10^{19} molecules
83. 1.3×10^{-20} **85.** 1.429×10^{19} **87.** 7.4×10^{-14}
89. (a) $\frac{\sqrt{10}}{10}$ **(b)** $\frac{\sqrt{2x}}{x}$ **(c)** $\frac{\sqrt{3x}}{3}$
91. (a) $\frac{2\sqrt[3]{x^2}}{x}$ **(b)** $\frac{\sqrt[4]{y}}{y}$ **(c)** $\frac{xy^{3/5}}{y}$
93. (a) Negative **(b)** Positive **(c)** Negative **(d)** Negative
(e) Positive **(f)** Negative **95.** 2.5×10^{13} mi **97.** 1.3×10^{21} L
99. 4.03×10^{27} molecules **101. (a)** 28 mi/h **(b)** 167 ft

SECTION 1.3 ▪ PAGE 32

1. $3; 2x^5, 6x^4, 4x^3; 2x^3, 2x^3(x^2 + 3x + 2)$
2. $10, 7; 2, 5; (x + 2)(x + 5)$
3. $A^2 + 2AB + B^2; 4x^2 + 12x + 9$ **4.** $A^2 - B^2; 25 - x^2$

A1

5. $(A + B)(A - B)$; $(2x - 5)(2x + 5)$ **6.** $(A + B)^2$; $(x + 5)^2$
7. Trinomial; x^2, $-3x$, 7; 2 **9.** Monomial; -8; 0
11. Four terms; $-x^4$, x^3, $-x^2$, x; 4 **13.** $7x + 5$
15. $5x^2 - 2x - 4$ **17.** $x^3 + 3x^2 - 6x + 11$ **19.** $9x + 103$
21. $-t^4 + t^3 - t^2 - 10t + 5$ **23.** $21t^2 - 26t + 8$
25. $6x^2 + 7x - 5$ **27.** $2x^2 + 5xy - 3y^2$ **29.** $9x^2 + 24x + 16$
31. $4u^2 + 4uv + v^2$ **33.** $4x^2 + 12xy + 9y^2$ **35.** $x^2 - 25$
37. $9x^2 - 16$ **39.** $x - 4$ **41.** $y^3 + 6y^2 + 12y + 8$
43. $-8r^3 + 12r^2 - 6r + 1$ **45.** $x^3 + 4x^2 + 7x + 6$
47. $2x^3 - 7x^2 + 7x - 5$ **49.** $x\sqrt{x} - x$ **51.** $y^2 + y$
53. $x^4 - a^4$ **55.** $a - b^2$ **57.** $-x^4 + x^2 - 2x + 1$
59. $4x^2 + 4xy + y^2 - 9$ **61.** $2x(-x^2 + 8)$
63. $(y - 6)(y + 9)$ **65.** $xy(2x - 6y + 3)$ **67.** $(x - 1)(x + 3)$
69. $(2x - 5)(4x + 3)$ **71.** $(3x - 1)(x - 5)$
73. $(3x + 4)(3x + 8)$ **75.** $(3a - 4)(3a + 4)$
77. $(3x + y)(9x^2 - 3xy + y^2)$
79. $(2s - 5t)(4s^2 + 10st + 25t^2)$ **81.** $(x + 6)^2$
83. $(x + 4)(x^2 + 1)$ **85.** $(2x + 1)(x^2 - 3)$
87. $(x + 1)(x^2 + 1)$ **89.** $\sqrt{x}(x - 1)(x + 1)$
91. $x^{-3/2}(1 + x)^2$ **93.** $(x^2 + 1)^{-1/2}(x^2 + 3)$ **95.** $6x(2x^2 + 3)$
97. $(x - 4)(x + 2)$ **99.** $(2x + 3)(x + 1)$
101. $9(x - 5)(x + 1)$ **103.** $(7 - 2y)(7 + 2y)$
105. $(t - 3)^2$ **107.** $(2x + y)^2$ **109.** $4ab$
111. $(x - 1)(x + 1)(x - 3)(x + 3)$
113. $(2x - 5)(4x^2 + 10x + 25)$ **115.** $x(x + 1)^2$
117. $x^2 y^3 (x + y)(x - y)$ **119.** $(x + 2)(2x^2 + 1)$
121. $3(x - 1)(x + 2)$ **123.** $(a - 1)(a + 1)(a - 2)(a + 2)$
125. $2(x^2 + 4)^4(x - 2)^3(7x^2 - 10x + 8)$
127. $(x^2 + 3)^{-4/3}(\frac{1}{3}x^2 + 3)$
129. **(d)** $(a + b + c)(a + b - c)(a - b + c)(b - a + c)$

SECTION 1.4 ■ PAGE 41

1. (a), (c)   **2.** numerator; denominator; $\dfrac{x + 1}{x + 3}$

3. numerators; denominators; $\dfrac{2x}{x^2 + 4x + 3}$

4. **(a)** 3 **(b)** $x(x + 1)^2$ **(c)** $\dfrac{-2x^2 + 1}{x(x + 1)^2}$

5. $\mathbb{R}$ **7.** $x \neq 4$ **9.** $x \geq -3$ **11.** $\{x \mid x \neq -1, 2\}$

13. $\dfrac{x + 2}{2(x - 1)}$ **15.** $\dfrac{1}{x + 2}$ **17.** $\dfrac{x + 2}{x + 1}$ **19.** $\dfrac{y}{y - 1}$

21. $\dfrac{x(2x + 3)}{2x - 3}$ **23.** $\dfrac{1}{4(x - 2)}$ **25.** $\dfrac{x + 3}{x - 3}$ **27.** $\dfrac{1}{t^2 + 9}$

29. $\dfrac{x + 4}{x + 1}$ **31.** $\dfrac{x + 5}{(2x + 3)(x + 4)}$ **33.** $\dfrac{(2x + 1)(2x - 1)}{(x + 5)^2}$

35. $x^2(x + 1)$ **37.** $\dfrac{x}{yz}$ **39.** $\dfrac{3(x + 2)}{x + 3}$ **41.** $\dfrac{3x + 7}{(x - 3)(x + 5)}$

43. $\dfrac{1}{(x + 1)(x + 2)}$ **45.** $\dfrac{3x + 2}{(x + 1)^2}$ **47.** $\dfrac{u^2 + 3u + 1}{u + 1}$

49. $\dfrac{2x + 1}{x^2(x + 1)}$ **51.** $\dfrac{2x + 7}{(x + 3)(x + 4)}$ **53.** $\dfrac{x - 2}{(x + 3)(x - 3)}$

55. $\dfrac{5x - 6}{x(x - 1)}$ **57.** $\dfrac{-5}{(x + 1)(x + 2)(x - 3)}$ **59.** $\dfrac{(x + 1)^2}{x^2 + 2x - 1}$

61. $\dfrac{4x - 7}{(x - 2)(x - 1)(x + 2)}$ **63.** $-xy$ **65.** $\dfrac{y - x}{xy}$ **67.** $\dfrac{1}{1 - x}$

69. $-\dfrac{1}{(1 + x)(1 + x + h)}$ **71.** $-\dfrac{2x + h}{x^2(x + h)^2}$ **73.** $\dfrac{1}{\sqrt{1 - x^2}}$

75. $\dfrac{(x + 2)^2(x - 13)}{(x - 3)^3}$ **77.** $\dfrac{x + 2}{(x + 1)^{3/2}}$ **79.** $\dfrac{2x + 3}{(x + 1)^{4/3}}$

81. $2 + \sqrt{3}$ **83.** $\dfrac{2(\sqrt{7} - \sqrt{2})}{5}$ **85.** $\dfrac{y\sqrt{3} - y\sqrt{y}}{3 - y}$

87. $\dfrac{-4}{3(1 + \sqrt{5})}$ **89.** $\dfrac{r - 2}{5(\sqrt{r} - \sqrt{2})}$ **91.** $\dfrac{1}{\sqrt{x^2 + 1} + x}$

93. True   **95.** False   **97.** False   **99.** True   **101.** **(a)** $\dfrac{R_1 R_2}{R_1 + R_2}$

(b) $\frac{20}{3} \approx 6.7$ ohms

SECTION 1.5 ■ PAGE 54

1. **(a)** True   **(b)** False (because quantity could be 0)   **(c)** False
2. **(a)** Factor into $(x + 1)(x - 5)$, and use the Zero-Product
Property.   **(b)** Add 5 to each side, then complete the square by
adding 4 to both sides.   **(c)** Insert coefficients into the Quadratic
Formula.   **3.** **(a)** $0, 4$ **(b)** factor   **4.** **(a)** $\sqrt{2x} = -x$
(b) $2x = x^2$ **(c)** $0, 2$ **(d)** 0
5. quadratic; $x + 1$; $W^2 - 5W + 6 = 0$
6. quadratic; x^3; $W^2 + 7W - 8 = 0$ **7.** **(a)** No   **(b)** Yes
9. **(a)** Yes   **(b)** No   **11.** 12 **13.** 18 **15.** -3 **17.** 12
19. $-\frac{3}{4}$ **21.** 30 **23.** $-\frac{1}{3}$ **25.** $\frac{13}{3}$ **27.** -2 **29.** $R = \dfrac{PV}{nT}$

31. $w = \dfrac{P - 2l}{2}$ **33.** $x = \dfrac{2d - b}{a - 2c}$ **35.** $x = \dfrac{1 - a}{a^2 - a - 1}$

37. $r = \pm \sqrt{\dfrac{3V}{\pi h}}$ **39.** $b = \pm\sqrt{c^2 - a^2}$

41. $t = \dfrac{-v_0 \pm \sqrt{v_0^2 + 2gh}}{g}$ **43.** $-4, 3$ **45.** $3, 4$ **47.** $-\frac{3}{2}, \frac{5}{2}$

49. $-2, \frac{1}{3}$ **51.** ± 2 **53.** $-\dfrac{2 \pm \sqrt{10}}{3}$ **55.** $-1 \pm \sqrt{6}$

57. $3 \pm 2\sqrt{5}$ **59.** $-2 \pm \frac{\sqrt{14}}{2}$ **61.** $0, \frac{1}{4}$ **63.** $-3, 5$ **65.** $2, 5$
67. $-\frac{3}{2}, 1$ **69.** $-1 \pm \frac{2\sqrt{6}}{3}$ **71.** $\frac{3}{4}$ **73.** $-\frac{9}{2}, \frac{1}{2}$
75. No real solution   **77.** $\dfrac{-8 \pm \sqrt{14}}{10}$ **79.** 2 **81.** 1

83. No real solution   **85.** $-\frac{7}{5}, 2$ **87.** $-50, 100$ **89.** -4
91. 4 **93.** 3 **95.** $\pm 2\sqrt{2}, \pm\sqrt{5}$ **97.** No real solution
99. $\pm 3\sqrt{3}, \pm 2\sqrt{2}$ **101.** $-1, 0, 3$ **103.** $27, 729$
105. $-2, -\frac{4}{3}$ **107.** $3.99, 4.01$ **109.** 4.24 s
111. **(a)** After 1 s and $1\frac{1}{2}$ s   **(b)** Never   **(c)** 25 ft
(d) After $1\frac{1}{4}$ s   **(e)** After $2\frac{1}{2}$ s   **113.** **(a)** 0.00055, 12.018 m
(b) 234.375 kg/m^3 **115.** **(a)** After 17 yr, on Jan. 1, 2019
(b) After 18.612 yr, on Aug. 12, 2020   **117.** 50 **119.** 132.6 ft

SECTION 1.6 ■ PAGE 67

2. principal; interest rate; time in years   **3.** **(a)** x^2 **(b)** lw

(c) πr^2 **4.** 1.6 **5.** $\dfrac{1}{x}$ **6.** $r = \dfrac{d}{t}, t = \dfrac{d}{r}$ **7.** $3n + 3$

9. $\dfrac{160 + s}{3}$ **11.** $0.025x$ **13.** $3w^2$ **15.** $\frac{3}{4}s$ **17.** $\dfrac{25}{3 + x}$

19. 400 mi   **21.** \$9000 at $4\frac{1}{2}$% and \$3000 at 4%   **23.** 7.5%
25. \$7400   **27.** \$45,000   **29.** Plumber, 70 h; assistant, 35 h
31. 40 years old   **33.** 9 pennies, 9 nickels, 9 dimes   **35.** 45 ft
37. 120 ft by 120 ft   **39.** 25 ft by 35 ft   **41.** 60 ft by 40 ft
43. 120 ft   **45.** **(a)** 9 cm   **(b)** 5 in.   **47.** 4 in.   **49.** 18 ft
51. 5 m   **53.** 200 mL   **55.** 18 g   **57.** 0.6 L   **59.** 35%
61. 37 min 20 s   **63.** 3 h   **65.** Irene 3 h, Henry $4\frac{1}{2}$ h   **67.** 4 h

69. 500 mi/h   **71.** 50 mi/h (or 240 mi/h)   **73.** 6 km/h
75. 6.4 ft from the fulcrum   **77.** 2 ft by 6 ft by 15 ft
79. 13 in. by 13 in.   **81.** 2.88 ft   **83.** 16 mi; no   **85.** 7.52 ft
87. 18 ft   **89.** 4.55 ft

SECTION 1.7 ■ PAGE 80

1. (a) $<$ **(b)** $\le$ **(c)** $\le$ **(d)** $>$ **2. (a)** True   **(b)** False
3. (a) $[-3, 3]$ **(b)** $(-\infty, -3], [3, \infty)$ **4. (a)** < 3 **(b)** > 3
5. $\{\sqrt{2}, 2, 4\}$ **7.** $\{4\}$ **9.** $\{-2, -1, 2, 4\}$
11. $\left(-\infty, \frac{7}{2}\right]$ **13.** $(4, \infty)$

15. $(-\infty, 2]$ **17.** $\left(-\infty, -\frac{1}{2}\right)$

19. $[1, \infty)$ **21.** $\left(\frac{16}{3}, \infty\right)$

23. $(-\infty, -18)$ **25.** $(-\infty, -1]$

27. $[-3, -1)$ **29.** $(2, 6)$

31. $\left[\frac{9}{2}, 5\right)$ **33.** $\left(\frac{15}{2}, \frac{21}{2}\right]$

35. $(-2, 3)$ **37.** $\left(-\infty, -\frac{7}{2}\right] \cup [0, \infty)$

39. $[-3, 6]$ **41.** $(-\infty, -1] \cup \left[\frac{1}{2}, \infty\right)$

43. $(-1, 4)$ **45.** $(-\infty, -3) \cup (6, \infty)$

47. $(-2, 2)$ **49.** $(-\infty, -2] \cup [1, 3]$

51. $(-\infty, -2] \cup (-2, 4)$ **53.** $[-1, 3]$

55. $(-2, 0) \cup (2, \infty)$ **57.** $(-\infty, -1) \cup [3, \infty)$

59. $\left(-\infty, -\frac{3}{2}\right)$ **61.** $(-\infty, 5) \cup [16, \infty)$

63. $(-2, 0) \cup (2, \infty)$ **65.** $[-2, -1) \cup (0, 1]$

67. $[-2, 0) \cup (1, 3]$ **69.** $\left(-3, -\frac{1}{2}\right) \cup (2, \infty)$

71. $(-\infty, -1) \cup (1, \infty)$ **73.** $[-4, 4]$

75. $\left(-\infty, -\frac{7}{2}\right) \cup \left(\frac{7}{2}, \infty\right)$ **77.** $[2, 8]$

79. $[1.3, 1.7]$ **81.** $(-\infty, -1] \cup \left[\frac{7}{3}, \infty\right)$

83. $(-4, 8)$ **85.** $(-6.001, -5.999)$

87. $\left[-\frac{1}{2}, \frac{3}{2}\right]$

89. $|x| < 3$ **91.** $|x - 7| \ge 5$ **93.** $|x| \le 2$ **95.** $|x| > 3$
97. $|x - 1| \le 3$ **99.** $-\dfrac{4}{3} \le x \le \dfrac{4}{3}$ **101.** $x < -2$ or $x > 7$

103. (a) $x \ge \dfrac{c}{a} + \dfrac{c}{b}$ **(b)** $\dfrac{a - c}{b} \le x < \dfrac{2a - c}{b}$

105. $68 \le F \le 86$ **107.** More than 200 mi
109. Between 12,000 mi and 14,000 mi
111. (a) $-\frac{1}{3}P + \frac{560}{3}$ **(b)** From \$215 to \$290
113. Distances between 20,000 km and 100,000 km
115. From 0 s to 3 s   **117.** Between 0 and 60 mi/h
119. Between 20 and 40 ft   **121.** Between 62.4 and 74.0 in.

SECTION 1.8 ■ PAGE 92

1. $(3, -5)$ **2.** $\sqrt{(c - a)^2 + (d - b)^2}$; 10
3. $\left(\dfrac{a + c}{2}, \dfrac{b + d}{2}\right)$; $(4, 6)$ **4.** 2; 3; No   **5. (a)** y; x; -1
(b) x; y; $\frac{1}{2}$ **6.** $(1, 2)$; 3

7.

9. (a) $\sqrt{13}$ **(b)** $\left(\frac{3}{2}, 1\right)$ **11. (a)** 10   **(b)** $(1, 0)$
13. (a)   **15. (a)**

(b) 10   **(c)** $(3, 12)$ **(b)** 25   **(c)** $\left(\frac{1}{2}, 6\right)$
17. (a)   **19.** 24

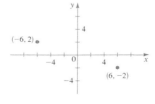

(b) $4\sqrt{10}$ **(c)** $(0, 0)$

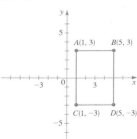

21. Trapezoid, area $= 9$

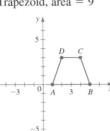

23.

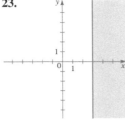

25.

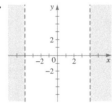

27.

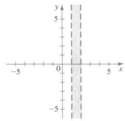

29.

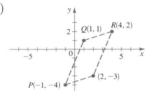

31.

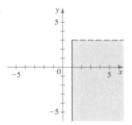

33. $A(6, 7)$ **35.** $Q(-1, 3)$ **39. (b)** 10 **43.** $(0, -4)$
45. $(2, -3)$

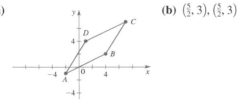

47. (a)

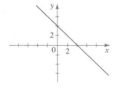

(b) $\left(\frac{5}{2}, 3\right), \left(\frac{5}{2}, 3\right)$

49. No, yes, yes   **51.** Yes, no, yes
53. x-intercepts $0, 4$; y-intercept 0
55. x-intercepts $-2, 2$; y-intercepts $-4, 4$
57. x-intercept 4,
  y-intercept 4,
  no symmetry

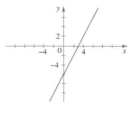

59. x-intercept 3,
  y-intercept -6,
  no symmetry

61. x-intercepts ± 1,
  y-intercept 1,
  symmetry about y-axis

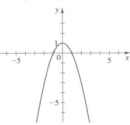

63. x-intercept 0,
  y-intercept 0,
  symmetry about y-axis

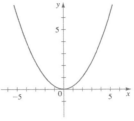

65. x-intercepts ± 3,
  y-intercept -9,
  symmetry about y-axis

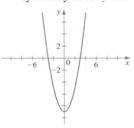

67. No intercepts,
  symmetry about origin

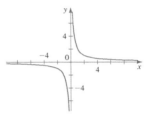

69. x-intercepts ± 2,
  y-intercept 2,
  symmetry about y-axis

71. x-intercept 4,
  y-intercepts $-2, 2$,
  symmetry about x-axis

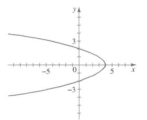

73. x-intercepts ± 2,
  y-intercept 16,
  symmetry about y-axis

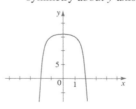

75. x-intercepts ± 4,
  y-intercept 4,
  symmetry about y-axis

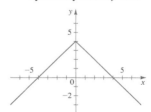

77. Symmetry about y-axis
79. Symmetry about origin
81. Symmetry about origin
83.

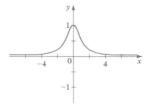

85.

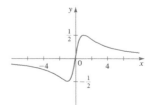

87. $(0, 0), 3$

89. $(3, 0), 4$

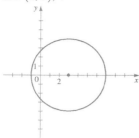

91. $(-3, 4), 5$

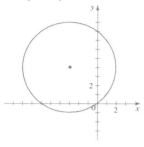

93. $(x - 2)^2 + (y + 1)^2 = 9$ **95.** $x^2 + y^2 = 65$
97. $(x - 2)^2 + (y - 5)^2 = 25$ **99.** $(x - 7)^2 + (y + 3)^2 = 9$
101. $(x + 2)^2 + (y - 2)^2 = 4$ **103.** $(2, -5), 4$ **105.** $\left(\frac{1}{4}, -\frac{1}{4}\right), \frac{1}{2}$
107. $\left(\frac{3}{4}, 0\right), \frac{3}{4}$
109.

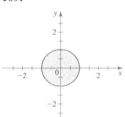

111. 12π **113. (a)** 5   **(b)** 31; 25   **(c)** Points P and Q must either be on the same street or the same avenue.
115. (a) 2 Mm, 8 Mm   **(b)** $-1.33, 7.33; 2.40$ Mm, 7.60 Mm

SECTION 1.9 ▪ PAGE 104

1. x **2.** above   **3. (a)** $x = -1, 0, 1, 3$ **(b)** $[-1, 0] \cup [1, 3]$
4. (a) $x = 1, 4$ **(b)** $(1, 4)$ **5.** (c)   **7.** (c)   **9.** (c)
11.

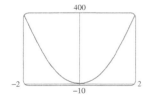

13.

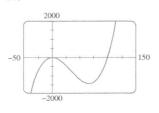

15.

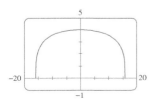

17.

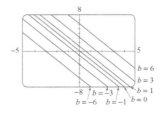

19.

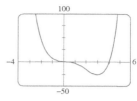

21.

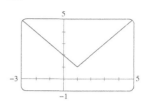

23. No   **25.** Yes, 2
27.

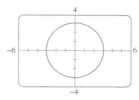

29.

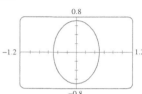

31. -4 **33.** $\frac{5}{14}$ **35.** $\pm 4\sqrt{2} \approx \pm 5.7$ **37.** No solution
39. $2.5, -2.5$ **41.** $5 + 2\sqrt[4]{5} \approx 7.99, 5 - 2\sqrt[4]{5} \approx 2.01$
43. $3.00, 4.00$ **45.** $1.00, 2.00, 3.00$ **47.** 1.62
49. $-1.00, 0.00, 1.00$ **51.** 4 **53.** No solution
55. 2.55 **57.** $-2.05, 0, 1.05$ **59.** $[-2.00, 5.00]$
61. $(-\infty, 1.00] \cup [2.00, 3.00]$ **63.** $(-1.00, 0) \cup (1.00, \infty)$
65. $(-\infty, 0)$ **67.** $(-1, 4)$ **69.** $[-1, 3]$ **71.** $0, 0.01$
73. (a)

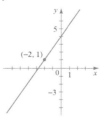

   (b) 67 mi

SECTION 1.10 ▪ PAGE 115

1. $y; x; 2$ **2. (a)** 3   **(b)** 3   **(c)** $-\frac{1}{3}$ **3.** $y - 2 = 3(x - 1)$
4. (a) $0; y = 3$ **(b)** Undefined; $x = 2$ **5.** $\frac{1}{2}$ **7.** $\frac{1}{6}$
9. $-\frac{1}{2}$ **11.** $-\frac{9}{2}$ **13.** $-2, \frac{1}{2}, 3, -\frac{1}{4}$ **15.** $x + y - 4 = 0$
17. $3x - 2y - 6 = 0$ **19.** $5x - y - 7 = 0$
21. $2x - 3y + 19 = 0$ **23.** $5x + y - 11 = 0$
25. $3x - y - 2 = 0$ **27.** $3x - y - 3 = 0$ **29.** $y = 5$
31. $x + 2y + 11 = 0$ **33.** $x = -1$ **35.** $5x - 2y + 1 = 0$
37. $x - y + 6 = 0$
39. (a)

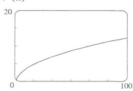

   (b) $3x - 2y + 8 = 0$

41. They all have the same slope.

43. They all have the same x-intercept.

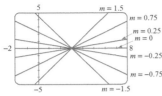

45. $-1, 3$

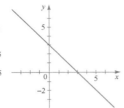

47. $-\frac{1}{3}, 0$

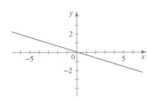

49. $\frac{3}{2}, 3$

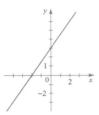

51. 0, 4

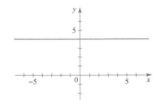

53. $\frac{3}{4}, -3$

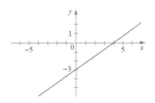

55. $-\frac{3}{4}, \frac{1}{4}$

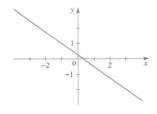

61. $x - y - 3 = 0$ **63.** (b) $4x - 3y - 24 = 0$ **65.** 16,667 ft
67. (a) 8.34; the slope represents the increase in dosage for a one-year increase in age.   (b) 8.34 mg
69. (a)

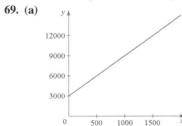

(b) The slope represents production cost per toaster; the y-intercept represents monthly fixed cost.

71. (a) $t = \frac{5}{24}n + 45$ (b) $76°F$
73. (a) $P = 0.434d + 15$, where P is pressure in lb/in^2 and d is depth in feet

(b)

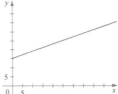

(c) The slope is the rate of increase in water pressure, and the y-intercept is the air pressure at the surface.   **(d)** 196 ft
75. (a) $C = \frac{1}{4}d + 260$
(b) $635
(c) The slope represents cost per mile.
(d) The y-intercept represents monthly fixed cost.

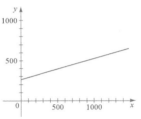

SECTION 1.11 ▪ PAGE 121

1. directly proportional; proportionality   **2.** inversely proportional; proportionality   **3.** directly proportional; inversely proportional   **4.** $\frac{1}{2}xy$ **5.** $T = kx$ **7.** $v = k/z$ **9.** $y = ks/t$

11. $z = k\sqrt{y}$ **13.** $V = klwh$ **15.** $R = k\dfrac{i}{Pt}$ **17.** $y = 7x$

19. $R = 12/s$ **21.** $M = 15x/y$ **23.** $W = 360/r^2$
25. $C = 16lwh$ **27.** $s = 500/\sqrt{t}$ **29.** (a) $F = kx$ (b) 8
(c) 32 N   **31.** (a) $C = kpm$ (b) 0.125   (c) $57,500
33. (a) $P = ks^3$ (b) 0.012   (c) 324   **35.** 0.7 dB   **37.** 4
39. 5.3 mi/h   **41.** (a) $R = kL/d^2$ (b) $0.00291\overline{6}$ (c) $R \approx 137\ \Omega$
43. (a) 160,000   (b) 1,930,670,340   **45.** 36 lb

47. (a) $f = \dfrac{k}{L}$ (b) Halves it

CHAPTER 1 REVIEW ▪ PAGE 125

1. Commutative Property for addition
3. Distributive Property

5. $-2 \le x < 6$

7. $[5, \infty)$

9. 6   **11.** $\frac{1}{72}$ **13.** $\frac{1}{6}$ **15.** 11   **17.** 4   **19.** $16x^3$ **21.** $12xy^8$

23. x^2y^2 **25.** $3x^{3/2}y^2$ **27.** $\dfrac{4r^{5/2}}{s^7}$ **29.** 7.825×10^{10}

31. 1.65×10^{-32} **33.** $3xy^2(4xy^2 - y^3 + 3x^2)$
35. $(x - 2)(x + 5)$ **37.** $(4t + 3)(t - 4)$ **39.** $(5 - 4t)(5 + 4t)$
41. $(x - 1)(x^2 + x + 1)(x + 1)(x^2 - x + 1)$
43. $x^{-1/2}(x - 1)^2$ **45.** $(x - 2)(4x^2 + 3)$
47. $\sqrt{x^2 + 2}(x^2 + x + 2)^2$ **49.** $6x^2 - 21x + 3$ **51.** $-7 + x$

53. $2x^3 - 6x^2 + 4x$ **55.** $\dfrac{3(x + 3)}{x + 4}$ **57.** $\dfrac{x + 1}{x - 4}$ **59.** $\dfrac{1}{x + 1}$

61. $-\dfrac{1}{2x}$ **63.** $3\sqrt{2} - 2\sqrt{3}$ **65.** 5   **67.** No solution

69. $2, 7$ **71.** $-1, \frac{1}{2}$ **73.** $0, \pm\frac{5}{2}$ **75.** $\dfrac{-2 \pm \sqrt{7}}{3}$ **77.** -5

79. $3, 11$ **81.** 20 lb raisins, 30 lb nuts

83. $\frac{1}{4}(\sqrt{329} - 3) \approx 3.78$ mi/h **85.** 1 h 50 min

87. $(-3, \infty)$

89. $(-\infty, -6) \cup (2, \infty)$

91. $(-\infty, -2) \cup (2, 4]$

93. $[2, 8]$

95. $-1, 7$ **97.** $[1, 3]$

99. (a)

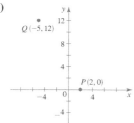

(b) $\sqrt{193}$ **(c)** $\left(-\frac{3}{2}, 6\right)$
(d) $y = -\frac{12}{7}x + \frac{24}{7}$ **(e)** $(x - 2)^2 + y^2 = 193$

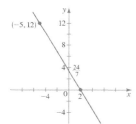

101.

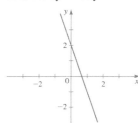

103. B **105.** $(x + 5)^2 + (y + 1)^2 = 26$
107. Circle, center $(-1, 3)$, radius 1 **109.** No graph
111. No symmetry **113.** No symmetry

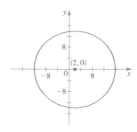

115. Symmetry about y-axis **117.** No symmetry

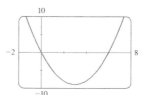
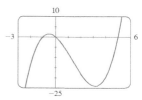

119. **121.**

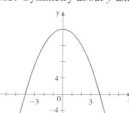
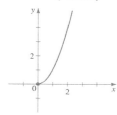

123. $2x - 3y - 16 = 0$ **125.** $3x + y - 12 = 0$
127. $x + 5y = 0$ **129.** $x^2 + y^2 = 169, 5x - 12y + 169 = 0$
131. (a) The slope represents the amount the spring
lengthens for a one-pound increase in weight. The S-intercept
represents the unstretched length of the spring. **(b)** 4 in.
133. $M = 8z$ **135. (a)** $I = k/d^2$ **(b)** 64,000 **(c)** 160 candles
137. 11.0 mi/h

CHAPTER 1 TEST ■ PAGE 128

1. (a)

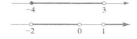

(b) $(-\infty, 3], [-1, 4)$ **(c)** 16
2. (a) 81 **(b)** -81 **(c)** $\frac{1}{81}$ **(d)** 25 **(e)** $\frac{9}{4}$ **(f)** $\frac{1}{8}$
3. (a) 1.86×10^{11} **(b)** 3.965×10^{-7}
4. (a) $6\sqrt{2}$ **(b)** $48a^5b^7$ **(c)** $\dfrac{x}{9y^7}$ **(d)** $\dfrac{x + 2}{x - 2}$ **(e)** $\dfrac{1}{x - 2}$

(f) $-(x + y)$ **5.** $5\sqrt{2} + 2\sqrt{10}$
6. (a) $11x - 2$ **(b)** $4x^2 + 7x - 15$ **(c)** $a - b$
(d) $4x^2 + 12x + 9$ **(e)** $x^3 + 6x^2 + 12x + 8$
7. (a) $(2x - 5)(2x + 5)$ **(b)** $(2x - 3)(x + 4)$
(c) $(x - 3)(x - 2)(x + 2)$
(d) $x(x + 3)(x^2 - 3x + 9)$
(e) $3x^{-1/2}(x - 1)(x - 2)$ **(f)** $xy(x - 2)(x + 2)$

8. (a) 6 **(b)** 1 **(c)** $-3, 4$ **(d)** $-1 \pm \dfrac{\sqrt{2}}{2}$

(e) No real solution **(f)** $\pm 1, \pm\sqrt{2}$ **(g)** $\frac{2}{3}, \frac{22}{3}$ **9.** 120 mi
10. 50 ft by 120 ft
11. (a) $[-4, 3)$

(b) $(-2, 0) \cup (1, \infty)$

(c) $(1, 7)$

(d) $(-1, 4]$

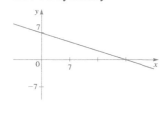

12. Between 41°F and 50°F **13.** $0 \le x \le 6$
14. (a) $-2.94, -0.11, 3.05$ **(b)** $[-1, 2]$

15. (a) $S(3, 6)$ **(b)** 18

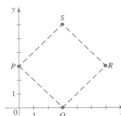

16. (a) **(b)** x-intercepts $-2, 2$
y-intercept -4
(c) Symmetric about y-axis

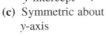

17. (a)

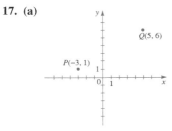

(b) $\sqrt{89}$ **(c)** $\left(1, \frac{7}{2}\right)$ **(d)** $\frac{5}{8}$ **(e)** $y = -\frac{8}{5}x + \frac{51}{10}$
(f) $(x - 1)^2 + \left(y - \frac{7}{2}\right)^2 = \frac{89}{4}$

18. (a) $(0, 0), 5$ **(b)** $(2, -1), 3$

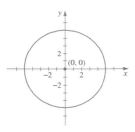

(c) $(-3, 1), 2$

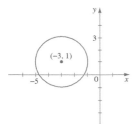

19. $y = \frac{2}{3}x - 5$

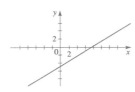

slope $\frac{2}{3}$; y-intercept -5

20. (a) $3x + y - 3 = 0$ **(b)** $2x + 3y - 12 = 0$
21. (a) $4°C$ **(b)**

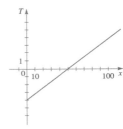

(c) The slope is the rate of change in temperature, the x-intercept is the depth at which the temperature is $0°C$, and the T-intercept is the temperature at ground level.
22. (a) $M = kwh^2/L$ **(b)** 400 **(c)** 12,000 lb

FOCUS ON MODELING ▪ PAGE 135

1. (a)

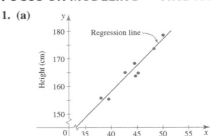

(b) $y = 1.8807x + 82.65$
(c) 191.7 cm

3. (a)

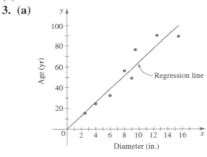

(b) $y = 6.451x - 0.1523$
(c) 116 years

5. (a)

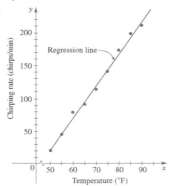

(b) $y = 4.857x - 220.97$
(c) 265 chirps/min

7. (a)

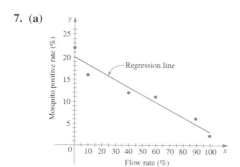

(b) $y = -0.168x + 19.89$ **(c)** 8.13%

9. (a)

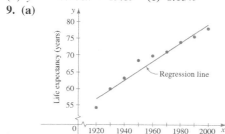

(b) $y = 0.2708x - 462.9$ **(c)** 80.3 years

11. (a) Men: $y = -0.1703x + 64.61$,
women $y = -0.2603x + 78.27$; x represents years since 1900

(b) 2052

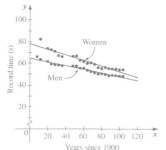

CHAPTER 2

SECTION 2.1 ▪ PAGE 149

1. value   **2.** domain, range   **3. (a)** f and g
(b) $f(5) = 10, g(5) = 0$ **4. (a)** square, add 3

(b)

x	0	2	4	6
$f(x)$	19	7	3	7

5. $f(x) = 2(x + 3)$ **7.** $f(x) = (x - 5)^2$ **9.** Square, then add 2
11. Subtract 4, then divide by 3

13.

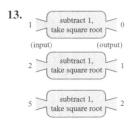

15.

x	$f(x)$
-1	8
0	2
1	0
2	2
3	8

17. $3, 3, -6, -\frac{23}{4}, 94$ **19.** $3, -3, 2, 2a + 1, -2a + 1, 2a + 2b + 1$

21. $-\dfrac{1}{3}, -3, \dfrac{1}{3}, \dfrac{1 - a}{1 + a}, \dfrac{2 - a}{a}$, undefined

23. $-4, 10, -2, 3\sqrt{2}, 2x^2 + 7x + 1, 2x^2 - 3x - 4$
25. $6, 2, 1, 2, 2|x|, 2(x^2 + 1)$ **27.** $4, 1, 1, 2, 3$
29. $8, -\frac{3}{4}, -1, 0, -1$ **31.** $x^2 + 4x + 5, x^2 + 6$
33. $x^2 + 4, x^2 + 8x + 16$ **35.** $3a + 2, 3(a + h) + 2, 3$
37. $5, 5, 0$ **39.** $\dfrac{a}{a + 1}, \dfrac{a + h}{a + h + 1}, \dfrac{1}{(a + h + 1)(a + 1)}$
41. $3 - 5a + 4a^2, 3 - 5a - 5h + 4a^2 + 8ah + 4h^2, -5 + 8a + 4h$
43. $(-\infty, \infty)$ **45.** $[-1, 5]$ **47.** $\{x \mid x \neq 3\}$ **49.** $\{x \mid x \neq \pm 1\}$
51. $[5, \infty)$ **53.** $(-\infty, \infty)$ **55.** $[\frac{5}{2}, \infty)$ **57.** $[-2, 3) \cup (3, \infty)$
59. $(-\infty, 0] \cup [6, \infty)$ **61.** $(4, \infty)$ **63.** $(\frac{1}{2}, \infty)$

65. (a) $f(x) = \dfrac{x}{3} + \dfrac{2}{3}$

(b)

x	$f(x)$
2	$\frac{4}{3}$
4	2
6	$\frac{8}{3}$
8	$\frac{10}{3}$

(c)

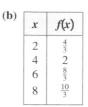

67. (a) $T(x) = 0.08x$

(b)

x	$T(x)$
2	0.16
4	0.32
6	0.48
8	0.64

(c)

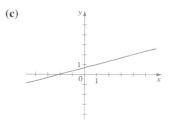

69. (a) $C(10) = 1532.1, C(100) = 2100$ **(b)** The cost of producing 10 yd and 100 yd   **(c)** $C(0) = 1500$ **71. (a)** $50, 0$ **(b)** $V(0)$ is the volume of the full tank, and $V(20)$ is the volume of the empty tank, 20 minutes later.

(c)

x	$V(x)$
0	50
5	28.125
10	12.5
15	3.125
20	0

73. (a) $v(0.1) = 4440, v(0.4) = 1665$
(b) Flow is faster near central axis.

(c)

r	$v(r)$
0	4625
0.1	4440
0.2	3885
0.3	2960
0.4	1665
0.5	0

75. (a) 8.66 m, 6.61 m, 4.36 m
(b) It will appear to get shorter.
77. (a) $90, $105, $100, $105
(b) Total cost of an order, including shipping
79. (a) $F(x) = \begin{cases} 15(40 - x) & \text{if } 0 < x < 40 \\ 0 & \text{if } 40 \le x \le 65 \\ 15(x - 65) & \text{if } x > 65 \end{cases}$

(b) $150, $0, $150   **(c)** Fines for violating the speed limits
81.

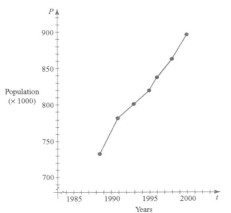

83.

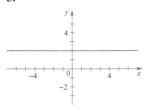

SECTION 2.2 ■ PAGE 159

1. $f(x)$, $x^3 + 2$, 10, 10   **2.** 3   **3.** 3
4. (a) IV   **(b)** II   **(c)** I   **(d)** III
5.   **7.**

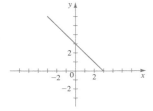   **9.**

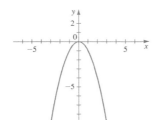   **11.**

13.

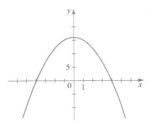

15.

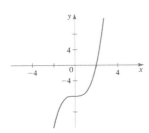

17.

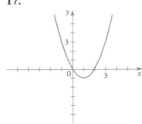

19.

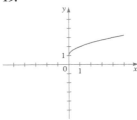

21.

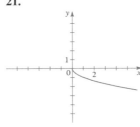

23.

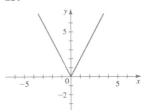

25.

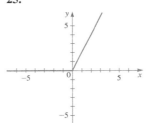

27.

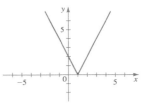

29. (a)

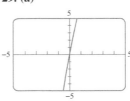

(b)

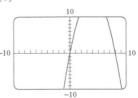

(c)

(d)

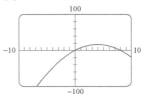

Graph (c) is the most appropriate.

31. (a)

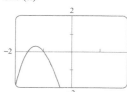

(b)

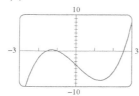

(c)

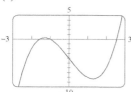

(d)

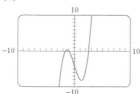

Graph (c) is the most appropriate.

33.

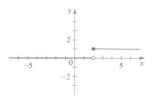

35.

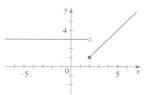

37.

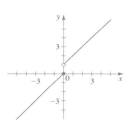

39.

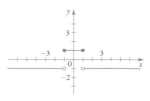

41.

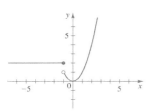

43.

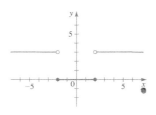

45.

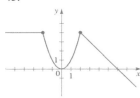

47.

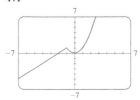

49. $f(x) = \begin{cases} -2 & \text{if } x < -2 \\ x & \text{if } -2 \leq x \leq 2 \\ 2 & \text{if } x > 2 \end{cases}$

51. (a) Yes **(b)** No **(c)** Yes **(d)** No
53. Function, domain $[-3, 2]$, range $[-2, 2]$ **55.** Not a function
57. Yes **59.** No **61.** No **63.** Yes **65.** Yes **67.** Yes
69. (a)

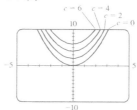

(b)

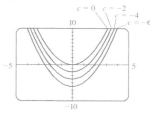

(c) If $c > 0$, then the graph of $f(x) = x^2 + c$ is the same as the graph of $y = x^2$ shifted upward c units. If $c < 0$, then the graph of $f(x) = x^2 + c$ is the same as the graph of $y = x^2$ shifted downward c units.

71. (a)

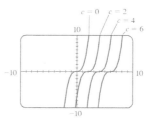

(b)

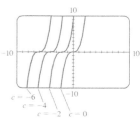

(c) If $c > 0$, then the graph of $f(x) = (x - c)^3$ is the same as the graph of $y = x^3$ shifted to the right c units. If $c < 0$, then the graph of $f(x) = (x - c)^3$ is the same as the graph of $y = x^3$ shifted to the left c units.

73. (a)

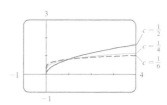

(b)

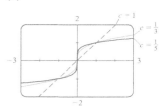

(c) Graphs of even roots are similar to $\sqrt{x}$; graphs of odd roots are similar to $\sqrt[3]{x}$. As c increases, the graph of $y = \sqrt[c]{x}$ becomes steeper near 0 and flatter when $x > 1$.

75. $f(x) = -\frac{7}{6}x - \frac{4}{3}, -2 \leq x \leq 4$

77. $f(x) = \sqrt{9 - x^2}, -3 \leq x \leq 3$

79.

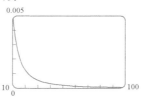

81. (a) $E(x) = \begin{cases} 6 + 0.10x & 0 \le x \le 300 \\ 36 + 0.06(x - 300), & x > 300 \end{cases}$

(b)

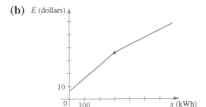

83. $P(x) = \begin{cases} 0.44 & \text{if } 0 < x \le 1 \\ 0.61 & \text{if } 1 < x \le 2 \\ 0.78 & \text{if } 2 < x \le 3 \\ 0.95 & \text{if } 3 < x \le 3.5 \end{cases}$

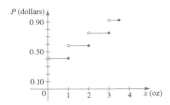

SECTION 2.3 ■ PAGE 168

1. $a, 4$ **2.** $x, y, [1, 6], [1, 7]$
3. (a) increase, $[1, 2], [4, 5]$ **(b)** decrease, $[2, 4], [5, 6]$
4. (a) largest, 7, 2   **(b)** smallest, 2, 4
5. (a) $1, -1, 3, 4$ **(b)** Domain $[-3, 4]$, range $[-1, 4]$
(c) $-3, 2, 4$ **(d)** $-3 \le x \le 2$ and $x = 4$
7. (a) $3, 2, -2, 1, 0$ **(b)** Domain $[-4, 4]$, range $[-2, 3]$
9. (a)   **11. (a)**

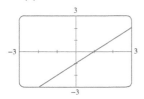

(b) Domain $(-\infty, \infty)$,   **(b)** Domain $[1, 3]$,
    range $(-\infty, \infty)$ range $\{4\}$
13. (a)   **15. (a)**

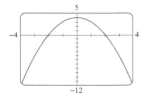

(b) Domain $(-\infty, \infty)$,   **(b)** Domain $[-4, 4]$,
    range $(-\infty, 4]$ range $[0, 4]$

17. (a)

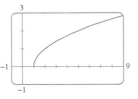

(b) Domain $[1, \infty)$,
    range $[0, \infty)$
19. (a) $[-1, 1], [2, 4]$ **(b)** $[1, 2]$
21. (a) $[-2, -1], [1, 2]$ **(b)** $[-3, -2], [-1, 1], [2, 3]$
23. (a)   **25. (a)**

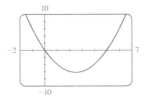

(b) Increasing on $[2.5, \infty)$;   **(b)** Increasing on $(-\infty, -1]$,
decreasing on $(-\infty, 2.5]$ $[2, \infty)$; decreasing on $[-1, 2]$
27. (a)   **29. (a)**

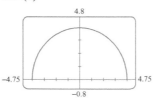

(b) Increasing on   **(b)** Increasing on $[0, \infty)$;
$(-\infty, -1.55], [0.22, \infty)$;   decreasing on $(-\infty, 0]$
decreasing on $[-1.55, 0.22]$
31. (a) Local maximum 2 when $x = 0$; local minimum -1 when
$x = -2$, local minimum 0 when $x = 2$ **(b)** Increasing on
$[-2, 0] \cup [2, \infty)$; decreasing on $(-\infty, -2] \cup [0, 2]$
33. (a) Local maximum 0 when $x = 0$; local maximum 1 when
$x = 3$, local minimum -2 when $x = -2$, local minimum -1 when
$x = 1$ **(b)** Increasing on $[-2, 0] \cup [1, 3]$; decreasing on
$(-\infty, -2] \cup [0, 1] \cup [3, \infty)$ **35. (a)** Local maximum ≈ 0.38
when $x \approx -0.58$; local minimum ≈ -0.38 when $x \approx 0.58$
(b) Increasing on $(-\infty, -0.58] \cup [0.58, \infty)$; decreasing on
$[-0.58, 0.58]$ **37. (a)** Local maximum ≈ 0 when $x = 0$; local
minimum ≈ -13.61 when $x \approx -1.71$, local minimum ≈ -73.32
when $x \approx 3.21$ **(b)** Increasing on $[-1.71, 0] \cup [3.21, \infty)$; decreasing on $(-\infty, -1.71] \cup [0, 3.21]$ **39. (a)** Local maximum
≈ 5.66 when $x \approx 4.00$ **(b)** Increasing on $(-\infty, 4.00]$; decreasing
on $[4.00, 6.00]$ **41. (a)** Local maximum ≈ 0.38 when
$x \approx -1.73$; local minimum ≈ -0.38 when $x \approx 1.73$
(b) Increasing on $(-\infty, -1.73] \cup [1.73, \infty)$; decreasing on
$[-1.73, 0) \cup (0, 1.73]$ **43. (a)** 500 MW, 725 MW
(b) Between 3:00 A.M. and 4:00 A.M.   **(c)** Just before noon
45. (a) Increasing on $[0, 30] \cup [32, 68]$; decreasing on $[30, 32]$
(b) He went on a crash diet and lost weight, only to regain
it again later.   **47. (a)** Increasing on $[0, 150] \cup [300, \infty)$;
decreasing on $[150, 300]$ **(b)** Local maximum when $x = 150$;
local minimum when $x = 300$

49. Runner A won the race. All runners finished. Runner B fell but got up again to finish second.

51. (a)

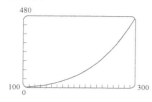

(b) Increases   **53.** 20 mi/h   **55.** $r \approx 0.67$ cm

SECTION 2.4 ■ PAGE 177

1. $\dfrac{100 \text{ miles}}{2 \text{ hours}} = 50$ mi/h   **2.** $\dfrac{f(b) - f(a)}{b - a}$ **3.** $\dfrac{25 - 1}{5 - 1} = 6$

4. (a) secant   **(b)** 3   **5.** $\frac{2}{3}$ **7.** $-\frac{4}{5}$ **9.** 3   **11.** 5   **13.** 60

15. $12 + 3h$ **17.** $-\dfrac{1}{a}$ **19.** $\dfrac{-2}{a(a + h)}$ **21. (a)** $\frac{1}{2}$

23. -0.25 ft/day   **25. (a)** 245 persons/yr
(b) -328.5 persons/yr   **(c)** 1997–2001   **(d)** 2001–2006
27. (a) 7.2 units/yr   **(b)** 8 units/yr   **(c)** -55 units/yr
(d) 2000–2001, 2001–2002   **29.** First 20 minutes: 4.05°F/min,
next 20 minutes: 1.5°F/min; first interval

SECTION 2.5 ■ PAGE 187

1. (a) up   **(b)** left   **2. (a)** down   **(b)** right   **3. (a)** *x*-axis
(b) *y*-axis   **4. (a)** II   **(b)** IV   **(c)** I   **(d)** III   **5. (a)** Shift
downward 5 units   **(b)** Shift to the right 5 units   **7. (a)** Reflect
in the *x*-axis   **(b)** Reflect in the *y*-axis   **9. (a)** Reflect in the *x*-
axis, then shift upward 5 units   **(b)** Stretch vertically by a factor
of 3, then shift downward 5 units   **11. (a)** Shift to the left 1 unit,
stretch vertically by a factor of 2, then shift downward 3 units
(b) Shift to the right 1 unit, stretch vertically by a factor of 2, then
shift upward 3 units   **13. (a)** Shrink horizontally by a factor of $\frac{1}{4}$
(b) Stretch horizontally by a factor of 4   **15. (a)** Shift to the left
2 units   **(b)** Shift upward 2 units   **17. (a)** Shift to the left
2 units, then shift downward 2 units   **(b)** Shift to the right 2
units, then shift upward 2 units

19. (a)

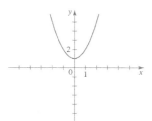

(b)

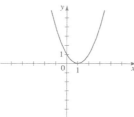

(c)

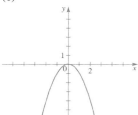

(d)

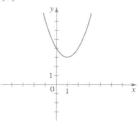

21.

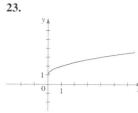

23.

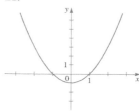

25.

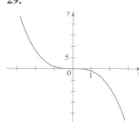

27.

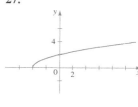

29.

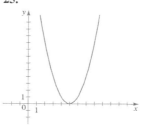

31.

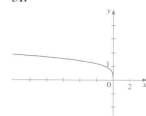

33.

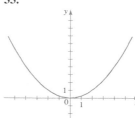

35.

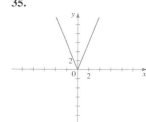

37.

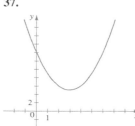

39.

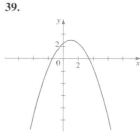

41.

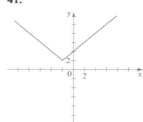

43.

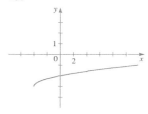

45. $f(x) = x^2 + 3$ **47.** $f(x) = \sqrt{x + 2}$
49. $f(x) = |x - 3| + 1$ **51.** $f(x) = \sqrt[4]{-x} + 1$
53. $f(x) = 2(x - 3)^2 - 2$ **55.** $g(x) = (x - 2)^2$
57. $g(x) = |x + 1| + 2$ **59.** $g(x) = -\sqrt{x + 2}$
61. (a) 3 **(b)** 1 **(c)** 2 **(d)** 4

63. (a) **(b)**

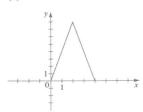

(c) **(d)**

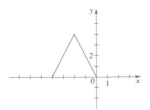
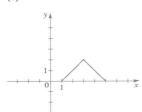

(e) **(f)**

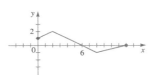

65. (a) **(b)**

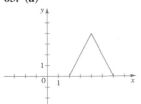
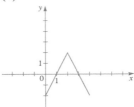

67.

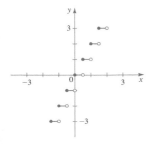

69.

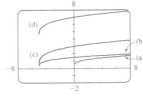

For part (b) shift the graph in (a) to the left 5 units; for part (c) shift the graph in (a) to the left 5 units and stretch vertically by a factor of 2; for part (d) shift the graph in (a) to the left 5 units, stretch vertically by a factor of 2, and then shift upward 4 units.

71.

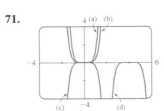

For part (b) shrink the graph in (a) vertically by a factor of $\frac{1}{3}$; for part (c) shrink the graph in (a) vertically by a factor of $\frac{1}{3}$ and reflect in the x-axis; for part (d) shift the graph in (a) to the right 4 units, shrink vertically by a factor of $\frac{1}{3}$, and then reflect in the x-axis.

73.

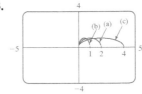

The graph in part (b) is shrunk horizontally by a factor of $\frac{1}{2}$ and the graph in part (c) is stretched by a factor of 2.

75. Even **77.** Neither

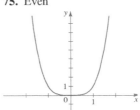

79. Odd **81.** Neither

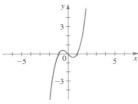

83. (a) **(b)**

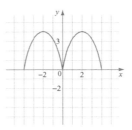
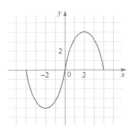

85. To obtain the graph of g, reflect in the x-axis the part of the graph of f that is below the x-axis.

87. (a)   **(b)**

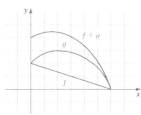

89. (a) Shift upward 4 units, shrink vertically by a factor of 0.01
(b) Shift to the right 10 units; $g(t) = 4 + 0.01(t - 10)^2$

SECTION 2.6 ■ PAGE 196

1. $8, -2, 15, \dfrac{3}{5}$ **2.** $f(g(x)), 12$ **3.** Multiply by 2, then add 1;
Add 1, then multiply by 2   **4.** $x + 1, 2x, 2x + 1, 2(x + 1)$

5. $(f + g)(x) = x^2 + x - 3, (-\infty, \infty)$;
$(f - g)(x) = -x^2 + x - 3, (-\infty, \infty)$;
$(fg)(x) = x^3 - 3x^2, (-\infty, \infty)$;
$\left(\dfrac{f}{g}\right)(x) = \dfrac{x - 3}{x^2}, (-\infty, 0) \cup (0, \infty)$

7. $(f + g)(x) = \sqrt{4 - x^2} + \sqrt{1 + x}, [-1, 2]$;
$(f - g)(x) = \sqrt{4 - x^2} - \sqrt{1 + x}, [-1, 2]$;
$(fg)(x) = \sqrt{-x^3 - x^2 + 4x + 4}, [-1, 2]$;
$\left(\dfrac{f}{g}\right)(x) = \sqrt{\dfrac{4 - x^2}{1 + x}}, (-1, 2]$

9. $(f + g)(x) = \dfrac{6x + 8}{x^2 + 4x}, x \neq -4, x \neq 0$;
$(f - g)(x) = \dfrac{-2x + 8}{x^2 + 4x}, x \neq -4, x \neq 0$;
$(fg)(x) = \dfrac{8}{x^2 + 4x}, x \neq -4, x \neq 0$;
$\left(\dfrac{f}{g}\right)(x) = \dfrac{x + 4}{2x}, x \neq -4, x \neq 0$

11. $[0, 1]$ **13.** $(3, \infty)$

15.   **17.**

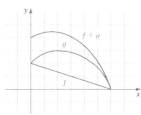
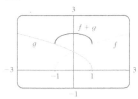

19.

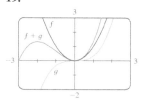

21. (a) 1   **(b)** -23 **23. (a)** -11 **(b)** -119
25. (a) $-3x^2 + 1$ **(b)** $-9x^2 + 30x - 23$
27. 4   **29.** 5   **31.** 4
33. $(f \circ g)(x) = 8x + 1, (-\infty, \infty)$;
$(g \circ f)(x) = 8x + 11, (-\infty, \infty)$; $(f \circ f)(x) = 4x + 9, (-\infty, \infty)$;
$(g \circ g)(x) = 16x - 5, (-\infty, \infty)$
35. $(f \circ g)(x) = (x + 1)^2, (-\infty, \infty)$;
$(g \circ f)(x) = x^2 + 1, (-\infty, \infty)$; $(f \circ f)(x) = x^4, (-\infty, \infty)$;
$(g \circ g)(x) = x + 2, (-\infty, \infty)$
37. $(f \circ g)(x) = \dfrac{1}{2x + 4}, x \neq -2; (g \circ f)(x) = \dfrac{2}{x} + 4, x \neq 0$;
$(f \circ f)(x) = x, x \neq 0, (g \circ g)(x) = 4x + 12, (-\infty, \infty)$
39. $(f \circ g)(x) = |2x + 3|, (-\infty, \infty)$;
$(g \circ f)(x) = 2|x| + 3, (-\infty, \infty)$; $(f \circ f)(x) = |x|, (-\infty, \infty)$;
$(g \circ g)(x) = 4x + 9, (-\infty, \infty)$
41. $(f \circ g)(x) = \dfrac{2x - 1}{2x}, x \neq 0; (g \circ f)(x) = \dfrac{2x}{x + 1} - 1, x \neq -1$;
$(f \circ f)(x) = \dfrac{x}{2x + 1}, x \neq -1, x \neq -\tfrac{1}{2}$;
$(g \circ g)(x) = 4x - 3, (-\infty, \infty)$
43. $(f \circ g)(x) = \dfrac{1}{x + 1}, x \neq -1, x \neq 0; (g \circ f)(x) = \dfrac{x + 1}{x}$,
$x \neq -1, x \neq 0; (f \circ f)(x) = \dfrac{x}{2x + 1}, x \neq -1, x \neq -\tfrac{1}{2}$;
$(g \circ g)(x) = x, x \neq 0$
45. $(f \circ g \circ h)(x) = \sqrt{x - 1} - 1$
47. $(f \circ g \circ h)(x) = (\sqrt{x} - 5)^4 + 1$
49. $g(x) = x - 9, f(x) = x^5$
51. $g(x) = x^2, f(x) = x/(x + 4)$
53. $g(x) = 1 - x^3, f(x) = |x|$
55. $h(x) = x^2, g(x) = x + 1, f(x) = 1/x$
57. $h(x) = \sqrt[3]{x}, g(x) = 4 + x, f(x) = x^9$
59. $R(x) = 0.15x - 0.000002x^2$
61. (a) $g(t) = 60t$ **(b)** $f(r) = \pi r^2$ **(c)** $(f \circ g)(t) = 3600\pi t^2$
63. $A(t) = 16\pi t^2$ **65. (a)** $f(x) = 0.9x$ **(b)** $g(x) = x - 100$
(c) $(f \circ g)(x) = 0.9x - 90, (g \circ f)(x) = 0.9x - 100, f \circ g$:
first rebate, then discount, $g \circ f$:
first discount, then rebate, $g \circ f$ is the better deal

SECTION 2.7 ■ PAGE 204

1. different, Horizontal Line   **2. (a)** one-to-one, $g(x) = x^3$
(b) $g^{-1}(x) = x^{1/3}$ **3. (a)** Take the cube root, subtract 5, then
divide the result by 3.   **(b)** $f(x) = (3x + 5)^3, f^{-1}(x) = \dfrac{x^{1/3} - 5}{3}$
4. (a) False **(b)** True   **5.** No   **7.** Yes   **9.** No   **11.** Yes
13. Yes   **15.** No   **17.** No   **19.** No   **21. (a)** 2   **(b)** 3   **23.** 1
37. $f^{-1}(x) = \frac{1}{2}(x - 1)$ **39.** $f^{-1}(x) = \frac{1}{4}(x - 7)$
41. $f^{-1}(x) = \sqrt[3]{\frac{1}{4}(5 - x)}$ **43.** $f^{-1}(x) = (1/x) - 2$
45. $f^{-1}(x) = \dfrac{4x}{1 - x}$ **47.** $f^{-1}(x) = \dfrac{7x + 5}{x - 2}$
49. $f^{-1}(x) = (5x - 1)/(2x + 3)$
51. $f^{-1}(x) = \frac{1}{5}(x^2 - 2), x \ge 0$
53. $f^{-1}(x) = \sqrt{4 - x}, x \le 4$
55. $f^{-1}(x) = (x - 4)^3$
57. $f^{-1}(x) = x^2 - 2x, x \ge 1$
59. $f^{-1}(x) = \sqrt[4]{x}$
61. (a)   **(b)**

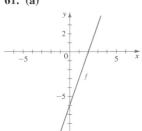   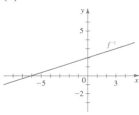

(c) $f^{-1}(x) = \frac{1}{3}(x + 6)$
63. (a)   **(b)**

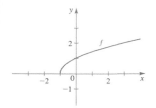   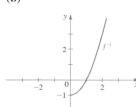

(c) $f^{-1}(x) = x^2 - 1, x \ge 0$
65. Not one-to-one   **67.** One-to-one

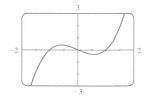   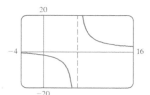

69. Not one-to-one

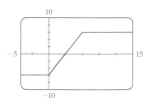

71. (a) $f^{-1}(x) = x - 2$ **73. (a)** $g^{-1}(x) = x^2 - 3, x \ge 0$
(b)   **(b)**

   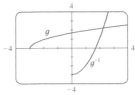

75. $x \ge 0, f^{-1}(x) = \sqrt{4 - x}$ **77.** $x \ge -2, h^{-1}(x) = \sqrt{x} - 2$
79.

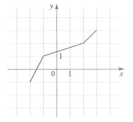

81. (a) $f(x) = 500 + 80x$ **(b)** $f^{-1}(x) = \frac{1}{80}(x - 500)$, the
number of hours worked as a function of the fee
(c) 9; if he charges $1220, he worked 9 h

83. (a) $v^{-1}(t) = \sqrt{0.25 - \dfrac{t}{18,500}}$ **(b)** 0.498; at a distance 0.498

from the central axis the velocity is 30
85. (a) $F^{-1}(x) = \frac{5}{9}(x - 32)$; the Celsius temperature when the
Fahrenheit temperature is x **(b)** $F^{-1}(86) = 30$; when the
temperature is 86°F, it is 30°C
87. (a) $f(x) = \begin{cases} 0.1x & \text{if } 0 \le x \le 20{,}000 \\ 2000 + 0.2(x - 20{,}000) & \text{if } x > 20{,}000 \end{cases}$

(b) $f^{-1}(x) = \begin{cases} 10x & \text{if } 0 \le x \le 2000 \\ 10{,}000 + 5x & \text{if } x > 2000 \end{cases}$

If you pay x euros (€) in taxes, your income is $f^{-1}(x)$.
(c) $f^{-1}(10{,}000) = €\,60{,}000$
89. $f^{-1}(x) = \frac{1}{2}(x - 7)$. A pizza costing x dollars has $f^{-1}(x)$
toppings.

CHAPTER 2 REVIEW ■ PAGE 208

1. $f(x) = x^2 - 5$ **3.** Add 10, then multiply the result by 3.

5.

x	$g(x)$
-1	5
0	0
1	-3
2	-4
3	-3

7. (a) $C(1000) = 34{,}000, C(10{,}000) = 205{,}000$ **(b)** The costs of
printing 1000 and 10,000 copies of the book   **(c)** $C(0) = 5000$;
fixed costs   **9.** 6, 2, 18, $a^2 - 4a + 6, a^2 + 4a + 6, x^2 - 2x + 3$,
$4x^2 - 8x + 6, 2x^2 - 8x + 10$ **11. (a)** Not a function
(b) Function   **(c)** Function, one-to-one   **(d)** Not a function
13. Domain $[-3, \infty)$, range $[0, \infty)$ **15.** $(-\infty, \infty)$

17. $[-4, \infty)$ **19.** $\{x \mid x \neq -2, -1, 0\}$ **21.** $(-\infty, -1] \cup [1, 4]$

23.
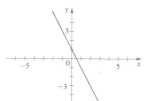

25.
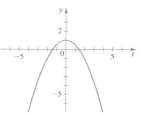

27.
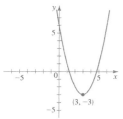

29.
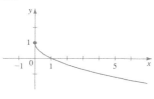

31.
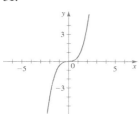

33.
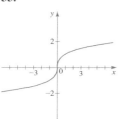

35.
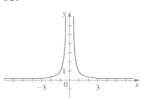

37.
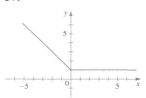

39.
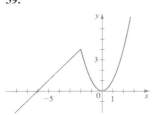

41. No **43.** Yes **45.** (iii)

47.
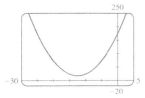

49.
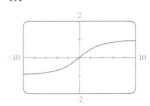

51. $[-2.1, 0.2] \cup [1.9, \infty)$

53.
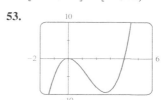
Increasing on $(-\infty, 0]$, $[2.67, \infty)$; decreasing on $[0, 2.67]$

55. 5 **57.** $\dfrac{-1}{3(3 + h)}$ **59. (a)** $P(10) = 5010, P(20) = 7040$; the populations in 1995 and 2005 **(b)** 203 people/yr; average annual population increase **61. (a)** $\frac{1}{2}, \frac{1}{2}$ **(b)** Yes, because it is a linear function **63. (a)** Shift upward 8 units **(b)** Shift to the left 8 units **(c)** Stretch vertically by a factor of 2, then shift upward 1 unit **(d)** Shift to the right 2 units and downward 2 units **(e)** Reflect in y-axis **(f)** Reflect in y-axis, then in x-axis **(g)** Reflect in x-axis **(h)** Reflect in line $y = x$
65. (a) Neither **(b)** Odd **(c)** Even **(d)** Neither
67. $g(-1) = -7$ **69.** 68 ft **71.** Local maximum ≈ 3.79 when $x \approx 0.46$; local minimum ≈ 2.81 when $x \approx -0.46$

73.
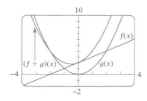

75. (a) $(f + g)(x) = x^2 - 6x + 6$
(b) $(f - g)(x) = x^2 - 2$
(c) $(fg)(x) = -3x^3 + 13x^2 - 18x + 8$
(d) $(f/g)(x) = (x^2 - 3x + 2)/(4 - 3x)$
(e) $(f \circ g)(x) = 9x^2 - 15x + 6$
(f) $(g \circ f)(x) = -3x^2 + 9x - 2$
77. $(f \circ g)(x) = -3x^2 + 6x - 1, (-\infty, \infty)$;
$(g \circ f)(x) = -9x^2 + 12x - 3, (-\infty, \infty)$;
$(f \circ f)(x) = 9x - 4, (-\infty, \infty)$;
$(g \circ g)(x) = -x^4 + 4x^3 - 6x^2 + 4x, (-\infty, \infty)$
79. $(f \circ g \circ h)(x) = 1 + \sqrt{x}$ **81.** Yes **83.** No
85. No **87.** $f^{-1}(x) = \dfrac{x + 2}{3}$
89. $f^{-1}(x) = \sqrt[3]{x} - 1$
91. (a), (b)
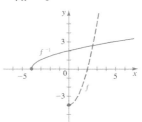

(c) $f^{-1}(x) = \sqrt{x + 4}$

CHAPTER 2 TEST ▪ PAGE 211

1. (a) and (b) are graphs of functions, (a) is one-to-one
2. (a) $2/3$, $\sqrt{6}/5$, $\sqrt{a}/(a-1)$ (b) $[-1, 0) \cup (0, \infty)$
3. (a) $f(x) = (x-2)^3$

(b)

x	$f(x)$
-1	-27
0	-8
1	-1
2	0
3	1
4	8

(c)

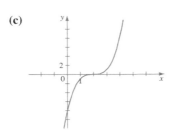

(d) By the Horizontal Line Test; take the cube root, then add 2
(e) $f^{-1}(x) = x^{1/3} + 2$ **4.** (a) $R(2) = 4000$, $R(4) = 4000$; total sales revenue with prices of \$2 and \$4

(b)

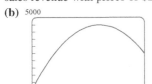

Revenue increases until price reaches \$3, then decreases

(c) \$4500; \$3   **5.** 5
6. (a)   **(b)**

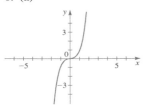

7. (a) Shift to the right 3 units, then shift upward 2 units
(b) Reflect in y-axis
8. (a) $3, 0$ **(b)**

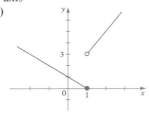

9. (a) $(f \circ g)(x) = (x-3)^2 + 1$ **(b)** $(g \circ f)(x) = x^2 - 2$
(c) 2   **(d)** 2   **(e)** $(g \circ g \circ g)(x) = x - 9$
10. (a) $f^{-1}(x) = 3 - x^2$, $x \geq 0$
(b)

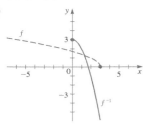

11. (a) Domain $[0, 6]$, range $[1, 7]$
(b)

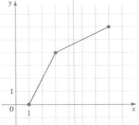

(c) $\frac{5}{4}$

12. (a)

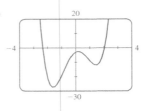

(b) No

(c) Local minimum ≈ -27.18 when $x \approx -1.61$; local maximum ≈ -2.55 when $x \approx 0.18$; local minimum ≈ -11.93 when $x \approx 1.43$ **(d)** $[-27.18, \infty)$
(e) Increasing on $[-1.61, 0.18] \cup [1.43, \infty)$; decreasing on $(-\infty, -1.61] \cup [0.18, 1.43]$

FOCUS ON MODELING ▪ PAGE 218

1. $A(w) = 3w^2$, $w > 0$ **3.** $V(w) = \frac{1}{2}w^3$, $w > 0$
5. $A(x) = 10x - x^2$, $0 < x < 10$
7. $A(x) = (\sqrt{3}/4)x^2$, $x > 0$
9. $r(A) = \sqrt{A/\pi}$, $A > 0$
11. $S(x) = 2x^2 + 240/x$, $x > 0$
13. $D(t) = 25t$, $t \geq 0$
15. $A(b) = b\sqrt{4 - b}$, $0 < b < 4$
17. $A(h) = 2h\sqrt{100 - h^2}$, $0 < h < 10$
19. (b) $p(x) = x(19 - x)$ (c) 9.5, 9.5
21. (b) $A(x) = x(2400 - 2x)$ (c) 600 ft by 1200 ft
23. (a) $f(w) = 8w + 7200/w$
(b) Width along road is 30 ft, length is 40 ft   **(c)** 15 ft to 60 ft

25. (a) $A(x) = 15x - \left(\dfrac{\pi + 4}{8}\right)x^2$

(b) Width ≈ 8.40 ft, height of rectangular part ≈ 4.20 ft
27. (a) $A(x) = x^2 + 48/x$ **(b)** Height ≈ 1.44 ft, width ≈ 2.88 ft

29. (a) $A(x) = 2x + \dfrac{200}{x}$ **(b)** 10 m by 10 m

31. (b) To point C, 5.1 mi from B

CHAPTER 3

SECTION 3.1 ▪ PAGE 229

1. square   **2.** (a) (h, k) (b) upward, minimum
(c) downward, maximum
3. upward, $(3, 5)$, 5, minimum
4. downward, $(3, 5)$, 5, maximum
5. (a) $(3, 4)$ (b) 4   (c) $\mathbb{R}, (-\infty, 4]$
7. (a) $(1, -3)$ (b) -3 (c) $\mathbb{R}, [-3, \infty)$

9. (a) $f(x) = (x - 3)^2 - 9$

(b) Vertex $(3, -9)$
x-intercepts 0, 6
y-intercept 0

(c)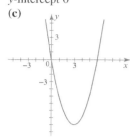

11. (a) $f(x) = 2\left(x + \frac{3}{2}\right)^2 - \frac{9}{2}$

(b) Vertex $\left(-\frac{3}{2}, -\frac{9}{2}\right)$
x-intercepts 0, -3,
y-intercept 0

(c)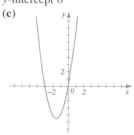

13. (a) $f(x) = (x + 2)^2 - 1$

(b) Vertex $(-2, -1)$, x-intercepts $-1, -3$, y-intercept 3

(c)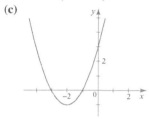

15. (a) $f(x) = -(x - 3)^2 + 13$

(b) Vertex $(3, 13)$; x-intercepts $3 \pm \sqrt{13}$; y-intercept 4

(c)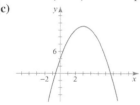

17. (a) $f(x) = 2(x + 1)^2 + 1$

(b) Vertex $(-1, 1)$; no x-intercept; y-intercept 3

(c)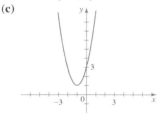

19. (a) $f(x) = 2(x - 5)^2 + 7$

(b) Vertex $(5, 7)$; no x-intercept; y-intercept 57

(c)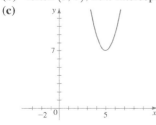

21. (a) $f(x) = -4(x + 2)^2 + 19$

(b) Vertex $(-2, 19)$; x-intercepts $-2 \pm \frac{1}{2}\sqrt{19}$; y-intercept 3

(c)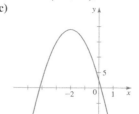

23. (a) $f(x) = (x + 1)^2 - 2$

(b)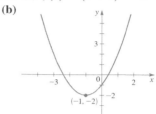

(c) Minimum $f(-1) = -2$

25. (a) $f(x) = 3(x - 1)^2 - 2$

(b)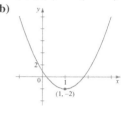

(c) Minimum $f(1) = -2$

27. (a) $f(x) = -\left(x + \frac{3}{2}\right)^2 + \frac{21}{4}$

(b)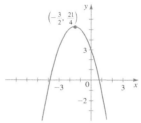

(c) Maximum $f\left(-\frac{3}{2}\right) = \frac{21}{4}$

29. (a) $g(x) = 3(x - 2)^2 + 1$

(b)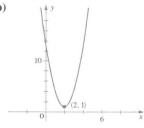

(c) Minimum $g(2) = 1$

31. (a) $h(x) = -\left(x + \frac{1}{2}\right)^2 + \frac{5}{4}$

(b)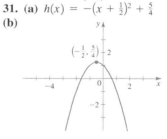

(c) Maximum $h\left(-\frac{1}{2}\right) = \frac{5}{4}$

33. Minimum $f\left(-\frac{1}{2}\right) = \frac{3}{4}$ **35.** Maximum $f(-3.5) = 185.75$

37. Minimum $f(0.6) = 15.64$ **39.** Minimum $h(-2) = -8$

41. Maximum $f(-1) = \frac{7}{2}$ **43.** $f(x) = 2x^2 - 4x$

45. $(-\infty, \infty), (-\infty, 1]$ **47.** $(-\infty, \infty), \left[-\frac{23}{2}, \infty\right)$

49. (a) -4.01 **(b)** -4.011025

51. Local maximum 2; local minima $-1, 0$

53. Local maxima 0, 1; local minima $-2, -1$

55. Local maximum ≈ 0.38 when $x \approx -0.58$;
local minimum ≈ -0.38 when $x \approx 0.58$

57. Local maximum ≈ 0 when $x = 0$; local minimum ≈ -13.61
when $x \approx -1.71$; local minimum ≈ -73.32 when $x \approx 3.21$

59. Local maximum ≈ 5.66 when $x \approx 4.00$

61. Local maximum ≈ 0.38 when $x \approx -1.73$;
local minimum ≈ -0.38 when $x \approx 1.73$ **63.** 25 ft

65. \$4000, 100 units   **67.** 30 times   **69.** 50 trees per acre

71. 600 ft by 1200 ft   **73.** Width 8.40 ft, height of rectangular
part 4.20 ft   **75. (a)** $f(x) = x(1200 - x)$ **(b)** 600 ft by 600 ft
77. (a) $R(x) = x(57,000 - 3000x)$ **(b)** \$9.50   **(c)** \$19.00

SECTION 3.2 ■ PAGE 243

1. II   **2. (a)** (ii)   **(b)** (iv)   **3. (a)**, (c)   **4. (a)**
5. (a)

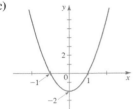

(b)

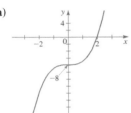

(c)

(d)

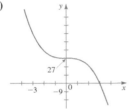

7. (a)

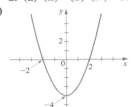

(b)

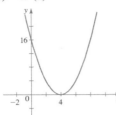

(c)

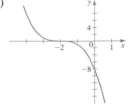

(d)

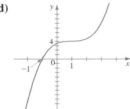

9. III   **11.** V   **13.** VI
15.

17.

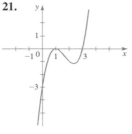

19.

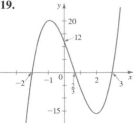

21.

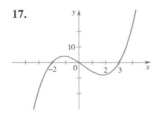

23.

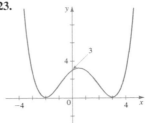

25.

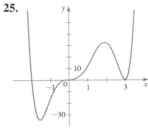

27. $P(x) = x(x + 2)(x - 3)$ **29.** $P(x) = -x(x + 3)(x - 4)$

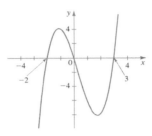

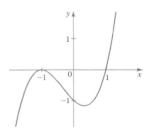

31. $P(x) = x^2(x - 1)(x - 2)$ **33.** $P(x) = (x + 1)^2(x - 1)$

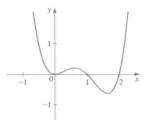

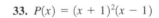

35. $P(x) = (2x - 1)(x + 3)(x - 3)$

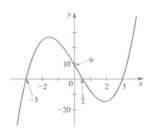

37. $P(x) = (x - 2)^2(x^2 + 2x + 4)$

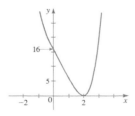

39. $P(x) = (x^2 + 1)(x + 2)(x - 2)$

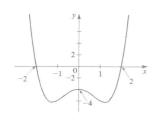

41. $y \to \infty$ as $x \to \infty$, $y \to -\infty$ as $x \to -\infty$
43. $y \to \infty$ as $x \to \pm\infty$
45. $y \to \infty$ as $x \to \infty$, $y \to -\infty$ as $x \to -\infty$
47. (a) x-intercepts 0, 4; y-intercept 0   (b) $(2, 4)$
49. (a) x-intercepts -2, 1; y-intercept -1 (b) $(-1, -2), (1, 0)$
51.

local maximum $(4, 16)$
53.

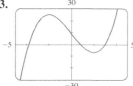

local maximum $(-2, 25)$,
local minimum $(2, -7)$

55.

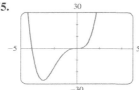

local minimum $(-3, -27)$

57.

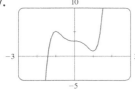

local maximum $(-1, 5)$,
local minimum $(1, 1)$
59. One local maximum, no local minimum
61. One local maximum, one local minimum
63. One local maximum, two local minima
65. No local extrema
67. One local maximum, two local minima
69.

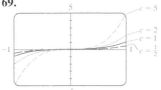

Increasing the value of c
stretches the graph vertically.

71.

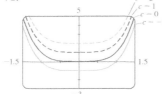

Increasing the value of c
moves the graph up.

73.

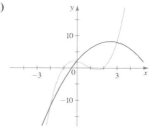

Increasing the value of c causes a deeper dip in the graph in the fourth quadrant and moves the positive x-intercept to the right.
75. (a)

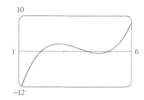

(b) Three   (c) $(0, 2), (3, 8), (-2, -12)$
77. (d) $P(x) = P_O(x) + P_E(x)$, where $P_O(x) = x^5 + 6x^3 - 2x$
and $P_E(x) = -x^2 + 5$
79. (a) Two local extrema

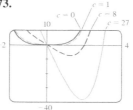

81. (a) 26 blenders   (b) No; $3276.22
83. (a) $V(x) = 4x^3 - 120x^2 + 800x$ (b) $0 < x < 10$
(c) Maximum volume ≈ 1539.6 cm^3

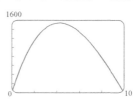

SECTION 3.3 ▪ PAGE 251
1. quotient, remainder   **2.** (a) factor   (b) k
3. $(x + 3)(3x - 4) + 8$ **5.** $(2x - 3)(x^2 - 1) - 3$
7. $(x^2 + 3)(x^2 - x - 3) + (7x + 11)$

9. $x + 1 + \dfrac{-11}{x + 3}$ **11.** $2x - \dfrac{1}{2} + \dfrac{-\frac{15}{2}}{2x - 1}$

13. $2x^2 - x + 1 + \dfrac{4x - 4}{x^2 + 4}$

In answers 15–37 the first polynomial given is the quotient, and the second is the remainder.
15. $x - 2, -16$ **17.** $2x^2 - 1, -2$ **19.** $x + 2, 8x - 1$
21. $3x + 1, 7x - 5$ **23.** $x^4 + 1, 0$ **25.** $x - 2, -2$
27. $3x + 23, 138$ **29.** $x^2 + 2, -3$ **31.** $x^2 - 3x + 1, -1$
33. $x^4 + x^3 + 4x^2 + 4x + 4, -2$ **35.** $2x^2 + 4x, 1$

37. $x^2 + 3x + 9, 0$ **39.** -3 **41.** 12 **43.** -7 **45.** -483
47. 2159 **49.** $\frac{7}{3}$ **51.** -8.279 **57.** $-1 \pm \sqrt{6}$
59. $x^3 - 3x^2 - x + 3$ **61.** $x^4 - 8x^3 + 14x^2 + 8x - 15$
63. $-\frac{3}{2}x^3 + 3x^2 + \frac{15}{2}x - 9$ **65.** $(x + 1)(x - 1)(x - 2)$
67. $(x + 2)^2(x - 1)^2$

SECTION 3.4 ■ PAGE 260

1. $a_0, a_n, \pm 1, \pm\frac{1}{2}, \pm\frac{1}{3}, \pm\frac{1}{6}, \pm 2, \pm\frac{2}{3}, \pm 5, \pm\frac{5}{2}, \pm\frac{5}{3}, \pm\frac{5}{6}, \pm 10, \pm\frac{10}{3}$
2. 1, 3, 5; 0 **3.** True **4.** False **5.** $\pm 1, \pm 3$ **7.** $\pm 1, \pm 2, \pm 4,$
$\pm 8, \pm\frac{1}{2}$ **9.** $\pm 1, \pm 7, \pm\frac{1}{2}, \pm\frac{7}{2}, \pm\frac{1}{4}, \pm\frac{7}{4}$ **11. (a)** $\pm 1, \pm\frac{1}{5}$
(b) $-1, 1, \frac{1}{5}$ **13. (a)** $\pm 1, \pm 3, \pm\frac{1}{2}, \pm\frac{3}{2}$ **(b)** $-\frac{1}{2}, 1, 3$
15. $-2, 1; P(x) = (x + 2)^2(x - 1)$
17. $-1, 2; P(x) = (x + 1)^2(x - 2)$ **19.** $2; P(x) = (x - 2)^3$
21. $-1, 2, 3; P(x) = (x + 1)(x - 2)(x - 3)$
23. $-3, -1, 1; P(x) = (x + 3)(x + 1)(x - 1)$
25. $\pm 1, \pm 2; P(x) = (x - 2)(x + 2)(x - 1)(x + 1)$
27. $-4, -2, -1, 1; P(x) = (x + 4)(x + 2)(x - 1)(x + 1)$
29. $\pm 2, \pm\frac{3}{2}; P(x) = (x - 2)(x + 2)(2x - 3)(2x + 3)$
31. $\pm 2, \frac{1}{3}, 3; P(x) = (x - 2)(x + 2)(x - 3)(3x - 1)$
33. $-1, \pm\frac{1}{2}; P(x) = (x + 1)(2x - 1)(2x + 1)$
35. $-\frac{3}{2}, \frac{1}{2}, 1; P(x) = (x - 1)(2x + 3)(2x - 1)$
37. $-\frac{5}{2}, -1, \frac{3}{2}; P(x) = (x + 1)(2x + 5)(2x - 3)$
39. $-\frac{1}{2}, \frac{2}{5}, \frac{1}{2}; P(x) = (2x - 1)(5x - 2)(2x + 1)$
41. $-1, \frac{1}{2}, 2; P(x) = (x + 1)(x - 2)^2(2x - 1)$
43. $-3, -2, 1, 3; P(x) = (x + 3)(x + 2)^2(x - 1)(x - 3)$
45. $-1, -\frac{1}{3}, 2, 5; P(x) = (x + 1)^2(x - 2)(x - 5)(3x + 1)$

47. $-2, -1 \pm \sqrt{2}$ **49.** $-1, 4, \dfrac{3 \pm \sqrt{13}}{2}$ **51.** $3, \dfrac{1 \pm \sqrt{5}}{2}$
53. $\frac{1}{2}, \dfrac{1 \pm \sqrt{3}}{2}$ **55.** $-1, -\frac{1}{2}, -3 \pm \sqrt{10}$
57. (a) $-2, 2, 3$ **(b)**

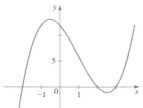

59. (a) $-\frac{1}{2}, 2$ **(b)**

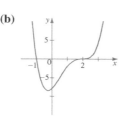

61. (a) $-1, 2$ **(b)**

63. (a) $-1, 2$ **(b)**

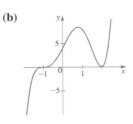

65. 1 positive, 2 or 0 negative; 3 or 1 real **67.** 1 positive,
1 negative; 2 real **69.** 2 or 0 positive, 0 negative; 3 or 1 real (since 0
is a zero but is neither positive nor negative) **75.** $3, -2$ **77.** $3, -1$
79. $-2, \frac{1}{2}, \pm 1$ **81.** $\pm\frac{1}{2}, \pm \sqrt{5}$ **83.** $-2, 1, 3, 4$ **89.** $-2, 2, 3$
91. $-\frac{3}{2}, -1, 1, 4$ **93.** $-1.28, 1.53$ **95.** -1.50 **99.** 11.3 ft
101. (a) It began to snow again. **(b)** No
(c) Just before midnight on Saturday night **103.** 2.76 m
105. 88 in. (or 3.21 in.)

SECTION 3.5 ■ PAGE 268

1. -1 **2.** 3, 4 **3. (a)** $3 - 4i$ **(b)** $9 + 16 = 25$ **4.** $3 - 4i$
5. Real part 5, imaginary part -7 **7.** Real part $-\frac{2}{3}$, imaginary part
$-\frac{5}{3}$ **9.** Real part 3, imaginary part 0 **11.** Real part 0, imaginary
part $-\frac{2}{3}$ **13.** Real part $\sqrt{3}$, imaginary part 2 **15.** $5 - i$
17. $3 + 5i$ **19.** $2 - 2i$ **21.** $-19 + 4i$ **23.** $-4 + 8i$
25. $30 + 10i$ **27.** $-33 - 56i$ **29.** $27 - 8i$ **31.** $-i$ **33.** 1
35. $-i$ **37.** $\frac{8}{5} + \frac{1}{5}i$ **39.** $-5 + 12i$ **41.** $-4 + 2i$ **43.** $2 - \frac{4}{3}i$
45. $-i$ **47.** $5i$ **49.** -6 **51.** $(3 + \sqrt{5}) + (3 - \sqrt{5})i$
53. 2 **55.** $-i\sqrt{2}$ **57.** $\pm 7i$ **59.** $2 \pm i$ **61.** $-1 \pm 2i$
63. $-\dfrac{1}{2} \pm \dfrac{\sqrt{3}}{2}i$ **65.** $\frac{1}{2} \pm \frac{1}{2}i$ **67.** $-\dfrac{3}{2} \pm \dfrac{\sqrt{3}}{2}i$ **69.** $\dfrac{-6 \pm \sqrt{6}i}{6}$
71. $1 \pm 3i$

SECTION 3.6 ■ PAGE 276

1. $5, -2, 3, 1$ **2. (a)** $x - a$ **(b)** $(x - a)^m$ **3.** n
4. $a - bi$ **5. (a)** $0, \pm 2i$ **(b)** $x^2(x - 2i)(x + 2i)$
7. (a) $0, 1 \pm i$ **(b)** $x(x - 1 - i)(x - 1 + i)$
9. (a) $\pm i$ **(b)** $(x - i)^2(x + i)^2$
11. (a) $\pm 2, \pm 2i$ **(b)** $(x - 2)(x + 2)(x - 2i)(x + 2i)$
13. (a) $-2, 1 \pm i\sqrt{3}$ **(b)** $(x + 2)(x - 1 - i\sqrt{3})(x - 1 + i\sqrt{3})$
15. (a) $\pm 1, \frac{1}{2} \pm \frac{1}{2}i\sqrt{3}, -\frac{1}{2} \pm \frac{1}{2}i\sqrt{3}$
(b) $(x - 1)(x + 1)(x - \frac{1}{2} - \frac{1}{2}i\sqrt{3})(x - \frac{1}{2} + \frac{1}{2}i\sqrt{3}) \times$
$(x + \frac{1}{2} - \frac{1}{2}i\sqrt{3})(x + \frac{1}{2} + \frac{1}{2}i\sqrt{3})$

*In answers 17–33 the factored form is given first, then
the zeros are listed with the multiplicity of each in parentheses.*
17. $(x - 5i)(x + 5i); \pm 5i\ (1)$
19. $[x - (-1 + i)][x - (-1 - i)]; -1 + i\ (1), -1 - i\ (1)$
21. $x(x - 2i)(x + 2i); 0\ (1), 2i\ (1), -2i\ (1)$
23. $(x - 1)(x + 1)(x - i)(x + i); 1\ (1), -1\ (1), i\ (1), -i\ (1)$
25. $16(x - \frac{3}{2})(x + \frac{3}{2})(x - \frac{3}{2}i)(x + \frac{3}{2}i); \frac{3}{2}\ (1), -\frac{3}{2}\ (1), \frac{3}{2}i\ (1), -\frac{3}{2}i\ (1)$
27. $(x + 1)(x - 3i)(x + 3i); -1\ (1), 3i\ (1), -3i\ (1)$
29. $(x - i)^2(x + i)^2; i\ (2), -i\ (2)$
31. $(x - 1)(x + 1)(x - 2i)(x + 2i); 1\ (1), -1\ (1), 2i\ (1), -2i\ (1)$
33. $x(x - i\sqrt{3})^2(x + i\sqrt{3})^2; 0\ (1), i\sqrt{3}\ (2), -i\sqrt{3}\ (2)$
35. $P(x) = x^2 - 2x + 2$ **37.** $Q(x) = x^3 - 3x^2 + 4x - 12$
39. $P(x) = x^3 - 2x^2 + x - 2$

41. $R(x) = x^4 - 4x^3 + 10x^2 - 12x + 5$

43. $T(x) = 6x^4 - 12x^3 + 18x^2 - 12x + 12$

45. $-2, \pm 2i$ **47.** $1, \dfrac{1 \pm i\sqrt{3}}{2}$ **49.** $2, \dfrac{1 \pm i\sqrt{3}}{2}$

51. $-\frac{3}{2}, -1 \pm i\sqrt{2}$ **53.** $-2, 1, \pm 3i$ **55.** $1, \pm 2i, \pm i\sqrt{3}$

57. 3 (multiplicity 2), $\pm 2i$ **59.** $-\frac{1}{2}$ (multiplicity 2), $\pm i$

61. 1 (multiplicity 3), $\pm 3i$ **63. (a)** $(x - 5)(x^2 + 4)$

(b) $(x - 5)(x - 2i)(x + 2i)$ **65. (a)** $(x - 1)(x + 1)(x^2 + 9)$

(b) $(x - 1)(x + 1)(x - 3i)(x + 3i)$

67. (a) $(x - 2)(x + 2)(x^2 - 2x + 4)(x^2 + 2x + 4)$

(b) $(x - 2)(x + 2)[x - (1 + i\sqrt{3})][x - (1 - i\sqrt{3})] \times$
$[x + (1 + i\sqrt{3})][x + (1 - i\sqrt{3})]$ **69. (a)** 4 real

(b) 2 real, 2 imaginary   **(c)** 4 imaginary

SECTION 3.7 ■ PAGE 289

1. $-\infty, \infty$ **2.** 2   **3.** $-1, 2$ **4.** $\frac{1}{3}$ **5.** $-2, 3$ **6.** 1

7. (a) $-3, -19, -199, -1999; 5, 21, 201, 2001;$
$1.2500, 1.0417, 1.0204, 1.0020; 0.8333, 0.9615, 0.9804, 0.9980$

(b) $r(x) \to -\infty$ as $x \to 2^-; r(x) \to \infty$ as $x \to 2^+$

(c) Horizontal asymptote $y = 1$

9. (a) $-22, -430, -40,300, -4,003,000;$
$-10, -370, -39,700, -3,997,000;$
$0.3125, 0.0608, 0.0302, 0.0030;$
$-0.2778, -0.0592, -0.0298, -0.0030$

(b) $r(x) \to -\infty$ as $x \to 2^-; r(x) \to -\infty$ as $x \to 2^+$

(c) Horizontal asymptote $y = 0$

11. x-intercept 1, y-intercept $-\frac{1}{4}$ **13.** x-intercepts $-1, 2$;

y-intercept $\frac{1}{3}$ **15.** x-intercepts $-3, 3$; no y-intercept

17. x-intercept 3, y-intercept 3, vertical $x = 2$; horizontal $y = 2$

19. x-intercepts $-1, 1$; y-intercept $\frac{1}{4}$; vertical $x = -2, x = 2$;
horizontal $y = 1$ **21.** Vertical $x = 2$; horizontal $y = 0$

23. Horizontal $y = 0$

25. Vertical $x = \frac{1}{2}, x = -1$; horizontal $y = 3$

27. Vertical $x = \frac{1}{3}, x = -2$; horizontal $y = \frac{5}{3}$

29. Vertical $x = 0$; horizontal $y = 3$

31. Vertical $x = 1$

33.    **35.**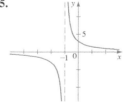

37. 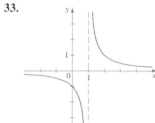   **39.**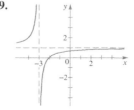

41.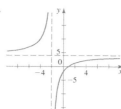

x-intercept 1
y-intercept -2
vertical $x = -2$
horizontal $y = 4$
domain $\{x \mid x \neq -2\}$
range $\{y \mid y \neq 4\}$

43.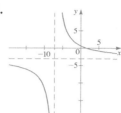

x-intercept $\frac{4}{3}$
y-intercept $\frac{4}{7}$
vertical $x = -7$
horizontal $y = -3$
domain $\{x \mid x \neq -7\}$
range $\{y \mid y \neq -3\}$

45.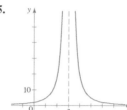

y-intercept 2
vertical $x = 3$
horizontal $y = 0$
domain $\{x \mid x \neq 3\}$
range $\{y \mid y > 0\}$

47.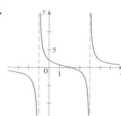

x-intercept 2
y-intercept 2
vertical $x = -1, x = 4$
horizontal $y = 0$
domain $\{x \mid x \neq -1, 4\}$
range $\mathbb{R}$

49.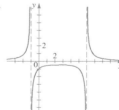

y-intercept -1
vertical $x = -1, x = 6$
horizontal $y = 0$
domain $\{x \mid x \neq -1, 6\}$
range $\{y \mid y \leq -0.5 \text{ or } y > 0\}$

51.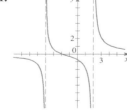

x-intercept -2
y-intercept $-\frac{3}{4}$
vertical $x = -4, x = 2$
horizontal $y = 0$
domain $\{x \mid x \neq -4, 2\}$
range $\mathbb{R}$

53.

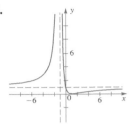

x-intercepts $-2, 1$
y-intercept $\frac{2}{3}$
vertical $x = -1, x = 3$
horizontal $y = 1$
domain $\{x \mid x \neq -1, 3\}$
range $\mathbb{R}$

55.

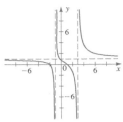

x-intercept 1
y-intercept 1
vertical $x = -1$
horizontal $y = 1$
domain $\{x \mid x \neq -1\}$
range $\{y \mid y \geq 0\}$

57.

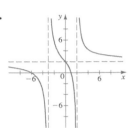

x-intercepts $-6, 1$
y-intercept 2
vertical $x = -3, x = 2$
horizontal $y = 2$
domain $\{x \mid x \neq -3, 2\}$
range $\mathbb{R}$

59.

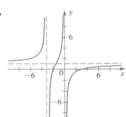

x-intercepts $-2, 3$
vertical $x = -3, x = 0$
horizontal $y = 1$
domain $\{x \mid x \neq -3, 0\}$
range $\mathbb{R}$

61.

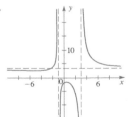

y-intercept -2
vertical $x = -1, x = 3$
horizontal $y = 3$
domain $\{x \mid x \neq -1, 3\}$
range $\{y \mid y \leq -1.5 \text{ or } y \geq 2.4\}$

63.

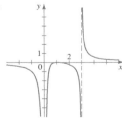

x-intercept 1
vertical $x = 0, x = 3$
horizontal $y = 0$
domain $\{x \mid x \neq 0, 3\}$
range $\mathbb{R}$

65.

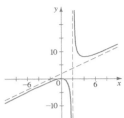

slant $y = x + 2$
vertical $x = 2$

67.

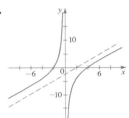

slant $y = x - 2$
vertical $x = 0$

69.

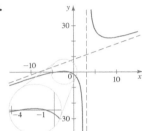

slant $y = x + 8$
vertical $x = 3$

71.

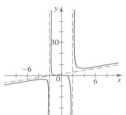

slant $y = x + 1$
vertical $x = 2, x = -2$

73.

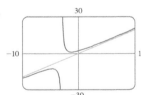

vertical $x = -3$

75.

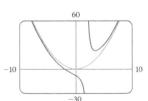

vertical $x = 2$

77.

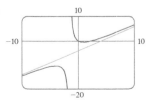

vertical $x = -1.5$
x-intercepts 0, 2.5
y-intercept 0, local
maximum $(-3.9, -10.4)$
local minimum $(0.9, -0.6)$
end behavior: $y = x - 4$

79.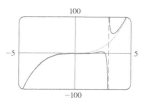

vertical $x = 1$
x-intercept 0
y-intercept 0
local minimum $(1.4, 3.1)$
end behavior: $y = x^2$

81.

vertical $x = 3$
x-intercepts 1.6, 2.7
y-intercept -2
local maxima $(-0.4, -1.8)$,
$(2.4, 3.8)$,
local minima $(0.6, -2.3)$,
$(3.4, 54.3)$
end behavior $y = x^3$

83. (a) 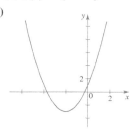   **(b)** It levels off at 3000.

85. (a) 2.50 mg/L   **(b)** It decreases to 0.   **(c)** 16.61 h

87.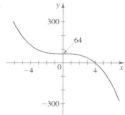

If the speed of the train approaches the speed of sound, then the pitch increases indefinitely (a sonic boom).

CHAPTER 3 REVIEW ▪ PAGE 292

1. (a) $f(x) = (x + 2)^2 - 3$

3. (a) $g(x) = -(x - 4)^2 + 17$

(b)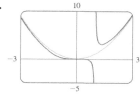

(b)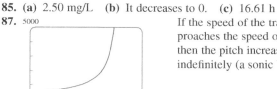

5. Minimum $f(-1) = -7$ **7.** 68 feet

9.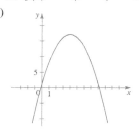

11.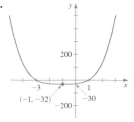

13.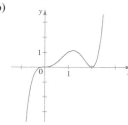

15. (a) 0 (multiplicity 3), 2 (multiplicity 2)

(b)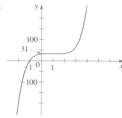

17.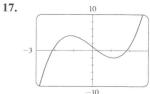

x-intercepts $-2.1, 0.3, 1.9$
y-intercept 1
local maximum $(-1.2, 4.1)$
local minimum $(1.2, -2.1)$
$y \to \infty$ as $x \to \infty$
$y \to -\infty$ as $x \to -\infty$

19.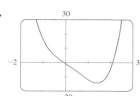

x-intercepts $-0.1, 2.1$
y-intercept -1
local minimum $(1.4, -14.5)$
$y \to \infty$ as $x \to \infty$
$y \to \infty$ as $x \to -\infty$

21. (a) $S = 13.8x(100 - x^2)$ **(b)** $0 \le x \le 10$
(c) 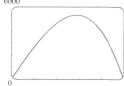   **(d)** 5.8 in.

In answers 23–29 the first polynomial given is the quotient, and the second is the remainder.

23. $x - 1, 3$ **25.** $x^2 + 3x + 23, 94$
27. $x^3 - 5x^2 + 17x - 83, 422$ **29.** $2x - 3, 12$
31. 3   **35.** 8   **37. (a)** $\pm 1, \pm 2, \pm 3, \pm 6, \pm 9, \pm 18$
(b) 2 or 0 positive, 3 or 1 negative
39. (a) $-4, 0, 4$ **41. (a)** $-2, 0$ (multiplicity 2), 1

(b)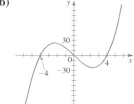

(b)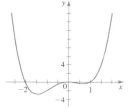

43. (a) $-2, -1, 2, 3$
(b)

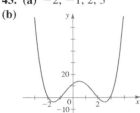

45. (a) $-\frac{1}{2}, 1$
(b)

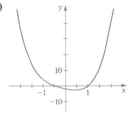

CHAPTER 3 TEST ■ PAGE 295

1. $f(x) = \left(x - \frac{1}{2}\right)^2 - \frac{25}{4}$

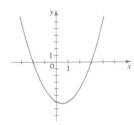

47. $3 + i$ **49.** $8 - i$ **51.** $\frac{6}{5} + \frac{8}{5}i$ **53.** i **55.** 2
57. $4x^3 - 18x^2 + 14x + 12$ **59.** No; since the complex conjugates of imaginary zeros will also be zeros, the polynomial would have 8 zeros, contradicting the requirement that it have degree 4.
61. $-3, 1, 5$ **63.** $-1 \pm 2i, -2$ (multiplicity 2)
65. $\pm 2, 1$ (multiplicity 3)   **67.** $\pm 2, \pm 1 \pm i\sqrt{3}$
69. $1, 3, \dfrac{-1 \pm i\sqrt{7}}{2}$ **71.** $x = -0.5, 3$ **73.** $x \approx -0.24, 4.24$
75. $2, P(x) = (x - 2)(x^2 + 2x + 2)$

2. Minimum $f\left(-\frac{3}{2}\right) = -\frac{3}{2}$ **3. (a)** 2500 ft   **(b)** 1000 ft

4.

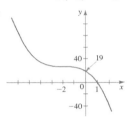

77.

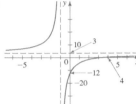

79.

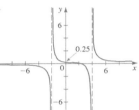

5. (a) $x^3 + 2x^2 + 2, 9$ **(b)** $x^3 + 2x^2 + \frac{1}{2}, \frac{15}{2}$
6. (a) $\pm 1, \pm 3, \pm \frac{1}{2}, \pm \frac{3}{2}$ **(b)** $2(x - 3)\left(x - \frac{1}{2}\right)(x + 1)$
(c) $-1, \frac{1}{2}, 3$ **(d)**

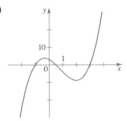

81.

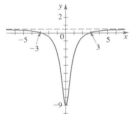

83.

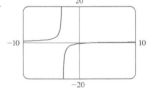

x-intercept 3
y-intercept -0.5
vertical $x = -3$
horizontal $y = 0.5$
no local extrema

85.

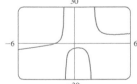

x-intercept -2
y-intercept -4
vertical $x = -1, x = 2$
slant $y = x + 1$
local maximum $(0.425, -3.599)$
local minimum $(4.216, 7.175)$

87. $(-2, -28), (1, 26), (2, 68), (5, 770)$

7. (a) $7 + i$ **(b)** $-1 - 5i$ **(c)** $18 + i$ **(d)** $\frac{6}{25} - \frac{17}{25}i$
(e) 1 **(f)** $6 - 2i$ **8.** $3, -1 \pm i$ **9.** $(x - 1)^2(x - 2i)(x + 2i)$
10. $x^4 + 2x^3 + 10x^2 + 18x + 9$
11. (a) 4, 2, or 0 positive; 0 negative
(c) 0.17, 3.93

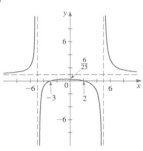

(d) Local minimum $(2.8, -70.3)$
12. (a) r, u **(b)** s **(c)** s **(d)**

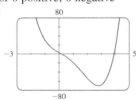

(e) $x^2 - 2x - 5$

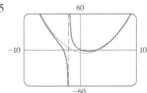

FOCUS ON MODELING ▪ PAGE 298

1. (a) $y = -0.275428x^2 + 19.7485x - 273.5523$
(b)

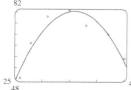

(c) 35.85 lb/in^2
3. (a) $y = 0.00203708x^3 - 0.104521x^2 + 1.966206x + 1.45576$
(b)

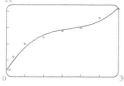

(c) 43 vegetables   (d) 2.0 s
5. (a) Degree 2
(b) $y = -16.0x^2 + 51.8429x + 4.20714$

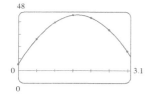

(c) 0.3 s and 2.9 s   (d) 46.2 ft

CHAPTER 4

SECTION 4.1 ▪ PAGE 307

1. $5; \frac{1}{25}, 1, 25, 15{,}625$ **2.** (a) III   (b) I   (c) II   (d) IV
3. (a) downward   (b) right   **4.** principal, interest rate per year, number of times interest is compounded per year, number of years, amount after t years; \$112.65   **5.** 2.000, 7.103, 77.880, 1.587
7. 0.885, 0.606, 0.117, 1.837
9.

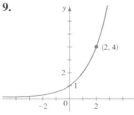

11.

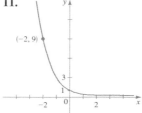

13.

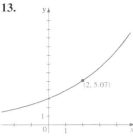

15.

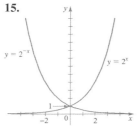

17.

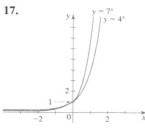

19. $f(x) = 3^x$ **21.** $f(x) = \left(\frac{1}{4}\right)^x$ **23.** II
25. $\mathbb{R}, (-\infty, 0), y = 0$ **27.** $\mathbb{R}, (-3, \infty), y = -3$

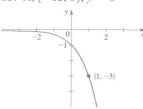   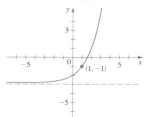

29. $\mathbb{R}, (4, \infty), y = 4$ **31.** $\mathbb{R}, (0, \infty), y = 0$

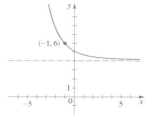   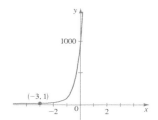

33. $\mathbb{R}, (1, \infty), y = 1$ **35.** $\mathbb{R}, (-\infty, 3), y = 3$

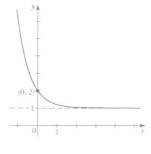   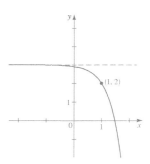

37. (a)

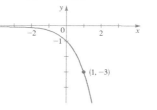

(b) The graph of g is steeper than that of f.

39.

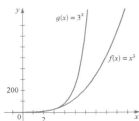

41. (a)

(i)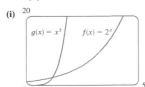

(ii)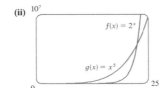

(iii)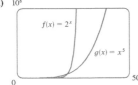

The graph of f ultimately increases much more quickly than that of g.

(b) 1.2, 22.4

43.

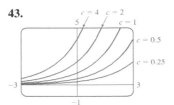

The larger the value of c, the more rapidly the graph increases.

45. (a) Increasing on $(-\infty, 0.50]$; decreasing on $[0.50, \infty)$
(b) $(0, 1.78]$ **47. (a)** $1500 \cdot 2^t$ **(b)** 25,165,824,000
49. $5203.71, $5415.71, $5636.36, $5865.99, $6104.98, $6353.71
51. (a) $11,605.41 **(b)** $13,468.55 **(c)** $15,630.80
53. (a) $519.02 **(b)** $538.75 **(c)** $726.23 **55.** $7678.96
57. 8.30%

SECTION 4.2 ▪ PAGE 312

1. natural; 2.71828 **2.** principal, interest rate per year, number of years; amount after t years; $112.75
3. 20.085, 1.259, 2.718, 0.135

5.

x	y
-2	0.41
-1	1.10
-0.5	1.82
0	3
0.5	4.95
1	8.15
2	22.17

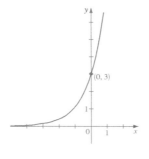

7. $\mathbb{R}, (-\infty, 0), y = 0$

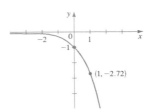

9. $\mathbb{R}, (-1, \infty), y = -1$

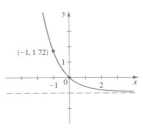

11. $\mathbb{R}, (0, \infty), y = 0$

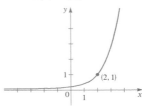

13. $\mathbb{R}, (-3, \infty), y = -3$

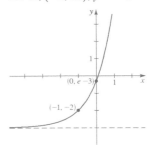

15. (a)

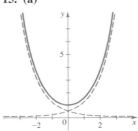

17. (a)

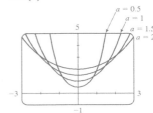

(b) The larger the value of a, the wider the graph.

19. Local minimum $\approx (0.27, 1.75)$
21. (a) 13 kg **(b)** 6.6 kg
23. (a) 0 **(b)** 50.6 ft/s, 69.2 ft/s
(c)

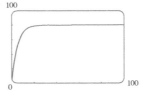

(d) 80 ft/s

25. (a) 100 **(b)** 482, 999, 1168 **(c)** 1200
27. (a) 11.79 billion, 11.97 billion
(b) **(c)** 12 billion

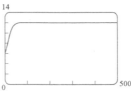

29. $7213.18, $7432.86, $7659.22, $7892.48, $8132.84, $8380.52
31. (a) $2145.02 **(b)** $2300.55 **(c)** $3043.92 **33. (a)** $768.05
(b) $769.22 **(c)** $769.82 **(d)** $770.42 **35. (a)** is best.

37. (a) $A(t) = 5000e^{0.09t}$ **(b)**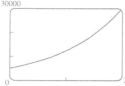

(c) After 17.88 yr

SECTION 4.3 ■ PAGE 322

1. 10^x

x	10^3	10^2	10^1	10^0	10^{-1}	10^{-2}	10^{-3}	$10^{1/2}$
log x	3	2	1	0	-1	-2	-3	$\frac{1}{2}$

2. $9; 1, 0, -1, 2, \frac{1}{2}$
3. (a) $\log_5 125 = 3$ **(b)** $5^2 = 25$ **4. (a)** III **(b)** II **(c)** I **(d)** IV
5.

Logarithmic form	Exponential form
$\log_8 8 = 1$	$8^1 = 8$
$\log_8 64 = 2$	$8^2 = 64$
$\log_8 4 = \frac{2}{3}$	$8^{2/3} = 4$
$\log_8 512 = 3$	$8^3 = 512$
$\log_8 \frac{1}{8} = -1$	$8^{-1} = \frac{1}{8}$
$\log_8 \frac{1}{64} = -2$	$8^{-2} = \frac{1}{64}$

7. (a) $5^2 = 25$ **(b)** $5^0 = 1$ **9. (a)** $8^{1/3} = 2$ **(b)** $2^{-3} = \frac{1}{8}$
11. (a) $e^x = 5$ **(b)** $e^5 = y$ **13. (a)** $\log_5 125 = 3$
(b) $\log_{10} 0.0001 = -4$ **15. (a)** $\log_8 \frac{1}{8} = -1$ **(b)** $\log_2 \frac{1}{8} = -3$
17. (a) $\ln 2 = x$ **(b)** $\ln y = 3$ **19. (a)** 1 **(b)** 0 **(c)** 2
21. (a) 2 **(b)** 2 **(c)** 10 **23. (a)** -3 **(b)** $\frac{1}{2}$ **(c)** -1
25. (a) 37 **(b)** 8 **(c)** $\sqrt{5}$ **27. (a)** $-\frac{2}{3}$ **(b)** 4 **(c)** -1
29. (a) 32 **(b)** 4 **31. (a)** 5 **(b)** 27 **33. (a)** 100 **(b)** 25
35. (a) 2 **(b)** 4 **37. (a)** 0.3010 **(b)** 1.5465 **(c)** -0.1761
39. (a) 1.6094 **(b)** 3.2308 **(c)** 1.0051
41. 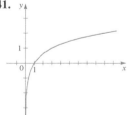 **43.**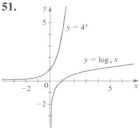

45. $y = \log_5 x$ **47.** $y = \log_9 x$ **49.** I
51.

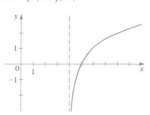

53. $(4, \infty), \mathbb{R}, x = 4$

55. $(-\infty, 0), \mathbb{R}, x = 0$ **57.** $(0, \infty), \mathbb{R}, x = 0$

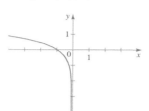 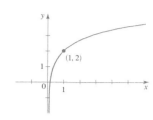

59. $(0, \infty), \mathbb{R}, x = 0$ **61.** $(0, \infty), [0, \infty), x = 0$

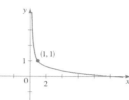 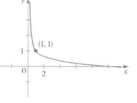

63. $(-3, \infty)$ **65.** $(-\infty, -1) \cup (1, \infty)$ **67.** $(0, 2)$
69.

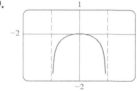

domain $(-1, 1)$
vertical asymptotes $x = 1$,
$x = -1$
local maximum $(0, 0)$

71.

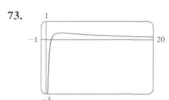

domain $(0, \infty)$
vertical asymptote $x = 0$
no maximum or minimum

73.

domain $(0, \infty)$
vertical asymptote $x = 0$
horizontal asymptote $y = 0$
local maximum
$\approx (2.72, 0.37)$

75. $(f \circ g)(x) = 2^{x+1}, (-\infty, \infty); (g \circ f)(x) = 2^x + 1, (-\infty, \infty)$
77. $(f \circ g)(x) = \log_2 (x - 2), (2, \infty)$;
$(g \circ f)(x) = \log_2 x - 2, (0, \infty)$
79. The graph of f grows more slowly than g.
81. (a)

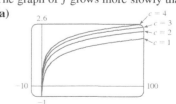

(b) The graph of
$f(x) = \log(cx)$
is the graph of
$f(x) = \log(x)$
shifted upward
log c units.

83. (a) $(1, \infty)$ **(b)** $f^{-1}(x) = 10^{2x}$

85. (a) $f^{-1}(x) = \log_2\left(\dfrac{x}{1 - x}\right)$ **(b)** $(0, 1)$ **87.** 2602 yr

89. 11.5 yr, 9.9 yr, 8.7 yr **91.** 5.32, 4.32

SECTION 4.4 ■ PAGE 329

1. sum; $\log_5 25 + \log_5 125 = 2 + 3$
2. difference; $\log_5 25 - \log_5 125 = 2 - 3$
3. times; $10 \cdot \log_5 25$
4. (a) $2 \log x + \log y - \log z$

(b) $\log\left(\dfrac{x^2 y}{z}\right)$

5. $10, e$; Change of Base; $\log_7 12 = \dfrac{\log 12}{\log 7} = 1.277$

6. True **7.** $\frac{3}{2}$ **9.** 2 **11.** 3 **13.** 3 **15.** 200 **17.** 4
19. $1 + \log_2 x$ **21.** $\log_2 x + \log_2(x - 1)$
23. $10 \log 6$ **25.** $\log_2 A + 2 \log_2 B$ **27.** $\log_3 x + \frac{1}{2} \log_3 y$
29. $\frac{1}{3} \log_5(x^2 + 1)$ **31.** $\frac{1}{2}(\ln a + \ln b)$
33. $3 \log x + 4 \log y - 6 \log z$
35. $\log_2 x + \log_2(x^2 + 1) - \frac{1}{2} \log_2(x^2 - 1)$
37. $\ln x + \frac{1}{2}(\ln y - \ln z)$ **39.** $\frac{1}{4} \log(x^2 + y^2)$
41. $\frac{1}{2}[\log(x^2 + 4) - \log(x^2 + 1) - 2 \log(x^3 - 7)]$
43. $3 \ln x + \frac{1}{2} \ln(x - 1) - \ln(3x + 4)$ **45.** $\log_3 160$

47. $\log_2(AB/C^2)$ **49.** $\log\left(\dfrac{x^4(x - 1)^2}{\sqrt[3]{x^2 + 1}}\right)$

51. $\ln(5x^2(x^2 + 5)^3)$

53. $\log\left(\dfrac{x^2}{x - 3}\right)$ **55.** 2.321928 **57.** 2.523719

59. 0.493008 **61.** 3.482892
63.

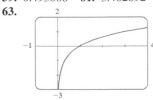

69. (a) $P = c/W^k$ **(b)** 1866, 64
71. (a) $M = -2.5 \log B + 2.5 \log B_0$

SECTION 4.5 ■ PAGE 338

1. (a) $e^x = 25$ **(b)** $x = \ln 25$ **(c)** 3.219
2. (a) $\log 3(x - 2) = \log x$ **(b)** $3(x - 2) = x$ **(c)** 3
3. 1.3979 **5.** −0.9730 **7.** −0.5850 **9.** 1.2040 **11.** 0.0767
13. 0.2524 **15.** 1.9349 **17.** −43.0677 **19.** 2.1492
21. 6.2126 **23.** −2.9469 **25.** −2.4423 **27.** 14.0055
29. $\ln 2 \approx 0.6931, 0$ **31.** $\frac{1}{2} \ln 3 \approx 0.5493$ **33.** ± 1 **35.** $0, \frac{4}{3}$
37. $e^{10} \approx 22026$ **39.** 0.01 **41.** $\frac{95}{3}$ **43.** −7 **45.** 5 **47.** 5
49. $\frac{13}{12}$ **51.** 4 **53.** 6 **55.** $\frac{3}{2}$ **57.** $1/\sqrt{5} \approx 0.4472$ **59.** 2.21
61. 0.00, 1.14 **63.** −0.57 **65.** 0.36
67. $2 < x < 4$ or $7 < x < 9$ **69.** $\log 2 < x < \log 5$

71. $f^{-1}(x) = \dfrac{\ln x}{2 \ln 2}$ **73.** $f^{-1}(x) = 2^x + 1$

75. (a) \$6435.09 **(b)** 8.24 yr **77.** 6.33 yr **79.** 8.15 yr

81. 13 days **83. (a)** 7337 **(b)** 1.73 yr **85. (a)** $P = P_0 e^{-h/k}$
(b) 56.47 kPa **87. (a)** $t = -\frac{5}{13} \ln(1 - \frac{13}{60} I)$ **(b)** 0.218 s

SECTION 4.6 ■ PAGE 350

1. (a) $n(t) = 10 \cdot 2^{2t/3}$ **(b)** 1.05×10^8 **(c)** After 14.9 h
3. (a) 3125 **(b)** 317,480
(c)

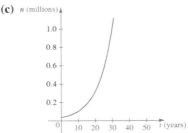

5. (a) $n(t) = 18,000 e^{0.08t}$ **(b)** 34,137

(c)

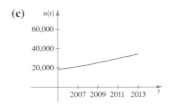

7. (a) 233 million **(b)** 181 million

9. (a) $n(t) = 112,000 \cdot 2^{t/18}$ **(b)** $n(t) = 112,000 e^{0.0385t}$
(c) **(d)** In the year 2045

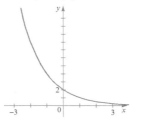

11. (a) 20,000 **(b)** $n(t) = 20,000 e^{0.1096t}$ **(c)** About 48,000
(d) 2017 **13. (a)** $n(t) = 8600 e^{0.1508t}$ **(b)** About 11,600
(c) 4.6 h **15. (a)** $n(t) = 29.76 e^{0.012936t}$ million
(b) 53.5 yr **(c)** 38.55 million **17. (a)** $m(t) = 22 \cdot 2^{-t/1600}$
(b) $m(t) = 22 e^{-0.000433t}$ **(c)** 3.9 mg **(d)** 463.4 yr
19. 18 yr **21.** 149 h **23.** 3560 yr
25. (a) 210°F **(b)** 153°F **(c)** 28 min
27. (a) 137°F **(b)** 116 min
29. (a) 2.3 **(b)** 3.5 **(c)** 8.3
31. (a) 10^{-3} M **(b)** 3.2×10^{-7} M
33. $4.8 \le \text{pH} \le 6.4$ **35.** $\log 20 \approx 1.3$ **37.** Twice as intense
39. 8.2 **41.** 73 dB **43. (b)** 106 dB

CHAPTER 4 REVIEW ■ PAGE 353

1. 0.089, 9.739, 55.902 **3.** 11.954, 2.989, 2.518
5. $\mathbb{R}, (0, \infty), y = 0$ **7.** $\mathbb{R}, (3, \infty), y = 3$

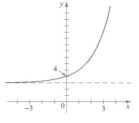

9. $(1, \infty)$, $\mathbb{R}$, $x = 1$

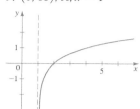

11. $(0, \infty)$, $\mathbb{R}$, $x = 0$

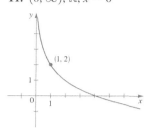

(1, 2)

13. $\mathbb{R}$, $(-1, \infty)$, $y = -1$

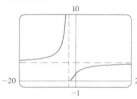

15. $(0, \infty)$, $\mathbb{R}$, $x = 0$

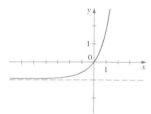

17. $\left(-\infty, \frac{1}{2}\right)$ **19.** $(-\infty, -2) \cup (2, \infty)$ **21.** $2^{10} = 1024$
23. $10^y = x$ **25.** $\log_2 64 = 6$ **27.** $\log 74 = x$ **29.** 7   **31.** 45
33. 6   **35.** -3 **37.** $\frac{1}{2}$ **39.** 2   **41.** 92   **43.** $\frac{2}{3}$
45. $\log A + 2 \log B + 3 \log C$ **47.** $\frac{1}{2}[\ln(x^2 - 1) - \ln(x^2 + 1)]$
49. $2 \log_5 x + \frac{3}{2} \log_5(1 - 5x) - \frac{1}{2} \log_5(x^3 - x)$
51. $\log 96$ **53.** $\log_2\left(\dfrac{(x - y)^{3/2}}{(x^2 + y^2)^2}\right)$ **55.** $\log\left(\dfrac{x^2 - 4}{\sqrt{x^2 + 4}}\right)$

57. 5   **59.** 2.60   **61.** -1.15 **63.** $-4, 2$
65. -15 **67.** 3   **69.** 0.430618
71. 2.303600
73.

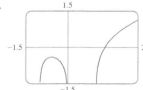

vertical asymptote
$x = -2$
horizontal asymptote
$y = 2.72$
no maximum or minimum

75.

vertical asymptotes
$x = -1$, $x = 0$, $x = 1$
local maximum
$\approx (-0.58, -0.41)$

77. 2.42   **79.** $0.16 < x < 3.15$
81. Increasing on $(-\infty, 0]$ and $[1.10, \infty)$, decreasing on $[0, 1.10]$
83. 1.953445   **85.** -0.579352 **87.** $\log_4 258$
89. (a) \$16,081.15   (b) \$16,178.18   (c) \$16,197.64
(d) \$16,198.31   **91.** 1.83 yr   **93.** 4.341%
95. (a) $n(t) = 30e^{0.15t}$ (b) 55   (c) 19 yr
97. (a) 9.97 mg   (b) 1.39×10^5 yr
99. (a) $n(t) = 150e^{-0.0004359t}$ (b) 97.0 mg   (c) 2520 yr
101. (a) $n(t) = 1500e^{0.1515t}$ (b) 7940
103. 7.9, basic   **105.** 8.0

CHAPTER 4 TEST ▪ PAGE 356

1. (a) $\mathbb{R}$, $(4, \infty)$, $y = 4$

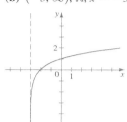

(b) $(-3, \infty)$, $\mathbb{R}$, $x = -3$

2. (a) $\log_6 25 = 2x$ (b) $e^3 = A$
3. (a) 36   (b) 3   (c) $\frac{3}{2}$ (d) 3   (e) $\frac{2}{3}$ (f) 2
4. $\frac{1}{3}[\log(x + 2) - 4 \log x - \log(x^2 + 4)]$
5. $\ln\left(\dfrac{x\sqrt{3 - x^4}}{(x^2 + 1)^2}\right)$ **6.** (a) 4.32   (b) 0.77   (c) 5.39   (d) 2
7. (a) $n(t) = 1000e^{2.07944t}$
(b) 22,627   (c) 1.3 h
(d)

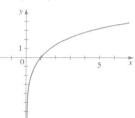

8. (a) $A(t) = 12,000\left(1 + \dfrac{0.056}{12}\right)^{12t}$
(b) \$14,195.06   (c) 9.249 yr
9. (a) $A(t) = 3e^{-0.069t}$ (b) 0.048 g   (c) after 3.6 min
10. 1995 times more intense

FOCUS ON MODELING ▪ PAGE 363

1. (a)

(b) $y = ab^t$, where $a = 1.180609 \times 10^{-15}$, $b = 1.0204139$, and y is the population in millions in the year t (c) 515.9 million
(d) 207.8 million   (e) No
3. (a) Yes   (b) Yes, the scatter plot appears linear.

(c) $\ln E = 4.551436 + 0.092383t$, where t is years since 1970 and E is expenditure in billions of dollars
(d) $E = 94.76838139e^{at}$, where $a = 0.0923827621$
(e) 3478.5 billion dollars

5. (a) $I_0 = 22.7586444$, $k = 0.1062398$

(b)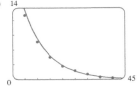

(c) 47.3 ft

7. (a) $S = 0.14A^{0.64}$

(b)

(c) 4 species

9. (a)

(b)

(c) Exponential function

(d) $y = ab^x$ where $a = 0.057697$ and $b = 1.200236$

11. (a) $y = \dfrac{c}{1 + ae^{-bx}}$, where $a = 49.10976596$,

$b = 0.4981144989$, and $c = 500.855793$ **(b)** 10.58 days

**CUMULATIVE REVIEW TEST FOR
CHAPTERS 2, 3, AND 4 ▪ PAGE 367**

1. (a) $(-\infty, \infty)$ **(b)** $[-4, \infty)$ **(c)** $12, 0, 0, 2, 2\sqrt{3}$, undefined
(d) $x^2 - 4$, $\sqrt{x + 6}$, $-4 + h^2$ **(e)** $\frac{1}{8}$
(f) $f \circ g = x + 4 - \sqrt{x + 4}$, $g \circ f = |x - 2|$, $f(g(12)) = 0$,
$g(f(12)) = 10$ **(g)** $g^{-1}(x) = x^2 - 4$, $x \geq 0$
2. (a) $4, 4, 4, 0, 1$ **(b)**

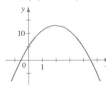

3. (a) $f(x) = -2(x - 2)^2 + 13$ **(b)** Maximum 13
(c) 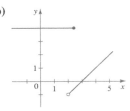 **(d)** Increasing on $(-\infty, 2]$;
decreasing on $[2, \infty)$
(e) Shift upward 5 units
(f) Shift to the left 3 units

4. f, D; g, C; r, A; s, F; h, B; k, E
5. (a) $\pm 1, \pm 2, \pm 4, \pm 8, \pm \frac{1}{2}$ **(b)** $2, 4, -\frac{1}{2}$
(c) $P(x) = 2(x - 2)(x - 4)(x + \frac{1}{2})$ **(d)**

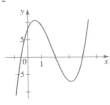

6. (a) 1 (multiplicity 2); -1, $1 + i$, $1 - i$ (multiplicity 1)
(b) $Q(x) = (x - 1)^2(x + 1)(x - 1 - i)(x - 1 + i)$
(c) $Q(x) = (x - 1)^2(x + 1)(x^2 - 2x + 2)$
7. x-intercepts $0, -2$; y-intercept 0; horizontal asymptote $y = 3$;
vertical asymptotes $x = 2$ and $x = -1$

8.

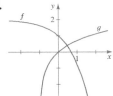

9. (a) -4 **(b)** $5 \log x + \frac{1}{2}\log(x - 1) - \log(2x - 3)$
10. (a) 4 **(b)** $\ln 2, \ln 4$ **11. (a)** $\$29{,}396.15$
(b) After 6.23 years **(c)** 12.837 years
12. (a) $P(t) = 120e^{0.0565t}$ **(b)** 917 **(c)** After 49.8 months

CHAPTER 5

SECTION 5.1 ▪ PAGE 375

1. (a) $(0, 0)$, 1 **(b)** $x^2 + y^2 = 1$ **(c)** (i) 0 (ii) 0 (iii) 0
(iv) 0 **2. (a)** terminal **(b)** $(0, 1), (-1, 0), (0, -1), (1, 0)$
9. $-\frac{4}{5}$ **11.** $-2\sqrt{2}/3$ **13.** $3\sqrt{5}/7$ **15.** $P(\frac{4}{5}, \frac{3}{5})$
17. $P(-\sqrt{5}/3, \frac{2}{3})$ **19.** $P(-\sqrt{2}/3, -\sqrt{7}/3)$
21. $t = \pi/4$, $(\sqrt{2}/2, \sqrt{2}/2)$; $t = \pi/2$, $(0, 1)$;
$t = 3\pi/4$, $(-\sqrt{2}/2, \sqrt{2}/2)$; $t = \pi$, $(-1, 0)$;
$t = 5\pi/4$, $(-\sqrt{2}/2, -\sqrt{2}/2)$; $t = 3\pi/2$, $(0, -1)$;
$t = 7\pi/4$, $(\sqrt{2}/2, -\sqrt{2}/2)$; $t = 2\pi$, $(1, 0)$
23. $(0, 1)$ **25.** $(-\sqrt{3}/2, \frac{1}{2})$ **27.** $(\frac{1}{2}, -\sqrt{3}/2)$
29. $(-\frac{1}{2}, \sqrt{3}/2)$ **31.** $(-\sqrt{2}/2, -\sqrt{2}/2)$
33. (a) $(-\frac{3}{5}, \frac{4}{5})$ **(b)** $(\frac{3}{5}, -\frac{4}{5})$ **(c)** $(-\frac{3}{5}, -\frac{4}{5})$ **(d)** $(\frac{3}{5}, \frac{4}{5})$
35. (a) $\pi/4$ **(b)** $\pi/3$ **(c)** $\pi/3$ **(d)** $\pi/6$
37. (a) $2\pi/7$ **(b)** $2\pi/9$ **(c)** $\pi - 3 \approx 0.14$ **(d)** $2\pi - 5 \approx 1.28$
39. (a) $\pi/3$ **(b)** $(-\frac{1}{2}, \sqrt{3}/2)$
41. (a) $\pi/4$ **(b)** $(-\sqrt{2}/2, \sqrt{2}/2)$
43. (a) $\pi/3$ **(b)** $(-\frac{1}{2}, -\sqrt{3}/2)$
45. (a) $\pi/4$ **(b)** $(-\sqrt{2}/2, -\sqrt{2}/2)$
47. (a) $\pi/6$ **(b)** $(-\sqrt{3}/2, -\frac{1}{2})$
49. (a) $\pi/3$ **(b)** $(\frac{1}{2}, \sqrt{3}/2)$ **51. (a)** $\pi/3$ **(b)** $(-\frac{1}{2}, -\sqrt{3}/2)$
53. $(0.5, 0.8)$ **55.** $(0.5, -0.9)$

SECTION 5.2 ▪ PAGE 384

1. y, x, y/x **2.** 1, 1   **3.** $t = \pi/4$, $\sin t = \sqrt{2}/2$, $\cos t = \sqrt{2}/2$; $t = \pi/2$, $\sin t = 1$, $\cos t = 0$; $t = 3\pi/4$, $\sin t = \sqrt{2}/2$, $\cos t = -\sqrt{2}/2$; $t = \pi$, $\sin t = 0$, $\cos t = -1$; $t = 5\pi/4$, $\sin t = -\sqrt{2}/2$, $\cos t = -\sqrt{2}/2$; $t = 3\pi/2$, $\sin t = -1$, $\cos t = 0$; $t = 7\pi/4$, $\sin t = -\sqrt{2}/2$, $\cos t = \sqrt{2}/2$; $t = 2\pi$, $\sin t = 0$, $\cos t = 1$
5. (a) $\sqrt{3}/2$ (b) $-1/2$ (c) $-\sqrt{3}$
7. (a) $-1/2$ (b) $-1/2$ (c) $-1/2$
9. (a) $-\sqrt{2}/2$ (b) $-\sqrt{2}/2$ (c) $\sqrt{2}/2$
11. (a) $\sqrt{3}/2$ (b) $2\sqrt{3}/3$ (c) $\sqrt{3}/3$
13. (a) -1 (b) 0 (c) 0
15. (a) 2 (b) $-2\sqrt{3}/3$ (c) 2
17. (a) $-\sqrt{3}/3$ (b) $\sqrt{3}/3$ (c) $-\sqrt{3}/3$
19. (a) $\sqrt{2}/2$ (b) $-\sqrt{2}$ (c) -1
21. (a) -1 (b) 1 (c) -1 **23.** (a) 0 (b) 1 (c) 0
25. $\sin 0 = 0$, $\cos 0 = 1$, $\tan 0 = 0$, $\sec 0 = 1$, others undefined
27. $\sin \pi = 0$, $\cos \pi = -1$, $\tan \pi = 0$, $\sec \pi = -1$, others undefined
29. $\frac{4}{5}, \frac{3}{5}, \frac{4}{3}$ **31.** $-\sqrt{11}/4$, $\sqrt{5}/4$, $-\sqrt{55}/5$
33. $\sqrt{13}/7$, $-6/7$, $-\sqrt{13}/6$ **35.** $-\frac{12}{13}, -\frac{5}{13}, \frac{12}{5}$ **37.** $\frac{21}{29}, -\frac{20}{29}, -\frac{21}{20}$
39. (a) 0.8 (b) 0.84147 **41.** (a) 0.9 (b) 0.93204
43. (a) 1 (b) 1.02964 **45.** (a) -0.6 (b) -0.57482
47. Negative   **49.** Negative   **51.** II   **53.** II
55. $\sin t = \sqrt{1 - \cos^2 t}$
57. $\tan t = (\sin t)/\sqrt{1 - \sin^2 t}$
59. $\sec t = -\sqrt{1 + \tan^2 t}$
61. $\tan t = \sqrt{\sec^2 t - 1}$
63. $\tan^2 t = (\sin^2 t)/(1 - \sin^2 t)$
65. $\cos t = -\frac{4}{5}$, $\tan t = -\frac{3}{4}$, $\csc t = \frac{5}{3}$, $\sec t = -\frac{5}{4}$, $\cot t = -\frac{4}{3}$
67. $\sin t = -2\sqrt{2}/3$, $\cos t = \frac{1}{3}$, $\tan t = -2\sqrt{2}$, $\csc t = -\frac{3}{4}\sqrt{2}$, $\cot t = -\sqrt{2}/4$
69. $\sin t = -\frac{3}{5}$, $\cos t = \frac{4}{5}$, $\csc t = -\frac{5}{3}$, $\sec t = \frac{5}{4}$, $\cot t = -\frac{4}{3}$
71. $\cos t = -\sqrt{15}/4$, $\tan t = \sqrt{15}/15$, $\csc t = -4$, $\sec t = -4\sqrt{15}/15$, $\cot t = \sqrt{15}$
73. Odd   **75.** Odd   **77.** Even   **79.** Neither
81. $y(0) = 4$, $y(0.25) = -2.828$, $y(0.50) = 0$, $y(0.75) = 2.828$, $y(1.00) = -4$, $y(1.25) = 2.828$
83. (a) 0.49870 amp   (b) -0.17117 amp

SECTION 5.3 ▪ PAGE 396

1. $1, 2\pi$

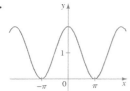

2. $3, \pi$

3.

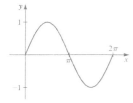

5.

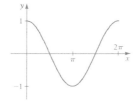

7.

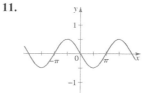

9.

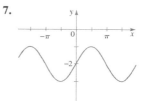

11.

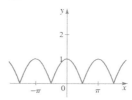

13.

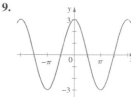

15.

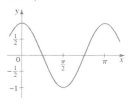

17. $1, \pi$

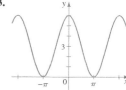

19. $3, 2\pi/3$

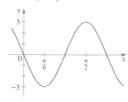

21. $10, 4\pi$

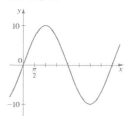

23. $\frac{1}{3}, 6\pi$

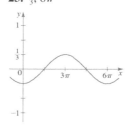

25. $2, 1$

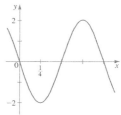

27. $\frac{1}{2}, 2$

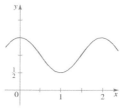

29. $1, 2\pi, \pi/2$

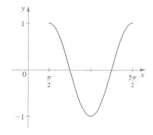

31. $2, 2\pi, \pi/6$

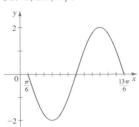

33. $4, \pi, -\pi/2$

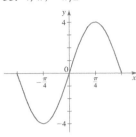

35. $5, 2\pi/3, \pi/12$

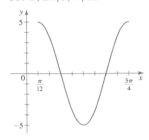

37. $\frac{1}{2}, \pi, \pi/6$

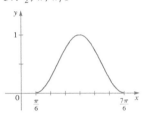

39. $3, 2, -\frac{1}{2}$

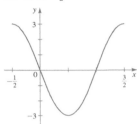

41. $1, 2\pi/3, -\pi/3$

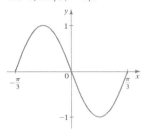

43. (a) $4, 2\pi, 0$ (b) $y = 4 \sin x$
45. (a) $\frac{3}{2}, \frac{2\pi}{3}, 0$ (b) $y = \frac{3}{2} \cos 3x$
47. (a) $\frac{1}{2}, \pi, -\frac{\pi}{3}$ (b) $y = -\frac{1}{2} \cos 2(x + \pi/3)$
49. (a) $4, \frac{3}{2}, -\frac{1}{2}$ (b) $y = 4 \sin \frac{4\pi}{3}(x + \frac{1}{2})$

51.

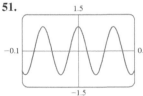

53.

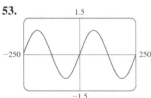

55.

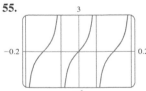

57.

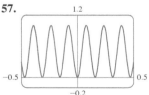

59.

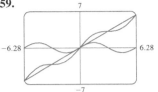

61.

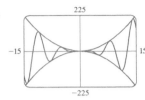

$y = x^2 \sin x$ is a sine curve that lies between the graphs of $y = x^2$ and $y = -x^2$

63.

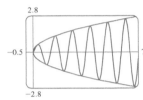

$y = \sqrt{x} \sin 5\pi x$ is a sine curve that lies between the graphs of $y = \sqrt{x}$ and $y = -\sqrt{x}$

65.

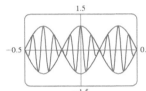

$y = \cos 3\pi x \cos 21\pi x$ is a cosine curve that lies between the graphs of $y = \cos 3\pi x$ and $y = -\cos 3\pi x$

67. Maximum value 1.76 when $x \approx 0.94$, minimum value -1.76 when $x \approx -0.94$ (The same maximum and minimum values occur at infinitely many other values of x.)
69. Maximum value 3.00 when $x \approx 1.57$, minimum value -1.00 when $x \approx -1.57$ (The same maximum and minimum values occur at infinitely many other values of x.)
71. 1.16   **73.** 0.34, 2.80
75. (a) Odd   (b) $0, \pm 2\pi, \pm 4\pi, \pm 6\pi, \ldots$
(c)

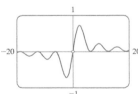

(d) $f(x)$ approaches 0
(e) $f(x)$ approaches 0

77. (a) 20 s   (b) 6 ft
79. (a) $\frac{1}{80}$ min   (b) 80
(c)

(d) $\frac{140}{90}$; it is higher than normal

SECTION 5.4 ■ PAGE 405

1. π; $\frac{\pi}{2} + n\pi$, n an integer

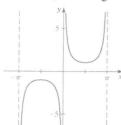

2. 2π; $n\pi$, n an integer

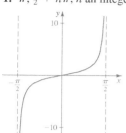

3. II   **5.** VI   **7.** IV

9. π

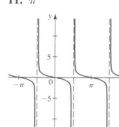

11. π

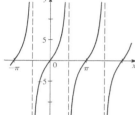

13. π

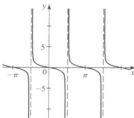

15. 2π

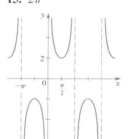

17. 2π

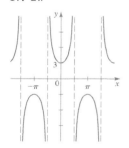

19. π

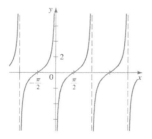

21. 2π

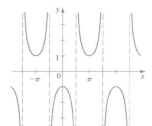

23. π

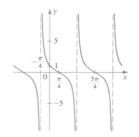

25. 2π

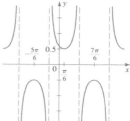

27. $\pi/4$

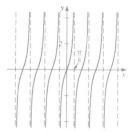

29. 4

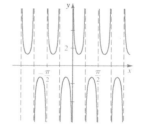

31. π

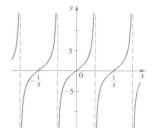

33. $\pi/2$

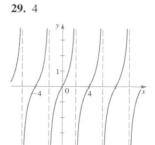

35. $\frac{1}{3}$

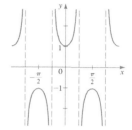

37. $\frac{4}{3}$

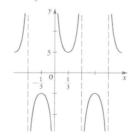

39. $\pi/2$

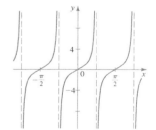

41. $\pi/2$

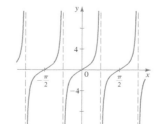

43. $\pi/2$

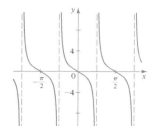

45. 2

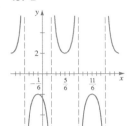

47. $2\pi/3$

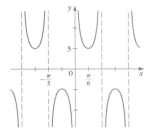

49. $3\pi/2$

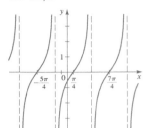

51. 2

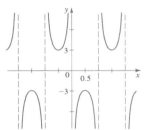

53. $\pi/2$

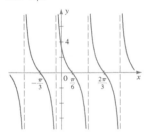

57. (a) 1.53 mi, 3.00 mi, 18.94 mi
(b)

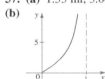

(c) $d(t)$ approaches ∞

SECTION 5.5 ■ PAGE 411

1. (a) $[-\pi/2, \pi/2], y, x, \pi/6, \pi/6, \frac{1}{2}$
(b) $[0, \pi]; y, x, \pi/3, \pi/3, \frac{1}{2}$ **2.** $[-1, 1]$; (b)
3. (a) $\pi/2$ (b) $\pi/3$ (c) Undefined
5. (a) π (b) $\pi/3$ (c) $5\pi/6$
7. (a) $-\pi/4$ (b) $\pi/3$ (c) $\pi/6$
9. (a) $2\pi/3$ (b) $-\pi/4$ (c) $\pi/4$ **11.** 0.72973
13. 2.01371 **15.** 2.75876 **17.** 1.47113 **19.** 0.88998
21. -0.26005 **23.** $\frac{1}{4}$ **25.** 5
27. Undefined **29.** $5\pi/6$ **31.** $-\pi/6$ **33.** $\pi/6$ **35.** $\pi/6$
37. $-\pi/3$ **39.** $\sqrt{3}/3$ **41.** $\frac{1}{2}$ **43.** $-\sqrt{2}/2$

SECTION 5.6 ■ PAGE 420

1. (a) $a \sin \omega t$ (b) $a \cos \omega t$
2. (a) $ke^{-ct} \sin \omega t$ (b) $ke^{-ct} \cos \omega t$

3. (a) $2, 2\pi/3, 3/(2\pi)$
(b)

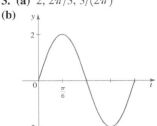

5. (a) $1, 20\pi/3, 3/(20\pi)$
(b)

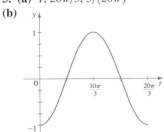

7. (a) $\frac{1}{4}, 4\pi/3, 3/(4\pi)$
(b)

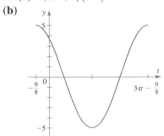

9. (a) $5, 3\pi, 1/(3\pi)$
(b)

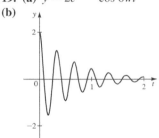

11. $y = 10 \sin\left(\dfrac{2\pi}{3}t\right)$ **13.** $y = 6 \sin(10t)$
15. $y = 60 \cos(4\pi t)$ **17.** $y = 2.4 \cos(1500\pi t)$
19. (a) $y = 2e^{-1.5t} \cos 6\pi t$
(b)

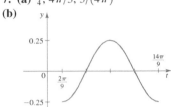

21. (a) $y = 100e^{-0.05t} \cos \dfrac{\pi}{2}t$
(b)

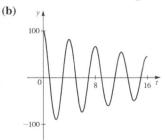

23. (a) $y = 7e^{-10t} \sin 12t$ **(b)**

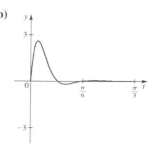

25. (a) $y = 0.3e^{-0.2t} \sin(40\pi t)$
(b)

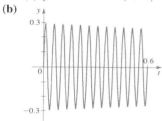

27. (a) 10 cycles per minute
(b)   **(c)** 0.4 m

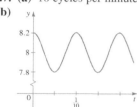

29. (a) 25, 0.0125, 80   **(b)**

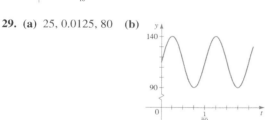

(c) The period decreases and the frequency increases.
31. $d(t) = 5 \sin(5\pi t)$

33. $y = 21 \sin\left(\dfrac{\pi}{6}t\right)$

35. $y = 5 \cos(2\pi t)$ **37.** $y = 11 + 10 \sin\left(\dfrac{\pi t}{10}\right)$

39. $y = 3.8 + 0.2 \sin\left(\dfrac{\pi}{5}t\right)$

41. $f(t) = 10 \sin\left(\dfrac{\pi}{12}(t - 8)\right) + 90$

43. (a) 45 V   **(b)** 40   **(c)** 40   **(d)** $E(t) = 45 \cos(80\pi t)$

45. $f(t) = e^{-0.9t} \sin \pi t$ **47.** $e = \dfrac{1}{3} \ln 4 \approx 0.46$

CHAPTER 5 REVIEW ■ PAGE 424

1. (b) $\frac{1}{2}, -\sqrt{3}/2, -\sqrt{3}/3$ **3. (a)** $\pi/3$ **(b)** $\left(-\frac{1}{2}, \sqrt{3}/2\right)$
(c) $\sin t = \sqrt{3}/2, \cos t = -\frac{1}{2}, \tan t = -\sqrt{3}, \csc t = 2\sqrt{3}/3,$
$\sec t = -2, \cot t = -\sqrt{3}/3$
5. (a) $\pi/4$ **(b)** $\left(-\sqrt{2}/2, -\sqrt{2}/2\right)$
(c) $\sin t = -\sqrt{2}/2, \cos t = -\sqrt{2}/2,$
$\tan t = 1, \csc t = -\sqrt{2}, \sec t = -\sqrt{2}, \cot t = 1$
7. (a) $\sqrt{2}/2$ **(b)** $-\sqrt{2}/2$ **9. (a)** 0.89121   **(b)** 0.45360
11. (a) 0   **(b)** Undefined   **13. (a)** Undefined   **(b)** 0
15. (a) $-\sqrt{3}/3$ **(b)** $-\sqrt{3}$ **17.** $(\sin t)/(1 - \sin^2 t)$
19. $(\sin t)/\sqrt{1 - \sin^2 t}$
21. $\tan t = -\frac{5}{12}, \csc t = \frac{13}{5}, \sec t = -\frac{13}{12}, \cot t = -\frac{12}{5}$
23. $\sin t = 2\sqrt{5}/5, \cos t = -\sqrt{5}/5,$
$\tan t = -2, \sec t = -\sqrt{5}$
25. $(16 - \sqrt{17})/4$ **27.** 3

29. (a) $10, 4\pi, 0$ **31. (a)** $1, 4\pi, 0$
(b)   **(b)**

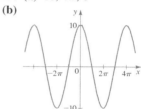   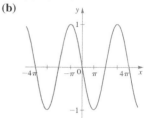

33. (a) $3, \pi, 1$ **35. (a)** $1, 4, -\frac{1}{3}$
(b)   **(b)**

   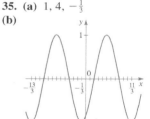

37. $y = 5 \sin 4x$ **39.** $y = \frac{1}{2} \sin 2\pi\left(x + \frac{1}{3}\right)$
41. π **43.** π

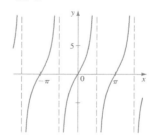   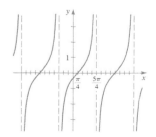

45. π **47.** 2π

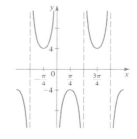

49. $\frac{\pi}{2}$ **51.** $\frac{\pi}{6}$

53. (a)

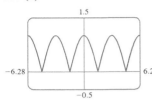

55. (a)

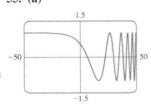

(b) Period π
(c) Even

(b) Not periodic
(c) Neither

57. (a)

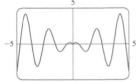

(b) Not periodic
(c) Even

59.

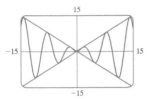

$y = x \sin x$ is a sine function whose graph lies between those of $y = x$ and $y = -x$

61.

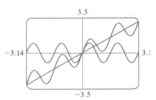

The graphs are related by graphical addition.

63. $1.76, -1.76$ **65.** $0.30, 2.84$
67. (a) Odd **(b)** $0, \pm\pi, \pm2\pi, \ldots$
(c)

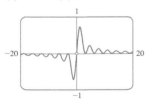

(d) $f(x)$ approaches 0
(e) $f(x)$ approaches 0
69. $y = 50 \cos(16\pi t)$
71. $y = 4 \cos\left(\frac{\pi}{6} t\right)$

CHAPTER 5 TEST ■ PAGE 426

1. $y = -\frac{5}{6}$ **2. (a)** $\frac{4}{5}$ **(b)** $-\frac{3}{5}$ **(c)** $-\frac{4}{3}$ **(d)** $-\frac{5}{3}$
3. (a) $-\frac{1}{2}$ **(b)** $-\sqrt{2}/2$ **(c)** $\sqrt{3}$ **(d)** -1
4. $\tan t = -(\sin t)/\sqrt{1 - \sin^2 t}$ **5.** $-\frac{2}{15}$

6. (a) $5, \pi/2, 0$
(b)

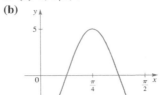

7. (a) $2, 4\pi, \pi/3$
(b)

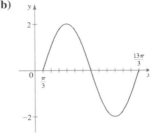

8. π

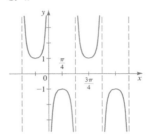

9. $\pi/2$

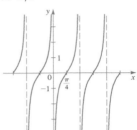

10. (a) $\pi/4$ **(b)** $5\pi/6$ **(c)** 0 **(d)** $1/2$
11. $y = 2 \sin 2(x + \pi/3)$
12. (a)

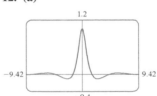

(b) Even
(c) Minimum value -0.11 when $x \approx \pm2.54$, maximum value 1 when $x = 0$

13. $y = 5 \sin(4\pi t)$
14. $y = 16e^{-0.1t} \cos 24\pi t$

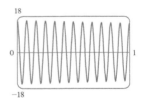

FOCUS ON MODELING ■ PAGE 430

1. (a) and **(c)**

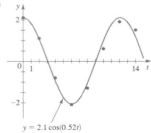

(b) $y = 2.1 \cos(0.52t)$
(d) $y = 2.05 \sin(0.50t + 1.55) - 0.01$ **(e)** The formula of (d) reduces to $y = 2.05 \cos(0.50t - 0.02) - 0.01$. Same as (b), rounded to one decimal.

3. (a) and **(c)**

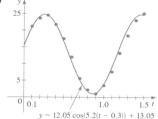

$y = 12.05 \cos(5.2(t - 0.3)) + 13.05$

(b) $y = 12.05 \cos(5.2(t - 0.3)) + 13.05$
(d) $y = 11.72 \sin(5.05t + 0.24) + 12.96$ **(e)** The formula of (d) reduces to $y = 11.72 \cos(5.05(t - 0.26)) + 12.96$. Close, but not identical, to (b).

5. (a) and **(c)**

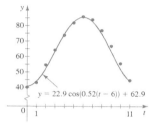

$y = 22.9 \cos(0.52(t - 6)) + 62.9$

(b) $y = 22.9 \cos(0.52(t - 6)) + 62.9$, where y is temperature (°F) and t is months (January = 0)
(d) $y = 23.4 \sin(0.48t - 1.36) + 62.2$

7. (a) and **(c)**

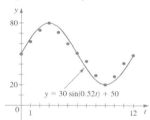

$y = 30 \sin(0.52t) + 50$

(b) $y = 30 \sin(0.52t) + 50$ where y is the owl population in year t
(d) $y = 25.8 \sin(0.52t - 0.02) + 50.6$

9. (a) and **(c)**

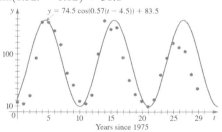

$y = 74.5 \cos(0.57(t - 4.5)) + 83.5$

Years since 1975

(b) $y = 74.5 \cos(0.57(t - 4.5)) + 83.5$, where y is the average daily sunspot count, and t is the years since 1975
(d) $y = 67.65 \sin(0.62t - 1.65) + 74.5$

CHAPTER 6

SECTION 6.1 ■ PAGE 440

1. (a) arc, 1   **(b)** $\pi/180$ **(c)** $180/\pi$ **2. (a)** $r\theta$ **(b)** $\frac{1}{2}r^2\theta$
3. $2\pi/5 \approx 1.257$ rad   **5.** $-\pi/4 \approx -0.785$ rad
7. $-5\pi/12 \approx -1.309$ rad   **9.** $6\pi \approx 18.850$ rad
11. $8\pi/15 \approx 1.676$ rad   **13.** $\pi/24 \approx 0.131$ rad   **15.** $210°$
17. $-225°$ **19.** $540/\pi \approx 171.9°$ **21.** $-216/\pi \approx -68.8°$

23. $18°$ **25.** $-24°$ **27.** $410°, 770°, -310°, -670°$
29. $11\pi/4, 19\pi/4, -5\pi/4, -13\pi/4$
31. $7\pi/4, 15\pi/4, -9\pi/4, -17\pi/4$ **33.** Yes   **35.** Yes   **37.** Yes
39. $13°$ **41.** $30°$ **43.** $280°$ **45.** $5\pi/6$ **47.** π **49.** $\pi/4$
51. $55\pi/9 \approx 19.2$ **53.** 4   **55.** 4 mi   **57.** 2 rad $\approx 114.6°$
59. $36/\pi \approx 11.459$ m   **61. (a)** 35.45 **(b)** 25   **63.** 50 m^2
65. 4 m   **67.** 6 cm^2 **69.** 13.9 mi   **71.** 330π mi ≈ 1037 mi
73. 1.6 million mi   **75.** 1.15 mi   **77.** 360π in$^2 \approx 1130.97$ in^2
79. (a) 90π rad/min   **(b)** 1440π in./min ≈ 4523.9 in./min
81. $32\pi/15$ ft/s ≈ 6.7 ft/s   **83.** 1039.6 mi/h   **85.** 2.1 m/s
87. (a) 10π cm ≈ 31.4 cm   **(b)** 5 cm   **(c)** 3.32 cm
(d) 86.8 cm^3

SECTION 6.2 ■ PAGE 448

1. (a)

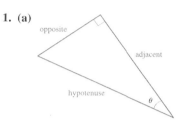

(b) $\dfrac{\text{opposite}}{\text{hypotenuse}}, \dfrac{\text{adjacent}}{\text{hypotenuse}}, \dfrac{\text{opposite}}{\text{adjacent}}$ **(c)** similar

2. $\sin \theta, \cos \theta, \tan \theta$
3. $\sin \theta = \frac{4}{5}, \cos \theta = \frac{3}{5}, \tan \theta = \frac{4}{3}, \csc \theta = \frac{5}{4}, \sec \theta = \frac{5}{3}, \cot \theta = \frac{3}{4}$
5. $\sin \theta = \frac{40}{41}, \cos \theta = \frac{9}{41}, \tan \theta = \frac{40}{9}, \csc \theta = \frac{41}{40}, \sec \theta = \frac{41}{9}, \cot \theta = \frac{9}{40}$
7. $\sin \theta = 2\sqrt{13}/13, \cos \theta = 3\sqrt{13}/13, \tan \theta = \frac{2}{3},$ $\csc \theta = \sqrt{13}/2, \sec \theta = \sqrt{13}/3, \cot \theta = \frac{3}{2}$
9. (a) $3\sqrt{34}/34, 3\sqrt{34}/34$ **(b)** $\frac{3}{5}, \frac{3}{5}$ **(c)** $\sqrt{34}/5, \sqrt{34}/5$
11. $\frac{25}{2}$ **13.** $13\sqrt{3}/2$ **15.** 16.51658
17. $x = 28 \cos \theta, y = 28 \sin \theta$
19. $\cos \theta = \frac{4}{5}, \tan \theta = \frac{3}{4}, \csc \theta = \frac{5}{3}, \sec \theta = \frac{5}{4}, \cot \theta = \frac{4}{3}$

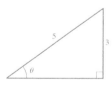

21. $\sin \theta = \sqrt{2}/2, \cos \theta = \sqrt{2}/2, \tan \theta = 1,$ $\csc \theta = \sqrt{2}, \sec \theta = \sqrt{2}$

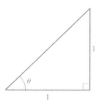

23. $\sin \theta = 3\sqrt{5}/7, \cos \theta = \frac{2}{7}, \tan \theta = 3\sqrt{5}/2,$ $\csc \theta = 7\sqrt{5}/15, \cot \theta = 2\sqrt{5}/15$

25. $(1 + \sqrt{3})/2$ **27.** 1   **29.** $\frac{1}{2}$

31.

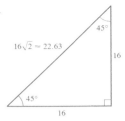

33.

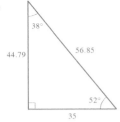

35.

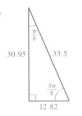

37.

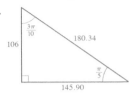

39. $\sin \theta \approx 0.45$, $\cos \theta \approx 0.89$, $\tan \theta = 0.50$, $\csc \theta \approx 2.24$, $\sec \theta \approx 1.12$, $\cot \theta = 2.00$ **41.** 230.9 **43.** 63.7
45. $x = 10 \tan \theta \sin \theta$ **47.** 1026 ft **49. (a)** 2100 mi **(b)** No
51. 19 ft **53.** 345 ft **55.** 415 ft, 152 ft **57.** 2570 ft
59. 5808 ft **61.** 91.7 million mi **63.** 3960 mi **65.** 0.723 AU

SECTION 6.3 ▪ PAGE 459

1. y/r, x/r, y/x **2.** quadrant, positive, negative, negative
3. (a) 30° **(b)** 30° **(c)** 30° **5. (a)** 45° **(b)** 90° **(c)** 75°
7. (a) $\pi/4$ **(b)** $\pi/6$ **(c)** $\pi/3$ **9. (a)** $2\pi/7$ **(b)** 0.4π **(c)** 1.4
11. $\frac{1}{2}$ **13.** $-\sqrt{3}/2$ **15.** $-\sqrt{3}$ **17.** 1 **19.** $-\sqrt{3}/2$
21. $\sqrt{3}/3$ **23.** $\sqrt{3}/2$ **25.** -1 **27.** $\frac{1}{2}$ **29.** 2 **31.** -1
33. Undefined **35.** III **37.** IV
39. $\tan \theta = -\sqrt{1 - \cos^2\theta}/\cos \theta$
41. $\cos \theta = \sqrt{1 - \sin^2\theta}$
43. $\sec \theta = -\sqrt{1 + \tan^2\theta}$
45. $\cos \theta = -\frac{4}{5}$, $\tan \theta = -\frac{3}{4}$, $\csc \theta = \frac{5}{3}$, $\sec \theta = -\frac{5}{4}$, $\cot \theta = -\frac{4}{3}$
47. $\sin \theta = -\frac{3}{5}$, $\cos \theta = \frac{4}{5}$, $\csc \theta = -\frac{5}{3}$, $\sec \theta = \frac{5}{4}$, $\cot \theta = -\frac{4}{3}$
49. $\sin \theta = \frac{1}{2}$, $\cos \theta = \sqrt{3}/2$, $\tan \theta = \sqrt{3}/3$, $\sec \theta = 2\sqrt{3}/3$, $\cot \theta = \sqrt{3}$
51. $\sin \theta = 3\sqrt{5}/7$, $\tan \theta = -3\sqrt{5}/2$, $\csc \theta = 7\sqrt{5}/15$, $\sec \theta = -\frac{7}{2}$, $\cot \theta = -2\sqrt{5}/15$
53. (a) $\sqrt{3}/2$, $\sqrt{3}$ **(b)** $\frac{1}{2}$, $\sqrt{3}/4$ **(c)** $\frac{3}{4}$, 0.88967 **55.** 19.1
57. 66.1° **59.** $(4\pi/3) - \sqrt{3} \approx 2.46$
63. (b)

θ	20°	60°	80°	85°
h	1922	9145	29,944	60,351

65. (a) $A(\theta) = 400 \sin \theta \cos \theta$
(b)

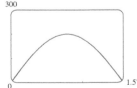

(c) width = depth ≈ 14.14 in.
67. (a) $9\sqrt{3}/4$ ft ≈ 3.897 ft, $\frac{9}{16}$ ft $= 0.5625$ ft
(b) 23.982 ft, 3.462 ft

69. (a)

(b) 0.946 rad or 54°

SECTION 6.4 ▪ PAGE 467

1. (a) $[-1, 1]$, $[-\pi/2, \pi/2]$ **(b)** $[-1, 1]$, $[0, \pi]$
(c) $\mathbb{R}$, $(-\pi/2, \pi/2)$ **2. (a)** $\frac{8}{10}$ **(b)** $\frac{6}{10}$ **(c)** $\frac{8}{6}$ **3. (a)** $\pi/6$
(b) $5\pi/6$ **(c)** $-\pi/4$ **5. (a)** $-\pi/6$ **(b)** $\pi/3$ **(c)** $\pi/6$
7. 0.46677 **9.** 1.82348 **11.** 1.24905 **13.** Undefined
15. 36.9° **17.** 34.7° **19.** 34.9° **21.** 30°, 150°
23. 44.4°, 135.6° **25.** 45.6° **27.** $\frac{4}{5}$ **29.** $\frac{13}{5}$ **31.** $\frac{12}{5}$
33. $\sqrt{1 - x^2}$ **35.** $x/\sqrt{1 - x^2}$ **37.** 72.5°, 19 ft
39. (a) $h = 2 \tan \theta$ **(b)** $\theta = \tan^{-1}(h/2)$
41. (a) $\theta = \sin^{-1}(h/680)$ **(b)** $\theta = 0.826$ rad
43. (a) 54.1° **(b)** 48.3°, 32.2°, 24.5°. The function $\sin^{-1}$ is undefined for values outside the interval $[-1, 1]$.

SECTION 6.5 ▪ PAGE 473

1. $\dfrac{\sin A}{a} = \dfrac{\sin B}{b} = \dfrac{\sin C}{c}$ **2.** ASA, SSA **3.** 318.8 **5.** 24.8
7. 44° **9.** $\angle C = 114°$, $a \approx 51$, $b \approx 24$ **11.** $\angle A = 44°$,
$\angle B = 68°$, $a \approx 8.99$ **13.** $\angle C = 62°$, $a \approx 200$, $b \approx 242$

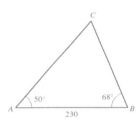

15. $\angle B = 85°$, $a \approx 5$, $c \approx 9$

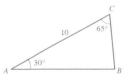

17. $\angle A = 100°$, $a \approx 89$, $c \approx 71$

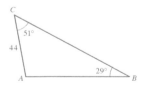

19. $\angle B \approx 30°$, $\angle C \approx 40°$, $c \approx 19$ **21.** No solution
23. $\angle A_1 \approx 125°$, $\angle C_1 \approx 30°$, $a_1 \approx 49$;
$\angle A_2 \approx 5°$, $\angle C_2 \approx 150°$, $a_2 \approx 5.6$ **25.** No solution
27. $\angle A_1 \approx 57.2°$, $\angle B_1 \approx 93.8°$, $b_1 \approx 30.9$;
$\angle A_2 \approx 122.8°$, $\angle B_2 \approx 28.2°$, $b_2 \approx 14.6$
29. (a) 91.146° **(b)** 14.427° **33. (a)** 1018 mi **(b)** 1017 mi
35. 219 ft **37.** 55.9 m **39.** 175 ft **41.** 192 m
43. 0.427 AU, 1.119 AU

SECTION 6.6 ▪ PAGE 480

1. $a^2 + b^2 - 2ab \cos C$ **2.** SSS, SAS **3.** 28.9 **5.** 47
7. 29.89° **9.** 15 **11.** $\angle A \approx 39.4°$, $\angle B \approx 20.6°$, $c \approx 24.6$

13. $\angle A \approx 48°$, $\angle B \approx 79°$, $c \approx 3.2$
15. $\angle A \approx 50°$, $\angle B \approx 73°$, $\angle C \approx 57°$
17. $\angle A_1 \approx 83.6°$, $\angle C_1 \approx 56.4°$, $a_1 \approx 193$;
$\angle A_2 \approx 16.4°$, $\angle C_2 \approx 123.6$, $a_2 \approx 54.9$ **19.** No such triangle
21. 2   **23.** 25.4   **25.** 89.2°   **27.** 24.3   **29.** 54   **31.** 26.83
33. 5.33   **35.** 40.77   **37.** 3.85 cm^2 **39.** 2.30 mi   **41.** 23.1 mi
43. 2179 mi   **45. (a)** 62.6 mi   **(b)** S 18.2° E   **47.** 96°
49. 211 ft   **51.** 3835 ft   **53.** $165,554

CHAPTER 6 REVIEW ▪ PAGE 483

1. (a) $\pi/3$ **(b)** $11\pi/6$ **(c)** $-3\pi/4$ **(d)** $-\pi/2$
3. (a) 450°   **(b)** $-30°$ **(c)** 405°   **(d)** $(558/\pi)° \approx 177.6°$
5. 8 m   **7.** 82 ft   **9.** 0.619 rad $\approx 35.4°$ **11.** 18,151 ft^2
13. 300π rad/min ≈ 942.5 rad/min,
7539.8 in./min $= 628.3$ ft/min
15. $\sin\theta = 5/\sqrt{74}$, $\cos\theta = 7/\sqrt{74}$, $\tan\theta = \frac{5}{7}$,
$\csc\theta = \sqrt{74}/5$, $\sec\theta = \sqrt{74}/7$, $\cot\theta = \frac{7}{5}$
17. $x \approx 3.83$, $y \approx 3.21$ **19.** $x \approx 2.92$, $y \approx 3.11$
21. $A = 70°$, $a \approx 2.819$, $b \approx 1.026$
23. $A \approx 16.3°$, $C \approx 73.7°$, $c \approx 24$
25. $a = \cot\theta$, $b = \csc\theta$ **27.** 48 m   **29.** 1076 mi   **31.** $-\sqrt{2}/2$
33. 1   **35.** $-\sqrt{3}/3$ **37.** $-\sqrt{2}/2$ **39.** $2\sqrt{3}/3$ **41.** $-\sqrt{3}$
43. $\sin\theta = \frac{12}{13}$, $\cos\theta = -\frac{5}{13}$, $\tan\theta = -\frac{12}{5}$,
$\csc\theta = \frac{13}{12}$, $\sec\theta = -\frac{13}{5}$, $\cot\theta = -\frac{5}{12}$ **45.** 60°
47. $\tan\theta = -\sqrt{1 - \cos^2\theta}/\cos\theta$
49. $\tan^2\theta = \sin^2\theta/(1 - \sin^2\theta)$
51. $\sin\theta = \sqrt{7}/4$, $\cos\theta = \frac{3}{4}$, $\csc\theta = 4\sqrt{7}/7$, $\cot\theta = 3\sqrt{7}/7$
53. $\cos\theta = -\frac{4}{5}$, $\tan\theta = -\frac{3}{4}$, $\csc\theta = \frac{5}{3}$, $\sec\theta = -\frac{5}{4}$, $\cot\theta = -\frac{4}{3}$
55. $-\sqrt{5}/5$ **57.** 1   **59.** $\pi/3$ **61.** $2/\sqrt{21}$ **63.** $x/\sqrt{1 + x^2}$
65. $\theta = \cos^{-1}(x/3)$ **67.** 5.32   **69.** 148.07   **71.** 9.17
73. 54.1° or 125.9°   **75.** 80.4°   **77.** 77.3 mi   **79.** 3.9 mi
81. 32.12

CHAPTER 6 TEST ▪ PAGE 487

1. $11\pi/6$, $-3\pi/4$ **2.** 240°, $-74.5°$
3. (a) 240π rad/min ≈ 753.98 rad/min
(b) 12,063.7 ft/min $= 137$ mi/h   **4. (a)** $\sqrt{2}/2$
(b) $\sqrt{3}/3$ **(c)** 2   **(d)** 1   **5.** $(26 + 6\sqrt{13})/39$
6. $a = 24\sin\theta$, $b = 24\cos\theta$ **7.** $(4 - 3\sqrt{2})/4$
8. $-\frac{13}{12}$ **9.** $\tan\theta = -\sqrt{\sec^2\theta - 1}$ **10.** 19.6 ft
11. (a) $\theta = \tan^{-1}(x/4)$ **(b)** $\theta = \cos^{-1}(3/x)$ **12.** $\frac{40}{41}$
13. 9.1   **14.** 250.5   **15.** 8.4   **16.** 19.5   **17.** 78.6°   **18.** 40.2°
19. (a) 15.3 m^2 **(b)** 24.3 m   **20. (a)** 129.9°   **(b)** 44.9
21. 554 ft

FOCUS ON MODELING ▪ PAGE 490

1. 1.41 mi   **3.** 14.3 m   **5. (c)** 2349.8 ft
7.

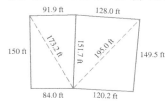

CHAPTER 7

SECTION 7.1 ▪ PAGE 498

1. all; 1   **2.** $\cos(-x) = \cos x$ **3.** $\sin t$ **5.** $\tan\theta$ **7.** -1
9. $\csc u$ **11.** $\tan\theta$ **13.** 1   **15.** $\cos y$ **17.** $\sin^2 x$ **19.** $\sec x$
21. $2\sec u$ **23.** $\cos^2 x$ **25.** $\cos\theta$

27. (a) LHS $= \dfrac{1 - \sin^2 x}{\sin x} =$ RHS

29. LHS $= \sin\theta\,\dfrac{\cos\theta}{\sin\theta} =$ RHS

31. LHS $= \cos u\,\dfrac{1}{\cos u}\cot u =$ RHS

33. LHS $= \sin B + \cos B\,\dfrac{\cos B}{\sin B}$

$= \dfrac{\sin^2 B + \cos^2 B}{\sin B} = \dfrac{1}{\sin B} =$ RHS

35. LHS $= -\dfrac{\cos\alpha}{\sin\alpha}\cos\alpha - \sin\alpha = \dfrac{-\cos^2\alpha - \sin^2\alpha}{\sin\alpha}$

$= \dfrac{-1}{\sin\alpha} =$ RHS

37. LHS $= \dfrac{\sin\theta}{\cos\theta} + \dfrac{\cos\theta}{\sin\theta} = \dfrac{\sin^2\theta + \cos^2\theta}{\cos\theta\sin\theta}$

$= \dfrac{1}{\cos\theta\sin\theta} =$ RHS

39. LHS $= 1 - \cos^2\beta = \sin^2\beta =$ RHS

41. LHS $= \dfrac{(\sin x + \cos x)^2}{(\sin x + \cos x)(\sin x - \cos x)} = \dfrac{\sin x + \cos x}{\sin x - \cos x}$

$= \dfrac{(\sin x + \cos x)(\sin x - \cos x)}{(\sin x - \cos x)(\sin x - \cos x)} =$ RHS

43. LHS $= \dfrac{\frac{1}{\cos t} - \cos t}{\frac{1}{\cos t}} \cdot \dfrac{\cos t}{\cos t} = \dfrac{1 - \cos^2 t}{1} =$ RHS

45. LHS $= \dfrac{1}{\cos^2 y} = \sec^2 y =$ RHS

47. LHS $= \cot x\cos x + \cot x - \csc x\cos x - \csc x$

$= \dfrac{\cos^2 x}{\sin x} + \dfrac{\cos x}{\sin x} - \dfrac{\cos x}{\sin x} - \dfrac{1}{\sin x} = \dfrac{\cos^2 x - 1}{\sin x}$

$= \dfrac{-\sin^2 x}{\sin x} =$ RHS

49. LHS $= \sin^2 x\left(1 + \dfrac{\cos^2 x}{\sin^2 x}\right) = \sin^2 x + \cos^2 x =$ RHS

51. LHS $= 2(1 - \sin^2 x) - 1 = 2 - 2\sin^2 x - 1 =$ RHS

53. LHS $= \dfrac{1 - \cos\alpha}{\sin\alpha} \cdot \dfrac{1 + \cos\alpha}{1 + \cos\alpha}$

$= \dfrac{1 - \cos^2\alpha}{\sin\alpha(1 + \cos\alpha)} = \dfrac{\sin^2\alpha}{\sin\alpha(1 + \cos\alpha)} =$ RHS

55. LHS $= \dfrac{\sin^2\theta}{\cos^2\theta} - \dfrac{\sin^2\theta\cos^2\theta}{\cos^2\theta}$

$= \dfrac{\sin^2\theta(1 - \cos^2\theta)}{\cos^2\theta} = \dfrac{\sin^2\theta\sin^2\theta}{\cos^2\theta} =$ RHS

57. LHS $= \dfrac{\sin x - 1}{\sin x + 1} \cdot \dfrac{\sin x + 1}{\sin x + 1} = \dfrac{\sin^2 x - 1}{(\sin x + 1)^2} =$ RHS

59. LHS $= \dfrac{\sin^2 t + 2 \sin t \cos t + \cos^2 t}{\sin t \cos t}$

$= \dfrac{\sin^2 t + \cos^2 t}{\sin t \cos t} + \dfrac{2 \sin t \cos t}{\sin t \cos t} = \dfrac{1}{\sin t \cos t} + 2$

$=$ RHS

61. LHS $= \dfrac{1 + \frac{\sin^2 u}{\cos^2 u}}{1 - \frac{\sin^2 u}{\cos^2 u}} \cdot \dfrac{\cos^2 u}{\cos^2 u} = \dfrac{\cos^2 u + \sin^2 u}{\cos^2 u - \sin^2 u} =$ RHS

63. LHS $= \dfrac{\sec x}{\sec x - \tan x} \cdot \dfrac{\sec x + \tan x}{\sec x + \tan x}$

$= \dfrac{\sec x(\sec x + \tan x)}{\sec^2 x - \tan^2 x} =$ RHS

65. LHS $= (\sec v - \tan v) \cdot \dfrac{\sec v + \tan v}{\sec v + \tan v}$

$= \dfrac{\sec^2 v - \tan^2 v}{\sec v + \tan v} =$ RHS

67. LHS $= \dfrac{\sin x + \cos x}{\frac{1}{\cos x} + \frac{1}{\sin x}} = \dfrac{\sin x + \cos x}{\frac{\sin x + \cos x}{\cos x \sin x}}$

$= (\sin x + \cos x)\dfrac{\cos x \sin x}{\sin x + \cos x} =$ RHS

69. LHS $= \dfrac{\frac{1}{\sin x} - \frac{\cos x}{\sin x}}{\frac{1}{\cos x} - 1} \cdot \dfrac{\sin x \cos x}{\sin x \cos x} = \dfrac{\cos x(1 - \cos x)}{\sin x(1 - \cos x)}$

$= \dfrac{\cos x}{\sin x} =$ RHS

71. LHS $= \dfrac{\sin^2 u}{\cos^2 u} - \dfrac{\sin^2 u \cos^2 u}{\cos^2 u} = \dfrac{\sin^2 u}{\cos^2 u}(1 - \cos^2 u) =$ RHS

73. LHS $= (\sec^2 x - \tan^2 x)(\sec^2 x + \tan^2 x) =$ RHS

75. RHS $= \dfrac{\sin \theta - \frac{1}{\sin \theta}}{\cos \theta - \frac{\cos \theta}{\sin \theta}} = \dfrac{\frac{\sin^2 \theta - 1}{\sin \theta}}{\frac{\cos \theta \sin \theta - \cos \theta}{\sin \theta}}$

$= \dfrac{\cos^2 \theta}{\cos \theta(\sin \theta - 1)} =$ LHS

77. LHS $= \dfrac{-\sin^2 t + \tan^2 t}{\sin^2 t} = -1 + \dfrac{\sin^2 t}{\cos^2 t} \cdot \dfrac{1}{\sin^2 t}$

$= -1 + \sec^2 t =$ RHS

79. LHS $= \dfrac{\sec x - \tan x + \sec x + \tan x}{(\sec x + \tan x)(\sec x - \tan x)}$

$= \dfrac{2 \sec x}{\sec^2 x - \tan^2 x} =$ RHS

81. LHS $= \tan^2 x + 2 \tan x \cot x + \cot^2 x = \tan^2 x + 2 + \cot^2 x$

$= (\tan^2 x + 1) + (\cot^2 x + 1) =$ RHS

83. LHS $= \dfrac{\frac{1}{\cos u} - 1}{\frac{1}{\cos u} + 1} \cdot \dfrac{\cos u}{\cos u} =$ RHS

85. LHS $= \dfrac{(\sin x + \cos x)(\sin^2 x - \sin x \cos x + \cos^2 x)}{\sin x + \cos x}$

$= \sin^2 x - \sin x \cos x + \cos^2 x =$ RHS

87. LHS $= \dfrac{1 + \sin x}{1 - \sin x} \cdot \dfrac{1 + \sin x}{1 + \sin x} = \dfrac{(1 + \sin x)^2}{1 - \sin^2 x}$

$= \dfrac{(1 + \sin x)^2}{\cos^2 x} = \left(\dfrac{1 + \sin x}{\cos x}\right)^2 =$ RHS

89. LHS $= \left(\dfrac{\sin x}{\cos x} + \dfrac{\cos x}{\sin x}\right)^4 = \left(\dfrac{\sin^2 x + \cos^2 x}{\sin x \cos x}\right)^4$

$= \left(\dfrac{1}{\sin x \cos x}\right)^4 =$ RHS

91. $\tan \theta$ **93.** $\tan \theta$ **95.** $3 \cos \theta$

97.

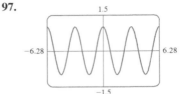

Yes

99.

3

No

SECTION 7.2 ■ PAGE 505

1. addition; $\sin x \cos y + \cos x \sin y$

2. subtraction; $\cos x \cos y + \sin x \sin y$

3. $\dfrac{\sqrt{6} + \sqrt{2}}{4}$ **5.** $\dfrac{\sqrt{2} - \sqrt{6}}{4}$ **7.** $2 - \sqrt{3}$ **9.** $-\dfrac{\sqrt{6} + \sqrt{2}}{4}$

11. $\sqrt{3} - 2$ **13.** $-\dfrac{\sqrt{6} + \sqrt{2}}{4}$ **15.** $\sqrt{2}/2$ **17.** $\tfrac{1}{2}$ **19.** $\sqrt{3}$

21. LHS $= \dfrac{\sin\left(\frac{\pi}{2} - u\right)}{\cos\left(\frac{\pi}{2} - u\right)} = \dfrac{\sin \frac{\pi}{2} \cos u - \cos \frac{\pi}{2} \sin u}{\cos \frac{\pi}{2} \cos u + \sin \frac{\pi}{2} \sin u}$

$= \dfrac{\cos u}{\sin u} =$ RHS

23. LHS $= \dfrac{1}{\cos\left(\frac{\pi}{2} - u\right)} = \dfrac{1}{\cos \frac{\pi}{2} \cos u + \sin \frac{\pi}{2} \sin u}$

$= \dfrac{1}{\sin u} =$ RHS

25. LHS $= \sin x \cos \frac{\pi}{2} - \cos x \sin \frac{\pi}{2} =$ RHS

27. LHS $= \sin x \cos \pi - \cos x \sin \pi =$ RHS

29. LHS $= \dfrac{\tan x - \tan \pi}{1 + \tan x \tan \pi} =$ RHS

31. LHS $= \cos x \cos \frac{\pi}{6} - \sin x \sin \frac{\pi}{6} + \sin x \cos \frac{\pi}{3} - \cos x \sin \frac{\pi}{3}$

$= \dfrac{\sqrt{3}}{2} \cos x - \tfrac{1}{2} \sin x + \tfrac{1}{2} \sin x - \dfrac{\sqrt{3}}{2} \cos x =$ RHS

33. LHS $= \sin x \cos y + \cos x \sin y$

$- (\sin x \cos y - \cos x \sin y) =$ RHS

35. LHS $= \dfrac{1}{\tan(x - y)} = \dfrac{1 + \tan x \tan y}{\tan x - \tan y}$

$= \dfrac{1 + \frac{1}{\cot x} \frac{1}{\cot y}}{\frac{1}{\cot x} - \frac{1}{\cot y}} \cdot \dfrac{\cot x \cot y}{\cot x \cot y} =$ RHS

37. LHS $= \dfrac{\sin x}{\cos x} - \dfrac{\sin y}{\cos y} = \dfrac{\sin x \cos y - \cos x \sin y}{\cos x \cos y} =$ RHS

39. LHS $= \dfrac{\sin x \cos y + \cos x \sin y - (\sin x \cos y - \cos x \sin y)}{\cos x \cos y - \sin x \sin y + \cos x \cos y + \sin x \sin y}$

$\quad = \dfrac{2 \cos x \sin y}{2 \cos x \cos y} =$ RHS

41. LHS $= \sin((x + y) + z)$

$\quad = \sin(x + y)\cos z + \cos(x + y)\sin z$

$\quad = \cos z[\sin x \cos y + \cos x \sin y]$

$\quad\quad + \sin z[\cos x \cos y - \sin x \sin y] =$ RHS

43. $\dfrac{\sqrt{1 - x^2} + xy}{\sqrt{1 + y^2}}$ **45.** $\dfrac{x - y}{\sqrt{1 + x^2}\sqrt{1 + y^2}}$

47. $\frac{1}{4}(\sqrt{6} + \sqrt{2})$ **49.** $\dfrac{3 - 2\sqrt{14}}{\sqrt{7} + 6\sqrt{2}}$ **51.** $-\frac{1}{10}(3 + 4\sqrt{3})$

53. $2\sqrt{5}/65$ **55.** $2\sin\left(x + \dfrac{5\pi}{6}\right)$ **57.** $5\sqrt{2}\sin\left(2x + \dfrac{7\pi}{4}\right)$

59. (a) $g(x) = 2\sin 2\left(x + \dfrac{\pi}{12}\right)$

(b)

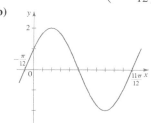

63. $\tan\gamma = \frac{17}{6}$

65. (a)

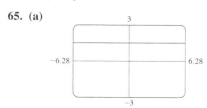

$\sin^2\left(x + \dfrac{\pi}{4}\right) + \sin^2\left(x - \dfrac{\pi}{4}\right) = 1$

67. $\pi/2$ **69.** (b) $k = 10\sqrt{3},\ \phi = \pi/6$

SECTION 7.3 ■ PAGE 514

1. Double-Angle; $2\sin x \cos x$

2. Half-Angle; $\pm\sqrt{(1 - \cos x)/2}$

3. $\frac{120}{169}, \frac{119}{169}, \frac{120}{119}$ **5.** $-\frac{24}{25}, \frac{7}{25}, -\frac{24}{7}$ **7.** $\frac{24}{25}, \frac{7}{25}, \frac{24}{7}$ **9.** $-\frac{3}{5}, \frac{4}{5}, -\frac{3}{4}$

11. $\frac{1}{2}\left(\frac{3}{4} - \cos 2x + \frac{1}{4}\cos 4x\right)$

13. $\frac{1}{16}(1 - \cos 2x - \cos 4x + \cos 2x \cos 4x)$

15. $\frac{1}{32}\left(\frac{3}{4} - \cos 4x + \frac{1}{4}\cos 8x\right)$

17. $\frac{1}{2}\sqrt{2 - \sqrt{3}}$ **19.** $\sqrt{2} - 1$ **21.** $-\frac{1}{2}\sqrt{2 + \sqrt{3}}$

23. $\sqrt{2} - 1$ **25.** $\frac{1}{2}\sqrt{2 + \sqrt{3}}$ **27.** $-\frac{1}{2}\sqrt{2 - \sqrt{2}}$

29. (a) $\sin 36°$ (b) $\sin 6\theta$ **31.** (a) $\cos 68°$ (b) $\cos 10\theta$

33. (a) $\tan 4°$ (b) $\tan 2\theta$ **37.** $\sqrt{10}/10,\ 3\sqrt{10}/10,\ \frac{1}{3}$

39. $\sqrt{(3 + 2\sqrt{2})}/6,\ \sqrt{(3 - 2\sqrt{2})}/6,\ 3 + 2\sqrt{2}$

41. $\sqrt{6}/6,\ -\sqrt{30}/6,\ -\sqrt{5}/5$

43. $\dfrac{2x}{1 + x^2}$ **45.** $\sqrt{\dfrac{1 - x}{2}}$ **47.** $\frac{336}{625}$ **49.** $\frac{8}{7}$ **51.** $\frac{7}{25}$

53. $-8\sqrt{3}/49$ **55.** $\frac{1}{2}(\sin 5x - \sin x)$ **57.** $\frac{1}{2}(\sin 5x + \sin 3x)$

59. $\frac{3}{2}(\cos 11x + \cos 3x)$ **61.** $2\sin 4x \cos x$

63. $2\sin 5x \sin x$ **65.** $-2\cos\frac{9}{2}x \sin\frac{5}{2}x$ **67.** $(\sqrt{2} + \sqrt{3})/2$

69. $\frac{1}{4}(\sqrt{2} - 1)$ **71.** $\sqrt{2}/2$ **73.** LHS $= \cos(2 \cdot 5x) =$ RHS

75. LHS $= \sin^2 x + 2\sin x \cos x + \cos^2 x$

$\quad = 1 + 2\sin x \cos x =$ RHS

77. LHS $= \dfrac{2\sin 2x \cos 2x}{\sin x} = \dfrac{2(2\sin x \cos x)(\cos 2x)}{\sin x} =$ RHS

79. LHS $= \dfrac{2(\tan x - \cot x)}{(\tan x + \cot x)(\tan x - \cot x)} = \dfrac{2}{\tan x + \cot x}$

$\quad = \dfrac{2}{\frac{\sin x}{\cos x} + \frac{\cos x}{\sin x}} \cdot \dfrac{\sin x \cos x}{\sin x \cos x} = \dfrac{2\sin x \cos x}{\sin^2 x + \cos^2 x}$

$\quad = 2\sin x \cos x =$ RHS

81. LHS $= \tan(2x + x) = \dfrac{\tan 2x + \tan x}{1 - \tan 2x \tan x}$

$\quad = \dfrac{\frac{2\tan x}{1 - \tan^2 x} + \tan x}{1 - \frac{2\tan x}{1 - \tan^2 x}\tan x}$

$\quad = \dfrac{2\tan x + \tan x(1 - \tan^2 x)}{1 - \tan^2 x - 2\tan x \tan x} =$ RHS

83. LHS $= (\cos^2 x + \sin^2 x)(\cos^2 x - \sin^2 x)$

$\quad = \cos^2 x - \sin^2 x =$ RHS

85. LHS $= \dfrac{2\sin 3x \cos 2x}{2\cos 3x \cos 2x} = \dfrac{\sin 3x}{\cos 3x} =$ RHS

87. LHS $= \dfrac{2\sin 5x \cos 5x}{2\sin 5x \cos 4x} =$ RHS

89. LHS $= \dfrac{2\sin\left(\frac{x + y}{2}\right)\cos\left(\frac{x - y}{2}\right)}{2\cos\left(\frac{x + y}{2}\right)\cos\left(\frac{x - y}{2}\right)}$

$\quad = \dfrac{\sin\left(\frac{x + y}{2}\right)}{\cos\left(\frac{x + y}{2}\right)} =$ RHS

95. LHS $= \dfrac{(\sin x + \sin 5x) + (\sin 2x + \sin 4x) + \sin 3x}{(\cos x + \cos 5x) + (\cos 2x + \cos 4x) + \cos 3x}$

$\quad = \dfrac{2\sin 3x \cos 2x + 2\sin 3x \cos x + \sin 3x}{2\cos 3x \cos 2x + 2\cos 3x \cos x + \cos 3x}$

$\quad = \dfrac{\sin 3x(2\cos 2x + 2\cos x + 1)}{\cos 3x(2\cos 2x + 2\cos x + 1)} =$ RHS

97. (a)

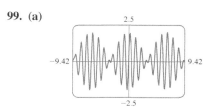

$\dfrac{\sin 3x}{\sin x} - \dfrac{\cos 3x}{\cos x} = 2$

99. (a)

(c)

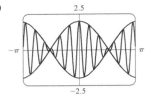

The graph of $y = f(x)$ lies between the two other graphs.

101. (a) $P(t) = 8t^4 - 8t^2 + 1$ **(b)** $Q(t) = 16t^5 - 20t^3 + 5t$
107. (a) and **(c)**

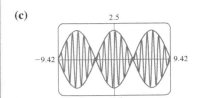

The graph of f lies between the graphs of $y = 2 \cos t$ and $y = -2 \cos t$. Thus, the loudness of the sound varies between $y = \pm 2 \cos t$.

SECTION 7.4 ■ PAGE 522

1. infinitely many **2.** no, infinitely many
3. $0.3; x \approx -9.7, -6.0, -3.4, 0.3, 2.8, 6.6, 9.1$
4. (a) $0.30, 2.84$ **(b)** $2\pi, 0.30 + 2k\pi, 2.84 + 2k\pi$
5. $\dfrac{\pi}{3} + 2k\pi, \dfrac{2\pi}{3} + 2k\pi$

7. $(2k + 1)\pi$ **9.** $1.32 + 2k\pi, 4.97 + 2k\pi$

11. $-0.47 + 2k\pi, 3.61 + 2k\pi$

13. $-\dfrac{\pi}{3} + k\pi$ **15.** $1.37 + k\pi$

17. $\dfrac{5\pi}{6} + 2k\pi, \dfrac{7\pi}{6} + 2k\pi$;

$-7\pi/6, -5\pi/6, 5\pi/6, 7\pi/6, 17\pi/6, 19\pi/6$

19. $\dfrac{\pi}{4} + 2k\pi, \dfrac{3\pi}{4} + 2k\pi$;

$-7\pi/4, -5\pi/4, \pi/4, 3\pi/4, 9\pi/4, 11\pi/4$
21. $1.29 + 2k\pi, 5.00 + 2k\pi; -5.00, -1.29, 1.29, 5.00, 7.57, 11.28$
23. $-1.47 + k\pi; -7.75, -4.61, -1.47, 1.67, 4.81, 7.95$

25. $(2k + 1)\pi$ **27.** $-\dfrac{\pi}{4} + 2k\pi, \dfrac{5\pi}{4} + 2k\pi$

29. $0.20 + 2k\pi, 2.94 + 2k\pi$ **31.** $-\dfrac{\pi}{6} + k\pi, \dfrac{\pi}{6} + k\pi$

33. $\dfrac{\pi}{4} + k\pi, \dfrac{3\pi}{4} + k\pi$ **35.** $-1.11 + k\pi, 1.11 + k\pi$

37. $\dfrac{\pi}{4} + k\pi, \dfrac{3\pi}{4} + k\pi$

39. $-1.11 + k\pi, 1.11 + k\pi, \dfrac{2\pi}{3} + 2k\pi, \dfrac{4\pi}{3} + 2k\pi$

41. $\dfrac{\pi}{3} + 2k\pi, \dfrac{5\pi}{3} + 2k\pi$ **43.** $0.34 + 2k\pi, 2.80 + 2k\pi$

45. $\dfrac{\pi}{3} + 2k\pi, \dfrac{5\pi}{3} + 2k\pi$ **47.** No solution **49.** $\dfrac{3\pi}{2} + 2k\pi$

51. $\dfrac{\pi}{2} + k\pi, \dfrac{7\pi}{6} + 2k\pi, \dfrac{11\pi}{6} + 2k\pi$

53. $\dfrac{\pi}{2} + k\pi$ **55.** $k\pi, 0.73 + 2k\pi, 2.41 + 2k\pi$ **57.** $44.95°$

59. (a) $0°$ **(b)** $60°, 120°$ **(c)** $90°, 270°$ **(d)** $180°$

SECTION 7.5 ■ PAGE 528

1. $\sin x = 0, k\pi$ **2.** $\sin x + 2 \sin x \cos x = 0$,
$\sin x = 0, 1 + 2 \cos x = 0$ **3.** $-\dfrac{\pi}{6} + 2k\pi, \dfrac{7\pi}{6} + 2k\pi, \dfrac{\pi}{2} + 2k\pi$

5. $(2k + 1)\pi, 1.23 + 2k\pi, 5.05 + 2k\pi$

7. $k\pi, 0.72 + 2k\pi, 5.56 + 2k\pi$ **9.** $\dfrac{\pi}{6} + 2k\pi, \dfrac{5\pi}{6} + 2k\pi$

11. $\dfrac{\pi}{3} + 2k\pi, \dfrac{5\pi}{3} + 2k\pi, (2k + 1)\pi$ **13.** $(2k + 1)\pi, \dfrac{\pi}{2} + 2k\pi$

15. $2k\pi$ **17. (a)** $\dfrac{\pi}{9} + \dfrac{2k\pi}{3}, \dfrac{5\pi}{9} + \dfrac{2k\pi}{3}$

(b) $\pi/9, 5\pi/9, 7\pi/9, 11\pi/9, 13\pi/9, 17\pi/9$

19. (a) $\dfrac{\pi}{3} + k\pi, \dfrac{2\pi}{3} + k\pi$ **(b)** $\pi/3, 2\pi/3, 4\pi/3, 5\pi/3$
21. (a) $\dfrac{5\pi}{18} + \dfrac{k\pi}{3}$ **(b)** $5\pi/18, 11\pi/18, 17\pi/18, 23\pi/18,$
$29\pi/18, 35\pi/18$ **23. (a)** $4k\pi$ **(b)** 0

25. (a) $4\pi + 6k\pi, 5\pi + 6k\pi$ **(b)** None

27. (a) $0.62 + \dfrac{k\pi}{2}$ **(b)** $0.62, 2.19, 3.76, 5.33$

29. (a) $k\pi$ **(b)** $0, \pi$ **31. (a)** $\dfrac{\pi}{6} + k\pi, \dfrac{\pi}{4} + k\pi, \dfrac{5\pi}{6} + k\pi$

(b) $\pi/6, \pi/4, 5\pi/6, 7\pi/6, 5\pi/4, 11\pi/6$

33. (a) $\dfrac{\pi}{6} + 2k\pi, \dfrac{5\pi}{6} + 2k\pi, \dfrac{3\pi}{4} + k\pi$

(b) $\pi/6, 3\pi/4, 5\pi/6, 7\pi/4$

35. (a)

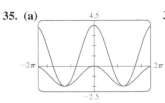

$(\pm 3.14, -2)$

(b) $((2k + 1)\pi, -2)$

37. (a)

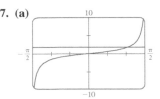

$(1.04, 1.73)$

(b) $\left(\dfrac{\pi}{3} + k\pi, \sqrt{3} \right)$

39. $\pi/8, 3\pi/8, 5\pi/8, 7\pi/8, 9\pi/8, 11\pi/8, 13\pi/8, 15\pi/8$
41. $\pi/3, 2\pi/3$ **43.** $\pi/2, 7\pi/6, 3\pi/2, 11\pi/6$ **45.** 0
47. $0, \pi$ **49.** $0, \pi/3, 2\pi/3, \pi, 4\pi/3, 5\pi/3$ **51.** $\pi/6, 3\pi/2$

53. $k\pi/2$ **55.** $\dfrac{\pi}{2} + k\pi, \dfrac{\pi}{9} + \dfrac{2k\pi}{3}, \dfrac{5\pi}{9} + \dfrac{2k\pi}{3}$

57. $0, \pm 0.95$ **59.** 1.92 **61.** ± 0.71
63. $0.94721°$ or $89.05279°$ **65. (a)** 34th day (February 3), 308th day (November 4) **(b)** 275 days

CHAPTER 7 REVIEW ■ PAGE 530

1. $\text{LHS} = \sin\theta\left(\dfrac{\cos\theta}{\sin\theta} + \dfrac{\sin\theta}{\cos\theta} \right) = \cos\theta + \dfrac{\sin^2\theta}{\cos\theta}$
$= \dfrac{\cos^2\theta + \sin^2\theta}{\cos\theta} = \text{RHS}$

3. LHS $= (1 - \sin^2 x) \csc x - \csc x$
$= \csc x - \sin^2 x \csc x - \csc x$
$= -\sin^2 x \dfrac{1}{\sin x} = $ RHS

5. LHS $= \dfrac{\cos^2 x}{\sin^2 x} - \dfrac{\tan^2 x}{\sin^2 x} = \cot^2 x - \dfrac{1}{\cos^2 x} = $ RHS

7. LHS $= \dfrac{\cos x}{\frac{1}{\cos x}(1 - \sin x)} = \dfrac{\cos x}{\frac{1}{\cos x} - \frac{\sin x}{\cos x}} = $ RHS

9. LHS $= \sin^2 x \dfrac{\cos^2 x}{\sin^2 x} + \cos^2 x \dfrac{\sin^2 x}{\cos^2 x} = \cos^2 x + \sin^2 x = $ RHS

11. LHS $= \dfrac{2 \sin x \cos x}{1 + 2\cos^2 x - 1} = \dfrac{2 \sin x \cos x}{2\cos^2 x} = \dfrac{2 \sin x}{2 \cos x} = $ RHS

13. LHS $= \dfrac{1 - \cos x}{\sin x} = \dfrac{1}{\sin x} - \dfrac{\cos x}{\sin x} = $ RHS

15. LHS $= \tfrac{1}{2}[\cos((x+y) - (x-y))$
$\qquad - \cos((x+y) + (x-y))]$
$= \tfrac{1}{2}(\cos 2y - \cos 2x)$
$= \tfrac{1}{2}[1 - 2\sin^2 y - (1 - 2\sin^2 x)]$
$= \tfrac{1}{2}(2\sin^2 x - 2\sin^2 y) = $ RHS

17. LHS $= 1 + \dfrac{\sin x}{\cos x} \cdot \dfrac{1 - \cos x}{\sin x} = 1 + \dfrac{1 - \cos x}{\cos x}$
$= 1 + \dfrac{1}{\cos x} - 1 = $ RHS

19. LHS $= \cos^2 \tfrac{x}{2} - 2\sin \tfrac{x}{2} \cos \tfrac{x}{2} + \sin^2 \tfrac{x}{2}$
$= 1 - \sin(2 \cdot \tfrac{x}{2}) = $ RHS

21. LHS $= \dfrac{2 \sin x \cos x}{\sin x} - \dfrac{2\cos^2 x - 1}{\cos x}$
$= 2\cos x - 2\cos x + \dfrac{1}{\cos x} = $ RHS

23. LHS $= \dfrac{\tan x + \tan \frac{\pi}{4}}{1 - \tan x \tan \frac{\pi}{4}} = $ RHS

25. (a)
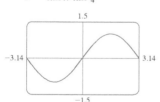
(b) Yes

27. (a)
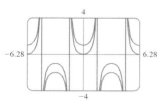
(b) No

29. (a)
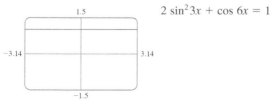
$2 \sin^2 3x + \cos 6x = 1$

31. $0.85, 2.29$ **33.** $0, \pi$ **35.** $\pi/6, 5\pi/6$ **37.** $\pi/3, 5\pi/3$
39. $2\pi/3, 4\pi/3$ **41.** $\pi/3, 2\pi/3, 3\pi/4, 4\pi/3, 5\pi/3, 7\pi/4$
43. $\pi/6, \pi/2, 5\pi/6, 7\pi/6, 3\pi/2, 11\pi/6$ **45.** $\pi/6$

47. 1.18 **49. (a)** $63.4°$ **(b)** No   **(c)** $90°$ **51.** $\tfrac{1}{2}\sqrt{2 + \sqrt{3}}$

53. $\sqrt{2} - 1$ **55.** $\sqrt{2}/2$ **57.** $\sqrt{2}/2$ **59.** $\dfrac{\sqrt{2} + \sqrt{3}}{4}$

61. $2\dfrac{\sqrt{10} + 1}{9}$ **63.** $\tfrac{2}{3}(\sqrt{2} + \sqrt{5})$ **65.** $\sqrt{(3 + 2\sqrt{2})}/6$

67. $-\dfrac{12\sqrt{10}}{31}$ **69.** $\dfrac{2x}{1 - x^2}$ **71. (a)** $\theta = \tan^{-1}\left(\dfrac{10}{x}\right)$

(b) 286.4 ft

CHAPTER 7 TEST ■ PAGE 532

1. (a) LHS $= \dfrac{\sin \theta}{\cos \theta} \sin \theta + \cos \theta = \dfrac{\sin^2 \theta + \cos^2 \theta}{\cos \theta} = $ RHS

(b) LHS $= \dfrac{\tan x}{1 - \cos x} \cdot \dfrac{1 + \cos x}{1 + \cos x} = \dfrac{\tan x(1 + \cos x)}{1 - \cos^2 x}$
$= \dfrac{\frac{\sin x}{\cos x}(1 + \cos x)}{\sin^2 x} = \dfrac{1}{\sin x} \cdot \dfrac{1 + \cos x}{\cos x} = $ RHS

(c) LHS $= \dfrac{2 \tan x}{\sec^2 x} = \dfrac{2 \sin x}{\cos x} \cdot \cos^2 x = 2 \sin x \cos x = $ RHS

2. $\tan \theta$ **3. (a)** $\tfrac{1}{2}$ **(b)** $\dfrac{\sqrt{2} + \sqrt{6}}{4}$ **(c)** $\tfrac{1}{2}\sqrt{2 - \sqrt{3}}$

4. $(10 - 2\sqrt{5})/15$
5. (a) $\tfrac{1}{2}(\sin 8x - \sin 2x)$ **(b)** $-2 \cos \tfrac{7}{2}x \sin \tfrac{3}{2}x$ **6.** -2
7. (a) $0.34, 2.80$ **(b)** $\pi/3, \pi/2, 5\pi/3$ **(c)** $2\pi/3, 4\pi/3$
(d) $\pi/6, \pi/2, 5\pi/6, 3\pi/2$ **8.** $0.58, 2.56, 3.72, 5.70$ **9.** $\tfrac{1519}{1681}$
10. $\dfrac{\sqrt{1 - x^2} - xy}{\sqrt{1 + y^2}}$

FOCUS ON MODELING ■ PAGE 536

1. (a) $y = -5 \sin\left(\dfrac{\pi}{2}t\right)$

(b)
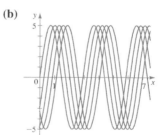

Yes, it is a traveling wave.
(c) $v = \pi/4$
3. $y(x, t) = 2.7 \sin(0.68x - 4.10t)$
5. $y(x, t) = 0.6 \sin(\pi x) \cos(40\pi t)$
7. (a) $1, 2, 3, 4$
(b) 5:
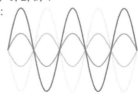

6:
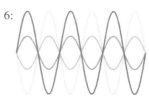

(c) 880π (d) $y(x, t) = \sin t \cos(880\pi t)$;
$y(x, t) = \sin(2t) \cos(880\pi t)$; $y(x, t) = \sin(3t) \cos(880\pi t)$;
$y(x, t) = \sin(4t) \cos(880\pi t)$

CUMULATIVE REVIEW TEST FOR CHAPTERS 5, 6 AND 7 ■ PAGE 539

1. (a) $\sqrt{5}/3$ (b) $-2/3$ (c) $-\sqrt{5}/2$ (d) $3\sqrt{3}/5$
2. (a) $2\sqrt{10}/7$ (b) $7/3$ (c) $3\sqrt{10}/20$
3. (a) $-\sqrt{3}/2$ (b) -1 (c) $2\sqrt{3}/3$ (d) -1
4. $\sin t = -24/25$, $\tan t = -24/7$, $\cot t = -7/24$, $\sec t = 25/7$, $\csc t = -25/24$ **5.** (a) $2, \pi, \pi/4$ (b)

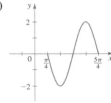

6. $y = 3 \cos \frac{1}{2}(x - \frac{\pi}{3})$ **7.** (a) $h(t) = 45 - 40 \cos 8\pi t$
(b) $2\sqrt{19} \approx 8.7$ cm   **8.** (a) 7.2   (b) 92.9°

9. (a) LHS $= \dfrac{(\sec \theta - 1)(\sec \theta + 1)}{\tan \theta (\sec \theta + 1)}$

$= \dfrac{\sec^2 \theta - 1}{\tan \theta (\sec \theta + 1)} = \dfrac{\tan^2 \theta}{\tan \theta (\sec \theta + 1)} = $ RHS

(b) RHS $= 1 - (1 - 2 \sin^2 2\theta) = 2 \sin^2 2\theta = 2(2 \sin \theta \cos \theta)^2$
$= $ LHS

10. $2 \cos \dfrac{7x}{2} \cos \dfrac{x}{2}$ **11.** (a) Domain $[-1, 1]$, range $[0, \pi]$

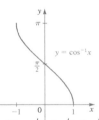

(b) $5\pi/6$ (c) $\sqrt{1 - x^2}/x$ **12.** $\pi/6, 5\pi/6, 3\pi/2$

CHAPTER 8

SECTION 8.1 ■ PAGE 546

1. coordinate; $(1, 1)$, $(\sqrt{2}, \pi/4)$ **2.** (a) $r \cos \theta, r \sin \theta$
(b) $x^2 + y^2, y/x$
3.

5.

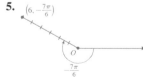

7.

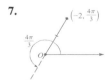

9.

 $\left(-3, \dfrac{3\pi}{2}\right), \left(3, \dfrac{5\pi}{2}\right)$

11.

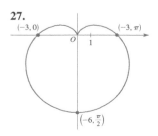 $\left(-1, -\dfrac{5\pi}{6}\right), \left(1, \dfrac{\pi}{6}\right)$

13. $(-5, 0)$ $(-5, 2\pi), (5, \pi)$

15. Q **17.** Q **19.** P **21.** P **23.** $(3\sqrt{2}, 3\pi/4)$
25. $\left(-\dfrac{5}{2}, -\dfrac{5\sqrt{3}}{2}\right)$ **27.** $(2\sqrt{3}, 2)$ **29.** $(1, -1)$ **31.** $(-5, 0)$
33. $(3\sqrt{6}, -3\sqrt{2})$ **35.** $(\sqrt{2}, 3\pi/4)$ **37.** $(4, \pi/4)$
39. $(5, \tan^{-1} \frac{4}{3})$ **41.** $(6, \pi)$ **43.** $\theta = \pi/4$ **45.** $r = \tan \theta \sec \theta$
47. $r = 4 \sec \theta$ **49.** $x^2 + y^2 = 49$ **51.** $x = 0$ **53.** $x = 6$
55. $x^2 + (y - 2)^2 = 4$ **57.** $x^2 + y^2 = (x^2 + y^2 - x)^2$
59. $(x^2 + y^2 - 2y)^2 = x^2 + y^2$ **61.** $y - x = 1$
63. $x^2 - 3y^2 + 16y - 16 = 0$ **65.** $x^2 + y^2 = \dfrac{y}{x}$
67. $y = \pm \sqrt{3} x$

SECTION 8.2 ■ PAGE 553

1. circles, rays   **2.** (a) satisfy   (b) circle, 3, pole; line, pole, 1
3. VI   **5.** II   **7.** I   **9.** Symmetric about $\theta = \pi/2$
11. Symmetric about the polar axis
13. Symmetric about $\theta = \pi/2$
15. All three types of symmetry
17.

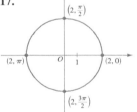

$x^2 + y^2 = 4$

19.

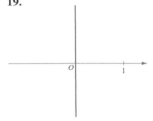

$x = 0$

21.

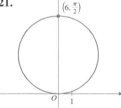

$x^2 + (y - 3)^2 = 9$

23.

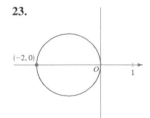

25.

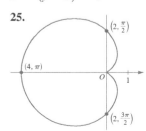

27.

29.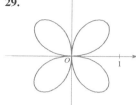

31.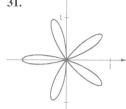

33.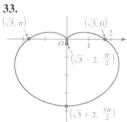

35.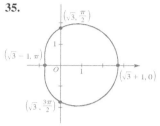

37.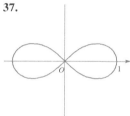

39.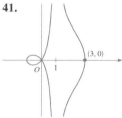

41.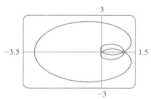

43. $0 \le \theta \le 4\pi$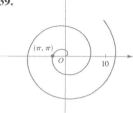

45. $0 \le \theta \le 4\pi$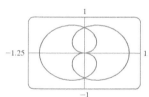

47. The graph of $r = 1 + \sin n\theta$ has n loops.   **49.** IV   **51.** III

53.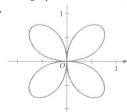

55.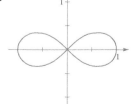

57. $\left(\dfrac{a}{2}, \dfrac{b}{2}\right)$, $\dfrac{\sqrt{a^2 + b^2}}{2}$

59. (a) Elliptical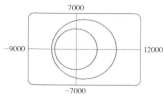

(b) π; 540 mi

SECTION 8.3 ■ PAGE 562

1. real, imaginary, (a, b) **2. (a)** $\sqrt{a^2 + b^2}$, b/a
(b) $r(\cos\theta + i\sin\theta)$

3. (a) $\sqrt{2}\left(\cos\dfrac{3\pi}{4} + i\sin\dfrac{3\pi}{4}\right)$; $\sqrt{3} + i$

(b) $1 + i$, $\sqrt{2}\left(\cos\dfrac{\pi}{4} + i\sin\dfrac{\pi}{4}\right)$

4. n; four; $2, 2i, -2, -2i$; 2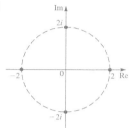

5. 4

7. 2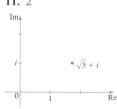

9. $\sqrt{29}$

11. 2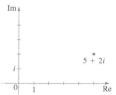

13. 1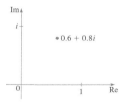

15.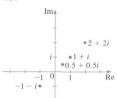

17.

19.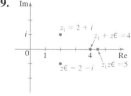

21.

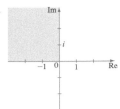

23.

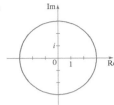

25.

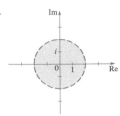

27.

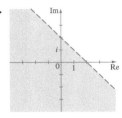

29. $\sqrt{2}\left(\cos\dfrac{\pi}{4} + i\sin\dfrac{\pi}{4}\right)$ **31.** $2\left(\cos\dfrac{7\pi}{4} + i\sin\dfrac{7\pi}{4}\right)$

33. $4\left(\cos\dfrac{11\pi}{6} + i\sin\dfrac{11\pi}{6}\right)$ **35.** $3\left(\cos\dfrac{3\pi}{2} + i\sin\dfrac{3\pi}{2}\right)$

37. $5\sqrt{2}\left(\cos\dfrac{\pi}{4} + i\sin\dfrac{\pi}{4}\right)$ **39.** $8\left(\cos\dfrac{11\pi}{6} + i\sin\dfrac{11\pi}{6}\right)$

41. $20(\cos\pi + i\sin\pi)$ **43.** $5[\cos(\tan^{-1}\tfrac{4}{3}) + i\sin(\tan^{-1}\tfrac{4}{3})]$

45. $3\sqrt{2}\left(\cos\dfrac{3\pi}{4} + i\sin\dfrac{3\pi}{4}\right)$ **47.** $8\left(\cos\dfrac{\pi}{6} + i\sin\dfrac{\pi}{6}\right)$

49. $\sqrt{5}[\cos(\tan^{-1}\tfrac{1}{2}) + i\sin(\tan^{-1}\tfrac{1}{2})]$

51. $2\left(\cos\dfrac{\pi}{4} + i\sin\dfrac{\pi}{4}\right)$

53. $z_1 z_2 = \cos\dfrac{4\pi}{3} + i\sin\dfrac{4\pi}{3}$

$\dfrac{z_1}{z_2} = \cos\dfrac{2\pi}{3} + i\sin\dfrac{2\pi}{3}$

55. $z_1 z_2 = 15\left(\cos\dfrac{3\pi}{2} + i\sin\dfrac{3\pi}{2}\right)$

$\dfrac{z_1}{z_2} = \dfrac{3}{5}\left(\cos\dfrac{7\pi}{6} - i\sin\dfrac{7\pi}{6}\right)$

57. $z_1 z_2 = 8(\cos 150° + i\sin 150°)$

$z_1/z_2 = 2(\cos 90° + i\sin 90°)$

59. $z_1 z_2 = 100(\cos 350° + i\sin 350°)$

$z_1/z_2 = \dfrac{4}{25}(\cos 50° + i\sin 50°)$

61. $z_1 = 2\left(\cos\dfrac{\pi}{6} + i\sin\dfrac{\pi}{6}\right)$

$z_2 = 2\left(\cos\dfrac{\pi}{3} + i\sin\dfrac{\pi}{3}\right)$

$z_1 z_2 = 4\left(\cos\dfrac{\pi}{2} + i\sin\dfrac{\pi}{2}\right)$

$\dfrac{z_1}{z_2} = \cos\dfrac{\pi}{6} - i\sin\dfrac{\pi}{6}$

$\dfrac{1}{z_1} = \dfrac{1}{2}\left(\cos\dfrac{\pi}{6} - i\sin\dfrac{\pi}{6}\right)$

63. $z_1 = 4\left(\cos\dfrac{11\pi}{6} + i\sin\dfrac{11\pi}{6}\right)$

$z_2 = \sqrt{2}\left(\cos\dfrac{3\pi}{4} + i\sin\dfrac{3\pi}{4}\right)$

$z_1 z_2 = 4\sqrt{2}\left(\cos\dfrac{7\pi}{12} + i\sin\dfrac{7\pi}{12}\right)$

$\dfrac{z_1}{z_2} = 2\sqrt{2}\left(\cos\dfrac{13\pi}{12} + i\sin\dfrac{13\pi}{12}\right)$

$\dfrac{1}{z_1} = \dfrac{1}{4}\left(\cos\dfrac{11\pi}{6} - i\sin\dfrac{11\pi}{6}\right)$

65. $z_1 = 5\sqrt{2}\left(\cos\dfrac{\pi}{4} + i\sin\dfrac{\pi}{4}\right)$

$z_2 = 4(\cos 0 + i\sin 0)$

$z_1 z_2 = 20\sqrt{2}\left(\cos\dfrac{\pi}{4} + i\sin\dfrac{\pi}{4}\right)$

$\dfrac{z_1}{z_2} = \dfrac{5\sqrt{2}}{4}\left(\cos\dfrac{\pi}{4} + i\sin\dfrac{\pi}{4}\right)$

$\dfrac{1}{z_1} = \dfrac{\sqrt{2}}{10}\left(\cos\dfrac{\pi}{4} - i\sin\dfrac{\pi}{4}\right)$

67. $z_1 = 20(\cos\pi + i\sin\pi)$

$z_2 = 2\left(\cos\dfrac{\pi}{6} + i\sin\dfrac{\pi}{6}\right)$

$z_1 z_2 = 40\left(\cos\dfrac{7\pi}{6} + i\sin\dfrac{7\pi}{6}\right)$

$\dfrac{z_1}{z_2} = 10\left(\cos\dfrac{5\pi}{6} + i\sin\dfrac{5\pi}{6}\right)$

$\dfrac{1}{z_1} = \dfrac{1}{20}(\cos\pi - i\sin\pi)$

69. -1024 **71.** $512(-\sqrt{3} + i)$ **73.** -1 **75.** 4096

77. $8(-1 + i)$ **79.** $\dfrac{1}{2048}(-\sqrt{3} - i)$

81. $2\sqrt{2}\left(\cos\dfrac{\pi}{12} + i\sin\dfrac{\pi}{12}\right)$,

$2\sqrt{2}\left(\cos\dfrac{13\pi}{12} + i\sin\dfrac{13\pi}{12}\right)$

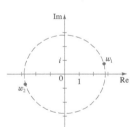

83. $3\left(\cos\dfrac{3\pi}{8} + i\sin\dfrac{3\pi}{8}\right)$,

$3\left(\cos\dfrac{7\pi}{8} + i\sin\dfrac{7\pi}{8}\right)$,

$3\left(\cos\dfrac{11\pi}{8} + i\sin\dfrac{11\pi}{8}\right)$,

$3\left(\cos\dfrac{15\pi}{8} + i\sin\dfrac{15\pi}{8}\right)$

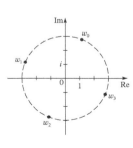

85. $\pm 1,\ \pm i,\ \pm\dfrac{\sqrt{2}}{2} \pm \dfrac{\sqrt{2}}{2}i$

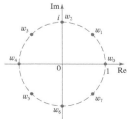

87. $\dfrac{\sqrt{3}}{2} + \dfrac{1}{2}i, \ -\dfrac{\sqrt{3}}{2} + \dfrac{1}{2}i, \ -i$

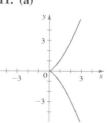

89. $\pm\dfrac{\sqrt{2}}{2} \pm \dfrac{\sqrt{2}}{2}i$

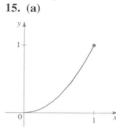

91. $\pm\dfrac{\sqrt{2}}{2} \pm \dfrac{\sqrt{2}}{2}i$

93. $2\left(\cos\dfrac{\pi}{18} + i\sin\dfrac{\pi}{18}\right), 2\left(\cos\dfrac{13\pi}{18} + i\sin\dfrac{13\pi}{18}\right),$
  $2\left(\cos\dfrac{25\pi}{18} + i\sin\dfrac{25\pi}{18}\right)$

95. $2^{1/6}\left(\cos\dfrac{5\pi}{12} + i\sin\dfrac{5\pi}{12}\right), 2^{1/6}\left(\cos\dfrac{13\pi}{12} + i\sin\dfrac{13\pi}{12}\right),$
  $2^{1/6}\left(\cos\dfrac{21\pi}{12} + i\sin\dfrac{21\pi}{12}\right)$

SECTION 8.4 ■ PAGE 569

1. (a) parameter **(b)** $(0,0), (1,1)$ **(c)** x^2; parabola
2. (a) True **(b)** $(0,0), (2,4)$ **(c)** x^2; path

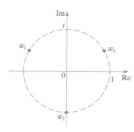

3. (a)

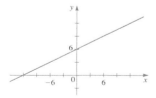

(b) $x - 2y + 12 = 0$
7. (a)

(b) $x = \sqrt{1-y}$

5. (a)

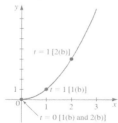

(b) $x = (y+2)^2$
9. (a)

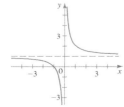

(b) $y = \dfrac{1}{x} + 1$

11. (a)

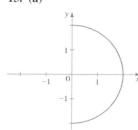

(b) $x^3 = y^2$
15. (a)

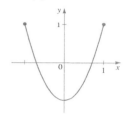

(b) $y = x^2, 0 \le x \le 1$
19. (a)

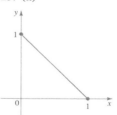

(b) $x^2 - y^2 = 1, x \ge 1, y \ge 0$
23. (a)

(b) $x + y = 1, 0 \le x \le 1$
25. $3, (3, 0)$, counterclockwise, 2π
27. $1, (0, 1)$, clockwise, π
29. $x = 4 + t, y = -1 + \frac{1}{2}t$
31. $x = 6 + t, y = 7 + t$
33. $x = a\cos t, y = a\sin t$
37.

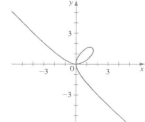

13. (a)

(b) $x^2 + y^2 = 4, x \ge 0$
17. (a)

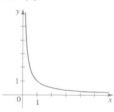

(b) $y = 2x^2 - 1, -1 \le x \le 1$
21. (a)

(b) $xy = 1, x \ge 0$

39.

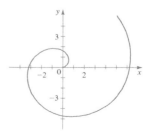

43.

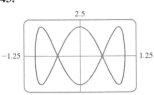

45.

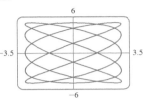

47.

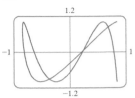

49. (a) $x = 2^{t/12} \cos t$, $y = 2^{t/12} \sin t$
(b)

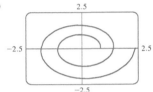

51. (a) $x = \dfrac{4 \cos t}{2 - \cos t}$, $y = \dfrac{4 \sin t}{2 - \cos t}$

(b)

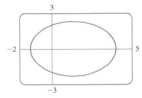

53. III   **55.** II
57.

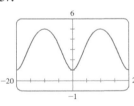

59. (b) $x^{2/3} + y^{2/3} = a^{2/3}$

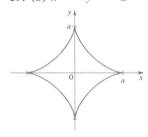

61. $x = a(\sin \theta \cos \theta + \cot \theta)$, $y = a(1 + \sin^2\theta)$
63. (a) $x = a \sec \theta$, $y = b \sin \theta$
(b)

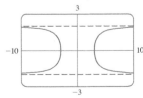

65. $y = a - a \cos\left(\dfrac{x + \sqrt{2ay - y^2}}{a}\right)$

67. (b)

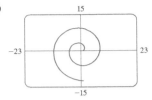

CHAPTER 8 REVIEW ▪ **PAGE 572**

1. (a)

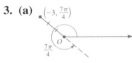

(b) $(6\sqrt{3}, 6)$

3. (a)

(b) $\left(\dfrac{-3\sqrt{2}}{2}, \dfrac{3\sqrt{2}}{2}\right)$

5. (a)

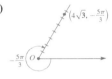

(b) $(2\sqrt{3}, 6)$

7. (a)

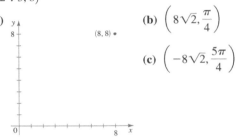

(b) $\left(8\sqrt{2}, \dfrac{\pi}{4}\right)$

(c) $\left(-8\sqrt{2}, \dfrac{5\pi}{4}\right)$

9. (a)

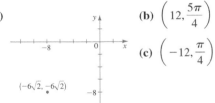

(b) $\left(12, \dfrac{5\pi}{4}\right)$

(c) $\left(-12, \dfrac{\pi}{4}\right)$

11. (a)

(b) $\left(2\sqrt{3}, \dfrac{5\pi}{6}\right)$

(c) $\left(-2\sqrt{3}, -\dfrac{\pi}{6}\right)$

13. (a) $r = \dfrac{4}{\cos \theta + \sin \theta}$

(b)

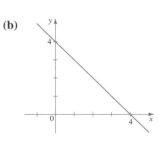

15. (a) $r = 4(\cos \theta + \sin \theta)$

(b)

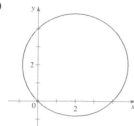

17. (a)

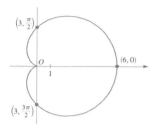

(b) $(x^2 + y^2 - 3x)^2 = 9(x^2 + y^2)$

19. (a)   **(b)** $(x^2 + y^2)^3 = 16x^2y^2$

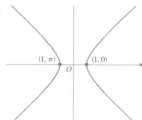

21. (a)   **(b)** $x^2 - y^2 = 1$

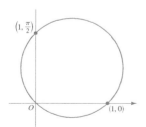

23. (a)   **(b)** $x^2 + y^2 = x + y$

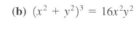

25. $0 \le \theta \le 6\pi$ **27.** $0 \le \theta \le 6\pi$

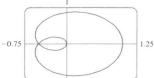

29. (a)

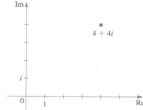

(b) $4\sqrt{2}, \dfrac{\pi}{4}$ **(c)** $4\sqrt{2}\left(\cos \dfrac{\pi}{4} + i \sin \dfrac{\pi}{4} \right)$

31. (a)

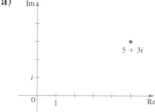

(b) $\sqrt{34}, \tan^{-1}\left(\frac{3}{5}\right)$ **(c)** $\sqrt{34}\left[\cos\left(\tan^{-1}\frac{3}{5}\right) + i \sin\left(\tan^{-1}\frac{3}{5}\right)\right]$

33. (a)

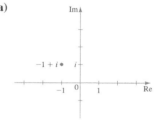

(b) $\sqrt{2}, \dfrac{3\pi}{4}$ **(c)** $\sqrt{2}\left(\cos \dfrac{3\pi}{4} + i \sin \dfrac{3\pi}{4} \right)$

35. $8(-1 + i\sqrt{3})$ **37.** $-\frac{1}{32}(1 + i\sqrt{3})$ **39.** $\pm 2\sqrt{2}(1 - i)$

41. $\pm 1, \pm\frac{1}{2} \pm \dfrac{\sqrt{3}}{2}i$

43. (a)   **45. (a)**

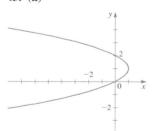
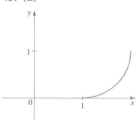

(b) $x = 2y - y^2$ **(b)** $(x - 1)^2 + (y - 1)^2 = 1,$
$1 \le x \le 2, 0 \le y \le 1$

47.

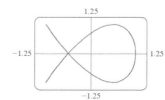

49. $x = \frac{1}{2}(1 + \cos \theta), y = \frac{1}{2}(\sin \theta + \tan \theta)$

CHAPTER 8 TEST ▪ PAGE 574

1. (a) $\left(-4\sqrt{2}, -4\sqrt{2}\right)$ **(b)** $\left(4\sqrt{3}, 5\pi/6\right), \left(-4\sqrt{3}, 11\pi/6\right)$

2. (a)   circle

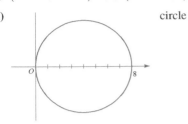

(b) $(x-4)^2 + y^2 = 16$

3.   limaçon

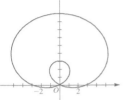

4. (a)

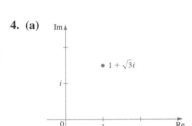

(b) $2\left(\cos\dfrac{\pi}{3} + i\sin\dfrac{\pi}{3}\right)$ **(c)** -512

5. $-8, \sqrt{3} + i$

6. $-3i, 3\left(\pm\dfrac{\sqrt{3}}{2} + \dfrac{1}{2}i\right)$

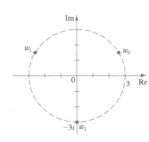

7. (a)

(b) $\dfrac{(x-3)^2}{9} + \dfrac{y^2}{4} = 1, x \geq 3$

8. $x = 3 + t, y = 5 + 2t$

FOCUS ON MODELING ▪ PAGE 577

1. $y = -\left(\dfrac{g}{2v_0^2 \cos^2\theta}\right)x^2 + (\tan\theta)x$

3. (a) 5.45 s   **(b)** 118.7 ft   **(c)** 5426.5 ft

(d)

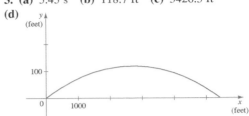

5. $\dfrac{v_0^2 \sin^2\theta}{2g}$ **7.** No, $\theta \approx 23°$

CHAPTER 9

SECTION 9.1 ▪ PAGE 587

1. (a) A, B

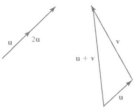

(b) $(2, 1), (4, 3), \langle 2, 2\rangle, \langle -3, 6\rangle, \langle 4, 4\rangle, \langle -1, 8\rangle$

2. (a) $\sqrt{a^2 + b^2}, 2\sqrt{2}$ **(b)** $(|\mathbf{w}|\cos\theta, |\mathbf{w}|\sin\theta)$

3.   **5.**

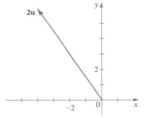

7.

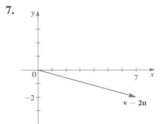

9. $\langle 3, 3\rangle$ **11.** $\langle 3, -1\rangle$ **13.** $\langle 5, 7\rangle$ **15.** $\langle -4, -3\rangle$ **17.** $\langle 0, 2\rangle$

19.   **21.**

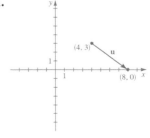

23.

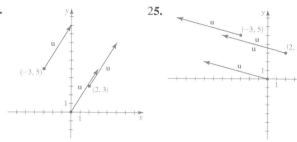

25.

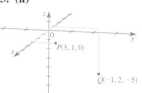

27. $\mathbf{i} + 4\mathbf{j}$ **29.** $3\mathbf{i}$ **31.** $\langle 4, 14 \rangle, \langle -9, -3 \rangle, \langle 5, 8 \rangle, \langle -6, 17 \rangle$
33. $\langle 0, -2 \rangle, \langle 6, 0 \rangle, \langle -2, -1 \rangle, \langle 8, -3 \rangle$
35. $4\mathbf{i}, -9\mathbf{i} + 6\mathbf{j}, 5\mathbf{i} - 2\mathbf{j}, -6\mathbf{i} + 8\mathbf{j}$
37. $\sqrt{5}, \sqrt{13}, 2\sqrt{5}, \frac{1}{2}\sqrt{13}, \sqrt{26}, \sqrt{10}, \sqrt{5} - \sqrt{13}$
39. $\sqrt{101}, 2\sqrt{2}, 2\sqrt{101}, \sqrt{2}, \sqrt{73}, \sqrt{145}, \sqrt{101} - 2\sqrt{2}$
41. $20\sqrt{3}\,\mathbf{i} + 20\mathbf{j}$ **43.** $-\dfrac{\sqrt{2}}{2}\mathbf{i} - \dfrac{\sqrt{2}}{2}\mathbf{j}$
45. $4\cos 10°\mathbf{i} + 4\sin 10°\mathbf{j} \approx 3.94\mathbf{i} + 0.69\mathbf{j}$
47. $5, 53.13°$ **49.** $13, 157.38°$ **51.** $2, 60°$ **53.** $15\sqrt{3}, -15$
55. $2\mathbf{i} - 3\mathbf{j}$ **57.** S $84.26°$ W **59.** (a) $40\mathbf{j}$ (b) $425\mathbf{i}$
(c) $425\mathbf{i} + 40\mathbf{j}$ (d) 427 mi/h, N $84.6°$ E
61. 794 mi/h, N $26.6°$ W **63.** (a) $10\mathbf{i}$ (b) $10\mathbf{i} + 17.32\mathbf{j}$
(c) $20\mathbf{i} + 17.32\mathbf{j}$ (d) 26.5 mi/h, N $49.1°$ E
65. (a) $22.8\mathbf{i} + 7.4\mathbf{j}$ (b) 7.4 mi/h, 22.8 mi/h
67. (a) $\langle 5, -3 \rangle$ (b) $\langle -5, 3 \rangle$ **69.** (a) $-4\mathbf{j}$ (b) $4\mathbf{j}$
71. (a) $\langle -7.57, 10.61 \rangle$ (b) $\langle 7.57, -10.61 \rangle$
73. $\mathbf{T}_1 \approx -56.5\mathbf{i} + 67.4\mathbf{j}, \mathbf{T}_2 \approx 56.5\mathbf{i} + 32.6\mathbf{j}$

SECTION 9.2 ■ PAGE 595

1. $a_1a_2 + b_1b_2$; real number or scalar **2.** $\dfrac{\mathbf{a} \cdot \mathbf{b}}{|\mathbf{a}||\mathbf{b}|}$; perpendicular

3. (a) $\dfrac{\mathbf{a} \cdot \mathbf{b}}{|\mathbf{b}|}$ (b) $\left(\dfrac{\mathbf{a} \cdot \mathbf{b}}{|\mathbf{b}|^2} \right)\mathbf{b}$

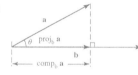

4. $\mathbf{F} \cdot \mathbf{D}$
5. (a) 2 (b) $45°$ **7.** (a) 13 (b) $56°$ **9.** (a) -1 (b) $97°$
11. (a) $5\sqrt{3}$ (b) $30°$ **13.** (a) 1 (b) $86°$ **15.** Yes **17.** No
19. Yes **21.** 9 **23.** -5 **25.** $-\frac{12}{5}$ **27.** -24
29. (a) $\langle 1, 1 \rangle$ (b) $\mathbf{u}_1 = \langle 1, 1 \rangle, \mathbf{u}_2 = \langle -3, 3 \rangle$
31. (a) $\langle -\frac{1}{2}, \frac{3}{2} \rangle$ (b) $\mathbf{u}_1 = \langle -\frac{1}{2}, \frac{3}{2} \rangle, \mathbf{u}_2 = \langle \frac{3}{2}, \frac{1}{2} \rangle$
33. (a) $\langle -\frac{18}{5}, \frac{24}{5} \rangle$ (b) $\mathbf{u}_1 = \langle -\frac{18}{5}, \frac{24}{5} \rangle, \mathbf{u}_2 = \langle \frac{28}{5}, \frac{21}{5} \rangle$
35. -28 **37.** 25 **45.** 16 ft-lb **47.** 8660 ft-lb **49.** 1164 lb
51. $23.6°$

SECTION 9.3 ■ PAGE 602

1. x, y, z; $(5, 2, 3)$; $y = 2$

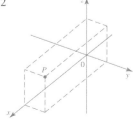

2. $\sqrt{(x_2 - x_1)^2 + (y_2 - y_1)^2 + (z_2 - z_1)^2};$
$\sqrt{38}; (x - 5)^2 + (y - 2)^2 + (z - 3)^2 = 9$

3. (a)

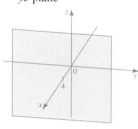

5. (a)

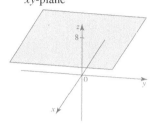

(b) $\sqrt{42}$ (b) $2\sqrt{29}$
7. Plane parallel to the **9.** Plane parallel to the
yz-plane xy-plane

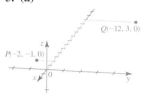

11. $(x - 2)^2 + (y + 5)^2 + (z - 3)^2 = 25$
13. $(x - 3)^2 + (y + 1)^2 + z^2 = 6$
15. Center: $(5, -1, -4)$, radius: $\sqrt{51}$
17. Center: $(6, 1, 0)$, radius: $\sqrt{37}$
19. (a) Circle, center: $(0, 2, -10)$, radius: $3\sqrt{11}$
(b) Circle, center: $(4, 2, -10)$, radius: $5\sqrt{3}$ **21.** (a) 3

SECTION 9.4 ■ PAGE 608

1. unit, $a_1\mathbf{i} + a_2\mathbf{j} + a_3\mathbf{k}$; $\sqrt{a_1^2 + a_2^2 + a_3^2}$; $4, (-2), 4, \langle 0, 7, -24 \rangle$
2. $\dfrac{\mathbf{u} \cdot \mathbf{v}}{|\mathbf{u}||\mathbf{v}|}$; 0; 0, perpendicular **3.** $\langle -1, -1, 5 \rangle$ **5.** $\langle -6, -2, 0 \rangle$
7. $(5, 4, -1)$ **9.** $(1, 0, -1)$ **11.** 3 **13.** $5\sqrt{2}$
15. $\langle 2, -3, 2 \rangle, \langle 2, -11, 4 \rangle, \langle 6, -23, \frac{19}{2} \rangle$
17. $\mathbf{i} - 2\mathbf{k}, \mathbf{i} + 2\mathbf{j} + 2\mathbf{k}, 3\mathbf{i} + \frac{7}{2}\mathbf{j} + \mathbf{k}$ **19.** $12\mathbf{i} + 2\mathbf{k}$
21. $3\mathbf{i} - 3\mathbf{j}$ **23.** (a) $\langle 3, 1, -2 \rangle$ (b) $3\mathbf{i} + \mathbf{j} - 2\mathbf{k}$ **25.** -4
27. 1 **29.** Yes **31.** No **33.** $116.4°$ **35.** $100.9°$
37. $\alpha \approx 65°, \beta \approx 56°, \gamma = 45°$ **39.** $\alpha \approx 73°, \beta \approx 65°, \gamma \approx 149°$
41. $\pi/4$ **43.** $125°$ **47.** (a) $-7\mathbf{i} - 24\mathbf{j} + 25\mathbf{k}$ (b) $25\sqrt{2}$

SECTION 9.5 ■ PAGE 615

1. $\begin{vmatrix} \mathbf{i} & \mathbf{j} & \mathbf{k} \\ a_1 & a_2 & a_3 \\ b_1 & b_2 & b_3 \end{vmatrix} = (a_2b_3 - a_3b_2)\mathbf{i} + (a_3b_1 - a_1b_3)\mathbf{j} + (a_1b_2 - a_2b_1)\mathbf{k}, -3\mathbf{i} + 2\mathbf{j} + 3\mathbf{k}$

2. perpendicular; perpendicular **3.** $9\mathbf{i} - 6\mathbf{j} + 3\mathbf{k}$
5. 0 **7.** $-4\mathbf{i} + 7\mathbf{j} - 3\mathbf{k}$ **9.** (a) $\langle 0, 2, 2 \rangle$ (b) $\left\langle 0, \dfrac{\sqrt{2}}{2}, \dfrac{\sqrt{2}}{2} \right\rangle$
11. (a) $14\mathbf{i} + 7\mathbf{j}$ (b) $\dfrac{2\sqrt{5}}{5}\mathbf{i} + \dfrac{\sqrt{5}}{5}\mathbf{j}$
13. $\dfrac{3\sqrt{3}}{2}$ **15.** 100 **17.** $\langle 0, 2, 2 \rangle$ **19.** $\langle 10, -10, 0 \rangle$ **21.** $4\sqrt{6}$
23. $\dfrac{5\sqrt{14}}{2}$ **25.** $\sqrt{14}$ **27.** $18\sqrt{3}$ **29.** (a) 0 (b) Yes

31. (a) 55 **(b)** No, 55 **33. (a)** -2 **(b)** No, 2
35. (a) $2{,}700{,}000\sqrt{3}$ **(b)** 4677 liters

SECTION 9.6 ■ PAGE 619

1. parametric; $x = x_0 + at$, $y = y_0 + bt$, $z = z_0 + ct$
2. $a(x - x_0) + b(y - y_0) + c(z - z_0) = 0$
3. $x = 1 + 3t$, $y = 2t$, $z = -2 - 3t$
5. $x = 3$, $y = 2 - 4t$, $z = 1 + 2t$
7. $x = 1 + 2t$, $y = 0$, $z = -2 - 5t$
9. $x = 1 + t$, $y = -3 + 4t$, $z = 2 - 3t$
11. $x = 1 - t$, $y = 1 + t$, $z = 2t$
13. $x = 3 + 4t$, $y = 7 - 4t$, $z = -5$
15. (a) $x + y - z = 5$ **(b)** x-intercept 5, y-intercept 5, z-intercept -5

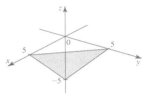

17. (a) $6x - z = 4$ **(b)** x-intercept $\frac{2}{3}$, no y-intercept, z-intercept -4

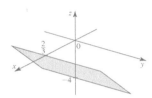

19. (a) $3x - y + 2z = -8$ **(b)** x-intercept $-\frac{8}{3}$, y-intercept 8, z-intercept -4

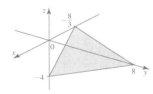

21. $5x - 3y - z = 35$ **23.** $x - 3y = 2$ **25.** $2x - 3y - 9z = 0$
27. $x = 2t$, $y = 5t$, $z = 4 - 4t$ **29.** $x = 2$, $y = -1 + t$, $z = 5$
31. $12x + 4y + 3z = 12$ **33.** $x - 2y + 4z = 0$

CHAPTER 9 REVIEW ■ PAGE 621

1. $\sqrt{13}$, $\langle 6, 4 \rangle$, $\langle -10, 2 \rangle$, $\langle -4, 6 \rangle$, $\langle -22, 7 \rangle$
3. $\sqrt{5}$, $3\mathbf{i} - \mathbf{j}$, $\mathbf{i} + 3\mathbf{j}$, $4\mathbf{i} + 2\mathbf{j}$, $4\mathbf{i} + 7\mathbf{j}$
5. $\langle 3, -4 \rangle$ **7.** 4, $120°$ **9.** $\langle 10, 10\sqrt{3} \rangle$
11. (a) $(4.8\mathbf{i} + 0.4\mathbf{j}) \times 10^4$ **(b)** 4.8×10^4 lb, N $85.2°$ E
13. 5, 25, 60 **15.** $2\sqrt{2}$, 8, 0 **17.** Yes **19.** No, $45°$
21. (a) $\dfrac{17\sqrt{37}}{37}$ **(b)** $\langle \frac{102}{37}, -\frac{17}{37} \rangle$
(c) $\mathbf{u}_1 = \langle \frac{102}{37}, -\frac{17}{37} \rangle$, $\mathbf{u}_2 = \langle \frac{9}{37}, \frac{54}{37} \rangle$
23. (a) $-\dfrac{14\sqrt{97}}{97}$ **(b)** $-\frac{56}{97}\mathbf{i} + \frac{126}{97}\mathbf{j}$
(c) $\mathbf{u}_1 = -\frac{56}{97}\mathbf{i} + \frac{126}{97}\mathbf{j}$, $\mathbf{u}_2 = \frac{153}{97}\mathbf{i} + \frac{68}{97}\mathbf{j}$

25. 3

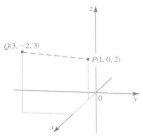

27. $x^2 + y^2 + z^2 = 36$
29. Center: $(1, 3, -2)$, radius: 4
31. 6, $\langle 6, 1, 3 \rangle$, $\langle 2, -5, 5 \rangle$, $\langle -1, -\frac{15}{2}, 5 \rangle$
33. (a) -1 **(b)** No, $92.8°$ **35. (a)** 0 **(b)** Yes
37. (a) $\langle -2, 17, -5 \rangle$ **(b)** $\left\langle -\dfrac{\sqrt{318}}{159}, \dfrac{17\sqrt{318}}{318}, -\dfrac{5\sqrt{318}}{318} \right\rangle$
39. (a) $\mathbf{i} + \mathbf{j} + 2\mathbf{k}$ **(b)** $\dfrac{\sqrt{6}}{6}\mathbf{i} + \dfrac{\sqrt{6}}{6}\mathbf{j} + \dfrac{\sqrt{6}}{3}\mathbf{k}$
41. $\frac{15}{2}$ **43.** 9 **45.** $x = 2 + 3t$, $y = t$, $z = -6$
47. $x = 6 - 2t$, $y = -2 + 3t$, $z = -3 + t$
49. $2x + 3y - 5z = 2$ **51.** $7x + 7y + 6z = 20$
53. $x = 2 - 2t$, $y = 0$, $z = -4t$

CHAPTER 9 TEST ■ PAGE 623

1. (a) **(b)** $-6\mathbf{i} + 10\mathbf{j}$ **(c)** $2\sqrt{34}$

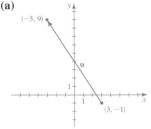

2. (a) $\langle 19, -3 \rangle$ **(b)** $5\sqrt{2}$ **(c)** 0 **(d)** Yes
3. (a) **(b)** 8, $150°$

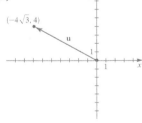

4. (a) $14\mathbf{i} + 6\sqrt{3}\mathbf{j}$ **(b)** 17.4 mi/h, N $53.4°$ E **5. (a)** $45.0°$
(b) $\dfrac{\sqrt{26}}{2}$ **(c)** $\frac{5}{2}\mathbf{i} - \frac{1}{2}\mathbf{j}$ **6.** 90 **7. (a)** 6
(b) $(x - 4)^2 + (y - 3)^2 + (z + 1)^2 = 36$
(c) $\langle 2, -4, 4 \rangle = 2\mathbf{i} - 4\mathbf{j} + 4\mathbf{k}$ **8. (a)** $11\mathbf{i} - 4\mathbf{j} - \mathbf{k}$ **(b)** $\sqrt{6}$
(c) -1 **(d)** $-3\mathbf{i} - 7\mathbf{j} - 5\mathbf{k}$ **(e)** $3\sqrt{35}$ **(f)** 18 **(g)** $96.3°$
9. $\left\langle \dfrac{7\sqrt{6}}{18}, \dfrac{\sqrt{6}}{9}, -\dfrac{\sqrt{6}}{18} \right\rangle$, $\left\langle -\dfrac{7\sqrt{6}}{18}, -\dfrac{\sqrt{6}}{9}, \dfrac{\sqrt{6}}{18} \right\rangle$

10. (a) $\langle 4, -3, 4 \rangle$ **(b)** $4x - 3y + 4z = 4$ **(c)** $\dfrac{\sqrt{41}}{2}$

11. $x = 2 - 2t, y = -4 + t, z = 7 - 2t$

CHAPTER 9 FOCUS ON MODELING ■ PAGE 626

1. 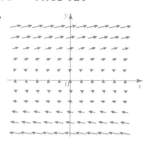 **3.**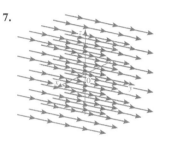

5. 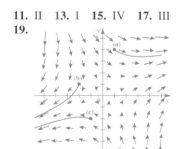 **7.**

9.

11. II **13.** I **15.** IV **17.** III
19.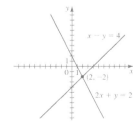

CUMULATIVE REVIEW TEST FOR CHAPTERS 8 AND 9 ■ PAGE 628

1. $(8\sqrt{2}, 7\pi/4), (-8\sqrt{2}, 3\pi/4)$
2. (a) 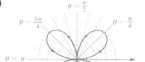   **(b)** $(x^2 + y^2)^{3/2} = 4xy$

3. (a) $z = 2\left(\cos \dfrac{11\pi}{6} + i \sin \dfrac{11\pi}{6} \right)$

(b) $zw = 12\left(\cos \dfrac{\pi}{4} + i \sin \dfrac{\pi}{4} \right) = 6\sqrt{2} + 6\sqrt{2}i$,
$z/w = \dfrac{1}{3}\left(\cos \dfrac{17\pi}{12} + i \sin \dfrac{17\pi}{12} \right)$

(c) $z^{10} = 1024\left(\cos \dfrac{\pi}{3} + i \sin \dfrac{\pi}{3} \right) = 512 + 512\sqrt{3}i$

(d) $\sqrt[3]{2}\left(\cos \dfrac{11\pi}{18} + i \sin \dfrac{11\pi}{18} \right)$, $\sqrt[3]{2}\left(\cos \dfrac{23\pi}{18} + i \sin \dfrac{23\pi}{18} \right)$,
$\sqrt[3]{2}\left(\cos \dfrac{35\pi}{18} + i \sin \dfrac{35\pi}{18} \right)$

4. (a) 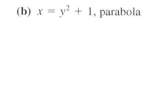   **(b)** $x = y^2 + 1$, parabola

5. (a) 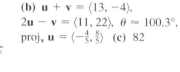   **(b)** $\mathbf{u} + \mathbf{v} = \langle 13, -4 \rangle$, $2\mathbf{u} - \mathbf{v} = \langle 11, 22 \rangle$, $\theta \approx 100.3°$, $\text{proj}_{\mathbf{v}} \mathbf{u} = \langle -\frac{4}{5}, \frac{8}{5} \rangle$ **(c)** 82

6. (a) 3 **(b)** $(x - 1)^2 + (y + 1)^2 + (z - 3)^2 = 9$
(c) $x = 1 + 2t, \quad y = -1 - t, \quad z = 3 - 2t$
7. (a) $\mathbf{a} \cdot \mathbf{b} = 0$, $\mathbf{a} \times \mathbf{b} = \langle 2, -13, -3 \rangle$, perpendicular
(b) $2x - 13y - 3z = 21$

CHAPTER 10

SECTION 10.1 ■ PAGE 638

1. x, y; equation; $(2, 1)$ **2.** substitution, elimination, graphical **3.** no, infinitely many **4.** infinitely many; $1 - t; (1, 0), (-3, 4), (5, -4)$ **5.** $(3, 2)$ **7.** $(3, 1)$
9. $(2, 1)$ **11.** $(1, 2)$ **13.** $(-2, 3)$
15. $(2, -2)$ **17.** No solution

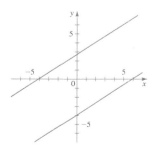

19. Infinitely many solutions

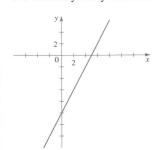

21. $(2, 2)$ **23.** $(3, -1)$ **25.** $(2, 1)$ **27.** $(3, 5)$ **29.** $(1, 3)$
31. $(10, -9)$ **33.** $(2, 1)$ **35.** No solution **37.** $(x, \frac{1}{3}x - \frac{5}{3})$
39. $(x, 3 - \frac{3}{2}x)$ **41.** $(-3, -7)$ **43.** $(x, 5 - \frac{5}{6}x)$ **45.** $(5, 10)$
47. No solution **49.** $(3.87, 2.74)$ **51.** $(61.00, 20.00)$
53. $\left(-\dfrac{1}{a-1}, \dfrac{1}{a-1} \right)$ **55.** $\left(\dfrac{1}{a+b}, \dfrac{1}{a+b} \right)$ **57.** 22, 12
59. 5 dimes, 9 quarters **61.** 200 gallons of regular gas, 80 gallons of premium gas **63.** Plane's speed 120 mi/h, wind speed 30 mi/h **65.** 200 g of A, 40 g of B **67.** 25%, 10%
69. \$14,000 at 5%, \$6,000 at 8% **71.** John $2\frac{1}{4}$ h, Mary $2\frac{1}{2}$ h
73. 25

SECTION 10.2 ▪ PAGE 646

1. $x + 3z = 1$ **2.** $-3; 4y - 5z = -4$ **3.** Linear **5.** Nonlinear
7. $(1, 3, 2)$ **9.** $(4, 0, 3)$ **11.** $(5, 2, -\frac{1}{2})$
13. $\begin{cases} x - 2y - z = 4 \\ \quad -y - 4z = 4 \\ 2x + y + z = 0 \end{cases}$ **15.** $\begin{cases} 2x - y + 3z = 2 \\ x + 2y - z = 4 \\ \quad 3y + 7z = 14 \end{cases}$
17. $(2, 1, -3)$ **19.** $(1, 2, 1)$ **21.** $(5, 0, 1)$ **23.** $(0, 1, 2)$
25. $(1 - 3t, 2t, t)$ **27.** No solution **29.** No solution
31. $(3 - t, -3 + 2t, t)$ **33.** $(2 - 2t, -\frac{2}{3} + \frac{4}{3}t, t)$
35. $(1, -1, 1, 2)$ **37.** \$30,000 in short-term bonds, \$30,000 in intermediate-term bonds, \$40,000 in long-term bonds
39. 250 acres corn, 500 acres wheat, 450 acres soybeans
41. Impossible **43.** 50 Midnight Mango, 60 Tropical Torrent, 30 Pineapple Power **45.** 1500 shares of A, 1200 shares of B, 1000 shares of C

SECTION 10.3 ▪ PAGE 659

1. dependent, inconsistent
2. $\begin{bmatrix} 1 & 1 & -1 & 1 \\ 1 & 0 & 2 & -3 \\ 0 & 2 & -1 & 3 \end{bmatrix}$
3. (a) x and y **(b)** dependent **(c)** $x = 3 + t, y = 5 - 2t, z = t$
4. (a) $x = 2, y = 1, z = 3$ **(b)** $x = 2 - t, y = 1 - t, z = t$
(c) No solution **5.** 3×2 **7.** 2×1 **9.** 1×3
11. (a) Yes **(b)** Yes **(c)** $\begin{cases} x = -3 \\ y = 5 \end{cases}$
13. (a) Yes **(b)** No **(c)** $\begin{cases} x + 2y + 8z = 0 \\ \quad y + 3z = 2 \\ \quad 0 = 0 \end{cases}$

15. (a) No **(b)** No **(c)** $\begin{cases} x \qquad\quad = 0 \\ \quad\quad 0 = 0 \\ y + 5z = 1 \end{cases}$
17. (a) Yes **(b)** Yes **(c)** $\begin{cases} x + 3y - \quad w = 0 \\ \quad z + 2w = 0 \\ \qquad\quad 0 = 1 \\ \qquad\quad 0 = 0 \end{cases}$
19. $(1, 1, 2)$ **21.** $(1, 0, 1)$ **23.** $(-1, 0, 1)$ **25.** $(-1, 5, 0)$
27. $(10, 3, -2)$ **29.** No solution **31.** $(2 - 3t, 3 - 5t, t)$
33. No solution **35.** $(-2t + 5, t - 2, t)$
37. $x = -\frac{1}{2}s + t + 6, y = s, z = t$ **39.** $(-2, 1, 3)$
41. No solution **43.** $(-9, 2, 0)$
45. $x = 5 - t, y = -3 + 5t, z = t$ **47.** $(0, -3, 0, -3)$
49. $(-1, 0, 0, 1)$ **51.** $x = \frac{1}{5}s - \frac{2}{3}t, y = \frac{1}{5}s + \frac{1}{3}t, z = s, w = t$
53. $\left(\frac{7}{4} - \frac{7}{4}t, -\frac{7}{4} + \frac{3}{4}t, \frac{9}{4} + \frac{3}{4}t, t \right)$ **55.** 2 VitaMax, 1 Vitron, 2 VitaPlus **57.** 5-mile run, 2-mile swim, 30-mile cycle
59. Impossible

SECTION 10.4 ▪ PAGE 669

1. dimension **2. (a)** columns, rows **(b)** (ii), (iii) **3.** (i), (ii)
4. $\begin{bmatrix} 4 & 9 & -7 \\ 7 & -7 & 0 \\ 4 & -5 & -5 \end{bmatrix}$ **5.** No **7.** $\begin{bmatrix} 1 & 3 \\ 1 & 5 \end{bmatrix}$ **9.** $\begin{bmatrix} 3 & 6 \\ 12 & -3 \\ 3 & 0 \end{bmatrix}$
11. Impossible **13.** $\begin{bmatrix} 5 & 2 & 1 \\ 7 & 10 & -7 \end{bmatrix}$ **15.** $\begin{bmatrix} -1 & -\frac{1}{2} \\ 1 & 2 \end{bmatrix}$
17. No solution **19.** $\begin{bmatrix} 0 & -5 \\ -25 & -20 \\ -10 & 10 \end{bmatrix}$ **21. (a)** $\begin{bmatrix} 5 & -2 & 5 \\ 1 & 1 & 0 \end{bmatrix}$
(b) Impossible **23. (a)** $\begin{bmatrix} 10 & -25 \\ 0 & 35 \end{bmatrix}$ **(b)** Impossible
25. (a) Impossible **(b)** $[14 \quad -14]$
27. (a) $\begin{bmatrix} -4 & 7 \\ 14 & -7 \end{bmatrix}$ **(b)** $\begin{bmatrix} 6 & -8 \\ 4 & -17 \end{bmatrix}$
29. (a) $\begin{bmatrix} 5 & -3 & 10 \\ 6 & 1 & 0 \\ -5 & 2 & 2 \end{bmatrix}$ **(b)** $\begin{bmatrix} -1 \\ 8 \\ -1 \end{bmatrix}$
31. (a) $\begin{bmatrix} 4 & -45 \\ 0 & 49 \end{bmatrix}$ **(b)** $\begin{bmatrix} 8 & -335 \\ 0 & 343 \end{bmatrix}$
33. (a) $\begin{bmatrix} 13 \\ -7 \end{bmatrix}$ **(b)** Impossible
35. $x = 2, y = -1$ **37.** $x = 1, y = -2$
39. $\begin{bmatrix} 2 & -5 \\ 3 & 2 \end{bmatrix}\begin{bmatrix} x \\ y \end{bmatrix} = \begin{bmatrix} 7 \\ 4 \end{bmatrix}$
41. $\begin{bmatrix} 3 & 2 & -1 & 1 \\ 1 & 0 & -1 & 0 \\ 0 & 3 & 1 & -1 \end{bmatrix}\begin{bmatrix} x_1 \\ x_2 \\ x_3 \\ x_4 \end{bmatrix} = \begin{bmatrix} 0 \\ 5 \\ 4 \end{bmatrix}$
43. Only ACB is defined. $ACB = \begin{bmatrix} -3 & -21 & 27 & -6 \\ -2 & -14 & 18 & -4 \end{bmatrix}$

45. (a) $[4{,}690 \quad 1{,}690 \quad 13{,}210]$ **(b)** Total revenue in Santa Monica, Long Beach, and Anaheim, respectively.

47. (a) $[105{,}000 \quad 58{,}000]$ **(b)** The first entry is the total amount (in ounces) of tomato sauce produced, and the second entry is the total amount (in ounces) of tomato paste produced.

49.

(a) $\begin{bmatrix} 1 & 0 & 1 & 0 & 1 & 1 \\ 0 & 3 & 0 & 1 & 2 & 1 \\ 1 & 2 & 0 & 0 & 3 & 0 \\ 1 & 3 & 2 & 3 & 2 & 0 \\ 0 & 3 & 0 & 0 & 2 & 1 \\ 1 & 2 & 0 & 1 & 3 & 1 \end{bmatrix}$
(b) $\begin{bmatrix} 2 & 1 & 2 & 1 & 2 & 2 \\ 1 & 3 & 1 & 2 & 3 & 2 \\ 2 & 3 & 1 & 1 & 3 & 1 \\ 2 & 3 & 3 & 3 & 3 & 1 \\ 1 & 3 & 1 & 1 & 3 & 2 \\ 2 & 3 & 1 & 2 & 3 & 2 \end{bmatrix}$

(c) $\begin{bmatrix} 2 & 3 & 2 & 3 & 2 & 2 \\ 3 & 0 & 3 & 2 & 1 & 2 \\ 2 & 1 & 3 & 3 & 0 & 3 \\ 2 & 0 & 1 & 0 & 1 & 3 \\ 3 & 0 & 3 & 3 & 1 & 2 \\ 2 & 1 & 3 & 2 & 0 & 2 \end{bmatrix}$

(d) $\begin{bmatrix} 3 & 3 & 3 & 3 & 3 & 3 \\ 3 & 0 & 3 & 3 & 0 & 3 \\ 3 & 0 & 3 & 3 & 0 & 3 \\ 3 & 0 & 0 & 0 & 0 & 3 \\ 3 & 0 & 3 & 3 & 0 & 3 \\ 3 & 0 & 3 & 3 & 0 & 3 \end{bmatrix}$
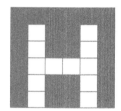

(e) The letter E

SECTION 10.5 ■ PAGE 680

1. (a) identity   **(b)** A, A   **(c)** inverse

2. (a) $\overset{A}{\begin{bmatrix} 5 & 3 \\ 3 & 2 \end{bmatrix}} \overset{X}{\begin{bmatrix} x \\ y \end{bmatrix}} = \overset{B}{\begin{bmatrix} 4 \\ 3 \end{bmatrix}}$ **(b)** $\begin{bmatrix} 2 & -3 \\ -3 & 5 \end{bmatrix}$

(c) $\overset{A^{-1}}{\begin{bmatrix} 2 & -3 \\ -3 & 5 \end{bmatrix}} \overset{B}{\begin{bmatrix} 4 \\ 3 \end{bmatrix}} = \overset{X}{\begin{bmatrix} x \\ y \end{bmatrix}}$ **(d)** $x = -1, y = 3$ **7.** $\begin{bmatrix} 1 & -2 \\ -\frac{3}{2} & \frac{7}{2} \end{bmatrix}$

9. $\begin{bmatrix} 3 & 5 \\ -2 & -3 \end{bmatrix}$ **11.** $\begin{bmatrix} 13 & 5 \\ -5 & -2 \end{bmatrix}$ **13.** No inverse

15. $\begin{bmatrix} 1 & 2 \\ -\frac{1}{2} & \frac{2}{3} \end{bmatrix}$ **17.** $\begin{bmatrix} -4 & -4 & 5 \\ 1 & 1 & -1 \\ 5 & 4 & -6 \end{bmatrix}$

19. No inverse   **21.** $\begin{bmatrix} -\frac{9}{2} & -1 & 4 \\ 3 & 1 & -3 \\ \frac{7}{2} & 1 & -3 \end{bmatrix}$

23. $\begin{bmatrix} 0 & 0 & -2 & 1 \\ -1 & 0 & 1 & 1 \\ 0 & 1 & -1 & 0 \\ 1 & 0 & 0 & -1 \end{bmatrix}$ **25.** $x = 12, y = -8$

27. $x = 126, y = -50$ **29.** $x = -38, y = 9, z = 47$
31. $x = -20, y = 10, z = 16$ **33.** $x = 3, y = 2, z = 1$
35. $x = 3, y = -2, z = 2$ **37.** $x = 8, y = 1, z = 0, w = 3$

39. $\begin{bmatrix} 7 & 2 & 3 \\ 10 & 3 & 5 \end{bmatrix}$ **41.** $\dfrac{1}{2a}\begin{bmatrix} 1 & 1 \\ -1 & 1 \end{bmatrix}$

43. $\begin{bmatrix} 1 & -\dfrac{1}{x} \\ -\dfrac{1}{x} & \dfrac{2}{x^2} \end{bmatrix}$; inverse does not exist for $x = 0$

45. $\dfrac{1}{2}\begin{bmatrix} 1 & e^{-x} & 0 \\ e^{-x} & -e^{-2x} & 0 \\ 0 & 0 & 1 \end{bmatrix}$; inverse exists for all x

47. (a) $\begin{bmatrix} 0 & 1 & -1 \\ -2 & \frac{3}{2} & 0 \\ 1 & -\frac{3}{2} & 1 \end{bmatrix}$ **(b)** 1 oz A, 1 oz B, 2 oz C

(c) 2 oz A, 0 oz B, 1 oz C   **(d)** No

49. (a) $\begin{cases} x + y + 2z = 675 \\ 2x + y + z = 600 \\ x + 2y + z = 625 \end{cases}$

(b) $\begin{bmatrix} 1 & 1 & 2 \\ 2 & 1 & 1 \\ 1 & 2 & 1 \end{bmatrix}\begin{bmatrix} x \\ y \\ z \end{bmatrix} = \begin{bmatrix} 675 \\ 600 \\ 625 \end{bmatrix}$ **(c)** $A^{-1} = \begin{bmatrix} -\frac{1}{4} & \frac{3}{4} & -\frac{1}{4} \\ -\frac{1}{4} & -\frac{1}{4} & \frac{3}{4} \\ \frac{3}{4} & -\frac{1}{4} & -\frac{1}{4} \end{bmatrix}$

She earns \$125 on a standard set, \$150 on a deluxe set, and \$200 on a leather-bound set.

SECTION 10.6 ■ PAGE 690

1. True   **2.** True   **3.** True   **4. (a)** $2 \cdot 4 - (-3) \cdot 1 = 11$
(b)
$+1(2 \cdot 4 - (-3) \cdot 1) - 0(3 \cdot 4 - 0 \cdot 1) + 2(3 \cdot (-3) - 0 \cdot 2) = -7$
5. 6   **7.** -4 **9.** Does not exist   **11.** $\frac{1}{8}$ **13.** 20, 20
15. $-12, 12$ **17.** 0, 0   **19.** 4, has an inverse
21. 5000, has an inverse   **23.** 0, does not have an inverse
25. -4, has an inverse   **27.** -18 **29.** 120   **31. (a)** -2
(b) -2 **(c)** Yes   **33.** $(-2, 5)$ **35.** $(0.6, -0.5)$ **37.** $(4, -1)$
39. $(4, 2, -1)$ **41.** $(1, 3, 2)$ **43.** $(0, -1, 1)$ **45.** $\left(\frac{189}{29}, -\frac{108}{29}, \frac{88}{29}\right)$
47. $\left(\frac{1}{2}, \frac{1}{4}, \frac{1}{4}, -1\right)$ **49.** $abcde$ **51.** 0, 1, 2   **53.** 1, -1 **55.** 21
57. $\frac{63}{2}$

61. (a) $\begin{cases} 100a + 10b + c = 25 \\ 225a + 15b + c = 33\frac{3}{4} \\ 1600a + 40b + c = 40 \end{cases}$

(b) $y = -0.05x^2 + 3x$

SECTION 10.7 ■ PAGE 697

1. (iii)   **2.** (ii)   **3.** $\dfrac{A}{x - 1} + \dfrac{B}{x + 2}$

5. $\dfrac{A}{x - 2} + \dfrac{B}{(x - 2)^2} + \dfrac{C}{x + 4}$ **7.** $\dfrac{A}{x - 3} + \dfrac{Bx + C}{x^2 + 4}$

9. $\dfrac{Ax + B}{x^2 + 1} + \dfrac{Cx + D}{x^2 + 2}$

11. $\dfrac{A}{x} + \dfrac{B}{2x - 5} + \dfrac{C}{(2x - 5)^2} + \dfrac{D}{(2x - 5)^3}$
$+ \dfrac{Ex + F}{x^2 + 2x + 5} + \dfrac{Gx + H}{(x^2 + 2x + 5)^2}$

13. $\dfrac{1}{x-1} - \dfrac{1}{x+1}$ **15.** $\dfrac{1}{x-1} - \dfrac{1}{x+4}$ **17.** $\dfrac{2}{x-3} - \dfrac{2}{x+3}$

19. $\dfrac{1}{x-2} - \dfrac{1}{x+2}$ **21.** $\dfrac{3}{x-4} - \dfrac{2}{x+2}$

23. $\dfrac{-\frac{1}{2}}{2x-1} + \dfrac{\frac{3}{2}}{4x-3}$ **25.** $\dfrac{2}{x-2} + \dfrac{3}{x+2} - \dfrac{1}{2x-1}$

27. $\dfrac{2}{x+1} - \dfrac{1}{x} + \dfrac{1}{x^2}$ **29.** $\dfrac{1}{2x+3} - \dfrac{3}{(2x+3)^2}$

31. $\dfrac{2}{x} - \dfrac{1}{x^3} - \dfrac{2}{x+2}$

33. $\dfrac{4}{x+2} - \dfrac{4}{x-1} + \dfrac{2}{(x-1)^2} + \dfrac{1}{(x-1)^3}$

35. $\dfrac{3}{x+2} - \dfrac{1}{(x+2)^2} - \dfrac{1}{(x+3)^2}$

37. $\dfrac{x+1}{x^2+3} - \dfrac{1}{x}$ **39.** $\dfrac{2x-5}{x^2+x+2} + \dfrac{5}{x^2+1}$

41. $\dfrac{1}{x^2+1} - \dfrac{x+2}{(x^2+1)^2} + \dfrac{1}{x}$ **43.** $x^2 + \dfrac{3}{x-2} - \dfrac{x+1}{x^2+1}$

45. $A = \dfrac{a+b}{2}, B = \dfrac{a-b}{2}$

SECTION 10.8 ■ PAGE 701

1. $(4, 8), (-2, 2)$ **3.** $(4, 16), (-3, 9)$
5. $(2, -2), (-2, 2)$ **7.** $(-25, 5), (-25, -5)$
9. $(-3, 4)\ (3, 4)$ **11.** $(-2, -1), (-2, 1), (2, -1), (2, 1)$
13. $(-1, \sqrt{2}), (-1, -\sqrt{2}), (\tfrac{1}{2}, \sqrt{\tfrac{7}{2}}), (\tfrac{1}{2}, -\sqrt{\tfrac{7}{2}})$
15. $(2, 4), (-\tfrac{5}{2}, \tfrac{7}{4})$ **17.** $(0, 0), (1, -1), (-2, -4)$
19. $(4, 0)$ **21.** $(-2, -2)$ **23.** $(6, 2), (-2, -6)$
25. No solution
27. $(\sqrt{5}, 2), (\sqrt{5}, -2), (-\sqrt{5}, 2), (-\sqrt{5}, -2)$
29. $(3, -\tfrac{1}{2}), (-3, -\tfrac{1}{2})$ **31.** $(\tfrac{1}{5}, \tfrac{1}{3})$
33. $(2.00, 20.00), (-8.00, 0)$ **35.** $(-4.51, 2.17), (4.91, -0.97)$
37. $(1.23, 3.87), (-0.35, -4.21)$
39. $(-2.30, -0.70), (0.48, -1.19)$ **41.** 12 cm by 15 cm
43. 15, 20 **45.** $(400.50, 200.25), 447.77$ m **47.** $(12, 8)$

SECTION 10.9 ■ PAGE 708

1. equation; $y = x + 1$; test

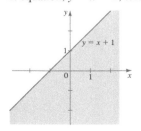

2. (a)

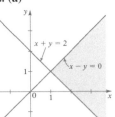

(b)

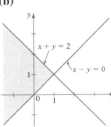

(c)

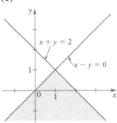

(d)

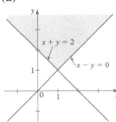

3.

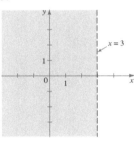

5.

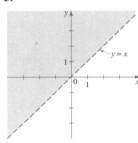

7.

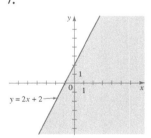

9.

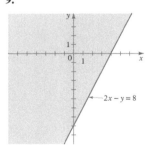

11.

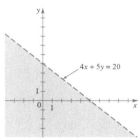

13.

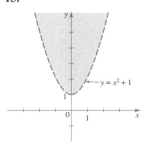

15.

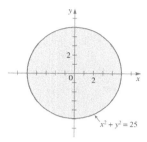

17. $y \leq \frac{1}{2}x - 1$ **19.** $x^2 + y^2 > 4$

21.

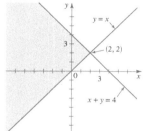

Not bounded

23.

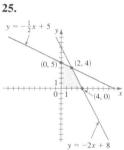

Not bounded

25.

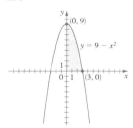

Bounded

27.

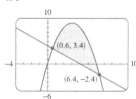

Bounded

29.

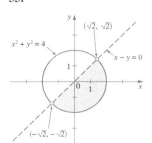

Bounded

31.

Bounded

33.

Bounded

35.

Bounded

37.

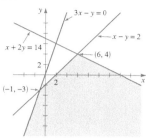

Not bounded

39.

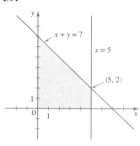

Bounded

41.

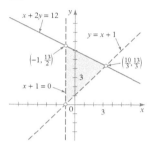

Bounded

43.

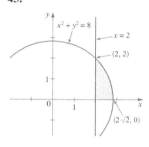

Bounded

45.

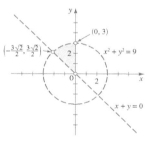

Bounded

47.

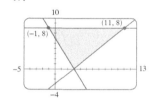

49.

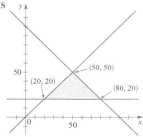

51. $x = $ number of fiction books
$y = $ number of nonfiction books

$$\begin{cases} x + y \leq 100 \\ 20 \leq y, \quad x \geq y \\ x \geq 0, \quad y \geq 0 \end{cases}$$

53. x = number of standard
    packages
y = number of deluxe
    packages
$\begin{cases} \frac{1}{4}x + \frac{5}{8}y \le 80 \\ \frac{3}{4}x + \frac{3}{8}y \le 90 \\ x \ge 0, \quad y \ge 0 \end{cases}$

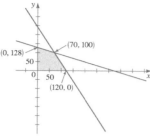

CHAPTER 10 REVIEW ■ PAGE 711

1. $(2, 1)$

3. x = any number
$y = \frac{2}{7}x - 4$

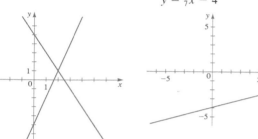

5. No solution

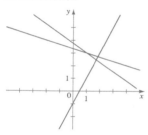

7. $(-3, 3), (2, 8)$ **9.** $\left(\frac{16}{7}, -\frac{14}{3}\right)$ **11.** $(21.41, -15.93)$
13. $(11.94, -1.39), (12.07, 1.44)$
15. (a) 2×3 **(b)** Yes **(c)** No
(d) $\begin{cases} x + 2y = -5 \\ \quad\quad y = \quad 3 \end{cases}$
17. (a) 3×4 **(b)** Yes **(c)** Yes
(d) $\begin{cases} x \quad + 8z = \quad 0 \\ \quad y + 5z = -1 \\ \quad\quad\quad 0 = \quad 0 \end{cases}$
19. (a) 3×4 **(b)** No **(c)** No
(d) $\begin{cases} \quad\quad y - 3z = 4 \\ x + \quad y \quad = 7 \\ x + 2y + \quad z = 2 \end{cases}$
21. $(1, 1, 2)$ **23.** No solution **25.** $(-8, -7, 10)$
27. No solution **29.** $(1, 0, 1, -2)$
31. $x = -4t + 1, y = -t - 1, z = t$
33. $x = 6 - 5t, y = \frac{1}{2}(7 - 3t), z = t$ **35.** $\left(-\frac{4}{3}t + \frac{4}{3}, \frac{5}{3}t - \frac{2}{3}, t\right)$
37. $(s + 1, 2s - t + 1, s, t)$ **39.** No solution
41. $(1, t + 1, t, 0)$ **43.** \$3000 at 6%, \$6000 at 7%
45. \$11,250 in bank A, \$22,500 in bank B, \$26,250 in bank C

47. Impossible **49.** $\begin{bmatrix} 4 & 18 \\ 4 & 0 \\ 2 & 2 \end{bmatrix}$

51. $\begin{bmatrix} 10 & 0 & -5 \end{bmatrix}$ **53.** $\begin{bmatrix} -\frac{7}{2} & 10 \\ 1 & -\frac{9}{2} \end{bmatrix}$ **55.** $\begin{bmatrix} 30 & 22 & 2 \\ -9 & 1 & -4 \end{bmatrix}$

57. $\begin{bmatrix} -\frac{1}{2} & \frac{11}{2} \\ \frac{15}{4} & -\frac{3}{2} \\ -\frac{1}{2} & 1 \end{bmatrix}$ **61.** $\frac{1}{3}\begin{bmatrix} -1 & -3 \\ -5 & 2 \end{bmatrix}$ **63.** $\begin{bmatrix} \frac{7}{2} & -2 \\ 0 & 8 \end{bmatrix}$

65. $\begin{bmatrix} 2 & -2 & 6 \\ -4 & 5 & -9 \end{bmatrix}$ **67.** $1, \begin{bmatrix} 9 & -4 \\ -2 & 1 \end{bmatrix}$ **69.** 0, no inverse

71. $-1, \begin{bmatrix} 3 & 2 & -3 \\ 2 & 1 & -2 \\ -8 & -6 & 9 \end{bmatrix}$ **73.** $24, \begin{bmatrix} 1 & 0 & 0 & -\frac{1}{4} \\ 0 & \frac{1}{2} & 0 & -\frac{1}{4} \\ 0 & 0 & \frac{1}{3} & -\frac{1}{4} \\ 0 & 0 & 0 & \frac{1}{4} \end{bmatrix}$

75. $(65, 154)$ **77.** $\left(-\frac{1}{12}, \frac{1}{12}, \frac{1}{12}\right)$ **79.** $\left(\frac{1}{5}, \frac{9}{5}\right)$ **81.** $\left(-\frac{87}{26}, \frac{21}{26}, \frac{3}{2}\right)$
83. 11 **85.** $\frac{2}{x - 5} + \frac{1}{x + 3}$ **87.** $\frac{-4}{x} + \frac{4}{x - 1} + \frac{-2}{(x - 1)^2}$
89. $\frac{-1}{x} + \frac{x + 2}{x^2 + 1}$
91. $(2, 1)$ **93.** $\left(-\frac{1}{2}, \frac{7}{4}\right), (2, -2)$ **95.** $x + y^2 \le 4$
97.

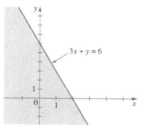

99.

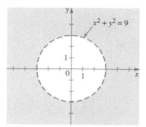

101.

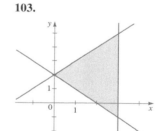

103.

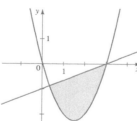

105.

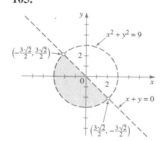

107.

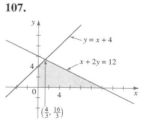

Bounded   Bounded

109. $x = \frac{b + c}{2}, y = \frac{a + c}{2}, z = \frac{a + b}{2}$ **111.** 2, 3

CHAPTER 10 TEST ▪ PAGE 714

1. **(a)** Linear　**(b)** $(-2, 3)$　**2.** **(a)** Nonlinear
(b) $(1, -2), \left(\frac{5}{3}, 0\right)$
3. $(-0.55, -0.78), (0.43, -0.29), (2.12, 0.56)$
4. Wind 60 km/h, airplane 300 km/h
5. **(a)** Row-echelon form　**(b)** Reduced row-echelon form
(c) Neither　**6.** **(a)** $\left(\frac{5}{2}, \frac{5}{2}, 0\right)$　**(b)** No solution
7. $\left(-\frac{3}{5} + \frac{2}{5}t, \frac{1}{5} + \frac{1}{5}t, t\right)$
8. Coffee $1.50, juice $1.75, donut $0.75
9. **(a)** Incompatible dimensions
(b) Incompatible dimensions

(c) $\begin{bmatrix} 6 & 10 \\ 3 & -2 \\ -3 & 9 \end{bmatrix}$　**(d)** $\begin{bmatrix} 36 & 58 \\ 0 & -3 \\ 18 & 28 \end{bmatrix}$　**(e)** $\begin{bmatrix} 2 & -\frac{3}{2} \\ -1 & 1 \end{bmatrix}$

(f) B is not square　**(g)** B is not square　**(h)** -3
10. **(a)** $\begin{bmatrix} 4 & -3 \\ 3 & -2 \end{bmatrix}\begin{bmatrix} x \\ y \end{bmatrix} = \begin{bmatrix} 10 \\ 30 \end{bmatrix}$　**(b)** $(70, 90)$

11. $|A| = 0, |B| = 2, B^{-1} = \begin{bmatrix} 1 & -2 & 0 \\ 0 & \frac{1}{2} & 0 \\ 3 & -6 & 1 \end{bmatrix}$

12. $(5, -5, -4)$
13. **(a)** $\dfrac{1}{x - 1} + \dfrac{1}{(x - 1)^2} - \dfrac{1}{x + 2}$　**(b)** $-\dfrac{1}{x} + \dfrac{x + 2}{x^2 + 3}$
14. **(a)**　**(b)**

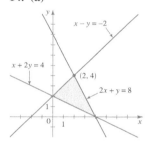

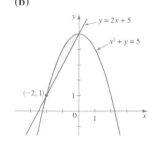

FOCUS ON MODELING ▪ PAGE 720

1. 198, 195
3.

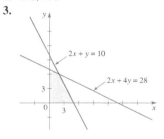

maximum 161
minimum 135

5. 3 tables, 34 chairs　**7.** 30 grapefruit crates, 30 orange crates
9. 15 Pasadena to Santa Monica, 3 Pasadena to El Toro, 0 Long
Beach to Santa Monica, 16 Long Beach to El Toro
11. 90 standard, 40 deluxe　**13.** $7500 in municipal bonds,
$2500 in bank certificates, $2000 in high-risk bonds
15. 4 games, 32 educational, 0 utility

CHAPTER 11

SECTION 11.1 ▪ PAGE 730

1. focus, directrix　**2.** $F(0, p), y = -p, F(0, 3), y = -3$
3. $F(p, 0), x = -p, F(3, 0), x = -3$

4. **(a)**　　　　　　**(b)**

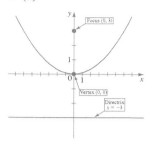

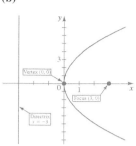

5. III　**7.** II　**9.** VI

Order of answers: focus; directrix; focal diameter

11. $F\left(0, \frac{9}{4}\right); y = -\frac{9}{4}; 9$　**13.** $F(1, 0); x = -1; 4$

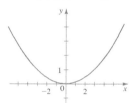

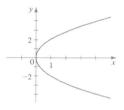

15. $F\left(0, \frac{1}{20}\right); y = -\frac{1}{20}; \frac{1}{5}$　**17.** $F\left(-\frac{1}{32}, 0\right); x = \frac{1}{32}; \frac{1}{8}$

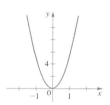

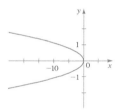

19. $F\left(0, -\frac{3}{2}\right); y = \frac{3}{2}; 6$　**21.** $F\left(-\frac{5}{12}, 0\right); x = \frac{5}{12}; \frac{5}{3}$

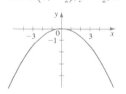

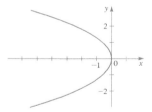

23.　　　　　　**25.**

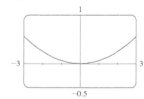

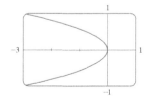

27.

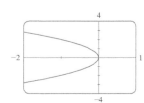

29. $x^2 = 8y$ **31.** $y^2 = -32x$ **33.** $y^2 = -8x$ **35.** $x^2 = 40y$
37. $y^2 = 4x$ **39.** $x^2 = 20y$ **41.** $x^2 = 8y$ **43.** $y^2 = -16x$
45. $y^2 = -3x$ **47.** $x = y^2$ **49.** $x^2 = -4\sqrt{2}y$
51. (a) $x^2 = -4py, p = \frac{1}{2}$, 1, 4, and 8

(b) The closer the directrix to the
vertex, the steeper the parabola.

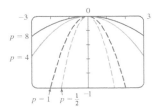

53. (a) $y^2 = 12x$ **(b)** $8\sqrt{15} \approx 31$ cm   **55.** $x^2 = 600y$

SECTION 11.2 ■ PAGE 738

1. sum; foci
2. $(a, 0), (-a, 0); c = \sqrt{a^2 - b^2}; (5, 0), (-5, 0), (3, 0), (-3, 0)$
3. $(0, a), (0, -a); c = \sqrt{a^2 - b^2}; (0, 5), (0, -5), (0, 3), (0, -3)$
4. (a)   **(b)**

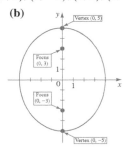

5. II   **7.** I

*Order of answers: vertices; foci; eccentricity; major axis
and minor axis*
9. $V(\pm 5, 0); F(\pm 4, 0);$ **11.** $V(0, \pm 3); F(0, \pm\sqrt{5});$
$\frac{4}{5}$; 10, 6 $\sqrt{5}/3$; 6, 4

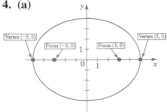

13. $V(\pm 4, 0); F(\pm 2\sqrt{3}, 0);$ **15.** $V(0, \pm\sqrt{3}); F(0, \pm\sqrt{3/2});$
$\sqrt{3}/2$; 8, 4 $1/\sqrt{2}; 2\sqrt{3}, \sqrt{6}$

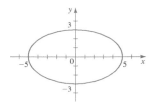

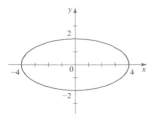

17. $V(\pm 1, 0); F(\pm\sqrt{3}/2, 0);$ **19.** $V(0, \pm\sqrt{2}); F(0, \pm\sqrt{3/2});$
$\sqrt{3}/2; 2, 1$ $\sqrt{3}/2; 2\sqrt{2}, \sqrt{2}$

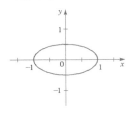

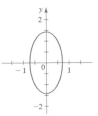

21. $V(0, \pm 1); F(0, \pm 1/\sqrt{2});$
$1/\sqrt{2}; 2, \sqrt{2}$

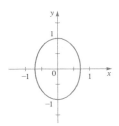

23. $\dfrac{x^2}{25} + \dfrac{y^2}{16} = 1$ **25.** $\dfrac{x^2}{4} + \dfrac{y^2}{8} = 1$ **27.** $\dfrac{x^2}{256} + \dfrac{y^2}{48} = 1$

29.   **31.**

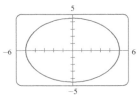

33. $\dfrac{x^2}{25} + \dfrac{y^2}{9} = 1$ **35.** $x^2 + \dfrac{y^2}{4} = 1$ **37.** $\dfrac{x^2}{9} + \dfrac{y^2}{13} = 1$

39. $\dfrac{x^2}{100} + \dfrac{y^2}{91} = 1$ **41.** $\dfrac{x^2}{25} + \dfrac{y^2}{5} = 1$ **43.** $\dfrac{64x^2}{225} + \dfrac{64y^2}{81} = 1$

45. $(0, \pm 2)$ **47.** $(\pm 1, 0)$

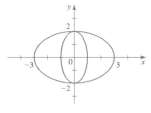

49. (a)   **(b)** Common major axes
and vertices; eccentricity
increases as k increases.

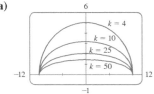

51. $\dfrac{x^2}{2.2500 \times 10^{16}} + \dfrac{y^2}{2.2491 \times 10^{16}} = 1$

53. $\dfrac{x^2}{1,455,642} + \dfrac{y^2}{1,451,610} = 1$

55. $5\sqrt{39}/2 \approx 15.6$ in.

SECTION 11.3 ▪ PAGE 747

1. difference; foci

2. $(-a, 0), (a, 0)$; $\sqrt{a^2 + b^2}$; $(-4, 0), (4, 0), (-5, 0), (5, 0)$

3. $(0, -a), (0, a)$; $\sqrt{a^2 + b^2}$; $(0, -4), (0, 4), (0, -5), (0, 5)$

4. (a)   **(b)**

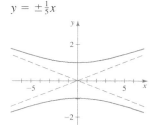

5. III   **7.** II

Order of answers: vertices; foci; asymptotes

9. $V(\pm 2, 0)$; $F(\pm 2\sqrt{5}, 0)$;   **11.** $V(0, \pm 1)$; $F(0, \pm\sqrt{26})$;
$y = \pm 2x$ $y = \pm\frac{1}{5}x$

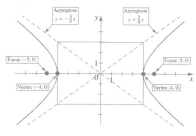

13. $V(\pm 1, 0)$; $F(\pm\sqrt{2}, 0)$;   **15.** $V(0, \pm 3)$; $F(0, \pm\sqrt{34})$;
$y = \pm x$ $y = \pm\frac{3}{5}x$

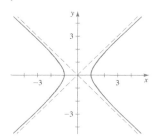

17. $V(\pm 2\sqrt{2}, 0)$; $F(\pm\sqrt{10}, 0)$;   **19.** $V(0, \pm\frac{1}{2})$; $F(0, \pm\sqrt{5}/2)$;
$y = \pm\frac{1}{2}x$ $y = \pm\frac{1}{2}x$

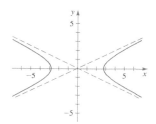
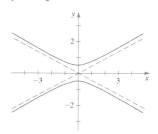

21. $\dfrac{x^2}{4} - \dfrac{y^2}{12} = 1$ **23.** $\dfrac{y^2}{16} - \dfrac{x^2}{16} = 1$ **25.** $\dfrac{x^2}{9} - \dfrac{4y^2}{9} = 1$

27.   **29.**

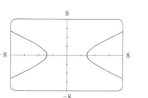

31. $\dfrac{x^2}{9} - \dfrac{y^2}{16} = 1$ **33.** $y^2 - \dfrac{x^2}{3} = 1$ **35.** $x^2 - \dfrac{y^2}{25} = 1$

37. $\dfrac{5y^2}{64} - \dfrac{5x^2}{256} = 1$ **39.** $\dfrac{x^2}{16} - \dfrac{y^2}{16} = 1$ **41.** $\dfrac{x^2}{9} - \dfrac{y^2}{16} = 1$

43. (b) $x^2 - y^2 = c^2/2$

47. (b)

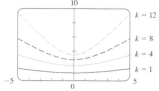

As k increases, the asymptotes get steeper.

49. $x^2 - y^2 = 2.3 \times 10^{19}$

SECTION 11.4 ▪ PAGE 755

1. (a) right; left   **(b)** upward; downward

2.

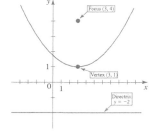

3.

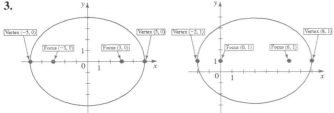

4.

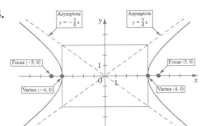

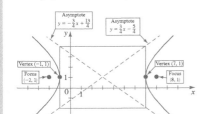

5. Center $C(2, 1)$;
foci $F(2 \pm \sqrt{5}, 1)$;
vertices $V_1(-1, 1)$, $V_2(5, 1)$;
major axis 6, minor axis 4

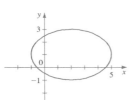

7. Center $C(0, -5)$;
foci $F_1(0, -1)$, $F_2(0, -9)$;
vertices $V_1(0, 0)$, $V_2(0, -10)$;
major axis 10, minor axis 6

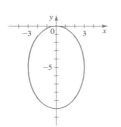

9. Vertex $V(3, -1)$;
focus $F(3, 1)$;
directrix $y = -3$

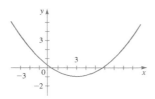

11. Vertex $V\left(-\frac{1}{2}, 0\right)$;
focus $F\left(-\frac{1}{2}, -\frac{1}{16}\right)$;
directrix $y = \frac{1}{16}$

13. Center $C(-1, 3)$;
foci $F_1(-6, 3)$, $F_2(4, 3)$;
vertices $V_1(-4, 3)$, $V_2(2, 3)$;
asymptotes
$y = \pm\frac{4}{3}(x + 1) + 3$

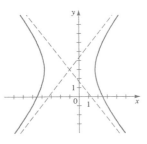

15. Center $C(-1, 0)$;
foci $F(-1, \pm\sqrt{5})$;
vertices $V(-1, \pm 1)$;
asymptotes $y = \pm\frac{1}{2}(x + 1)$

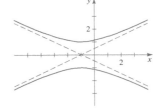

17. $x^2 = -\frac{1}{4}(y - 4)$ **19.** $\dfrac{(x - 5)^2}{25} + \dfrac{y^2}{16} = 1$

21. $(y - 1)^2 - x^2 = 1$

23. Parabola;
$V(-4, 4)$;
$F(-3, 4)$;
$x = -5$

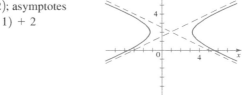

25. Hyperbola;
$C(1, 2)$; $F_1\left(-\frac{3}{2}, 2\right)$, $F_2\left(\frac{7}{2}, 2\right)$;
$V(1 \pm \sqrt{5}, 2)$; asymptotes
$y = \pm\frac{1}{2}(x - 1) + 2$

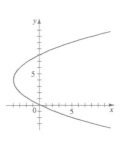

27. Ellipse; $C(3, -5)$;
$F(3 \pm \sqrt{21}, -5)$;
$V_1(-2, -5)$, $V_1(8, -5)$;
major axis 10,
minor axis 4

29. Hyperbola; $C(3, 0)$;
$F(3, \pm 5)$; $V(3, \pm 4)$;
asymptotes $y = \pm\frac{4}{3}(x - 3)$

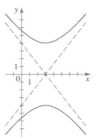

31. Degenerate conic
(pair of lines),
$y = \pm\frac{1}{2}(x - 4)$

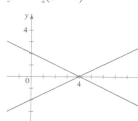

33. Point $(1, 3)$

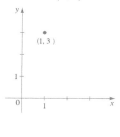

35.

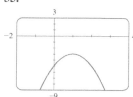

37.

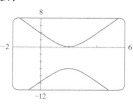

39. (a) $F < 17$ (b) $F = 17$ (c) $F > 17$
41. (a)

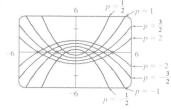

(c) The parabolas become narrower.
43. $\dfrac{(x + 150)^2}{18{,}062{,}500} + \dfrac{y^2}{18{,}040{,}000} = 1$

SECTION 11.5 ■ PAGE 764

1. $x = X \cos \phi - Y \sin \phi,\ y = X \sin \phi + Y \cos \phi$,
$X = x \cos \phi + y \sin \phi,\ Y = -x \sin \phi + y \cos \phi$
2. (a) conic section   (b) $(A - C)/B$
(c) $B^2 - 4AC$, parabola, ellipse, hyperbola   **3.** $\left(\sqrt{2}, 0\right)$
5. $\left(0, -2\sqrt{3}\right)$ **7.** $(1.6383, 1.1472)$
9. $X^2 + \sqrt{3}XY + 2 = 0$
11. $7Y^2 - 48XY - 7X^2 - 40X - 30Y = 0$
13. $X^2 - Y^2 = 2$
15. (a) Hyberbola   (b) $X^2 - Y^2 = 16$
(c) $\phi = 45°$

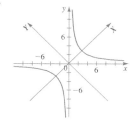

17. (a) Hyberbola
(b) $Y^2 - X^2 = 1$
(c) $\phi = 30°$

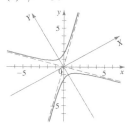

19. (a) Hyberbola
(b) $\dfrac{X^2}{4} - Y^2 = 1$
(c) $\phi \approx 53°$

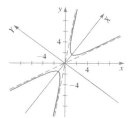

21. (a) Hyberbola
(b) $3X^2 - Y^2 = 2\sqrt{3}$
(c) $\phi = 30°$

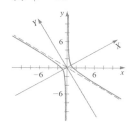

23. (a) Parabola
(b) $Y = \sqrt{2}X^2$
(c) $\phi = 45°$

25. (a) Hyberbola
(b) $(X - 1)^2 - 3Y^2 = 1$
(c) $\phi = 60°$

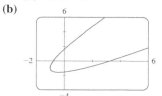

27. (a) Ellipse
(b) $X^2 + \dfrac{(Y + 1)^2}{4} = 1$
(c) $\phi \approx 53°$

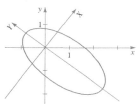

29. (a) Parabola
(b)

31. (a) Hyperbola
(b)

33. (a) $(X - 5)^2 - Y^2 = 1$
(b) *XY*-coordinates:
$C(5, 0)$; $V_1(6, 0)$, $V_2(4, 0)$; $F(5 \pm \sqrt{2}, 0)$;
xy-coordinates:
$C(4, 3)$; $V_1\left(\frac{24}{5}, \frac{18}{5}\right)$, $V_2\left(\frac{16}{5}, \frac{12}{5}\right)$; $F_1\left(4 + \frac{4}{5}\sqrt{2}, 3 + \frac{3}{5}\sqrt{2}\right)$,
$F_2\left(4 - \frac{4}{5}\sqrt{2}, 3 - \frac{3}{5}\sqrt{2}\right)$
(c) $Y = \pm(X - 5)$; $7x - y - 25 = 0$, $x + 7y - 25 = 0$
35. $X = x \cos\phi + y \sin\phi$; $Y = -x \sin\phi + y \cos\phi$

SECTION 11.6 ■ PAGE 770

1. focus, directrix; $\dfrac{\text{distance from } P \text{ to } F}{\text{distance from } P \text{ to } \ell}$, conic section; parabola, ellipse, hyperbola, eccentricity

2. $\dfrac{ed}{1 \pm e \cos\theta}$, $\dfrac{ed}{1 \pm e \sin\theta}$

3. $r = 6/(3 + 2\cos\theta)$

5. $r = 2/(1 + \sin\theta)$

7. $r = 20/(1 + 4\cos\theta)$

9. $r = 10/(1 + \sin\theta)$

11. II **13.** VI **15.** IV

17.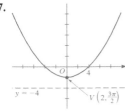

19.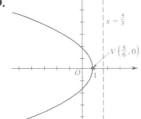

21. (a), (b)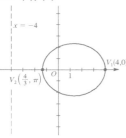

23. (a), (b)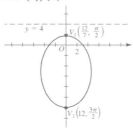

(c) $C\left(\frac{4}{3}, 0\right)$, major axis: $\frac{16}{3}$, minor axis: $\frac{8\sqrt{3}}{3}$

(c) $C\left(\frac{36}{7}, \frac{3\pi}{2}\right)$, major axis: $\frac{96}{7}$, minor axis: $\frac{24\sqrt{7}}{7}$

25. (a), (b)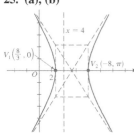

27. (a), (b)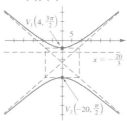

(c) $\left(\frac{16}{3}, 0\right)$

(c) $\left(12, \frac{3\pi}{2}\right)$

29. (a) 3, hyperbola
(b)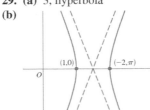

31. (a) 1, parabola
(b)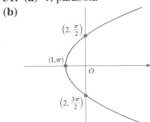

33. (a) $\frac{1}{2}$, ellipse
(b)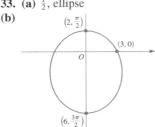

35. (a) $\frac{5}{2}$, hyperbola
(b)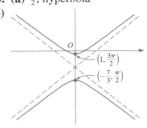

37. (a) eccentricity $\frac{3}{4}$, directrix $x = -\frac{1}{3}$
(b) $r = \dfrac{1}{4 - 3\cos\left(\theta - \frac{\pi}{3}\right)}$
(c)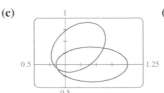

39. (a) eccentricity 1, directrix $y = 2$
(b) $r = \dfrac{2}{1 + \sin\left(\theta + \frac{\pi}{4}\right)}$
(c)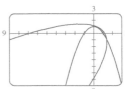

41. The ellipse is nearly circular when e is close to 0 and becomes more elongated as $e \to 1^-$. At $e = 1$, the curve becomes a parabola.

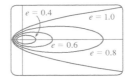

43. (b) $r = (1.49 \times 10^8)/(1 - 0.017\cos\theta)$
45. 0.25

CHAPTER 11 REVIEW ■ PAGE 773

1. $V(0, 0)$; $F(1, 0)$; $x = -1$

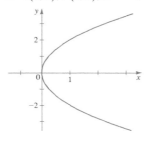

3. $V(0, 0)$; $F(0, -2)$; $y = 2$

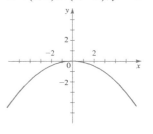

5. $V(-2, 2)$; $F\left(-\frac{7}{4}, 2\right)$; $x = -\frac{9}{4}$

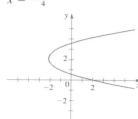

7. $V(-2, -3)$; $F(-2, -2)$; $y = -4$

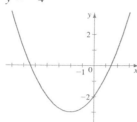

23. $C(-3, -1)$; $V(-3, -1 \pm \sqrt{2})$; $F(-3, -1 \pm 2\sqrt{5})$; asymptotes $y = \frac{1}{3}x$, $y = -\frac{1}{3}x - 2$

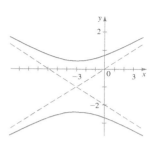

9. $C(0, 0)$; $V(0, \pm 5)$; $F(0, \pm 4)$; axes 10, 6

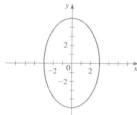

11. $C(0, 0)$; $V(\pm 4, 0)$; $F(\pm 2\sqrt{3}, 0)$; axes 8, 4

25. $y^2 = 8x$ **27.** $\dfrac{y^2}{16} - \dfrac{x^2}{9} = 1$ **29.** $\dfrac{(x-4)^2}{16} + \dfrac{(y-2)^2}{4} = 1$

31. Parabola; $F(0, -2)$; $V(0, 1)$

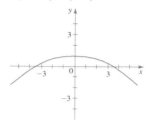

13. $C(3, 0)$; $V(3, \pm 4)$; $F(3, \pm\sqrt{7})$; axes 8, 6

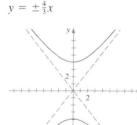

15. $C(0, 2)$; $V(\pm 3, 2)$; $F(\pm\sqrt{5}, 2)$; axes 6, 4

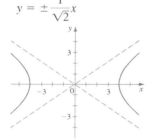

33. Hyperbola; $F(0, \pm 12\sqrt{2})$; $V(0, \pm 12)$

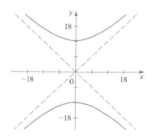

17. $C(0, 0)$; $V(0, \pm 4)$; $F(0, \pm 5)$; asymptotes $y = \pm\frac{4}{3}x$

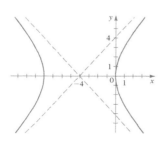

19. $C(0, 0)$; $V(\pm 4, 0)$; $F(\pm 2\sqrt{6}, 0)$; asymptotes $y = \pm\dfrac{1}{\sqrt{2}}x$

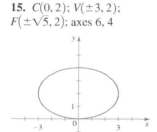

35. Ellipse; $F(1, 4 \pm \sqrt{15})$; $V(1, 4 \pm 2\sqrt{5})$

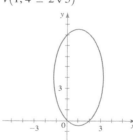

37. Parabola; $F\left(-\frac{255}{4}, 8\right)$; $V(-64, 8)$

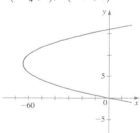

21. $C(-4, 0)$; $V_1(-8, 0)$, $V_2(0, 0)$; $F(-4 \pm 4\sqrt{2}, 0)$; asymptotes $y = \pm(x + 4)$

39. Ellipse; $F(3, -3 \pm 1/\sqrt{2})$; $V_1(3, -4)$, $V_2(3, -2)$

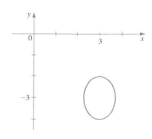

41. Has no graph

43. $x^2 = 4y$ **45.** $\dfrac{y^2}{4} - \dfrac{x^2}{16} = 1$

47. $\dfrac{(x-1)^2}{3} + \dfrac{(y-2)^2}{4} = 1$

49. $\dfrac{4(x-7)^2}{225} + \dfrac{(y-2)^2}{100} = 1$

51. (a) 91,419,000 mi   **(b)** 94,581,000 mi

53. (a)

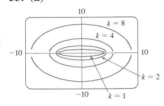

55. (a) Hyperbola   **(b)** $3X^2 - Y^2 = 1$
(c) $\phi = 45°$

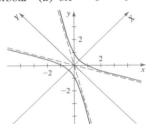

57. (a) Ellipse
(b) $(X-1)^2 + 4Y^2 = 1$
(c) $\phi = 30°$

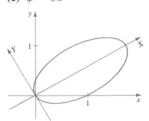

59. Ellipse

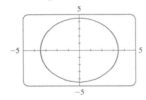

61. Parabola

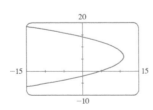

63. (a) $e = 1$, parabola
(b)

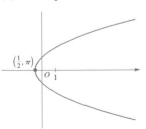

65. (a) $e = 2$, hyperbola

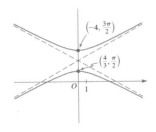

CHAPTER 11 TEST ▪ PAGE 775

1. $F(0, -3), y = 3$

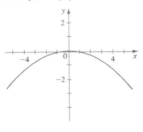

2. $V(\pm 4, 0); F(\pm 2\sqrt{3}, 0); 8, 4$

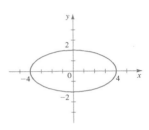

3. $V(0, \pm 3); F(0, \pm 5); y = \pm\frac{3}{4}x$

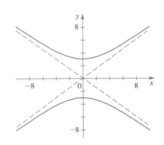

4. $y^2 = -x$ **5.** $\dfrac{x^2}{16} + \dfrac{(y-3)^2}{9} = 1$ **6.** $(x-2)^2 - \dfrac{y^2}{3} = 1$

7. $\dfrac{(x-3)^2}{9} + \dfrac{(y+\frac{1}{2})^2}{4} = 1$ **8.** $\dfrac{(x+2)^2}{8} - \dfrac{(y-4)^2}{9} = 1$

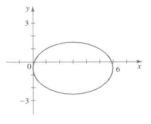   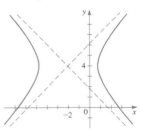

9. $(y+4)^2 = -2(x-4)$

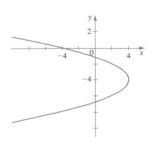

10. $\dfrac{y^2}{9} - \dfrac{x^2}{16} = 1$ **11.** $x^2 - 4x - 8y + 20 = 0$ **12.** $\frac{3}{4}$ in.

13. (a) Ellipse   **(b)** $\dfrac{X^2}{3} + \dfrac{Y^2}{18} = 1$

(c) $\phi \approx 27°$

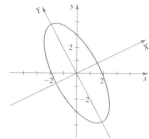

(d) $\left(-3\sqrt{2/5}, 6\sqrt{2/5}\right), \left(3\sqrt{2/5}, -6\sqrt{2/5}\right)$

14. (a) $r = \dfrac{1}{1 + 0.5\cos\theta}$

(b) Ellipse

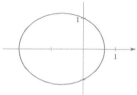

FOCUS ON MODELING ▪ PAGE 778

5. (c) $x^2 - mx + (ma - a^2) = 0$,
discriminant $m^2 - 4ma + 4a^2 = (m - 2a)^2, m = 2a$

CUMULATIVE REVIEW TEST FOR CHAPTERS 10 AND 11 ▪ PAGE 780

1. (a) Nonlinear   **(b)** $(0,0), (2,2), (-2,2)$ **(c)** Circle, parabola   **(d), (e)**

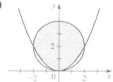

2. (a) $(3, 0, 1)$ **(b)** $x = t - 1, y = t + 2, z = t$
3. Xavier 4, Yolanda 10, Zachary 6
4. (a) $A + B$ impossible; $C - D =$
$\begin{bmatrix} 0 & -4 & -2 \\ -1 & -4 & -4 \\ -1 & -1 & -1 \end{bmatrix}$; $AB = \begin{bmatrix} -\frac{9}{2} & 1 & 5 \\ -4 & 2 & 0 \end{bmatrix}$; CB impossible;

$BD = \begin{bmatrix} -1 & -2 & -1 \\ -\frac{1}{2} & -1 & -\frac{1}{2} \end{bmatrix}$; $\det(B)$ impossible; $\det(C) = 2$;
$\det(D) = 0$

(b) $C^{-1} = \begin{bmatrix} 0 & 0 & -1 \\ -\frac{1}{2} & \frac{1}{2} & -\frac{1}{2} \\ 1 & 0 & 1 \end{bmatrix}$ **5. (a)** $\begin{bmatrix} 5 & -3 \\ 6 & -4 \end{bmatrix}\begin{bmatrix} x \\ y \end{bmatrix} = \begin{bmatrix} 5 \\ 0 \end{bmatrix}$

(b) $\begin{bmatrix} 2 & -\frac{3}{2} \\ 3 & -\frac{5}{2} \end{bmatrix}$ **(c)** $X = \begin{bmatrix} 10 \\ 15 \end{bmatrix}$ **(d)** $x = 10, y = 15$

6. $\dfrac{1}{x} + \dfrac{2}{x^2} - \dfrac{x+2}{x^2+4}$ **7.** $x^2 = 12y$

8. (a)

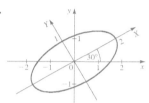

$F_1(0, 3 + \sqrt{5}), F_2(0, 3 - \sqrt{5})$, ellipse

(b)

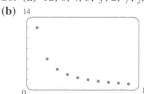

$F_1(0, 0), F_2(8, \pi)$, hyperbola

9. $\dfrac{(x-5)^2}{16} - \dfrac{y^2}{9} = 1$ **10.**

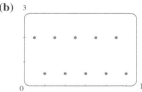

CHAPTER 12

SECTION 12.1 ▪ PAGE 792

1. the natural numbers   **2.** n; $1^2 + 2^2 + 3^2 + 4^2 = 30$
3. 2, 3, 4, 5; 101   **5.** $\frac{1}{2}, \frac{1}{3}, \frac{1}{4}, \frac{1}{5}; \frac{1}{101}$ **7.** $-1, \frac{1}{4}, -\frac{1}{9}, \frac{1}{16}; \frac{1}{10,000}$
9. 0, 2, 0, 2; 2   **11.** 1, 4, 27, 256; 100^{100} **13.** 3, 2, 0, -4, -12
15. 1, 3, 7, 15, 31   **17.** 1, 2, 3, 5, 8
19. (a) 7, 11, 15, 19, 23, 27, 31, 35, 39, 43
(b)

21. (a) $12, 6, 4, 3, \frac{12}{5}, 2, \frac{12}{7}, \frac{3}{2}, \frac{4}{3}, \frac{6}{5}$
(b)

23. (a) $2, \frac{1}{2}, 2, \frac{1}{2}, 2, \frac{1}{2}, 2, \frac{1}{2}, 2, \frac{1}{2}$
(b)

25. 2^n **27.** $3n - 2$ **29.** $(2n - 1)/n^2$ **31.** $1 + (-1)^n$

33. $1, 4, 9, 16, 25, 36$ **35.** $\frac{1}{3}, \frac{4}{9}, \frac{13}{27}, \frac{40}{81}, \frac{121}{243}, \frac{364}{729}$

37. $\frac{2}{3}, \frac{8}{9}, \frac{26}{27}, \frac{80}{81}$; $S_n = 1 - \dfrac{1}{3^n}$

39. $1 - \sqrt{2}, 1 - \sqrt{3}, -1, 1 - \sqrt{5}$; $S_n = 1 - \sqrt{n + 1}$

41. 10 **43.** $\frac{11}{6}$ **45.** 8 **47.** 31 **49.** 385 **51.** $46{,}438$

53. 22 **55.** $\sqrt{1} + \sqrt{2} + \sqrt{3} + \sqrt{4} + \sqrt{5}$

57. $\sqrt{4} + \sqrt{5} + \sqrt{6} + \sqrt{7} + \sqrt{8} + \sqrt{9} + \sqrt{10}$

59. $x^3 + x^4 + \cdots + x^{100}$ **61.** $\displaystyle\sum_{k=1}^{100} k$ **63.** $\displaystyle\sum_{k=1}^{10} k^2$

65. $\displaystyle\sum_{k=1}^{999} \frac{1}{k(k + 1)}$ **67.** $\displaystyle\sum_{k=0}^{100} x^k$ **69.** $2^{(2^n - 1)/2^n}$

71. (a) $2004.00, 2008.01, 2012.02, 2016.05, 2020.08, 2024.12$
(b) $\$2149.16$
73. (a) $35{,}700, 36{,}414, 37{,}142, 37{,}885, 38{,}643$ **(b)** $42{,}665$
75. (b) 6898 **77. (a)** $S_n = S_{n-1} + 2000$ **(b)** $\$38{,}000$

SECTION 12.2 ▪ PAGE 798

1. difference **2.** common difference; $2, 5$ **3.** True **4.** True
5. (a) $5, 7, 9, 11, 13$ **7. (a)** $\frac{5}{2}, \frac{3}{2}, \frac{1}{2}, -\frac{1}{2}, -\frac{3}{2}$
(b) 2 **(b)** -1
(c)

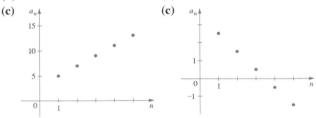

9. $a_n = 3 + 5(n - 1), a_{10} = 48$
11. $a_n = \frac{5}{2} - \frac{1}{2}(n - 1), a_{10} = -2$

13. Arithmetic, 3 **15.** Not arithmetic **17.** Arithmetic, $-\frac{3}{2}$
19. Arithmetic, 1.7
21. $11, 18, 25, 32, 39$; 7; $a_n = 11 + 7(n - 1)$
23. $\frac{1}{3}, \frac{1}{5}, \frac{1}{7}, \frac{1}{9}, \frac{1}{11}$; not arithmetic
25. $-4, 2, 8, 14, 20$; 6; $a_n = -4 + 6(n - 1)$
27. $3, a_5 = 14, a_n = 2 + 3(n - 1), a_{100} = 299$
29. $5, a_5 = 24, a_n = 4 + 5(n - 1), a_{100} = 499$
31. $4, a_5 = 4, a_n = -12 + 4(n - 1), a_{100} = 384$
33. $1.5, a_5 = 31, a_n = 25 + 1.5(n - 1), a_{100} = 173.5$
35. $s, a_5 = 2 + 4s, a_n = 2 + (n - 1)s, a_{100} = 2 + 99s$
37. $\frac{1}{2}$ **39.** $-100, -98, -96$ **41.** 30th
43. 100 **45.** 460 **47.** 1090 **49.** $20{,}301$ **51.** 832.3
53. 46.75 **57.** Yes **59.** 50 **61.** $\$1250$
63. $\$403{,}500$ **65.** 20 **67.** 78

SECTION 12.3 ▪ PAGE 805

1. ratio **2.** common ratio; $2, 5$ **3.** True **4. (a)** $a\left(\dfrac{1 - r^n}{1 - r}\right)$

(b) geometric; converges, $a/(1 - r)$; diverges

5. (a) $5, 10, 20, 40, 80$ **7. (a)** $\frac{5}{2}, -\frac{5}{4}, \frac{5}{8}, -\frac{5}{16}, \frac{5}{32}$
(b) 2 **(b)** $-\frac{1}{2}$
(c)   **(c)**

9. $a_n = 3 \cdot 5^{n-1}, a_4 = 375$ **11.** $a_n = \frac{5}{2}\left(-\frac{1}{2}\right)^{n-1}, a_4 = -\frac{5}{16}$
13. Geometric, 2 **15.** Geometric, $\frac{1}{2}$
17. Not geometric **19.** Geometric, 1.1
21. $6, 18, 54, 162, 486$; geometric, common ratio 3;
$a_n = 6 \cdot 3^{n-1}$
23. $\frac{1}{4}, \frac{1}{16}, \frac{1}{64}, \frac{1}{256}, \frac{1}{1024}$; geometric, common ratio $\frac{1}{4}$; $a_n = \frac{1}{4}\left(\frac{1}{4}\right)^{n-1}$
25. $0, \ln 5, 2 \ln 5, 3 \ln 5, 4 \ln 5$; not geometric
27. $3, a_5 = 162, a_n = 2 \cdot 3^{n-1}$
29. $-0.3, a_5 = 0.00243, a_n = (0.3)(-0.3)^{n-1}$
31. $-\frac{1}{12}, a_5 = \frac{1}{144}, a_n = 144\left(-\frac{1}{12}\right)^{n-1}$
33. $3^{2/3}, a_5 = 3^{11/3}, a_n = 3^{(2n+1)/3}$
35. $s^{2/7}, a_5 = s^{8/7}, a_n = s^{2(n-1)/7}$
37. $\frac{1}{2}$ **39.** $\frac{25}{4}$ **41.** 11th **43.** 315 **45.** 441
47. 3280
49. $\frac{6141}{1024}$ **51.** $\frac{3}{2}$ **53.** $\frac{3}{4}$ **55.** divergent
57. 2 **59.** divergent **61.** $\sqrt{2} + 1$ **63.** $\frac{7}{9}$ **65.** $\frac{1}{33}$
67. $\frac{112}{999}$ **69.** $10, 20, 40$
71. (a) $V_n = 160{,}000(0.80)^{n-1}$ **(b)** 4th year
73. 19 ft, $80\left(\frac{3}{4}\right)^n$ **75.** $\frac{64}{25}, \frac{1024}{625}, 5\left(\frac{4}{5}\right)^n$
77. (a) $17\frac{8}{9}$ ft **(b)** $18 - \left(\frac{1}{3}\right)^{n-3}$
79. 2801 **81.** 3 m
83. (a) 2 **(b)** $8 + 4\sqrt{2}$ **85.** 1

SECTION 12.4 ▪ PAGE 812

1. amount **2.** present value **3.** $\$13{,}180.79$
5. $\$360{,}262.21$ **7.** $\$5{,}591.79$ **9.** $\$572.34$
11. $\$13{,}007.94$ **13.** $\$2{,}601.59$ **15.** $\$307.24$
17. $\$733.76, \$264{,}153.60$
19. $\$583{,}770.65$
21. $\$9020.60$
23. (a) $\$859.15$ **(b)** $\$309{,}294.00$ **(c)** $\$1{,}841{,}519.29$
25. 18.16% **27.** 11.68%

SECTION 12.5 ▪ PAGE 819

1. natural; $P(1)$ **2.** (ii)
3. Let $P(n)$ denote the statement $2 + 4 + \cdots + 2n = n(n + 1)$.

Step 1 $P(1)$ is true, since $2 = 1(1 + 1)$.
Step 2 Suppose $P(k)$ is true. Then

$$2 + 4 + \cdots + 2k + 2(k + 1)$$
$$= k(k + 1) + 2(k + 1) \qquad \text{Induction hypothesis}$$
$$= (k + 1)(k + 2)$$

So $P(k + 1)$ follows from $P(k)$. Thus by the Principle of Mathematical Induction $P(n)$ holds for all n.

5. Let $P(n)$ denote the statement

$$5 + 8 + \cdots + (3n + 2) = \frac{n(3n + 7)}{2}.$$

Step 1 $P(1)$ is true, since $5 = \dfrac{1(3 \cdot 1 + 7)}{2}$

Step 2 Suppose $P(k)$ is true. Then

$$5 + 8 + \cdots + (3k + 2) + [3(k + 1) + 2]$$

$$= \frac{k(3k + 7)}{2} + (3k + 5) \qquad \text{Induction hypothesis}$$

$$= \frac{3k^2 + 13k + 10}{2}$$

$$= \frac{(k + 1)[3(k + 1) + 7]}{2}$$

So $P(k + 1)$ follows from $P(k)$. Thus by the Principle of Mathematical Induction $P(n)$ holds for all n.

7. Let $P(n)$ denote the statement

$$1 \cdot 2 + 2 \cdot 3 + \cdots + n(n + 1) = \frac{n(n + 1)(n + 2)}{3}.$$

Step 1 $P(1)$ is true, since $1 \cdot 2 = \dfrac{1 \cdot (1 + 1) \cdot (1 + 2)}{3}.$

Step 2 Suppose $P(k)$ is true. Then

$$1 \cdot 2 + 2 \cdot 3 + \cdots + k(k + 1) + (k + 1)(k + 2)$$

$$= \frac{k(k + 1)(k + 2)}{3} + (k + 1)(k + 2) \qquad \text{Induction hypothesis}$$

$$= \frac{(k + 1)(k + 2)(k + 3)}{3}$$

So $P(k + 1)$ follows from $P(k)$. Thus by the Principle of Mathematical Induction $P(n)$ holds for all n.

9. Let $P(n)$ denote the statement

$$1^3 + 2^3 + \cdots + n^3 = \frac{n^2(n + 1)^2}{4}.$$

Step 1 $P(1)$ is true, since $1^3 = \dfrac{1^2 \cdot (1 + 1)^2}{4}.$

Step 2 Suppose $P(k)$ is true. Then

$$1^3 + 2^3 + \cdots + k^3 + (k + 1)^3$$

$$= \frac{k^2(k + 1)^2}{4} + (k + 1)^3 \qquad \text{Induction hypothesis}$$

$$= \frac{(k + 1)^2[k^2 + 4(k + 1)]}{4}$$

$$= \frac{(k + 1)^2(k + 2)^2}{4}$$

So $P(k + 1)$ follows from $P(k)$. Thus by the Principle of Mathematical Induction $P(n)$ holds for all n.

11. Let $P(n)$ denote the statement
$2^3 + 4^3 + \cdots + (2n)^3 = 2n^2(n + 1)^2$.

Step 1 $P(1)$ is true, since $2^3 = 2 \cdot 1^2(1 + 1)^2$.
Step 2 Suppose $P(k)$ is true. Then

$$2^3 + 4^3 + \cdots + (2k)^3 + [2(k + 1)]^3$$

$$= 2k^2(k + 1)^2 + [2(k + 1)]^3 \qquad \text{Induction hypothesis}$$

$$= (k + 1)^2(2k^2 + 8k + 8)$$

$$= 2(k + 1)^2(k + 2)^2$$

So $P(k + 1)$ follows from $P(k)$. Thus by the Principle of Mathematical Induction $P(n)$ holds for all n.

13. Let $P(n)$ denote the statement
$1 \cdot 2 + 2 \cdot 2^2 + \cdots + n \cdot 2^n = 2[1 + (n - 1)2^n]$.

Step 1 $P(1)$ is true, since $1 \cdot 2 = 2[1 + 0]$.
Step 2 Suppose $P(k)$ is true. Then

$$1 \cdot 2 + 2 \cdot 2^2 + \cdots + k \cdot 2^k + (k + 1) \cdot 2^{k+1}$$

$$= 2[1 + (k - 1)2^k] + (k + 1) \cdot 2^{k+1} \qquad \text{Induction hypothesis}$$

$$= 2 + (k - 1)2^{k+1} + (k + 1) \cdot 2^{k+1}$$

$$= 2 + 2k2^{k+1} = 2(1 + k2^{k+1})$$

So $P(k + 1)$ follows from $P(k)$. Thus by the Principle of Mathematical Induction $P(n)$ holds for all n.

15. Let $P(n)$ denote the statement $n^2 + n$ is divisible by 2.

Step 1 $P(1)$ is true, since $1^2 + 1$ is divisible by 2.
Step 2 Suppose $P(k)$ is true. Now

$$(k + 1)^2 + (k + 1) = k^2 + 2k + 1 + k + 1$$

$$= (k^2 + k) + 2(k + 1)$$

But $k^2 + k$ is divisible by 2 (by the induction hypothesis), and $2(k + 1)$ is clearly divisible by 2, so $(k + 1)^2 + (k + 1)$ is divisible by 2. So $P(k + 1)$ follows from $P(k)$. Thus by the Principle of Mathematical Induction $P(n)$ holds for all n.

17. Let $P(n)$ denote the statement $n^2 - n + 41$ is odd.

Step 1 $P(1)$ is true, since $1^2 - 1 + 41$ is odd.
Step 2 Suppose $P(k)$ is true. Now

$$(k + 1)^2 - (k + 1) + 41 = (k^2 - k + 41) + 2k$$

But $k^2 - k + 41$ is odd (by the induction hypothesis), and $2k$ is clearly even, so their sum is odd. So $P(k + 1)$ follows from $P(k)$. Thus by the Principle of Mathematical Induction $P(n)$ holds for all n.

19. Let $P(n)$ denote the statement $8^n - 3^n$ is divisible by 5.

Step 1 $P(1)$ is true, since $8^1 - 3^1$ is divisible by 5.
Step 2 Suppose $P(k)$ is true. Now

$$8^{k+1} - 3^{k+1} = 8 \cdot 8^k - 3 \cdot 3^k$$

$$= 8 \cdot 8^k - (8 - 5) \cdot 3^k = 8 \cdot (8^k - 3^k) + 5 \cdot 3^k$$

which is divisible by 5 because $8^k - 3^k$ is divisible by 5 (by the induction hypothesis) and $5 \cdot 3^k$ is clearly divisible by 5. So $P(k + 1)$ follows from $P(k)$. Thus by the Principle of Mathematical Induction $P(n)$ holds for all n.

21. Let $P(n)$ denote the statement $n < 2^n$.

Step 1 $P(1)$ is true, since $1 < 2^1$.
Step 2 Suppose $P(k)$ is true. Then

$$k + 1 < 2^k + 1 \qquad \text{Induction hypothesis}$$
$$< 2^k + 2^k \qquad \text{Because } 1 < 2^k$$
$$= 2 \cdot 2^k = 2^{k+1}$$

So $P(k + 1)$ follows from $P(k)$. Thus by the Principle of Mathematical Induction $P(n)$ holds for all n.

23. Let $P(n)$ denote the statement $(1 + x)^n \geq 1 + nx$ for $x > -1$.

Step 1 $P(1)$ is true, since $(1 + x)^1 \geq 1 + 1 \cdot x$.
Step 2 Suppose $P(k)$ is true. Then

$$(1 + x)^{k+1} = (1 + x)(1 + x)^k$$
$$\geq (1 + x)(1 + kx) \qquad \text{Induction hypothesis}$$
$$= 1 + (k + 1)x + kx^2$$
$$\geq 1 + (k + 1)x$$

So $P(k + 1)$ follows from $P(k)$. Thus by the Principle of Mathematical Induction $P(n)$ holds for all n.

25. Let $P(n)$ denote the statement $a_n = 5 \cdot 3^{n-1}$.

Step 1 $P(1)$ is true, since $a_1 = 5 \cdot 3^0 = 5$.
Step 2 Suppose $P(k)$ is true. Then

$$a_{k+1} = 3 \cdot a_k \qquad \text{Definition of } a_{k+1}$$
$$= 3 \cdot 5 \cdot 3^{k-1} \qquad \text{Induction hypothesis}$$
$$= 5 \cdot 3^k$$

So $P(k + 1)$ follows from $P(k)$. Thus by the Principle of Mathematical Induction $P(n)$ holds for all n.

27. Let $P(n)$ denote the statement $x - y$ is a factor of $x^n - y^n$.

Step 1 $P(1)$ is true, since $x - y$ is a factor of $x^1 - y^1$.
Step 2 Suppose $P(k)$ is true. Now

$$x^{k+1} - y^{k+1} = x^{k+1} - x^k y + x^k y - y^{k+1}$$
$$= x^k(x - y) + (x^k - y^k)y$$

But $x^k(x - y)$ is clearly divisible by $x - y$, and $(x^k - y^k)y$ is divisible by $x - y$ (by the induction hypothesis), so their sum is divisible by $x - y$. So $P(k + 1)$ follows from $P(k)$. Thus by the Principle of Mathematical Induction $P(n)$ holds for all n.

29. Let $P(n)$ denote the statement F_{3n} is even.

Step 1 $P(1)$ is true, since $F_{3 \cdot 1} = 2$, which is even.
Step 2 Suppose $P(k)$ is true. Now, by the definition of the Fibonacci sequence

$$F_{3(k+1)} = F_{3k+3} = F_{3k+2} + F_{3k+1}$$
$$= F_{3k+1} + F_{3k} + F_{3k+1}$$
$$= F_{3k} + 2 \cdot F_{3k+1}$$

But F_{3k} is even (by the induction hypothesis), and $2 \cdot F_{3k+1}$ is clearly even, so $F_{3(k+1)}$ is even. So $P(k + 1)$ follows from $P(k)$. Thus by the Principle of Mathematical Induction $P(n)$ holds for all n.

31. Let $P(n)$ denote the statement
$F_1^2 + F_2^2 + \cdots + F_n^2 = F_n \cdot F_{n+1}$.

Step 1 $P(1)$ is true, since $F_1^2 = F_1 \cdot F_2$ (because $F_1 = F_2 = 1$).
Step 2 Suppose $P(k)$ is true. Then

$$F_1^2 + F_2^2 + \cdots + F_k^2 + F_{k+1}^2$$
$$= F_k \cdot F_{k+1} + F_{k+1}^2 \qquad \text{Induction hypothesis}$$
$$= F_{k+1}(F_k + F_{k+1}) \qquad \text{Definition of the}$$
$$\qquad\qquad\qquad\qquad\qquad \text{Fibonacci sequence}$$
$$= F_{k+1} \cdot F_{k+2}$$

So $P(k + 1)$ follows from $P(k)$. Thus by the Principle of Mathematical Induction $P(n)$ holds for all n.

33. Let $P(n)$ denote the statement $\begin{bmatrix} 1 & 1 \\ 1 & 0 \end{bmatrix}^n = \begin{bmatrix} F_{n+1} & F_n \\ F_n & F_{n-1} \end{bmatrix}$.

Step 1 $P(2)$ is true, since $\begin{bmatrix} 1 & 1 \\ 1 & 0 \end{bmatrix}^2 = \begin{bmatrix} 2 & 1 \\ 1 & 1 \end{bmatrix} = \begin{bmatrix} F_3 & F_2 \\ F_2 & F_1 \end{bmatrix}$.
Step 2 Suppose $P(k)$ is true. Then

$$\begin{bmatrix} 1 & 1 \\ 1 & 0 \end{bmatrix}^{k+1} = \begin{bmatrix} 1 & 1 \\ 1 & 0 \end{bmatrix}^k \begin{bmatrix} 1 & 1 \\ 1 & 0 \end{bmatrix}$$
$$= \begin{bmatrix} F_{k+1} & F_k \\ F_k & F_{k-1} \end{bmatrix} \begin{bmatrix} 1 & 1 \\ 1 & 0 \end{bmatrix} \qquad \text{Induction hypothesis}$$
$$= \begin{bmatrix} F_{k+1} + F_k & F_{k+1} \\ F_k + F_{k-1} & F_k \end{bmatrix}$$
$$= \begin{bmatrix} F_{k+2} & F_{k+1} \\ F_{k+1} & F_k \end{bmatrix} \qquad \text{Definition of the}$$
$$\qquad\qquad\qquad\qquad \text{Fibonacci sequence}$$

So $P(k + 1)$ follows from $P(k)$. Thus by the Principle of Mathematical Induction $P(n)$ holds for all $n \geq 2$.

35. Let $P(n)$ denote the statement $F_n \geq n$.

Step 1 $P(5)$ is true, since $F_5 \geq 5$ (because $F_5 = 5$).
Step 2 Suppose $P(k)$ is true. Now

$$F_{k+1} = F_k + F_{k-1} \qquad \text{Definition of the Fibonacci sequence}$$
$$\geq k + F_{k-1} \qquad \text{Induction hypothesis}$$
$$\geq k + 1 \qquad \text{Because } F_{k-1} \geq 1$$

So $P(k + 1)$ follows from $P(k)$. Thus by the Principle of Mathematical Induction $P(n)$ holds for all $n \geq 5$.

SECTION 12.6 ■ PAGE 827

1. binomial **2.** Pascal's; 1, 4, 6, 4, 1

3. $\dfrac{n!}{k!(n - k)!}$; $\dfrac{4!}{3!(4 - 3)!} = 4$

4. Binomial; $\dbinom{4}{0}, \dbinom{4}{1}, \dbinom{4}{2}, \dbinom{4}{3}, \dbinom{4}{4}$

5. $x^6 + 6x^5y + 15x^4y^2 + 20x^3y^3 + 15x^2y^4 + 6xy^5 + y^6$

7. $x^4 + 4x^2 + 6 + \dfrac{4}{x^2} + \dfrac{1}{x^4}$

9. $x^5 - 5x^4 + 10x^3 - 10x^2 + 5x - 1$
11. $x^{10}y^5 - 5x^8y^4 + 10x^6y^3 - 10x^4y^2 + 5x^2y - 1$
13. $8x^3 - 36x^2y + 54xy^2 - 27y^3$

15. $\dfrac{1}{x^5} - \dfrac{5}{x^{7/2}} + \dfrac{10}{x^2} - \dfrac{10}{x^{1/2}} + 5x - x^{5/2}$

17. 15   **19.** 4950   **21.** 18   **23.** 32
25. $x^4 + 8x^3y + 24x^2y^2 + 32xy^3 + 16y^4$

27. $1 + \dfrac{6}{x} + \dfrac{15}{x^2} + \dfrac{20}{x^3} + \dfrac{15}{x^4} + \dfrac{6}{x^5} + \dfrac{1}{x^6}$

29. $x^{20} + 40x^{19}y + 760x^{18}y^2$ **31.** $25a^{26/3} + a^{25/3}$
33. $48,620x^{18}$ **35.** $300a^2b^{23}$ **37.** $100y^{99}$ **39.** $13,440x^4y^6$
41. $495a^8b^8$ **43.** $(x + y)^4$ **45.** $(2a + b)^3$ **47.** $3x^2 + 3xh + h^2$

CHAPTER 12 REVIEW ▪ PAGE 829

1. $\frac{1}{2}, \frac{4}{3}, \frac{9}{4}, \frac{16}{5}; \frac{100}{11}$ **3.** $0, \frac{1}{4}, 0, \frac{1}{32}; \frac{1}{500}$ **5.** 1, 3, 15, 105; 654,729,075
7. 1, 4, 9, 16, 25, 36, 49   **9.** 1, 3, 5, 11, 21, 43, 85
11. (a) 7, 9, 11, 13, 15   **13. (a)** $\frac{3}{4}, \frac{9}{8}, \frac{27}{16}, \frac{81}{32}, \frac{243}{64}$
(b)   **(b)**

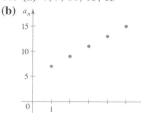   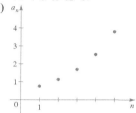

(c) 55   **(c)** $\frac{633}{64}$
(d) Arithmetic, common   **(d)** Geometric, common
difference 2   ratio $\frac{3}{2}$

15. Arithmetic, 7   **17.** Arithmetic, $t + 1$ **19.** Geometric, $\dfrac{1}{t}$
21. Geometric, $\frac{4}{27}$ **23.** $2i$ **25.** 5   **27.** $\frac{81}{4}$

29. (a) $A_n = 32,000(1.05)^{n-1}$ **(b)** \$32,000, \$33,600, \$35,280,
\$37,044, \$38,896.20, \$40,841.01, \$42,883.06, \$45,027.21
31. 12,288   **35. (a)** 9   **(b)** $\pm 6\sqrt{2}$ **37.** 126   **39.** 384

41. $0^2 + 1^2 + 2^2 + \cdots + 9^2$ **43.** $\dfrac{3}{2^2} + \dfrac{3^2}{2^3} + \dfrac{3^3}{2^4} + \cdots + \dfrac{3^{50}}{2^{51}}$

45. $\displaystyle\sum_{k=1}^{33} 3k$ **47.** $\displaystyle\sum_{k=1}^{100} k2^{k+2}$ **49.** Geometric; 4.68559

51. Arithmetic, $5050\sqrt{5}$ **53.** Geometric, 9831   **55.** $\frac{5}{7}$
57. Divergent   **59.** Divergent   **61.** 13   **63.** 65,534
65. \$2390.27

67. Let $P(n)$ denote the statement
$$1 + 4 + 7 + \cdots + (3n - 2) = \frac{n(3n - 1)}{2}.$$
Step 1 $P(1)$ is true, since $1 = \dfrac{1(3 \cdot 1 - 1)}{2}$.

Step 2 Suppose $P(k)$ is true. Then
$$1 + 4 + 7 + \cdots + (3k - 2) + [3(k + 1) - 2]$$
$$= \frac{k(3k - 1)}{2} + [3k + 1] \quad \text{Induction hypothesis}$$
$$= \frac{3k^2 - k + 6k + 2}{2}$$
$$= \frac{(k + 1)(3k + 2)}{2}$$
$$= \frac{(k + 1)[3(k + 1) - 1]}{2}$$

So $P(k + 1)$ follows from $P(k)$. Thus by the Principle of
Mathematical Induction $P(n)$ holds for all n.

69. Let $P(n)$ denote the statement
$\left(1 + \frac{1}{1}\right)\left(1 + \frac{1}{2}\right) \cdots \left(1 + \frac{1}{n}\right) = n + 1.$

Step 1 $P(1)$ is true, since $\left(1 + \frac{1}{1}\right) = 1 + 1.$
Step 2 Suppose $P(k)$ is true. Then
$$\left(1 + \frac{1}{1}\right)\left(1 + \frac{1}{2}\right) \cdots \left(1 + \frac{1}{k}\right)\left(1 + \frac{1}{k + 1}\right)$$
$$= (k + 1)\left(1 + \frac{1}{k + 1}\right) \quad \text{Induction hypothesis}$$
$$= (k + 1) + 1$$
So $P(k + 1)$ follows from $P(k)$. Thus by the Principle of
Mathematical Induction $P(n)$ holds for all n.

71. Let $P(n)$ denote the statement $a_n = 2 \cdot 3^n - 2.$
Step 1 $P(1)$ is true, since $a_1 = 2 \cdot 3^1 - 2 = 4.$
Step 2 Suppose $P(k)$ is true. Then
$$a_{k+1} = 3a_k + 4$$
$$= 3(2 \cdot 3^k - 2) + 4 \quad \text{Induction hypothesis}$$
$$= 2 \cdot 3^{k+1} - 2$$
So $P(k + 1)$ follows from $P(k)$. Thus by the Principle of
Mathematical Induction $P(n)$ holds for all n.

73. 100   **75.** 32   **77.** $A^3 - 3A^2B + 3AB^2 - B^3$
79. $1 - 6x^2 + 15x^4 - 20x^6 + 15x^8 - 6x^{10} + x^{12}$
81. $1540a^3b^{19}$ **83.** $17,010A^6B^4$

CHAPTER 12 TEST ▪ PAGE 832

1. 1, 6, 15, 28, 45, 66; 161   **2.** 2, 5, 13, 36, 104, 307   **3. (a)** 3
(b) $a_n = 2 + (n - 1)3$ **(c)** 104   **4. (a)** $\frac{1}{4}$ **(b)** $a_n = 12\left(\frac{1}{4}\right)^{n-1}$
(c) $3/4^8$ **5. (a)** $\frac{1}{5}, \frac{1}{25}$ **(b)** $\dfrac{5^8 - 1}{12,500}$ **6. (a)** $-\frac{8}{9}, -78$ **(b)** 60

8. (a) $(1 - 1^2) + (1 - 2^2) + (1 - 3^2) + (1 - 4^2) +$
$(1 - 5^2) = -50$
(b) $(-1)^3 2^1 + (-1)^4 2^2 + (-1)^5 2^3 + (-1)^6 2^4 = 10$
9. (a) $\frac{58,025}{59,049}$ **(b)** $2 + \sqrt{2}$

10. Let $P(n)$ denote the statement
$$1^2 + 2^2 + \cdots + n^2 = \frac{n(n + 1)(2n + 1)}{6}.$$

Step 1 $P(1)$ is true, since $1^2 = \dfrac{1(1 + 1)(2 \cdot 1 + 1)}{6}.$
Step 2 Suppose $P(k)$ is true. Then
$$1^2 + 2^2 + \cdots + k^2 + (k + 1)^2$$
$$= \frac{k(k + 1)(2k + 1)}{6} + (k + 1)^2 \quad \text{Induction hypothesis}$$
$$= \frac{k(k + 1)(2k + 1) + 6(k + 1)^2}{6}$$
$$= \frac{(k + 1)[k(2k + 1) + 6(k + 1)]}{6}$$
$$= \frac{(k + 1)(2k^2 + 7k + 6)}{6}$$
$$= \frac{(k + 1)[(k + 1) + 1][2(k + 1) + 1]}{6}$$

So $P(k + 1)$ follows from $P(k)$. Thus by the Principle of
Mathematical Induction $P(n)$ holds for all n.

11. $32x^5 + 80x^4y^2 + 80x^3y^4 + 40x^2y^6 + 10xy^8 + y^{10}$

12. $\binom{10}{3}(3x)^3(-2)^7 = -414{,}720x^3$

13. **(a)** $a_n = (0.85)(1.24)^n$ **(b)** 3.09 lb   **(c)** Geometric

FOCUS ON MODELING ■ PAGE 835

1. **(a)** $A_n = 1.0001A_{n-1}$, $A_0 = 275{,}000$ **(b)** $A_0 = 275{,}000$,
$A_1 = 275{,}027.50$, $A_2 = 275{,}055.00$, $A_3 = 275{,}082.51$,
$A_4 = 275{,}110.02$, $A_5 = 275{,}137.53$, $A_6 = 275{,}165.04$,
$A_7 = 275{,}192.56$ **(c)** $A_n = 1.0001^n(275{,}000)$
3. **(a)** $A_n = 1.0025A_{n-1} + 100$, $A_0 = 100$ **(b)** $A_0 = 100$,
$A_1 = 200.25$, $A_2 = 300.75$, $A_3 = 401.50$, $A_4 = 502.51$
(c) $A_n = 100[(1.0025^{n+1} - 1)/0.0025]$ **(d)** \$6580.83
5. **(b)** $A_0 = 2400$, $A_1 = 3120$, $A_2 = 3336$, $A_3 = 3400.8$,
$A_4 = 3420.2$ **(c)** $A_n = 3428.6(1 - 0.3^{n+1})$
(d) 3427.8 tons, 3428.6 tons
(e)

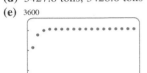

7. **(b)** In the 35th year
9. **(a)** $R_1 = 104$, $R_2 = 108$, $R_3 = 112$, $R_4 = 116$, $R_5 = 120$,
$R_6 = 124$, $R_7 = 127$ **(b)** It approaches 200.

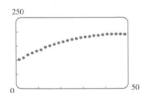

CHAPTER 13

SECTION 13.1 ■ PAGE 846

1. L, a; $5, 1$ **2.** limit, left, L; less; left, right, equal
3. 10   **5.** $\frac{1}{4}$ **7.** $\frac{1}{3}$ **9.** 1   **11.** -1 **13.** 0.51 **15.** $\frac{1}{2}$
17. **(a)** 2   **(b)** 3   **(c)** Does not exist   **(d)** 4   **(e)** Not defined
19. **(a)** -1 **(b)** -2 **(c)** Does not exist   **(d)** 2   **(e)** 0
(f) Does not exist   **(g)** 1   **(h)** 3
21. -8 **23.** Does not exist
25. Does not exist
27. Does not exist
29. **(a)** 4   **(b)** 4   **(c)** 4

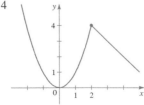

31. **(a)** 4   **(b)** 3   **(c)** Does not exist

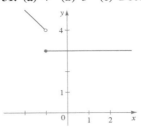

SECTION 13.2 ■ PAGE 855

1. $\lim\limits_{x \to a} f(x) + \lim\limits_{x \to a} g(x)$, $\lim\limits_{x \to a} f(x) \cdot \lim\limits_{x \to a} g(x)$; sum, product   **2.** $f(a)$
3. **(a)** 5   **(b)** 9   **(c)** 2   **(d)** $-\frac{1}{3}$ **(e)** $-\frac{3}{8}$ **(f)** 0
(g) Does not exist   **(h)** $-\frac{6}{11}$
5. 75   **7.** $\frac{1}{2}$ **9.** -3 **11.** 5   **13.** 2
15. $\frac{6}{5}$ **17.** 12   **19.** $\frac{1}{6}$ **21.** $-\frac{1}{16}$
23. 4   **25.** $-\frac{3}{2}$

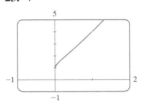   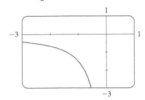

27. **(a)** 0.667

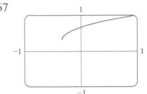

(b) 0.667

x	$f(x)$
0.1	0.71339
0.01	0.67163
0.001	0.66717
0.0001	0.66672

x	$f(x)$
-0.1	0.61222
-0.01	0.66163
-0.001	0.66617
-0.0001	0.66662

(c) $\frac{2}{3}$
29. 0   **31.** Does not exist
33. Does not exist
35. **(a)** 1, 2   **(b)** Does not exist
(c)

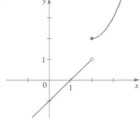

SECTION 13.3 ■ PAGE 863

1. $\dfrac{f(a + h) - f(a)}{h}$; slope, $(a, f(a))$

2. $\dfrac{f(x) - f(a)}{x - a}$, instantaneous, a **3.** 3   **5.** -11 **7.** 24

9. $y = -x - 1$

11. $y = -x + 4$

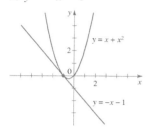

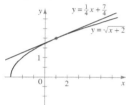

13. $y = \frac{1}{4}x + \frac{7}{4}$

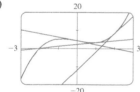

15. $f'(2) = -12$ **17.** $g'(1) = 4$ **19.** $F'(4) = -\frac{1}{16}$

21. $f'(a) = 2a + 2$ **23.** $f'(a) = \dfrac{1}{(a + 1)^2}$

25. (a) $f'(a) = 3a^2 - 2$
(b) $y = -2x + 4$, $y = x + 2$, $y = 10x - 12$
(c)

27. -24 ft/s   **29.** $12a^2 + 6$ m/s, 18 m/s, 54 m/s, 114 m/s
31. $0.75°$/min   **33. (a)** -38.3 gal/min, -27.8 gal/min
(b) -33.3 gal/min

SECTION 13.4 ■ PAGE 871

1. L, x; horizontal asymptote; 0, 0   **2.** L, large; converges,
diverges   **3. (a)** $-1, 2$ **(b)** $y = -1, y = 2$ **5.** 0   **7.** $\frac{2}{5}$ **9.** $\frac{4}{3}$
11. 2   **13.** Does not exist   **15.** 7   **17.** Does not exist
19. $-\frac{1}{4}$ **21.** 0   **23.** 0   **25.** Divergent   **27.** 0   **29.** Divergent
31. $\frac{3}{2}$ **33.** 8   **35. (b)** 30 g/L

SECTION 13.5 ■ PAGE 879

1. rectangles;
$f(x_1)(x_1 - a) + f(x_2)(x_2 - x_1) + f(x_3)(x_3 - x_2) + f(b)(b - x_3)$
2. $\displaystyle\sum_{k=1}^{n} f(x_k)\Delta x$

3. (a) 40, 52

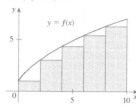
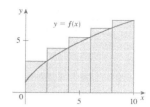

(b) 43.2, 49.2
5. 5.25   **7.** $\frac{223}{35}$
9. (a) $\frac{77}{60}$, underestimate   **(b)** $\frac{25}{12}$, overestimate

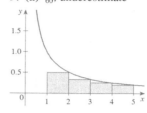
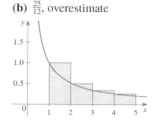

11. (a) 8, 6.875   **(b)** 5, 5.375

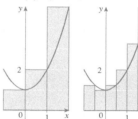
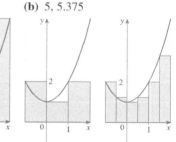

13. 37.5   **15.** 8   **17.** 166.25   **19.** 133.5

CHAPTER 13 REVIEW ■ PAGE 881

1. 1   **3.** 0.69   **5.** Does not exist   **7. (a)** Does not exist
(b) 2.4   **(c)** 2.4   **(d)** 2.4   **(e)** 0.5   **(f)** 1   **(g)** 2   **(h)** 0
9. -3 **11.** 7   **13.** 2   **15.** -1 **17.** 2   **19.** Does not exist
21. $f'(4) = 3$ **23.** $f'(16) = \frac{1}{8}$
25. (a) $f'(a) = -2$ **(b)** $-2, -2$
27. (a) $f'(a) = 1/(2\sqrt{a + 6})$ **(b)** $1/(4\sqrt{2}), 1/4$
29. $y = 2x + 1$ **31.** $y = 2x$ **33.** $y = -\frac{1}{4}x + 1$
35. (a) -64 ft/s   **(b)** $-32a$ ft/s   **(c)** $\sqrt{40} \approx 6.32$ s
(d) -202.4 ft/s   **37.** $\frac{1}{5}$ **39.** $\frac{1}{2}$ **41.** Divergent   **43.** 3.83
45. 10   **47.** $\frac{5}{6}$

CHAPTER 13 TEST ■ PAGE 883

1. (a) $\frac{1}{2}$ **(b)**

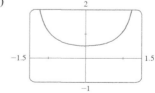

2. (a) 1 **(b)** 1 **(c)** 1 **(d)** 0 **(e)** 0 **(f)** 0 **(g)** 4 **(h)** 2
(i) Does not exist **3. (a)** 6 **(b)** -2 **(c)** Does not exist
(d) Does not exist **(e)** $\frac{1}{4}$ **(f)** 2 **4. (a)** $f'(x) = 2x - 2$
(b) $-4, 0, 2$ **5.** $y = \frac{1}{6}x + \frac{3}{2}$ **6. (a)** 0 **(b)** Does not exist
7. (a) $\frac{89}{25}$ **(b)** $\frac{11}{3}$

FOCUS ON MODELING ▪ PAGE 886

1. $57,333\frac{1}{3}$ ft-lb **3. (b)** Area under the graph of $p(x) = 375x$
between $x = 0$ and $x = 4$ **(c)** 3000 lb **(d)** 1500 lb
5. (a) 1625.28 heating degree-hours **(b)** $70°F$
(c) 1488 heating degree-hours **(d)** $75°F$ **(e)** The day in part (a)

CUMULATIVE REVIEW TEST FOR CHAPTERS 12 AND 13 ▪ PAGE 888

1. (a) $\frac{7}{15}, \frac{20}{41}, \frac{1}{2}$ **(b)** $\frac{99}{340}, \frac{801}{7984}, 0$ **(c)** $\frac{37}{2}, \frac{115}{2}$, no limit
(d) $12(\frac{5}{6})^6, 12(\frac{5}{6})^{19}, 0$ **(e)** $0.64, -5242.88$, no limit
2. (a) 41.4 **(b)** 88.572 **(c)** 5115/512 **(d)** 9
3. $2658.15 **4.** Hint: Induction step is
$a_{n+1} = a_n + 2(n + 1) - 1 = n^2 + 2n + 1 = (n + 1)^2.$
5. (a) $32x^5 - 40x^4 + 20x^3 - 5x^2 + \frac{5}{8}x - \frac{1}{32}$ **(b)** $\frac{495}{16}x^4$

6. (a) 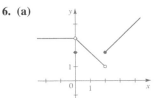 **(b) (i)** 2 **(ii)** 3 **(iii)** 2
(iv) 1 **(v)** 2

7. $\frac{1}{2}$ **8. (a)** 10 **(b)** 4 **(c)** Does not exist
9. (a) $3x^2$ **(b)** $27, 0, 3a^2$ **(c)** $y = 12x - 16$
10. (a) 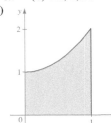 **(b)** *A* lies between the 1×1
square in the first quadrant, with
corner at the origin, which has
area 1, and the trapezoid with
corners $(0, 0), (1, 0), (1, 2)$, and
$(0, 1)$, which has area $\frac{3}{2}$.
(c) 78/64 **(d)** 4/3

WebAssign Student Quick Start Guide

WebAssign allows you to access your homework, quizzes, and tests—whatever your instructor chooses—at any time of day or night, from any computer with a connection to the Internet and a Web browser. Your instructor creates your assignments, schedules them and decides how many submissions you get, whether you can have an extension, whether you can save your work without submitting, and how much feedback you get after you submit an assignment.

The WebAssign support staff cannot change your username or password, give extensions, change your score, give you extra submissions, or help you with the content of your assignments.

Logging In

You can log in to WebAssign using any Web browser connected to the Internet. There are two different ways to log in to WebAssign. Each requires information from your teacher. If you are unsure about how to log in, please check with your teacher or another student in your class.

Go to the login page at https://webassign.net/login.html or the web address provided by your teacher.

If your teacher has created a WebAssign account for you, they will provide you with a **Username**, an **Institution** code and a **Passwor**d. Simply enter this information in the boxes provided and click the Log In button.

If your teacher wants you to **self-enroll** in the WebAssign course they will provide you with a **Class Key**. You will create your own username and password. It is important that you remember this information so you can log in for the remainder of the class.

- Click the **I have a Class Key** button. You don't need to enter any other information on this page.

- Enter the **class key** your instructor provided and click **Submit.** Verify you are enrolling in the correct class on the next page.

Class Key

Enter the Class Key that you received from your instructor. You will only need to complete this once. After you have created your account, you can log in on the main page.

Class Key

Class Keys generally start with an institution code, followed by two sets of four digits.

Submit

WebAssign.

- Enter your preferred Login and Student information.

- Click the **Create My Account** button to complete the enrollment process.

- A review screen will display, showing your username, institution code, and password. **Retain a copy of this information.** You will need it to log into WebAssign.

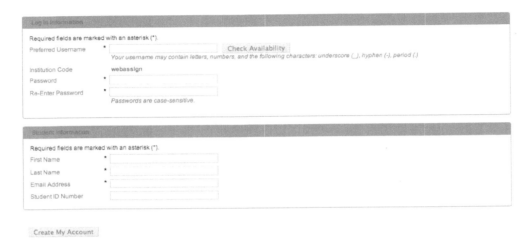

Access Codes

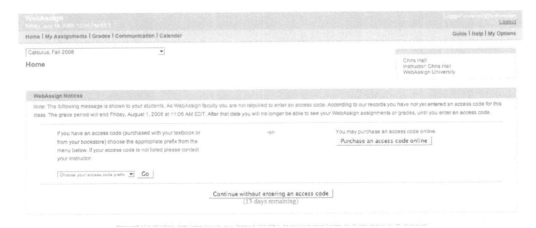

Once you log in, you may see a WebAssign Notice about entering an access code for your class. You can get an Access Code from any of the following places if you need to use one:

- A new textbook you purchased for the class.
- Your bookstore, which may sell Access Code cards.
- Online, where you can purchase an access code with a credit card.

You have a 14 day grace period to use WebAssign, starting with the WebAssign class start date. During this time you can work on and view your WebAssign assignments without registering a code.

After the grace period is over you will only see the code registration message until you submit or purchase a code.

There are two types of WebAssign access code cards.

The small card requires you to scratch off the silver surface in order to reveal the complete access code.

The larger security envelope card requires you to open the card to reveal the access code number.

If you would like to purchase an access code directly from WebAssign online, you may do so with a credit card. Your code will be automatically registered to your WebAssign account as soon as the transaction is complete. You will receive an email confirmation. Please keep a copy for your records.

Your WebAssign Home Page

Once you have successfully logged in you will see your WebAssign homepage. If you are taking more than one WebAssign class, you will need to select which class you wish to view first.

The upper right corner features links to a complete Student **Guide**, as well as a link to WebAssign Technical Support under **Help**. If you want to change your password or add or update your email address, simply click **My Options** in the upper right hand corner.

You will see your assignments and due dates listed, as well as any Communications, Grades, and Announcements posted by your teacher.

Answering Questions

WebAssign has a variety of different question types, ranging from multiple choice to fill-in-the-blank to symbolic questions. Here are some things to keep in mind as you work through your assignments:

• Some questions may include numbers or words that appear in red. This signifies that the number or word has been randomized, so that you receive a different version of the same basic question from your classmates.

• Some WebAssign questions check the number of significant figures in your answer. If you enter the correct value with the wrong number of significant figures, you will not receive credit, but you will receive a hint that your number does not have the correct number of significant figures.

• Some questions require entering symbolic notation. Answer symbolic questions by using calculator notation. You must use the exact variables specified in the questions. The order is not important as long as it is mathematically correct. Clicking on the eye button previews the expression you enter in proper mathematical notation. Clicking on the symbolic formatting help button provides tips for using the correct keystrokes.

When you click on some WebAssign chemistry or math questions an input palette will open. These palettes, called chemPad and mathPad, will help you enter your answer in proper notation.

• Some questions may require the use of an Active Figure simulation. Active Figures require the free Macromedia Flash Player plug-in, downloadable from www.macromedia.com.

• If your instructor allows it, you can save your work without grading by selecting the Save Work button at the end of the question. After you save your work, it will be available to you the next time you click the assignment.

Please note that WebAssign will **not** automatically submit your answers for scoring if you only Save your work. Your teacher will not be able to see your submissions. Please be sure to Submit prior to the due date and time.

• If your instructor allows it, you can submit answers by question part or for the entire assignment. To submit an individual question answer for grading, click the **Submit New Answers to Question __** button at the bottom of each question. To submit the entire assignment for grading, click the **Submit All New Answers** button at the end of the assignment.

Technical Support

If you are having difficulty logging in, please be sure to check with your teacher and verify whether an account has been created for you or whether you need to self-enroll. In either case your teacher needs to provide the appropriate information (username, institution code and password OR Class Key).

To email WebAssign Support go to http://www.webassign.net/info/support/report.html. This page also lists answers to **Common Problems**, and provides links to the **Student Guide**.

August 1, 2008